World Survey of Climatology Volume 1B

GENERAL CLIMATOLOGY, 1B

World Survey of Climatology

Editor in Chief:

H. E. LANDSBERG, College Park, Md. (U.S.A.)

Editors:

H. ARAKAWA, Tokyo (Japan)
R. A. BRYSON, Madison, Wisc. (U.S.A.)
O. M. ESSENWANGER, Huntsville, Al. (U.S.A.)
H. FLOHN, Bonn (F.R. Germany)
J. GENTILLI, Nedlands, W. A. (Australia)
J. F. GRIFFITHS, College Station, Texas (U.S.A.)
F. K. HARE, Ottawa, Ont. (Canada)
H. E. LANDSBERG, College Park, Md. (U.S.A.)
P. E. LYDOLPH, Milwaukee, Wisc. (U.S.A.)
S. ORVIG, Montreal, Que. (Canada)
D. F. REX, Boulder, Colo. (U.S.A.)
W. SCHWERDTFEGER, Madison, Wisc. (U.S.A.)
K. TAKAHASHI, Tokyo (Japan)
H. VAN LOON, Boulder, Colo. (U.S.A.)
C. C. WALLÉN, Geneva (Switzerland)

World Survey of Climatology Volume 1B

General Climatology, 1B

Elements of Statistical Analysis

by O. M. ESSENWANGER

610 Mountain Gap Drive,
Huntsville, AL 35803 (U.S.A.)

ELSEVIER Amsterdam-London-New York-Tokyo 1986

ELSEVIER SCIENCE PUBLISHERS B.V.
Sara Burgerhartstraat 25
P.O. Box 211, 1000 AE Amsterdam, The Netherlands

Distributors for the United States and Canada:

ELSEVIER SCIENCE PUBLISHING COMPANY INC.
52, Vanderbilt Avenue
New York, NY 10017, U.S.A.

With 14 illustrations and 89 tables

ISBN 0-444-42426-1 (Vol. 1B)
ISBN 0-444-40734-0 (Series)

Printed in The Netherlands

World Survey of Climatology

Editor in Chief: H. E. LANDSBERG

Volume 1A	General Climatology, 1A Editor: O. M. ESSENWANGER
Volume 1B	General Climatology, 1B by O. M. ESSENWANGER
Volume 2	General Climatology, 2 Editor: H. FLOHN
Volume 3	General Climatology, 3 Editor: H. E. LANDSBERG
Volume 4	Climate of the Free Atmosphere Editor: D. F. REX
Volume 5	Climates of Northern and Western Europe Editor: C. C. WALLÉN
Volume 6	Climates of Central and Southern Europe Editor: C. C. WALLÉN
Volume 7	Climates of the Soviet Union by P. E. LYDOLPH
Volume 8	Climates of Northern and Eastern Asia Editor: H. ARAKAWA
Volume 9	Climates of Southern and Western Asia Editors: K. TAKAHASHI and H. ARAKAWA
Volume 10	Climates of Africa Editor: J. F. GRIFFITHS
Volume 11	Climates of North America Editors: R. A. BRYSON and F. K. HARE
Volume 12	Climates of Central and South America Editor: W. SCHWERDTFEGER
Volume 13	Climates of Australia and New Zealand Editor: J. GENTILLI
Volume 14	Climates of the Polar Regions Editor: S. ORVIG
Volume 15	Climates of the Oceans Editor: H. VAN LOON

Foreword

With the development of electronic data processing, the field of statistical analysis has mushroomed in the past 30 years. Today, "canned" programs permit the meteorologist (climatologist) to use statistics as a tool to a high degree, and sophisticated statistical analysis of meteorological data is now possible which was lengthy and tedious prior to the existence of high speed computers. This development is paralleled in the field of numerical prediction. In turn, the availability of "canned" programs can lead to meaningless formalism unless the basic statistical background is understood. In addition, the reader must be aware that statistical analysis remains a tool in the aim to understand and formulate the physical (atmospheric) processes rather than a purpose.

It is impossible to discuss recent statistical theories in detail and evaluate every impact upon climatology in the frame of this volume of the World Survey of Climatology. Therefore, only a limited number of topics was selected for inclusion comprising a mixture of familiar and modern subjects of statistical analysis. These sections may give the reader an introduction to the field of climatological data processing.

The principle goal of this volume was the demonstration of practical applications. The examples were selected and presented so that the reader can personally perform most of the calculations except in a few cases where electronic data processing is essential such as in the power spectrum. These examples serve primarily to illustrate the practical application, outline the problems one may encounter, and may aid in the climatological interpretation of the results.

Although some theoretical background in statistical analysis is presented, this book is not thought primarily as a textbook in sophisticated statistical theory. For the interested reader, various references are given. For many problems of practical application, however, this discussion of the statistical basic background may suffice.

The section on frequency distributions comprises a mixture of the well known distributions and others with applications in the atmospheric sciences, but the treatment is by no means complete. Supplementary distributions can be found in the author's 1976 text.

In the sections on linear regression, curve fitting, and smoothing and filtering, only basic problems were treated which were considered to be most useful in practical applications and understanding of some "canned" programs.

The section on statistical tests, although not exhaustive, should be sufficient to solve many of the basic problems in hypothesis testing. Unfortunately, only a limited number of test tables could be included but formulae for test statistics were added. These approximations permit the reader to quickly evaluate whether more sophisticated methods are appropriate. In some cases the same data samples were treated by different tests to demonstrate the effects of differences in the statistical background.

A section on the analysis of variance was later dropped. Although it is a very important topic in modern statistical analysis, the reader may refer to the cited statistical literature. Instead, goodness-of-fit tests and quality control (assurance) of climatological data were included. For the average climatologist these topics may be more useful than the advanced topic of variance analysis because only a few climatologists deal with experiments for which analysis of variance is primarily used.

The section on "characteristics of meteorological elements" had to be kept short and only the most basic elements in climatology have been included. The author is planning a supplement at some future date.

If this volume stimulates statistical analysis in climatology and leads to a better understanding of the problems in automatic data processing of atmospheric data, the author has reached the goal.

O. M. Essenwanger
Huntsville, Alabama
August, 1985

Acknowledgements

The author's thanks must go to the Editor in Chief, Prof. Dr. H. E. Landsberg, for his continual encouragement and advice during the completion of the text and editing process. Without his continued support this volume would not be ready to-day. The author is saddened by Prof. Landsberg's sudden death before the final printing.

The author is indebted to several persons who contributed to the manuscript draft. Mrs. Clara Brooks typed the revised version, Mrs. Mona White drafted parts of the index , and Mr. Pete Bonholzer edited the text for grammar. Finally, my wife deserves my thanks for assistance in the proof-reading process.

I also wish to acknowledge the encouragement of some colleagues to write this text such as Prof. Dr. Elmar Reiter, Prof. Dr. Eberhard Wahl, Dr. Harold Crutcher, and Prof. Dr. Konrad Cehak.

The author appreciates permission from authors, journals and publishers to include copyrighted material and from the Army Missile Command to include some unpublished work in atmospheric data analysis. The following authors are thanked: J. R. Green, Y. A. S. Hegazy, D. M. Hershfield, A. F. Jenkinson, P. Lester, H. W. Lilliefors, P. W. Mielke, R. H. Moore, R. E. Schafer, L. R. Shenton, P. Skees, G. L. Tietjen, and M. A. J. van Montfort. Journals and publishers are the American Meteorological Society, the American Statistical Association, Biometrika, the Royal Statistical Society, and Technometrics (for fee).

Contents

Chapter 1

Introduction

Every day a multitude of observations is being made in meteorology. If our minds were able to absorb all the individual observations of one day and/or of the past years, then analysis could be performed, data could be compared, and conclusions from the data could be drawn by the individual without any help. This has not been possible, and our goal is the derivation of meaningful characteristics describing the physical processes of weather and climate in condensed form. One of the tools to express typical properties of climatological data is statistical analysis. Modern techniques and availability of electronic data processing equipment that permit data preparation even from huge data collections in a relatively short time have enhanced the use of this tool in climatological work. The major methods and characteristics of statistical analysis will be described in the following, although in the framework of this book no comprehensive treatment of the subject can be given. As a first step we must become familiar with some fundamental concepts, mathematical operations, and data preparation techniques.

An excellent introduction into the collection of climatological data can be found in texts by BAUR (1953), WMO (1968), LANDSBERG (1969), or STRINGER (1972). The reader may refer to these references for details. The following sections place major emphasis on the problem of statistical evaluation and examination of data.

Caution should be exercised in the utilization of data. Outliers, missing observations, data bias, wrong calibration factors, or erroneous units and other errors, could lead to incorrect interpretations unless they are recognized. A detailed discussion of these errors will follow in the section about quality control. Until then it is assumed that corrective measures have been taken to free the data from any corrigible error. Other texts of interest to readers dealing with statistical analysis in climatology are SNEYERS (1975) or SCHÖNWIESE (1983), although they are less comprehensive.

Probability and expectancy

Let a set or collection of objects denoted by A be every possible outcome of a random experiment, then in mathematical terms A is a sample space. If a set A is part of A then A is a subset of A, written $A \subset \mathrm{A}$. An element X of A is expressed by $X \in A$.

Assume A contains all outcomes for which a certain event has occurred, e.g., certain temperatures from a set of temperatures. If we make N experiments, then we can count the number of times, n, the event A occurred during the performance N. The ratio $f = n/N$ is called relative frequency of the event A. Relative frequencies tend to fluctuate considerably for small N, as can be discovered by throwing a die a few times and counting the ones, or any other number. For large N the relative frequency stabilizes. This stabilized relative frequency is called the probability p of an event A and is also designated as its expected value for large N (infinite):

$$\frac{n}{N} = f \rightarrow p = P(A) \text{ for } N \rightarrow \infty \tag{1}$$

If $A = A$ contains every possible outcome:

$$P(\mathrm{A}) = P(\mathrm{A}) = 1.0 \tag{2}$$

The event occurs with certainty. If we denote the complement of A by A* then:

$$P(\mathrm{A}^*) = 0 \tag{3}$$

In this sample space A^* no event can occur.
For $A \subset \mathrm{A}$:

$$0 \leq P(A) \leq 1$$

Further, for each $A \subset \mathrm{A}$:

$$P(A^*) = 1 - P(A) \tag{4a}$$

This complementary probability is often expressed as q. Hence:

$$q = 1 - p \tag{4b}$$

It follows that the expected number N_e:

$$N_e = N \cdot p = N \cdot P(A) \tag{5}$$

$n \rightarrow N_e$ for $N \rightarrow \infty$ (see eq. 1).
If A_1 and A_2 are subsets of A and $A_1 \subset A_2$, then:

$$P(A_1) \leq P(A_2) \tag{6}$$

If the symbol $\cup$ stands for the union of A_1 and A_2, and the symbol $\cap$ for the intersection of A_1 and A_2, then:

$$P(A_1 \cup A_2) = P(A_1) + P(A_2) - P(A_1 \cap A_2) \tag{7a}$$

$P(A_1 \cap A_2)$ denotes the probability that both events occur simultaneously. If A_1 and A_2 are mutually exclusive, $P(A_1 \cap A_2) = 0$, and:

$$P(A_1 \cup A_2) = P(A_1) + P(A_2). \tag{7b}$$

This rule is also called the addition rule of probabilities.
Hughes and Sangster (1979) have utilized combined probabilities to forecast precipitations when longer period probabilities are required but are not available.
Let us assume we are interested in the event of a random experiment whose outcome is an element of subset A_2 in a sample space, if and only if this event is also an element of a subset A_1. Then A_1 becomes the sample space A and the defined probability of A_2 with respect to A_1 is called the conditional probability, symbolized $P(A_2|A_1)$ for the elements $A_1 \cap A_2$:

$$P(A_2|A_1) = P(A_1 \cap A_2|A_1) = \frac{P(A_1 \cap A_2)}{P(A_1)} \tag{8a}$$

$$P(A_1 \cap A_2) = P(A_1) \cdot P(A_2|A_1) \tag{8b}$$

The latter is frequently called the multiplication rule for probabilities, also expressed as:

$$p = p_1 \cdot p_2 \tag{9a}$$

for events that are not mutually exclusive.
The conditional probability leads to Bayes' formula:

$$P(A_i|A) = \frac{P(A_i)P(A|A_i)}{\sum_{j=1}^{n} P(A_j) \cdot P(A|A_j)} \tag{9b}$$

where the A_j are mutually exclusive events whose union is the sample space A and A is any arbitrary event of A such that $P(A) > 0$.

Probability density, cumulative distribution, and classes

Up to now we have introduced only the probability and that an event is part of a set A or A, where $A \subset$ A. Because A or any other set A_i may show a distribution, two expansions are in order.
Let a random variable X have a probability set function $P(A)$ and assume that the set*[1] is unbounded from $-\infty$ to x. The probability of all such sets $P(X \in A) = P(X \leq x)$ depends on the value of x. Let:

$$F(x) = P(A) = P(X \leq x) \tag{10}$$

where $F(x)$ is called the cumulative distribution function (c.d.f.)
Let us assume that the Rieman integral for the one-dimensional set A is:

$$\int_A f(x)\, \mathrm{d}x = 1 \tag{11a}$$

then:

$$P(X \in A) = \int_A f(x)\, \mathrm{d}x \tag{12a}$$

and $f(x)$ is called the probability density function (p.d.f.). In eqs. 11a and 12a $f(x)$ is a continuous function. A similar relationship can be established when X is a discrete random variable with an upper and lower boundary, x_u, x_l respectively, and $x_l \leq X \leq x_u$. Then:

$$w = x_u - x_l \tag{13a}$$

is the width of the class interval. It may be necessary to assign a certain representative value x_c to the class:

$$x_l < x_c < x_u \tag{13b}$$

This value x_c can also be called the central class value. Very often we find:

$$x_c = (x_u + x_l)/2 \tag{13c}$$

*[1] In climatology it is automatically assumed that we deal with real numbers unless specifically mentioned.

but other definitions such as the logarithmic mean, etc., may be of more practical value. For discrete variables analogous to the continuous case:

$$\sum_{A} f(x)=1 \tag{11b}$$

and for $A \subset \mathrm{A}$:

$$P(A)=P(X\in A)=\sum_{A} f(x) \tag{12b}$$

For the discrete type the following relationship exists between c.d.f. and p.d.f.:

$$F(x)=\sum_{y\leq x} f(y) \tag{14a}$$

For the continuous case:

$$F(x)=\int_{-\infty}^{x} f(y)\,\mathrm{d}y \tag{14b}$$

Since by definition $F(x)$ is a probability set function, several properties can be derived: (a) $0\leq F(x)\leq 1$ because $0\leq P(X\leq x)\leq 1$; (b) $F(x)$ increases with increasing x; (c) $F(\infty)=1$ and $F(-\infty)=0$; (d) If $a<b$, then $P(a<X\leq b)=F(b)-F(a)$.
If the interval between a and b represents a class interval according to eq. 13b then:

$$P(X=c)=F(x_{\mathrm{u}})-F(x_{\mathrm{l}})=F(x_{\mathrm{b}})-F(x_{\mathrm{a}}) \tag{15a}$$

For a continuous function c is a point value, $x_{\mathrm{u}}=x_{\mathrm{l}}$, hence:

$$P(X=c)=0.$$

The cumulative distribution function can be represented for a discrete type of variate as a step function, the p.d.f. in the form of a histogram (see Fig. 1).
The one-dimensional case can be expanded to multidimensions. Some applications have been treated by the author in a different text (ESSENWANGER, 1976).
The choice of the class width (eq. 13a) and consequently the number of classes is arbitrary, e.g. we may select $W=R_{\mathrm{x}}/20$ where R_{x} is the range (see eq. 17). Another option is $W\geq\sigma/3$ where σ is the standard deviation (see eq. 26d). STURGES (1926) proposed an optimal class width:

$$W=R_{x}/(1+1.4427\ \ln N) \tag{16a}$$

which is based on the binomial distribution and its number of classes:

$$n=1+1.4427\ \ln N \tag{16b}$$

If the distribution is skewed DOANE (1976) recommended to add n_{D} classes:

$$n_{\mathrm{D}}=0.43429\ \ln\,(1+\gamma_1[(N+1)(N+3)/6(N-2)]^{1/2}) \tag{16c}$$

where γ_1 is the skewness (see eq. 27a). When $\gamma_1=0$ no classes will be added.

Contingency tables

We have discussed the dividing of a continuous or discrete function into classes, for which the p.d.f. can be established. If two variables X_{ji} and X_{ki}, exist , and both variables are

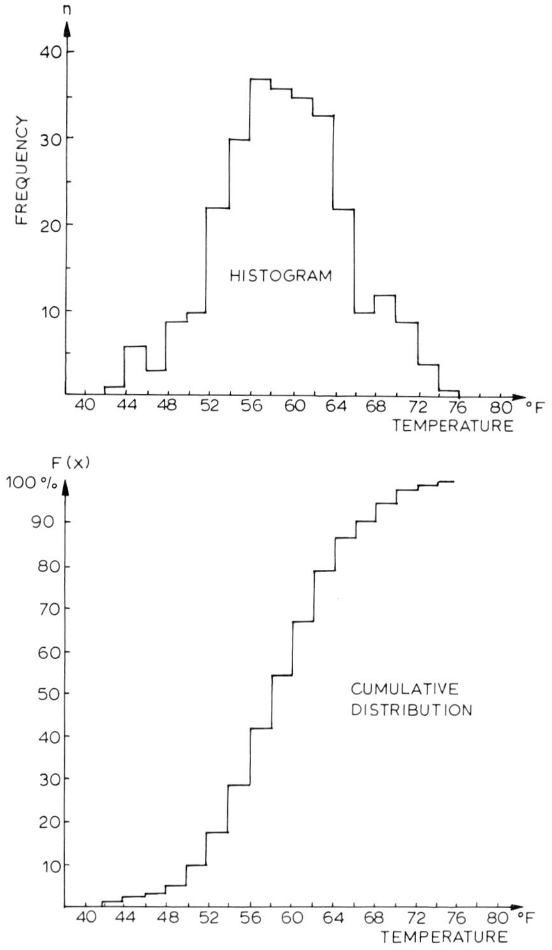

Fig. 1. Histogram and cumulative distribution for data of Table II.

divided into classes, a field of boxes can be constructed. The number n_{kj} in each box gives the joint probability density (simultaneous occurrence) of both variables, the marginal summations (either columns n_k or lines n_j) provide the p.d.f. of each separate variable. The relative frequency is $f_{kj}=n_{kj}/N$.

Division into categories can also be applied to attributes that are not susceptible to accurate measurements (e.g., cloud types), these tables are called contingency tables, as they represent a certain contingency for a specified category. An example of a contingency table is given in Table XXXIX (see also p. 296).

Contingency tables have found widespread utilization in statistical analysis. Details on usage and testing are found in subsequent sections. An excellent summary was given by KULLBACK (1974). The application of contingency tables to forecasting was treated in a special report by WMO (1966).

Example 1. Probability density function and cumulative probability. Table I contains the daily average temperature computed from 24 hourly observations at Yuma (Arizona) in February for a ten-year period 1955–1964. For simplicity the data of 29 February have been omitted. This example serves as an illustration how to establish the p.d.f. and the c.d.f. A discussion of the homogeneity of the sample is postponed until p. 14.

TABLE I

DAILY AVERAGE TEMPERATURE (°F) IN FEBRUARY (FROM 24 HOURLY OBSERVATIONS) FOR YUMA, ARIZONA

Feb.	1955	1956	1957	1958	1959	1960	1961	1962	1963	1964
1	55.6	50.3	50.9	60.6	54.0	59.3	63.6	62.4	66.4	59.8
2	52.3	43.8	51.8	59.1	54.6	63.0	63.1	62.0	68.8	57.0
3	47.8	45.7	53.9	59.5	53.2	56.5	63.8	61.6	72.8	56.0
4	45.9	48.1	56.9	59.1	54.0	58.3	63.1	61.2	70.8	52.8
5	49.2	51.1	56.0	57.3	56.3	60.1	61.0	63.6	70.6	52.3
6	49.6	51.7	58.4	58.5	59.6	61.3	57.2	62.0	72.2	53.0
7	52.0	52.3	59.7	60.8	58.1	62.0	59.8	61.4	70.8	52.0
8	54.8	54.0	65.8	61.4	54.3	62.6	59.8	61.4	69.5	55.1
9	57.5	54.0	68.9	61.7	52.9	60.7	61.5	65.2	67.4	58.9
10	56.4	53.3	71.5	59.3	53.5	54.6	64.3	68.8	61.6	60.4
11	56.3	55.9	70.4	60.8	55.2	56.3	66.0	66.5	62.0	62.0
12	58.3	59.5	72.1	61.5	57.2	59.2	64.5	62.8	59.7	56.1
13	60.4	59.9	74.1	63.6	53.1	57.1	61.1	60.0	56.3	53.1
14	63.7	58.6	73.5	61.2	54.4	56.9	64.5	63.0	59.6	51.9
15	67.9	56.5	71.1	62.7	57.5	56.5	64.0	64.9	60.8	48.9
16	68.0	48.2	68.0	63.4	63.3	56.9	60.5	60.3	60.4	46.9
17	65.6	44.8	65.0	65.6	62.2	57.0	59.3	56.8	61.7	53.7
18	56.1	50.5	62.4	65.5	60.8	55.5	58.1	56.8	61.8	58.5
19	44.8	53.7	63.2	64.3	60.0	54.1	59.5	54.0	64.3	62.2
20	45.5	55.5	62.5	60.5	59.8	54.0	62.8	53.5	67.0	59.5
21	46.4	60.2	62.3	64.4	56.3	55.8	64.4	54.0	68.0	55.5
22	48.8	62.0	63.7	65.8	54.4	55.0	65.1	53.5	65.6	54.8
23	51.2	65.9	65.8	65.8	55.9	51.7	62.0	56.0	68.9	56.0
24	53.4	57.5	63.9	66.4	57.2	49.5	58.1	54.8	69.1	55.1
25	60.2	55.4	66.8	62.6	60.2	49.7	61.0	53.5	69.0	57.8
26	56.9	56.4	71.6	59.9	61.3	55.4	64.6	51.3	70.7	53.8
27	57.8	57.3	71.5	56.5	63.5	58.2	59.0	48.1	67.5	52.0
28	58.7	59.3	68.6	56.6	68.0	58.2	59.8	45.4	67.2	55.2

TABLE II

CUMULATIVE FREQUENCY DISTRIBUTION AND PROBABILITY DENSITY OF TEMPERATURE FROM TABLE I

i	X_i	x_{ci}	n_i	$f(x_i)$	$F(x_i)$
1	42.0–43.9	42.95	1	0.3%	0.3%
2	44.0–45.9	44.95	6	2.1	2.4
3	46.0–47.9	46.95	3	1.1	3.5
4	48.0–49.9	48.95	9	3.2	6.7
5	50.0–51.9	50.95	10	3.6	10.3
6	52.0–53.9	52.95	22	7.9	18.2
7	54.0–55.9	54.95	30	10.7	28.9
8	56.0–57.9	56.95	37	13.2	42.1
9	58.0–59.9	58.95	36	12.8	54.9
10	60.0–61.9	60.95	35	12.5	67.4
11	62.0–63.9	62.95	33	11.8	79.2
12	64.0–65.9	64.95	22	7.9	87.1
13	66.0–67.9	66.95	10	3.6	90.7
14	68.0–69.9	68.95	12	4.3	95.0
15	70.0–71.9	70.95	9	3.2	98.2
16	72.0–73.9	72.95	4	1.5	99.7
17	74.0–75.9	74.95	1	0.3	100.0

TABLE III

AUXILIARY TO COMPUTATION OF MOMENTS (Example 3)

X_i	n_i	y_{ci}	$n_i y_{ci}$	$n_i y_{ci}^2$	$n_i y_{ci}^3$	$n_i y_{ci}^4$
42.0–43.9	1	−8	−8	64	−512	4096
44.0–45.9	6	−7	−42	294	−2058	14406
46.0–47.9	3	−6	−18	108	−648	3888
48.0–49.9	9	−5	−45	225	−1125	5625
50.0–51.9	10	−4	−40	160	−640	2560
52.0–53.9	22	−3	−66	198	−594	1782
54.0–55.9	30	−2	−60	120	−240	480
56.0–57.9	37	−1	−37	37	−37	37
58.0–59.9	36	0				
60.0–61.9	35	1	35	35	35	35
62.0–63.9	33	2	66	132	264	528
64.0–65.9	22	3	66	198	574	1722
66.0–67.9	10	4	40	160	640	2560
68.0–69.9	12	5	60	300	1500	7500
70.0–71.9	9	6	54	324	1944	11664
72.0–73.9	4	7	28	196	1372	9604
74.0–75.9	1	8	8	64	512	4096
$\sum$	280		41	2615	987	70583

In our case let us arbitrarily select $w=2$ degrees Fahrenheit. The first four columns of Table II with headings*[1] i, X_i, x_{ci} and n_i are self-explanatory. Next follows $f(x_i)$ which is n_i/N or the probability density function. $\sum f(x_i)=1.0$ can be checked. The last column displays the cumulative frequency distribution.

The data are given in tenths of a degree. Thus, the central class value (eq. 13b) for $i=5$ is $(51.9+50.0)/2=50.95$, etc. In electronic data processing the carrying of decimals is not connected with extra work. Otherwise a whole number such as 51 could have been chosen. Calculations of moments, etc. on ordinary desk calculators could be cumbersome if decimals are kept. The correction to the true value must then be made after computations. For further details see the moments computation (Table III).

Since the origin of the observations is not known, e.g., 50.0 is the lower and 51.9 is the upper class boundary, it must be taken at face value. If we assume that 50.0 represents data from 49.95 to 50.05 and similarly 51.9 data from 51.85 to 51.95, the central class value would be the same, namely $(51.95+49.95)/2=50.95$, although the boundaries have expanded.

Primitive and elementary characteristics

The p.d.f. or c.d.f. has now been established. The next step is the selection and definition of some primitive and elementary characteristics. $F(x)$ for $x=\pm\infty$, i.e., infinite boundaries, was discussed. Table II shows, however, that climatological sets of data are in general limited by finite numbers. Therefore, we may write:

$$F(x_2)=1;\ F(x_1)=0 \qquad \text{(15b and 15c)}$$

$$R_x=x_{max}-x_{min}=x_2-x_1 \qquad (17)$$

*[1] The central class value is here denoted by x_{ci}. In the following parts of the section the c subscript will be omitted. It is automatically assumed that the respective class characteristic for the frequency of x_i is the central class value.

is called the range of a (climatological) set of data, where x_{max} and x_{min} are the maximum and minimum, respectively. In climatology ranges, maxima and minima commonly display high variabilities which limit their usefulness. They have practical value, however, as characteristics for the boundaries of a particular set of observations.
Another primitive characteristic is the mode, defined for the variable x_j by:

$$P(x_j \in A) > P(x_i \in A) \qquad (18a)$$

for all values of $i \neq j$. A relative mode exists if:

$$P(x_j \in A_k) > P(x_i \in A_k) \qquad (18b)$$

for $A_k \in A$ and $(i-a) < j < (i+b)$, where $(a+b) \leq k$. This last condition is necessary because for a relative mode of any subset A_k of A at least one class interval exists on either side of the main mode x_j for which eq. 18b is valid without being a peak in the p.d.f. The mode or relative mode, however, must always be a maximum or relative maximum in the p.d.f.
Although the modal class is defined by eq. 18a or 18b, a refinement can be made under the assumption that the elements x_{ji} within a class x_j are not equally distributed and the probability densities of the two adjacent classes reflect the distribution within x_j. Then the mode x_{mo} becomes:

$$x_{mo} = x_l + \frac{f_{j+1}}{f_{j+1} + f_{j-1}} \cdot w \qquad (19)$$

where f_{j+1} and f_{j-1} are the probability densities of the class intervals above and below the modal class, respectively, and x_l is the lower class limit of the modal class x_j.
Some elementary characteristics refer to threshold values in the c.d.f.

Median: $F(x_{med}) = 0.5$ (20a)

Quartile: $F(x_{qu}) = 0.25$ or 0.75 (20b)

Decile: $F(x_d) = 0.1$ or $0.2 \ldots 0.9$ (20c)

Other threshold values x_{th} can be computed from ranked (ordered) data by:

$$x_{th} = x_j + \{(x_{j+1} - x_j)[F(x_{th}) - F(x_j)]\}/[F(x_{j+1}) - F(x_j)] \qquad (20d)$$

where $x_j < x_{th} < x_{j+1}$. E.g., GORDON and WELLS (1976) derived the quantiles to examine month-to-month temperature changes.
If the data are only available in the form of class groupings, the c.d.f. should be employed, and x_j is identical with x_l, x_{j+1} with x_u. Then:

$$x_l < x_{th} < x_u \qquad (20e)$$

or $x_{j+1} - x_j$ could then be replaced by the class width w (see eq. 13a). Eq. 20d is unnecessary if $x_{th} = x_j$ or $= x_l$.

Example 2. The maximum in Table I is 74.1 and the minimum 43.8. Hence the range $R_x = 30.3$°F. The mode from Table II is $x_j = 56.95$ with $n_j = 37$ and $f(x_j) = 13.2$. The adjusted mode is $x_{mo} = 56.0 + [12.8/(10.7 + 12.8)] \times 2 = 57.09$. Secondary modes appear at 44.95 and 68.95. The median is $F(x_{med}) = 57.95 + (7.9/12.8) \times 2 = 59.18$. $F(x_{0.25}) = 55.22$ and $F(x_{0.75}) = 63.27$. The reader may compute the deciles as an exercise.

Mathematical characteristics, moments

In the previous section some characteristics based on the c.d.f. or the p.d.f. were introduced. Although the maximum and minimum (x_{max} and x_{min}) can be determined without a frequency distribution, the other characteristics necessitate the establishment of $F(x)$ or $f(x)$. Sometimes this may be inconvenient or may consume extra time in data processing. Therefore, descriptive characteristics are sought which are independent from the establishment of a frequency distribution. Ideally, we also should be able to determine these descriptors if $F(x)$ or $f(x)$ are known. Such mathematical characteristics exist in the statistical theory of games. In problems involving distributions of random variables the following mathematical term has been defined:

$$E(X^{\nu}) = \mu_{\nu} = \int_{-\infty}^{\infty} X^{\nu} \, dX \qquad (21a)$$

The terms for $\nu = 0, 1 \ldots n$ are called moments in mechanics and the expression has been adopted in statistics. The letter ν denotes the order of the moment. For discrete variables:

$$E(X^{\nu}) = \mu_{\nu} = \frac{1}{N} \sum_{1}^{N} X^{\nu} \qquad (21b)$$

If a frequency distribution is available, then:

$$E(X^{\nu}) = \mu_{\nu} = \int_{-\infty}^{\infty} f(x) x^{\nu} \, dx \qquad (22a)$$

or:

$$E(X^{\nu}) = \mu_{\nu} = \sum_{1}^{n} f(x) \, x^{\nu} \qquad (22b)$$

where n corresponds to the number of classes.
Clearly, $f(x)$ appears here as the weighting function of x.
Let us now analyze the various moments.*[1]
When $\nu = 0$, we obtain unity, because $f(x)$ is the p.d.f. and relative frequency, and:

$$E(X^{0}) = \mu_{0} = \sum_{1}^{n} f(x_j) = \sum_{1}^{N} X_i^{0}/N = 1.0. \qquad (23)$$

The first moment for $\nu = 1$ leads to:

$$E(X) = \mu_1 = \sum_{1}^{n} f(x_j) x_j = \frac{1}{N} \sum_{1}^{N} X_i = \bar{X}. \qquad (24)$$

This is called the mathematical expectation of X and often denoted by $\bar{X}$, or the identically equivalent $\bar{x}$. The x_j correspond to the central class values or to:

$$x_j = \left(\sum_{1}^{n_j} X_i \right) \Big/ n_j$$

*[1] In climatology we have mostly discrete variables, thus the discussion refers to the use of discrete variables. For continuous variables the sum can be replaced by the integral.

We could continue with an expansion of μ_ν to a higher order. In climatology these expressions are seldom used. Instead, the higher moments are normalized with reference to the mean and we obtain a series of "central moments":

$$E[(X-\bar{X})^\nu]=\nu_\nu=\sum_1^n f(x_j)(x_j-\bar{x})^\nu=\frac{1}{N}\sum_1^N (X_i-\bar{X})^\nu/N \tag{25a}$$

Hence:

$$\nu_1=0 \tag{25b}$$

Further:

$$E(X-\bar{X})^2=\nu_2=\sum_1^n f(x_j)(x_j-\bar{x})^2=\sum_1^N (X_i-\bar{X})^2/N \tag{26a}$$

$$E(X-\bar{X})^3=\nu_3=\sum_1^n f(x_j)(x_j-\bar{x})^3=\sum_1^N (X_i-\bar{X})^3/N \tag{26b}$$

$$E(X-\bar{X})^4=\nu_4=\sum_1^n f(x_j)(x_j-\bar{x})^4=\sum_1^N (X_i-\bar{X})^4/N. \tag{26c}$$

Higher order moments beyond the fourth are rare in climatology. Although they can be computed their accuracy and reliability may be very low, e.g. because of the shortness of records.

The second central moment, also called variance, is usually designated*[1] by σ^2:

$$\sigma^2\equiv\nu_2=\mu_2-\bar{x}^2 \tag{26d}$$

and σ is customarily called the standard deviation (positive root of the square). The standard deviation can be interpreted as a measure of dispersion of the X_i values relative to $\bar{X}$.

The third central moment is used to compute a measure of skewness.

$$\gamma_1=\frac{\nu_3}{\sigma^3} \tag{27a}$$

The fourth central moment is often used as an expression of the flatness or excess (compared with the Gaussian normal distribution). Usually we define the kurtosis:

$$k_u=\gamma_2=\frac{\nu_4}{\sigma^4}-3 \tag{27b}$$

Bimodal distributions commonly display a large positive kurtosis. Therefore, DARLINGTON (1970) pointed out that the kurtosis is best described as a measure of bimodality versus unimodality instead of "peakedness." The reader is cautioned, however: not all frequency curves with high positive kurtosis are bimodal (DARLINGTON, 1970).

PEARSON (1894, 1895) defined parameters β_1 and β_2 to describe the relationship between the Gaussian normal distribution and his type of curves; these correspond to our symbols:

$$\beta_1=(\gamma_1)^2 \tag{28a}$$

*[1] As discussed later (eq. 48a) we must divide by $N-1$ in eq. 26a in order to obtain an unbiased estimator for σ^2.

$$\beta_2 = \gamma_2 + 3 = \frac{\nu_4}{\sigma^4}. \tag{28b}$$

For the Gaussian normal distribution

$$\gamma_1 = \gamma_2 = 0. \tag{28c}$$

Eqs. 29a–d are useful for simplification of computations, although for electronic data processing great accuracy is necessary and regular 8 digit precision may be insufficient for deriving μ_3 or μ_4.

$$\nu_3 = \mu_3 - 3\bar{X}\nu_2 - \bar{X}^3 \tag{29a}$$

$$\nu_3 = \mu_3 - 3\bar{X}\mu_2 + 2\bar{X}^3 \tag{29b}$$

$$\nu_4 = \mu_4 - 4\bar{X}\nu_3 - 6\bar{X}^2\nu_2 - \bar{X}^4 \tag{29c}$$

$$\nu_4 = \mu_4 - 4\bar{X}\mu_3 + 6\bar{X}^2\mu_2 - 3\bar{X}^4 \tag{29d}$$

We define a mixed moment:

$$\nu_{xy} = \sum_1^n f(x_j y_j)(x_j - \bar{x})(y_j - \bar{y}) = \frac{1}{N}\sum_1^N (X_i - \bar{X})(Y_i - \bar{Y}) \tag{30a}$$

or:

$$\mu_{xy} = \sum_1^n f(x_j y_j) x_j y_j = \frac{1}{N}\sum_1^N X_i Y_i \tag{30b}$$

Sometimes a different reference point instead of the mean $\bar{x}$ or zero is used. The reference point is denoted by x_R. Then:

$$\bar{x} = \sum (X - x_R)/N + x_R \tag{31a}$$

$$\sigma^2 = \sum (X - x_r)^2/N - (x_R - \bar{x})^2 \tag{31b}$$

$$\nu_3 = \sum (X - x_r)^3/N + 3(x_R - \bar{x})\sigma^2 + (x_R - \bar{x})^3 \tag{31c}$$

$$\nu_4 = \sum (X - x_R)^4/N + 4(x_R - \bar{x})\nu^3 - 6(x_R - \bar{x})^2\sigma^2 - (x_R - \bar{x})^4 \tag{31d}$$

This set of equations is useful if a precise numerical value of the moments is needed because the arbitrary reference x_R can be a convenient number (e.g., a whole number if X is given in whole numbers). The numbers requiring more precision do not appear in the summation terms but only in the correction terms with a single multiplication. For $x_R = 0$ the set of eq. 31 reduces to eqs. 24 and 26.

In empirical distributions $f(x_j)$ we may find a grouping of data into classes rather than a continuous $f(X_i)$. According to Sheppard*[1] (see KENDALL and STUART, 1958), a correction is necessary for ν_2 and ν_4. Corrected values are denoted by a prime:

$$\nu_2' = \nu_2 - \frac{w^2}{12} \quad \text{(corrected variance)} \tag{32a}$$

*[1] Correctly, Sheppard's correction should be applied to continuous variables. It is not suitable for frequency distributions having a maximum at or near one or both ends of the distribution. The correction is applicable to distributions with a central hump and $N > 100$, as e.g. in Table II.

and

$$\nu_4' = \nu_4 - \tfrac{1}{2}\nu_2 w^2 + 0.02917 w^4 \qquad (32b)$$

where w is the class width (eq. 13a).

Example 3. The computation of the parameters from grouped data (2° class intervals) in Table II is compared with the results obtained from Table I.

Grouped	Ungrouped
$\mu_1 = 59.24$; $\nu_1 = 0$	$\mu_1 = 59.22$; $\nu_1 = 0$
$\nu_2 = \sigma^2 = 37.27$; $\sigma = 6.10$	$\sigma^2 = 36.75$; $\sigma = 6.06$
$\nu_3 = -4.48$; $\gamma_1 = -0.020$	$\nu_3 = -0.016$; $\gamma_1 = -0.00$
$\nu_4 = 3908.096$; $\gamma_2 = -0.187$	$\nu_4 = 3793.688$; $\gamma_2 = -0.190$

$\nu_2' = 37.27 - 0.33 = 36.94$ $(w = 2)$
$\sigma' = 6.08$
$\nu_4' = 3908.096 - 74.51 + 0.758 = 3834.314$
with $\gamma_2' = -0.190$.
$\bar{y} = 0.146$
$\sigma_y^2 = 9.3180$; $\sigma_y = 3.053$
$\nu_3' = -0.560$; $\gamma_1 = -0.560/28.45 = -0.020$
$\nu_4' = 244.25$; $\beta_2 = 244.246/86.825 = 2.813$; $\gamma_2 = -0.187$
An adjustment must be made for the arbitrary reference point $x_R = 58.95$.
Further, $w_x = 2$ and $w_y = 1$.
Hence:

$\mu_1 = x_{ci} + (w_x/w_y)\bar{y} = 58.95 + 2 \times 0.146 = 59.26$
$\nu_2 = \sigma_y^2 \times (w_x/w_y)^2 = 9.3180 \times 4 = 37.272$
The calculated γ_1, β_2 and γ_2 above need no adjustment. If ν_3 and ν_4 are required they can be computed by eqs. 27a and b.

Moment generating function and cumulants

We have seen that the moments are important characteristics of a distribution. Since the integral in eq. 21a or 22a is often difficult to solve, other methods have been sought to derive the analytical expression for the moments. When all moments are finite, the integral exists and a "moment-generating" function $g(t)$ can be defined:

$$g(t) = E(e^{xt}) = \int_{-\infty}^{\infty} e^{xt} f(x)\,dx = \int_{-\infty}^{\infty} e^{xt}\,dF(x) \qquad (33)$$

For the discrete type the integral is replaced by the sum sign. By differentiation we can write:

$$\frac{d^{\nu} g(t)}{dt^{\nu}} = \int_{-\infty}^{\infty} x^{\nu} e^{xt} f(x)\,dx \qquad (34a)$$

For $t = 0$:

$$\frac{d^{\nu} g(0)}{dt^{\nu}} = E(x^{\nu}) = \mu_{\nu} \qquad (34b)$$

This is a simple differentiation process, where the ν-th moment follows from the ν-th derivative of $g(t)$.
We notice that the moment-generating function results in the non-central moments μ_ν. The central moment must then be computed by eq. 25a, or for the first four moments

eqs. 26d and 29b, d. The theoretical background for the moment-generating function can be found in several texts, e.g., HOYT (1972).

The calculation of the moments by the moment-generating function of the binomial distribution (see eq. 58) is illustrated by:

$$g(t)=(q+pe^t)^n \tag{34c}$$

Then:

$$\frac{dg(t)}{dt}=n(q+pe^t)^{n-1}(pe^t)$$

$$t=0: \quad \frac{dg(0)}{dt}=n(q+p)^{n-1}\times p=np.$$

Hence:

$$\mu_1=np$$

When $g(t)$ does not exist, a function:

$$g'(t)=E(e^{itx})=\int_{-\infty}^{\infty} e^{itx}\,dF(x) \tag{34d}$$

can be defined, which always exists. It is called the "characteristic function" of the distribution ($i=\sqrt{-1}$).

The moments are not the only set of descriptive parameters. Another series of important functions is the "cumulants". The "cumulant-generating function" is obtained by expanding ln $g(t)$ into a power series:

$$k(t)=\ln g(t)=k_1t+k_2t^2/2+\ldots+k_\nu t^\nu/\nu! \tag{35a}$$

We can transform $g(t)$ by multiplying with $e^{-\mu_1 t}$, which results in:

$$g(t)\,e^{-\mu_1 t}=g_1(t)=1+\nu_2t^2/2!\ \ldots\ +\nu_\nu t^\nu/\nu! \tag{35b}$$

Now:

$$\frac{dk_1(t)}{dt}=\frac{1}{g_1(t)}\times\frac{dg_1(t)}{dt} \tag{35c}$$

Hence:

$$(1+\nu_2t^2/2\ \ldots\ \nu_\nu t^\nu/\nu!)[k_1+k_2t+k_3t^2/2+\ \ldots\ k_\nu t^{\nu-1}/(\nu-1)!]$$
$$=\nu_2t+\nu_3t^2/2+\nu_4t^3/3!+\ldots\ \nu_\nu t^{\nu-1}/(\nu-1)! \tag{36}$$

with identity of coefficients of like powers of t.

$$\left.\begin{aligned}
&\mu_1=k_1\\
&\nu_2=k_2=\mu_2-k_1^2\\
&\nu_3=k_3=\mu_3-3k_2k_1-k_1^3\\
&\nu_4=k_4+3\nu_2k_2=\mu_4-4k_3k_1-6k_2k_1^2-k_1^4\\
&\nu_5=k_5+6\nu_2k_3+4\nu_3k_2=k_5+10k_3k_2
\end{aligned}\right\} \tag{37}$$

The cumulants (except the first) are invariant to any change of the origin; the non-central moments are not.
Again, the complex variable it sometimes is used instead of t. More details can be found in textbooks on statistical analysis such as MOOD (1950), KENNEY and KEEPING (1954), KENDALL and STUART (1961) or HOGG and CRAIG (1967).

Homogeneity

The problem of homogeneity presents severe difficulties in the statistical analysis of meteorological data. Customarily the population is an infinite or finite set of elements of a random variable formed by one or several controllable and defined repetitive, physical, uniform processes. A "random" sample designed so that every item of a single population has an equal chance to be selected is a set of homogeneous data. A random, homogeneous sample is needed to derive valid conclusions regarding the properties of the population. Inhomogeneity of climatological series can be caused by alterations in physical processes, by trend or by oscillation. Other causes may be instrumental effects such as changes of instrumentation or instrumentation site, or in vegetation cover around sites, etc. Homogeneity requires that the measurement properties remain the same within the sampling period.
In the practice of taking meteorological observations, samples usually are not selected to fill this rigid requirement of homogeneity, because the data commonly are successive or nearly successive. The daily temperature or precipitation of an individual calendar date (e.g. the 15th of July) for every year through a given time period could be a homogeneous sample, if, e.g., the existence of only one air mass for a specific location on this calendar date can be assumed; no climatological trend or oscillation in the given time period prevails; and no heterogeneous influence by instrumentation or incompatible physical characteristic exists.
Only a few data collections can be considered homogeneous under these strict rules. We can, however, adopt a working hypothesis and accept meteorological data as homogeneous if a valid statistical test gives a high probability of evidence for homogeneity. Some tests are discussed on p. 254ff. It is most likely that monthly averages for several meteorological elements will provide a homogeneous sample (e.g., all monthly averages of January). Homogeneous seasonal combinations (e.g., December, January, February) may be possible under certain circumstances. For most climates annual combinations yield inhomogeneous data.
It may be extremely difficult to correct for alterations in physical processes, but trends or oscillations can sometimes be eliminated. Determination of trends and oscillations is treated on p. 108ff (linear trend) and p. 146ff (oscillations). Corrections are also applied for changes in station location or instrumental bias. Generally it is not possible to reconstruct a series of corrected individual observations although data gaps can sometimes be bridged by specially designed rules and adopted objective techniques. It is customary, however, to adjust the characteristics of a set of inhomogeneous observations.
The most common problem is the derivation of a representative mean value for a total time period when the station location has changed. The difference and the ratio (or logarithmic difference) methods are commonly used but they require a homogeneous

auxiliary station preferably close in altitude*[1].

Adjustment by difference (e.g., temperature records) can be computed by:

$$\bar{x}_a = \bar{x} + \Delta x \tag{38a}$$

where $\bar{x}_a$ is the adjusted mean and $\bar{x}$ is the mean of a homogeneous supplementary location.

We obtain Δx from the following relationship:

$$\Delta x = \bar{u} - \bar{v} \tag{38b}$$

where $\bar{u}$ and $\bar{v}$ are the means from a homogeneous period with simultaneous records at the auxiliary and prime location, respectively. The mean for the total period must be weighted according to homogeneous subperiods.

Ratio method:

$$\bar{x}_a = (\Delta X) \times \bar{x} \tag{39a}$$

$$\ln \Delta X = \ln \bar{u} - \ln \bar{v} \tag{39b}$$

This method is usually adopted for precipitation records with the symbols equivalent to eq. 38a.

Sometimes one finds instead of eq. 39b:

$$\ln \Delta X = \frac{1}{N} \sum (\ln u_i - \ln v_i) \tag{39c}$$

A more sophisticated method utilizing several stations was developed by MITCHELL (1961). In this connection it seems appropriate to discuss the length of the "normal" period. The problem cannot be solved unconditionally. The length depends largely on the time variability of the meteorological element. The goal should be to establish a stable characteristic such as the mean or other parameters. Other factors include the accuracy of the parameters (see standard error, p. 247), the homogeneity of the time period, the availability of records and the purpose of computing a normal value. Although the use of a 30-year period is widespread, a shorter period may sometimes suffice. A longer period may introduce climatological trends into the set of data. Tests to check the homogeneity of the time series will be presented on pp. 170, 254ff (see also SNEYERS, 1979a).

Example 4. Assume we are interested in the 30-year average temperature of a station A for which the instrumentation has been moved twice during the period. In the first 11 years of record at station A_1, the mean was 19.5°C. The next seven years for station A_2 had a mean of 18.7 and finally, the 12 years at station A show 19.3°C. Let us assume that station B has a 30-year record and can be used as an auxiliary station with the temperature as given in Table IV. The problem is solved with the help of eqs. 38a and 38b.

Table IV displays the mean temperatures for the respective periods. Notice that the total mean for the 30 years at station B is the weighted mean, as the years n are not equal. The example demonstrates that locations A and A_1 show closeness of the average temperature conditions, but station A_2 is much colder.

Notice: $\bar{x}_A = 21.0 - 1.5$; $\bar{x}_{A_1} = 21.0 - 1.4$; $\bar{x}_{A_2} = 21.0 - 2.8$.

---

*[1] Mountain observatories, although generally possessing long homogeneous data series cannot be used for regular stations without special investigations (see TENTER, 1970).

TABLE IV

COMPUTATION OF THE MEAN TEMPERATURE FOR A HETEROGENEOUS STATION

Years	n	B	A_1	A_2	A	Δ	A	A_1	A_2
1–11	11	20.9	19.5	–	–	−1.4	(19.4)	19.5	(18.1)
12–18	7	21.5	–	18.7	–	−2.8	(20.0)	(20.1)	18.7
19–30	12	20.8			19.3	−1.5	19.3	(19.4)	(18.0)
1–30	30	21.0					19.5	19.6	18.2

Note: values between brackets are estimated.

Persistence

Meteorological observations usually are not independent of preceding conditions. This is quite obvious, e.g., a high or low pressure system needs time to develop or disappear. Some of them may "persist" a long time. Thus we can expect persistence to decrease with an increase in the length of the time interval between subsequent observations. E.g., the daily amount of rainfall may not have any correlation to the amount in a preceding year, but it frequently is influenced by the condition on the day before.
One of the best measurements of persistence is the autocorrelation (see eq. 43i or 292a). Oscillations can be measured by the Fourier series (see eq. 384a). Often persistence is measured by the number of runs (see p. 265). Some discussion of persistence in this section appears appropriate.

Simple tools

Besson (1924) defined persistence as:

$$B_p = \frac{1-p}{1-p_1} - 1 = \frac{1-P(A_2)}{1-P(A_2|A_1)} - 1 \tag{40a}$$

where p is the probability of an event A_2 and p_1 the probability of the occurrence of the event A_2 after another event A_1 has taken place. $B_p = 1$ for $p = p_1$ and ∞ for $p_1 = 1.0$, i.e., the event is always followed by the same event.
The coefficient can be transformed to:

$$r_B = 1 - \left(\frac{1-p_1}{1-p}\right)^2 = 1 - 1/(B_p+1)^2 \tag{40b}$$

where the boundaries are now 0 for $p = p_1$ and 1 for $p_1 = 1$.
Another coefficient of persistence has been formulated by Goutereau (1906):

$$G_p = \frac{\sigma\sqrt{2}}{\sigma_d} - 1 \tag{41a}$$

where σ is the standard deviation of the series and σ_d the standard deviation of the differences between observations. In a random series $\sigma_d = \sigma\sqrt{2}$, and $G_p = 0$. Reformulation of eq. 41a renders:

$$r_G = 1 - \frac{\sigma_d^2}{2\sigma^2} = 1 - 1/(G_p + 1)^2 \tag{41b}$$

For large N the correlation coefficient (see eq. 280a) and r_G are the same.
Persistence can also be measured by the number of runs, i.e. an unbroken succession of occurrences or non-occurrences. Tests are discussed on p. 265.
In meteorology an additional persistence measurement is important: the directional constancy of the wind. This persistence can be expressed as the ratio between the vector mean $R_{x,y}$ and the mean of the magnitudes of the vectors (scalar mean).

$$q = \frac{R_{x,y}}{\bar{v}} \tag{42a}$$

where:

$$R_{x,y}^2 = \bar{x}^2 + \bar{y}^2 \tag{42b}$$

or:

$$R_{x,y}^2 = \left(\frac{1}{N}\sum v \cos \phi\right)^2 + \left(\frac{1}{N}\sum v \sin \phi\right)^2 \tag{42c}$$

$$\bar{v} = \frac{1}{N}\sum v \tag{42d}$$

With no directional change $R_{x,y} = \bar{v}$ and q becomes 1.0. A completely random variation leads to $R_{x,y} = 0$ with $q = 0$. The quotient q, therefore, is similar to the correlation coefficient or other persistence criteria (e.g., see p. 171).

Example 5. Assume, we are interested in the persistence of the temperature above the average, after the temperature was above normal the day before. For January–February 1955–1964 at Yuma (Arizona) at 12 h noon the following probabilities result. The temperature was above 64°F on 302 out of 580 days, $P(A_2) = 302/580 = 0.521$.
The temperature was above 64° on 243 days for which the temperature the day before was also 64°. Hence $P(A_2|A_1) = 243/302 = 0.805$.
According to the persistence coefficient by Besson:

$$B_p = \frac{1 - 0.521}{1 - 0.805} - 1 = 1.456$$

$$r_B = 1 - 1/(1.456 + 1)^2 = 0.874.$$

For Goutereau's coefficient of persistence, σ for the 12 h noon temperature is 6.8221, the $\sigma_d = 3.9476$. Hence:

$$G_p = \frac{6.8221\sqrt{2}}{3.9476} - 1 = 1.443$$

Then:

$$r_G = 1 - 1/(2.443)^2 = 0.832$$

The similarities in the value between B_p and G_p are coincidental and depend on the threshold for Besson's coefficient. Had we chosen e.g. 51°F, then the results would be $P(A_2) = 561/580 = 0.967$ and $P(A_2|A_1) = 547/561 = 0.975$. This results in $B_p = 0.320$ and $r_B = 0.426$. Only 14 of the days $(561 - 547)$ display a change at such a low threshold, but the computed criteria illustrate that the persistence is low and a change is more likely. This agrees with normal expectation in this climate, where a warming trend at low temperatures is more likely than persisting cold weather. Another example of persistence for hourly data was given by LUND and GRANTHAM (1975).

Autocorrelation and repetitions

BARTELS (1943) introduced ω_R, the "equivalent number" of repetitions. This measure is expressed as the ratio:

$$\omega_R = n/N_I \tag{43a}$$

where n is the number of observations within a group (series) of observations and N_I is the "effective number" of independent values. It is self-evident that the effective number of independent observations must be at least one and cannot exceed n within a group. Hence, $1 \leq N_I \leq n$. Consequently, $n \geq \omega_R \geq 1.0$.
Specifically, Bartels has given the effective number of independent observations as the ratio:

$$N_I = \sigma^2/\sigma_g^2 \tag{43b}$$

where σ^2 denotes the customary variance of the total observations and:

$$\sigma_g^2 = \sum (\bar{x}_j - \bar{X})^2/n_k \tag{43c}$$

where $\bar{x}_j$ is the group mean and $\bar{X}$ the overall mean. In terms of past notation, with $N = n \times n_j$, we can write:

$$\bar{x}_j = \sum_{i=1}^{n} x_{ij}/n \tag{43d}$$

and:

$$\bar{X} = \sum_{j=1}^{n_j} \bar{x}_j/n_j = \sum_j (\sum_i x_{ij})/N \tag{43e}$$

The expected value for $\sigma_g^2 = \sigma^2/n$ for independence, and $\sigma_g^2 = \sigma^2$ for optimal persistence, i.e. for $x_{ij} = \text{const} = \bar{x}_j$ within a group ($i = 1, ..., n$; $j = 1, ..., n_j$). These differences in the expectancy can be readily illustrated from the formula:

$$\sigma^2 = \sum_j \sum_i (x_{ij} - \bar{x}_j)^2/N + \sum_j (\bar{x}_j - \bar{X})^2/n_j \tag{43f}$$

because the variance within a group is:

$$\sigma_j^2 = \sum_i (x_{ij} - \bar{x}_j)^2/N \tag{43g}$$

we can write:

$$\sigma_g^2 = \sum_j (\bar{x}_j - \bar{X})^2/n_j = \sigma^2 - \sum \sigma_j^2/n_j \tag{43h}$$

For independence $\sigma_j^2 \neq 0$. Consequently, $\sigma_g^2 < \sigma^2$, specifically $\sigma_g^2 = \sigma^2/n$. For optimal persistence $x_{ij} = \bar{x}_j$ and $\sigma_j^2 = 0$. Consequently, $\sigma_g^2 = \sigma^2$.

The measure ω_R can also be expressed by the autocorrelation function (see eq. 292a):

$$\omega_R = r_0 + (2/n) \sum_{i=1}^{n} (n-i) r_i, \tag{43i}$$

where r_i denotes the autocorrelation coefficients and $r_0 = 1.0$. For independence $r_i = 0$ with $i \geq 1$, and $\omega_R = 1.0$, i.e. there are no repetitions (see later eq. 493b).
A certain pattern of persistence is the Markov chain (see eq. 423a, or ESSENWANGER, 1976, p. 299) in which the autocorrelation can be expressed by:

$$r_i = \rho^i \tag{43j}$$

and ω_R transforms to:

$$\omega_R = (1+\rho)/(1-\rho) - 2\rho(1-\rho^n)/[n(1-\rho)^2] \tag{43k}$$

where $-1.0 < \rho < 1.0$. Again, $\rho = 0$ renders $\omega_R = 1.0$.
SNEYERS (1971) developed a maximum likelihood estimator of ρ for a Markov chain:

$$\hat{\rho} = \sum_j \sum_i x_{ij} x_{i(j-1)} / (\sum_j \sum_i x_{ij}^2) \tag{44a}$$

It is assumed that x_{ij} is given in deviations from the mean $\bar{X}$, i.e., $\bar{x} = 0$. In simpler notation we may write:

$$\hat{\rho} = \overline{\mathrm{Cov}}_j / \sigma^2 \tag{44b}$$

with:

$$\mathrm{Cov}_j = \sum x_{ij} x_{i(j-1)} / n \tag{44c}$$

and:

$$\overline{\mathrm{Cov}}_j = \sum_j \mathrm{Cov}_j / n_k \tag{44d}$$

In other words, the observations are divided into n_k groups with n observations each. Then the covariance between subsequent groups (i.e. j and $j-1$; $j \geq 2$) is computed (eq. 44c) and averaged (eq. 44d). In order to derive $\hat{\rho}$ we divide by σ^2 (see eq. 44b).
Combination of eq. 43a with 43b gives:

$$\omega_R = n\sigma_g^2 / \sigma^2 \tag{44e}$$

Another estimator for ω_R can be obtained by substituting estimators for σ_g^2 and σ^2. Additional theoretical background can be found in SNEYERS (1971), who presented a table of relations between ρ and ω_R. Persistence and correspondence with filters is discussed on p. 213.

Areal persistence

Areal persistence relates the probability of an event at a single location to the probability of occurrence within a (surrounding) area. Simple models relate the decrease of the (linear) correlation coefficient with distance, e.g.:

$$r_1(s) = \exp[-as^c] \tag{45a}$$

where r denotes the (linear) correlation coefficient, s the distance between stations and a and c are model constants. Sometimes a modified expression can be found such as:

$$r_2(s) = r_1(s) \times \cos(\alpha \times s) \tag{45b}$$

The trigonometric term causes $r_2(s)$ to become slightly negative after $\cos(\alpha \times s)$ crosses zero, but with increasing distance between stations $r_2(s)$ approximates zero. Generally, $1.0 \leq c \leq 2.0$, but models utilizing the boundary values of c are more frequently found.
GRINGORTEN (1973) suggested a different approach. In his first model the weighting function $F(R)$ decreases exponentially with the square of the distance, $F(R) = \exp(-R^2/A)$, and:

$$r_3(s) = \exp[-s^2/(2A)] \tag{45c}$$

where R stands for the Cartesian coordinates of an area, $R^2 = x^2 + y^2$. Gringorten defined a "characteristic" distance $d_c = s_1/s$, where s_1 is a specific distance. A convenient setting of $A = 50$ in eq. 45c results in:

$$r_3(s_1) = \exp - [s_1/(10d_c)]^2 \tag{45d}$$

Over the distance $s_1 = d_c$ (miles) r_3 remains almost exactly 0.99.
In the second model a uniform weighting function within a circular area surrounding the location is assumed, i.e.:

$$F(R) = \begin{cases} 1 \text{ for } R \leq R_0 \\ 0 \text{ for } R > R_0 \end{cases} \tag{45e}$$

For a short distance the following approximation is valid:

$$r_4(s_1) = r_4(s) = \exp - [2s/(\pi R_0)] \tag{45f}$$

In other words r_4 decreases exponentially with linear distance, and becomes zero for $2R_0$, according to:

$$\left.\begin{aligned} r_4(s_1) &= (2/\pi)[\sin^{-1}\sqrt{(1-d_2^2} - d_2\sqrt{1-d_2^2}] && \text{for } d_2 < 1 \\ &= 0 && \text{for } d_2 \geqq 1 \end{aligned}\right\} \tag{45g}$$

where $d_2 = s/(2R_0)$. For $R_0 = 64$ we find $d_2 = s_1/(128d_c)$, where again $r_4(s_1) = 0.99$ for d_c (miles).
According to Gringorten, the first model works well for temperature distribution while the second model may be better suited for mesoscale rainfall.
GRINGORTEN (1983) later expanded his work of climatological modelling of areal coverage to include sky cover, temperature, and visibility.

Significance and confidence

We pointed out that the relative frequency fluctuates for small N and stabilizes for large N. In practice we are interested whether these fluctuations are caused by chance or whether they are real and/or significant. Thus, we test the result against a hypothetical random model or expectation. The test is called a significance test and provides a criterion for deciding whether differences between theory and observation can reasonably be attributed to chance. The probability of erroneously rejecting a true hypothesis is called the significance level of a test. Individual authors may arbitrarily select different levels of significance, but 5%, 1% or 2σ levels frequently are chosen.

Another object of the statistical analysis is the estimation of parameters. Generally an interval can be computed for which one may assert a certain probability that it will contain the parameter. This interval is called the confidence interval and the probability the degree of confidence. The confidence interval can be one-sided or two-sided. More details are presented on p. 243. We define*[1]:

$$P[c_l < \text{par} < c_u] = 1 - \alpha \tag{46}$$

where c_u and c_l are the upper and lower boundaries, respectively, of the confidence interval and α is the level of signficance.

It should be cautioned that standard significance tests developed in modern theory of statistics can be misleading, because the assumptions upon which the tests are based may not be valid for a set of meteorological observations. Furthermore, significance does not guarantee the usefulness of the result for meteorological application, e.g., we may compute a correlation coefficient which is highly significant, but which is so low that it is worthless for practical application. Additional information on confidence and significance is found throughout this text.

Estimation

Assume we have a p.d.f. of a random variable X. The p.d.f. may have several parameters, one of which is θ in a set D. We denote this by writing $f(x,\theta)$, $\theta \in D$ and D is called the parameter space. The family of distributions for all θ in D is denoted by $\{f(x_i,\theta);\ \theta \in D\}$. Assume, for a special purpose we want to select precisely one member of the family to be the p.d.f. of the random variable. We need a point estimate of θ as opposed to the space D with the boundaries θ_l and θ_u, (i.e., $\theta_l < \theta < \theta_u$) which could be $\pm\infty$ for some parameter space D. Because there are infinitely many ways of selecting a point estimator θ, the problem is to choose a good rather than a poor estimator. The determination of an appropriate parameter is treated comprehensively in modern statistical literature and many textbooks deal in detail with the problem (e.g. Mood, 1950; Kenney and Keeping, 1954; Hald, 1957; Kendall and Stuart, 1961; Hogg and Craig, 1967; Snedecor and Cochran, 1967; Chakravarti et al., 1967; Sneyers, 1975). Only a few facts on estimators are summarized here.

The estimator is used in place of the unknown parameters of the p.d.f. In order to distinguish between the unknown parameter and its replacement, the estimator is called a statistic, let us assume S. It is usually obtained by sampling.

Four properties are desirable for a good estimator: unbiasedness, efficiency, sufficiency, and consistency. The first two conditions are combined under the term “best” statistic.

Definitions

(*a*) *Definition 1*: unbiased statistic. The mathematical expectation is equal to the true value:

$$E(S) = \theta \tag{47}$$

*[1] par = parameter.

The mean value $\bar{x}$ is an unbiased estimator, but the variance σ^2 is not. In order to fulfil eq. 47 for the variance (eq. 26d), we must divide by $N-1$ instead of N.

$$S^2 = \frac{1}{N-1}\sum (X - X_{\mathrm{m}})^2 \tag{48a}$$

The unbiased estimator for σ is given by (see DEMING and BIRGE, 1934; HOLTZMAN, 1950; HALD, 1952; CURETON, 1968; BOLCH, 1968):

$$S_{\mathrm{u}} = C_N S \tag{48b}$$

where:

$$C_N = \Gamma\left(\frac{N-1}{2}\right)\sqrt{\frac{N-1}{2}}\Big/\Gamma\left(\frac{N}{2}\right) \tag{48c}$$

and S is the square root of the unbiased variance. (For the definition of Γ see eq. 90a.) GURLAND and TRIPATHI (1971) have given some simple approximations for C_N and K_N where:

$$C_N = [(N-1)/K_N]^{1/2} \tag{48d}$$

$$C_N \approx 1 + 1/[4(N-1)] \tag{48e}$$

$$K_N \approx N - 1.5 + 1/[8(N-1)] \tag{48f}$$

These approximations simplify the computation of C_N and eliminate the lengthy process of calculating Γ. The standard deviation is then:

$$\hat{\sigma} = [\sum (X - X_{\mathrm{m}})^2/K_N]^{1/2} \tag{48g}$$

The second numerical term in eq. 48f is negligible for $N \geq 6$ if the precision of K_N can be relaxed to two digits. Then $K_N \sim N - 1.5$ (see also BRUGGER, 1969a).
The variance of $\hat{\sigma}$ for a Gaussian distribution is (HALD, 1952):

$$\mathrm{Var}\,(\hat{\sigma}) = B_k\sigma^2 \approx \sigma^2/(2k) \tag{48h}$$

where:

$$B_k^2 = 1 - (2/k)\left[\Gamma\left(\frac{k+1}{2}\right)\Big/\Gamma\left(\frac{k}{2}\right)\right]^2 \tag{48i}$$

and k denotes the degrees of freedom (see p. 247).
(*b*) *Definition 2*: efficient statistic. The previous definition of an unbiased estimator can only be filled "in the limit" if the variance of S is a minimum. In mathematical notation:

$$\left.\begin{aligned} &E(S) \to \theta \quad &(49a)\\ &\mathrm{Var}\,(S) \to 0 \quad &(49b)\end{aligned}\right\} \text{ as } N \to \infty$$

Another formulation is the requirement that $\sqrt{N(S-\theta)}$ has a Gaussian distribution with 0 mean for $N \to \infty$. Although efficient estimators need not be unbiased for finite samples, they are clearly unbiased in the limit. The minimum variance $\mathrm{Var}_{\min}$ is defined by:

$$\mathrm{Var}_{\min} = \frac{1}{N \cdot E\left[\frac{\partial(\ln f)}{\partial S}\right]^2} \tag{49c}$$

The ratio $\mathrm{Var}_{\min}/\mathrm{Var}_S$ is called the efficiency of S. A most efficient statistic has a ratio of 100%. When a most efficient statistic exists, it can be found by the method of maximum likelihood (discussed later).

Inefficient statistics are more easily obtained (e.g., by the method of moments), and the loss may not be serious. Often it is worthwhile to apply a small correction to an inefficient statistic S^* rather than make elaborate computations to derive an efficient statistic. Corrections can be made by:

$$S = S^* + \sigma_S^2 \left(\frac{\partial L}{\partial \theta}\right)_{S^*} \tag{49d}$$

where:

$$\left(\frac{\partial L}{\partial \theta}\right)_{S^*} = \left(\frac{\partial L}{\partial \theta}\right)_S + S^* - S\left(\frac{\partial L}{\partial \theta}\right)_{S^2} + \ldots \tag{49e}$$

(For L see eqs. 52a and 53a.)

Minimum variance estimators have become the subject of discussions in the recent statistical literature. E.g., BLOM (1976) has analyzed that the arithmetic mean is the best linear unbiased estimator (Blue).

(*c*) *Definition 3*: sufficient statistic. The value of S does not depend on θ. It contains all the information in the sample regarding the parameter.

$$\prod_1^n f(x_i,\theta) = g(x_1, x_2, \ldots, x_n; S)h(S,\theta) \tag{50}$$

where g does not depend on θ. This includes the domain of g.

Sufficient estimators do not exist for a considerable number of parameters. Maximum likelihood estimators, however, are sufficient (see BARTLETT, 1937b).

(*d*) *Definition 4*: consistent statistic. The statistic S tends toward the true population parameter:

$$P(S \rightarrow \theta) \rightarrow 1 \text{ for } n \rightarrow \infty \tag{51}$$

Maximum-likelihood estimation

There are several methods by which estimators can be obtained. In modern statistical theory the principle of maximum likelihood is preferred. The definition of a maximum-likelihood estimator $\hat{\theta}$ of a parameter θ is based on the maximum-likelihood function. Any parameter $\hat{\theta}$ that maximizes the likelihood function $L(\theta, x_1, x_2, \ldots, x_n)$ of the frequency function $f(\theta, x_i)$ is a maximum-likelihood estimator. Thus, the critical problem is to find the likelihood function L.

The likelihood function is defined as the joint probability density function, which is based on the principle of eq. 9a and can be generally expressed by:

$$L(\theta, x_1, x_2, \ldots, x_n) = \prod_1^n f(x_i, \theta) \tag{52a}$$

We are seeking a maximum, and according to calculus methods we must find the derivative (or as many derivatives as parameters):

$$\frac{\partial L}{\partial \theta} = 0 \tag{52b}$$

In most cases it is silently assumed that this derivative provides the maximum-likelihood estimator. This can be checked, however, by requiring:

$$\prod_1^n f(x_i, \hat{\theta}) > \prod_1^n f(x_i, \theta_j) \tag{52c}$$

for any j between $\pm\infty$, and n usually is the number of observations N. In practice it is sometimes difficult to determine the correct p.d.f., $f(x_i, \theta)$, for the individual observation. Then n denotes the number of classes and the density function can be considered as the weight of the individual class values x_i. Whether individual observations can enter eq. 52b or whether class grouping should be made can generally be determined from the form of the solution for eq. 52b.

In many practical applications the derivative $\partial L/\partial \theta$ may be difficult to obtain. A much simpler form is the calculation of:

$$L' = \ln L = \sum \ln f(x_i, \theta) \tag{53a}$$

Instead of $\partial L/\partial \theta$ we substitute:

$$\frac{\partial L'}{\partial \theta} = 0 = \frac{\partial}{\partial \theta}[\sum \ln f(x_i, \theta)] \tag{53b}$$

Usually maximum-likelihood estimators are denoted by ˆ in the statistical literature.

Example 6. An example may demonstrate the difference between eqs. 52b and 53b. Assume that:

$$f(\theta, x_i) = \theta\, e^{-\theta x_i}$$

Then:

$$L = \prod_1^n \theta\, e^{-\theta x_i} = \theta\, e^{-\theta x_1} \times \theta\, e^{-\theta x_2} \ldots \theta\, e^{-\theta x_n} \tag{53c}$$

or:

$$L = \theta^n e^{-\theta \sum_{i=1}^{n} x_i} \tag{53d}$$

We need:

$$\frac{\partial L}{\partial \theta} = (-\theta \sum x_i + n)\theta^{n-1} e^{-\theta \sum x_i} = 0 \tag{53e}$$

The solution is:

$$\hat{\theta} = n/\sum x_i \tag{53f}$$

Instead of the above procedure we could have substituted:

$$L'=\ln L=\sum(\ln\theta-\theta x_i)=n\ln\theta-\theta\sum_{i=1}^{n}x_i \tag{53g}$$

$$\frac{\partial L'}{\partial\theta}=n/\theta-\sum_{i=1}^{n}x_i=0 \tag{53h}$$

It is obvious that eq. 55b is a simpler expression than eq. 54c but it leads to the same answer, $\hat{\theta}$. We can check whether $\hat{\theta}$ provides a maximum. Assume $n=6$, $\sum x_i=15$, then $\hat{\theta}=0.4$

θ	$\ln\theta$	$n\ln\theta$	$-\theta\sum x_i$	L'	
0.2	−1.60	−9.60	−3.0	−12.60	
0.3	−1.20	−7.20	−4.5	−11.70	
0.4	−0.92	−5.52	−6.0	−11.52	maximum
0.5	−0.69	−4.14	−7.5	−11.64	
0.6	−0.51	−3.06	−9.0	−12.06	

Other maximum likelihood solutions can be found in sections of pp. 29–101.

Moments estimation

An alternative method to obtain estimators is the moments fit*[1] for which the moments of a distribution are used as defined in eq. 21a. Moments estimators are not always efficient, but they are efficient for the Gaussian normal distribution. If we are mainly concerned with properties of populations rather than the reliability of estimates, the moments fit can be adopted without the question of efficiency. Details about the moments of the distributions are later presented by individual types of frequency curves.

Least square estimation

Another method of determining parameters is the least square fit, which is often applied in correlation analysis and curve fitting processes.
The method minimizes:

$$L_{\text{sq.}}=\sum_{1}^{n}[f(\text{obs}_i)-f(x_i\cdot\theta)]^2 \tag{54a}$$

or:

$$\frac{\partial(L_{\text{sq.}})}{\partial\theta}=0=\tfrac{1}{2}\frac{\partial}{\partial\theta}\{\sum[f(\text{obs})-f(x_i,\theta)]\} \tag{54b}$$

A solution which is later shown (eqs. 360 and 361) is generally based on solving sets of linear equations by matrix analysis. Some of the estimators are simultaneously maximum likelihood estimators.

Bayesian estimation

One recent trend in statistical research is the application of Bayesian statistics. The conditional probability of eq. 9b was introduced.

*[1] The two different approaches were subject of discussion between R. A. Fisher and Karl Pearson. It is sometimes beneficial to remember PEARSON's reply, 1936.

We may call $f_p(\theta)$ the prior p.d.f. of a parameter $\tilde{\theta}$ and the conditional p.d.f. $f(\theta|y)$ the posterior p.d.f. of $\tilde{\theta}$. In many instances, $f_p(\theta)$ is not known, yet the choice of $f_p(\theta)$ affects the interval $\theta_l < \tilde{\theta} < \theta_u$. One solution is to take into account all prior knowledge of the experiment and assign a p.d.f. $f_p(\theta)$. This injects a subjective probability into the problem of estimation. Some solutions exist, however, where the estimation is independent of the knowledge of the distribution, as discussed below.

The classical approach to a problem of estimating θ_n for a given set A_j of observations x_{ij}, here called experience, for which a sufficient statistic X_n can be computed, is the use of a limited set of observations for X_n in estimating θ_n. If the relationship:

$$F(X_1, X_2 \ldots X_n|\theta_1, \theta_2 \ldots \theta_n) = \prod_1^n F(X_i|\theta_i) \tag{55a}$$

exists, we would ignore the prior experiences $X_1 \ldots X_{n-1}$.

The pure Bayesian approach assumes a distribution for θ, here called $G(\theta)$. We obtain the estimator from:

$$E(\theta|X_n) = \frac{\int \theta \, \mathrm{d}F(X_n|\theta) \, \mathrm{d}G(\theta)}{\int \mathrm{d}F(X_n|\theta) \, \mathrm{d}G(\theta)} \tag{55b}$$

(the posterior mean) as the minimizing estimator. This depends on the choice of $G(\theta)$.

The empirical Bayesian approach expresses $E(\theta|X_n)$ in a form such that θ can be estimated from the prior data sets $A_1 \ldots A_{j-1}$ for which sufficient statistics $X_1 \ldots X_{n-1}$ have been computed, without the knowledge of assumptions about the unknown distribution. The solution depends on the problem (CLEMMER and KRUTCHKOFF, 1968). Bayesian statistics are more common in problems of quality control (e.g., see LOCKE, 1964) than in atmospheric science.

Other estimations

Other methods exist which generally are not applied in meteorology. We could require, for example, that C_{sq} goes to a minimum (see eq. 645, chi square):

$$C_{sq} = \sum \frac{[f(\text{obs})_i - f(x_i, \theta)]^2}{f(x_i, \theta)} \tag{56}$$

Order statistics

The estimators previously introduced can be calculated without special sequence of the observational data. We have discussed other characteristic quantities of the frequency distribution such as the median, percentiles, etc. For these the order of data was necessary. Whenever a sequence of the observations by magnitude is needed for computing an estimator, we speak of an "order statistic". Sometimes the name "systematic statistic" may be employed.

The exact distribution of order statistics for evaluation of the quality of the statistics is usually difficult to derive. Therefore, order statistics have previously not had widespread application. A detailed discussion of important results in the utilization of order statistics can be found in WILKS (1948). Recently BEHBOODIAN (1977) related the order statistics with the moments of non-ordered variates:

$$\sum Y_i^k = \sum X_i^k \tag{57}$$

where Y_i is the ordered and X_i the ordinary observed value. Although explicit solutions can be found for eq. 57 they are not easy to obtain and produce often lengthy expressions.

Mathematical and empirical symbols

In order to distinguish between theoretical parameter or its mathematical expectation and its empirical counterpart (from data samples, i.e. estimators) the following nomenclature will be adopted in the subsequent parts whenever applicable.

Theoretical parameter:	Observed or estimator*[1]:	
$\bar{x} \equiv \bar{X}$	$X_m \equiv x_m = (1/N) \sum X_i$	(57a)
σ^2	S^2 or $s^2 = (N-1)^{-1} \sum (X_i - X_m)^2$	(57b)
σ	s or S	(57c)
ν_3	$M_3 = (1/N) \sum (X_i - X_m)^3$	(57d)
ν_4	$M_4 = (1/N) \sum (X_i - X_m)^3$	(57e)
μ_j	m_j	(57f)

*[1] Unbiased estimator for s see eq. 48b. In common statistical practice $s = \sqrt{s^2}$ is utilized.

Chapter 2

Frequency Distributions

In the previous section general statistical principles were introduced. This section will acquaint the reader with some of the frequency distribution models that are often utilized in statistical analysis in meteorology. It is obvious that in a short description many details on the theoretical background of frequency curves and related problems must be left unanswered. The reader interested in more details of the theoretical background or other types of frequency models is referred to the statistical literature such as MOOD (1950), HALD (1957), KENDALL and STUART (1958), BROWNLEE (1960a), CHAKRAVARTI et al. (1967), JOHNSON and KOTZ (1969, 1970a, 1970b, 1972) ESSENWANGER (1976), etc.

The variety of distributions presented in this section will not solve all problems encountered in the atmospheric sciences. A selection has been made to delineate some of the important and most common types. They will be useful in many of the problems. Karl Pearson's system (see ELDERTON, 1953 or ESSENWANGER, 1976), many of the less frequently utilized systems, and multi-dimensional distributions were omitted for brevity. Supplementation of the subsequent models and the treatment of mixture of distributions can be found in the author's earlier text (ESSENWANGER, 1976).

The binomial distribution

Although the binomial distribution has only limited application in climatology as a p.d.f., some other important distributions are derived from it. Further, some important tests are based upon the binomial distribution, which is also called the Bernoulli distribution in memory of its inventor.

Generally it is known that:

$$(a+b)^n = \sum_{x=0}^{n} \binom{n}{x} b^x a^{n-x} \tag{58}$$

Let us define a function:

$$f(x) = \binom{n}{x} p^x (1-p)^{n-x} \begin{cases} \text{for } x=0, 1, 2 \ldots n \\ 0 \text{ elsewhere} \end{cases} \tag{59a}$$

with parameters n and p, where $0<p<1$. From eq. 58 it follows that $\sum_x f(x)=1$; we have a p.d.f. The definition of eq. 59a implies that n represents the possible maximum occurrence of x. The distribution is discrete with mutually exclusive elements, denoted in eq. 58 as a

and b. Eq. 59a can be found in modified form by substituting:

$$q=(1-p) \tag{59b}$$

Further:

$$\binom{n}{x}=\frac{n!}{x!(n-x)!} \tag{59c}$$

and:

$$F(x)=\int_0^n f(x)\,\mathrm{d}x \tag{59d}$$

The moments of the distribution are given by:

$$\mu_1=np \tag{60a}$$

$$\nu_2=npq=\mu_1 q \tag{60b}$$

$$\mu_2=np(np+q) \tag{60c}$$

$$\nu_3=npq(q-p)=\nu_2(1-2p) \tag{60d}$$

$$\nu_4=npq[1+3pq(n-2)] \tag{60e}$$

$$\gamma_1=(q-p)/\sqrt{npq} \tag{60f}$$

$$\gamma_2=(1-6pq)/(npq) \tag{60g}$$

The mode occurs at:

$$[p\cdot(n+1)-1]\leq x_{\mathrm{mo}}\leq p\cdot(n+1) \tag{60h}$$

For p between 0.25 and 0.75 the p.d.f. is nearly symmetrical with a central hump. It becomes assymetric with smaller p. For $p<0.10$ or >0.90 the distribution changes to the Poisson distribution of rare events (see eq. 63a).
Parameter estimation:

Moments:

$$x_{\mathrm{m}}=np \tag{61a}$$

$$s^2=npq \tag{61b}$$

Maximum likelihood:

$$\hat{p}=\frac{x_{\mathrm{m}}}{n} \tag{61c}$$

with:

$$\mathrm{Var}\,(\hat{p})=pq/n \tag{61d}$$

and:

$$n=\frac{x_{\mathrm{m}}^2}{x_{\mathrm{m}}-s^2} \tag{61e}$$

The likelihood function ($\sum f(x)=1$):

$$L=n \ln q+N \ln (p/q)+\sum_{x=1}^{n} f(x) \ln [(n-x+1)/x] \tag{61f}$$

The computation of confidence intervals by the use of the binomial distribution is presented on p. 244. The hypergeometric distribution was discussed by ESSENWANGER (1976).

The binomial distribution may conveniently be computed by the recursion formula:

$$f(x+1)=\frac{n-x}{x+1}\cdot\frac{p}{q}\cdot f(x) \tag{62a}$$

for

$x=0, \ldots, n-1$

with:

$$f(0)=q^n \tag{62b}$$

Several tables of the binomial distribution exist (e.g., NATIONAL BUREAU OF STANDARDS, 1950, etc.).

Example 7. Pure binomial distributions are rare in meteorology because of the influence of persistence upon the meteorological elements. The sample selected here shows the application of the theory, although it may have no general validity for all similar kinds of cloud data.

In this particular example the departures from the binomial model are small. For exemplification the data sample was divided into three groups: clear days = 0 and 1 tenth, cloudy days = 2 to 8 tenths, and overcast days with 9 and 10 tenths sky cover. We are interested in the frequency of occurrence for days of each group within a ten-day period, e.g., what is the expectancy that all 10 days fall into the overcast group.

The data sample for Boston (Mass.) in the period 1924–48 during April at 07h30 was selected to illustrate the method. There are 75 ten-day periods for a total of $N=750$ days, with $n_1=234$,

TABLE V

APPLICATION OF THE BINOMIAL FREQUENCY DISTRIBUTION TO CLOUD COVER DATA

n	Clear days		Cloudy		Overcast	
	obs.	analyt.	obs.	analyt.	obs.	analyt.
0	3	1.8	6	5.4	0	0.2
1	10	8.1	20	16.3	3	1.4
2	14	16.5	17	22.0	5	5.3
3	22	19.9	15	17.6	10	11.9
4	13	15.8	12	9.3	20	17.6
5	6	8.6	4	3.4	17	17.8
6	3	3.3	1	0.8	9	12.5
7	2	0.8	0	0.2	8	6.0
8	2	0.2	0	0.0	2	1.9
9	0	0.0	0	0.0	1	0.4
10	0	0.0	0	0.0	0	0.0
$\sum$	75	75.0	75	75.0	75	75.0

$n_2=173$, $n_3=373$ for the three groups. These observed data lead to the probabilities $p_1=234/750=0.312$, $p_2=0.231$ and $p_3=0.457$. The task is the calculation of the binomial series for $n=10$, $x=0, 1, \ldots, 10$ with $N_1=75=n_1/x_{m_1}$ (where $x_{m_1}=np_1=10\cdot0.312=3.12$). The binomial series is exhibited in the second column of Table V. Similarly, we calculate the binomial model for the remaining two groups. A comparison with the observed data discloses that the deviations are small. Testing of the statistical significance of the deviations is described on p. 281ff. Because the sample was selected for illustration of the method no discussion of the predictive value of the model is given. Table V discloses, however, that the chances are low for the occurrence of either 10 subsequent clear, cloudy or overcast days, and that the event of 10 consecutive days of one group has not been observed in the 25 years of record.

The Poisson distribution

Assume that $p<0.1$ in the binomial distribution (i.e., the occurrence is a rare event). Function 59a can then be substituted by:

$$f(x)=\frac{e^{-h}h^x}{x!} \begin{cases} \text{for } x=0, 1, 2 \ldots \\ 0 \text{ elsewhere} \end{cases} \tag{63a}$$

which is called the Poisson distribution.
Since again $\sum_x f(x)=1$, we have a p.d.f. The c.d.f. is:

$$F(x)=\int_0^n f(x)\,dx \tag{63b}$$

Notice that the distribution has only one parameter: h.
The moments of the distribution are:

$$\mu_1=h \tag{64a}$$

$$\nu_2=h \tag{64b}$$

$$\nu_3=h \tag{64c}$$

$$\nu_4=h(3h+1) \tag{64d}$$

For a more convenient computation, the p.d.f. can be transformed to:

$$f(x+1)=f(x)\cdot\frac{h}{x+1} \quad \text{for } x\geq 0 \tag{65a}$$

with:

$$f(0)=e^{-h} \tag{65b}$$

The distribution is used for rare independent events such as frequency of tropical storms, hail or sometimes thunderstorms. When observations display persistence, the negative binomial (see eq. 70a) is more suitable. Estimator:

$$h=x_m \tag{66}$$

Since $\sigma^2/\bar{x}=1$, we can define the following criterion:

$$\sigma^2/\bar{x}-1=\gamma \tag{67a}$$

and:

$$\gamma = q - 1 \tag{67b}$$

$$\gamma \begin{cases} = \text{negative for binomial } (q < 1.0) \\ = 0 \text{ for Poisson } (q = 1.0) \\ = \text{positive for negative binomial } (q > 1.0) \end{cases}$$

where γ represents the population parameter. In practice, the estimator s^2/x_m from the data sample is used to decide whether Poisson's law applies. SUKHATME (1938) showed that the χ^2 test*[1] can be applied when $x_m > 1$ and $N > 5$. If $x_m < 1$, then N must be > 15.

$$\chi^2_{N-1}/(N-1) = s^2/x_m = \gamma + 1 \tag{67c}$$

For the χ^2 test see eq. 645. If the χ^2 value is below the 95% significance level, the hypothesis that the distribution follows the Poisson model is accepted, otherwise the hypothesis is rejected because the high value of χ^2 indicates persistence in the observed data.
The likelihood function is:

$$L = h + N \ln h - \sum_{x=1}^{n} f(x) \ln x \tag{68}$$

The additive property of the Poisson distribution is called to the reader's attention. Given are these Poisson distributions:

$$f(x) = \frac{e^{-h_1} h_1^x}{x!}$$

and:

$$f(y) = \frac{e^{-h_1} h_2^y}{y!}$$

Then for $z = x + y$ and $h = h_1 + h_2$:

$$f(z) = \frac{e^{-h} h^z}{z!} \tag{69}$$

An example is postponed until after the discussion of the negative binomial in order to treat both types simultaneously.

The negative binomial distribution

The function:

$$f(x) = \binom{-k}{x} (-1)^x \frac{1}{(1+\gamma)^k} \left(\frac{\gamma}{1+\gamma}\right)^x \tag{70a}$$

---

*[1] It is assumed that s^2 is obtained by division through $N-1$.

is called the negative binomial, because the factorial can be written:

$$\binom{-k}{x}(-1)^x = \binom{x+k-1}{x} = \binom{x+k-1}{k-1} = \frac{(k+x-1)!}{(k-1)!x!} \tag{70b}$$

In notation of the binomial:

$$-p = \gamma = \sigma^2/\bar{x} - 1 = q - 1.0 \tag{70c}$$

It follows from eq. 67b that for the negative binomial $q > 1.0$.
We introduce $-p = Q'/P'$; $q = 1/P'$. Then $\gamma = (1/P') - 1 = Q'/P'$ with $P' + Q' = 1$ analogous to the binomial. Now eq. 68 transforms into the Pascal form (see TODHUNTER, 1865):

$$f(x) = \binom{-k}{x}(-1)^x (P')^k (Q')^x \tag{71a}$$

a form similar to eq. 59a. The analogy can be expanded by setting $1 + \gamma = Q$; $\gamma = P$, where $Q = 1 + P$ or $Q - P = 1$.
Then:

$$f(x) = \binom{-k}{x}(-1)^x (P)^x (Q)^{-x-k} \tag{71b}$$

and $-k$ assumes the role of n.
The distribution is also known as the Polya distribution (see POLYA and EGGENBERGER, 1923). The conversion to the incomplete beta function and comparison of the various versions may be omitted here (see ESSENWANGER, 1976, p. 42).
BOSWELL and PATIL (1969) have analyzed the underlying chance mechanism leading to the negative binomial distribution. In their comprehensive analysis they demonstrated that several chance mechanisms exist that apparently are not related.

$$F(x) = \int_0^n f(x)\,\mathrm{d}x \tag{72}$$

and:

$$f(x+1) = f(x)\frac{(k+x)}{(1+\gamma)}\frac{\gamma}{(x+1)} \qquad \text{for } x = 0, 1 \ldots n \tag{73a}$$

where:

$$\gamma = \frac{Q'}{P'} = P \tag{73b}$$

and:

$$f(0) = \frac{1}{(1+\gamma)^k}. \tag{73c}$$

The moments are:

$$\mu_1 = k\gamma \tag{74a}$$

$$\sigma^2 = (\gamma + 1)\, k\gamma \tag{74b}$$

$$\nu_3 = k\gamma\,(1 + 3\gamma + 2\gamma^2) \tag{74c}$$

$$\nu_4 = k\gamma\,(1+\gamma)\,[3(\gamma+1)\,(k\gamma+2\gamma)+1] \tag{74d}$$

$$= k\gamma(1+\gamma)[3\gamma(\gamma+1)(k+2)+1] \tag{74e}$$

Consequently, the moments fit is based on:

$$\gamma = d = \frac{s^2}{x_{\mathrm{m}}} - 1 \tag{75a}$$

$$k = \frac{x_{\mathrm{m}}}{d} = \frac{x_{\mathrm{m}}^2}{s^2 - x_{\mathrm{m}}} \tag{75b}$$

It can be used, if $C > 20$ (see THOM, 1958a). For $C < 20$ the maximum-likelihood fit should be employed:

$$C = \left(1 + \frac{1}{\gamma}\right)(k+2) \tag{75c}$$

The maximum-likelihood estimators are obtained from:

$$x_{\mathrm{m}} = \widehat{k\gamma} \tag{76a}$$

This equation can be utilized to determine $\hat{\gamma}$. The parameter $\hat{k}$ must be found by Newton's approximation method:

$$\hat{k}_1 = k + h_1 \tag{76b}$$

$$\hat{k}_2 = \hat{k}_1 + h_2 \tag{76c}$$

etc.
from the following relationship:

$$-h_i = \frac{\sum \psi(x+k) - n\psi(k) - n\ln\left(1 + \frac{x_{\mathrm{m}}}{k}\right)}{\sum \psi'(x+k) - n\psi'(k) + \frac{n x_{\mathrm{m}}}{k(k+x_{\mathrm{m}})}} \tag{76d}$$

where $\psi(x) = \mathrm{d}\,(\ln \Gamma_x)/\mathrm{d}x$ is the digamma function and ψ' is its derivative (see ABRAMOWITZ and STEGUN, 1964). The first k is taken from the moments fit, eq. 75b.
HALDANE (1941) gave the following formula, solved by trial and error:

$$L = 0 = kn\ln\left(1 - \frac{x_{\mathrm{m}}}{k}\right) - (f_1 + f_2 \ldots f_r) + \frac{k}{k+1}(f_2 + f_3 + \ldots f_r) + \ldots \frac{kf_r}{k+r-1} \tag{77}$$

where f_1, f_2 ... are the observed frequencies at $x = 1, 2 \ldots r$. Haldane's formula has eliminated the digamma function.
Another formula was given by JOHNSON and KOTZ (1969) (see also PIETERS et al., 1977), using $f(0)$ of the zero class:

$$\hat{\gamma}/\ln(1+\hat{\gamma}) = x_{\mathrm{m}}(-\ln f(0)) \tag{78}$$

where $\hat{\gamma}$ must also be found by an iterative process (e.g., Newton-Raphson, see ESSENWANGER, 1976). A unique solution exists for $x_{\mathrm{m}} > -\ln f_0$.
In eq. 71a it was stated that $F(x) = \int f(x)\,\mathrm{d}x \sim \sum f(x)$. BEST and GIPPS (1974) recommended an approximation of the cumulative negative binomial distribution by the incomplete

gamma distribution (see eq. 91). This requires:

$$F(x,k,p) \sim \int^{X} g(\alpha,\beta)\, dy \tag{79a}$$

where $g(\alpha,\beta)$ is the incomplete gamma function (see eq. 90a).
Although this transformation can be achieved by setting:

$$\alpha = 4k(1-P')/(2-P')^2 \tag{79b}$$

$$\beta = (2-P')/(2P') \tag{79c}$$

$$X = x + 0.5 + \bar{x}_\Delta \tag{79d}$$

$$\bar{x}_\Delta = k(1-P')/(2-P') \tag{79e}$$

$$P' = 1/(1+\gamma) \tag{79f}$$

the only advantage is the availability of tables.
The transformation by Best and Gipps (1974) is apparently closer, especially for $k \leq 2$, than the gamma transformations by Ord (1968) and Guenther (1972), while the Gaussian approximation by Peizer and Pratt (1968) is more accurate for larger k.
Kaiser and Stefansky (1972) expanded Polya's urn scheme to the bivariate Polya distribution and Schenzle (1979) investigated the fitting of the truncated negative binomial distribution.

Example 8. A numerical example is the thunderstorm occurrence at Oklahoma City, Oklahoma during the period 1924–1948. Table VI displays the observed frequency of days with thunderstorms by months. Table VII provides the related statistical parameters x_m, s^2, χ^2, γ, k and C. A difference between mean value x_m and s^2 is considered significant (per cent level) for $\chi^2 = 36.415$. Therefore, pronounced persistence exists in August. In December, the persistence rests in the great number of days without a thunderstorm. This can be concluded from k, which is completely different in the summer and winter months. Consequently, in August and December the negative binomial model is appropriate.
Table VI shows further the variety of models and calculation of estimators. January through July and September through November are closely approximated by the Poisson model, August by the negative binomial with moments fit and December by the negative binomial with maximum-likelihood fit. Table VI exhibits the recomputed values. The reader may compare the analytical and observed frequency densities. The negative binomial model has been included into Table VI for May, June, July and October because the calculated χ^2 is close to significance (5% level) which implies a deviation from the Poisson distribution. Although systematic differences between Poisson model and negative binomial model emerge, in this example the numerical difference in terms of the p.d.f. is not very large. It must be considered, however, that a data sample of 25 cases is not very large. (For application of the χ^2 test to frequency distributions see p. 281ff.)

The Gaussian distribution

If we assume $q = p = \frac{1}{2}$ in eq. 59a, substitute x by $np + x$, σ for $\sqrt{npq}$, and make n infinitely large, a limiting form of the binomial model and a frequency distribution is obtained, which is usually called the Gaussian "normal" distribution. In many sources it is designated as the "normal" distribution but in this text we refer to it as Gaussian distribution. The names Maxwell and Laplace are also associated with the formulation of the distribution. The Gaussian distribution is the most important continuous distribution

TABLE VI

NUMBER OF DAYS WITH THUNDERSTORMS BY MONTH FOR OKLAHOMA CITY, 1924–1948

Days	January		February		March		April		May			June			July			August		September		October			November		December	
	obs.	Po.	obs.	Po.	obs.	Po.	obs.	Po.	obs.	Po.	n.b.	obs.	Po.	n.b.	obs.	Po.	n.b.	obs.	n.b.	obs.	Po.	obs.	Po.	n.b.	obs.	Po.	obs.	n.b.*
0	13	13.2	6	5.1	3	2.2		0.2		0.0	0.0		0.0	0.0		0.1	0.3		0.2		0.2	2	0.6	1.1	7	6.7	17	16.9
1	8	8.4	6	8.1	6	5.3	2	1.0		0.1	0.3		0.1	0.1		0.6	1.1	1	0.8	1	1.1		2.3	3.0	9	8.8	5	5.2
2	4	2.7	6	6.5	5	6.4	4	2.3	1	0.4	0.7		0.2	0.3	3	1.6	2.1	2	1.6	3	2.5	6	4.2	4.3	5	5.8	1	1.8
3		0.7	6	3.5	4	5.3	1	3.7	1	1.0	1.4	1	0.4	0.6	6	2.9	3.1	2	2.4	3	3.9	6	5.2	4.7	3	2.6	2	0.7
4			1	1.4	3	3.2	2	4.5	1	1.8	2.2	1	0.9	1.2	2	4.0	3.6	4	3.1	4	4.6	3	4.8	4.0		0.8		0.3
5				0.4	3	1.7	5	4.4	3	2.8	2.8	1	1.6	1.8	2	4.3	3.6	3	3.3	6	4.4	4	3.6	3.1	1	0.2		0.1
6					1	0.6	6	3.5	5	3.4	3.1	2	2.4	2.4	3	3.9	3.2	2	3.2	2	3.4	1	2.2	2.1		0.1		
7						0.2	2	2.4	4	3.7	3.1	5	3.0	2.9	5	3.0	2.6	2	2.8	5	2.3		1.2	1.3				
8						0.1	2	1.5	3	3.4	2.9	1	3.4	3.0	1	2.1	1.9	2	2.3		1.4	2	0.6	0.8				
9							1	1.0	2	2.9	2.4	7	3.3	2.9		1.3	1.3	3	1.8	1	0.7	1	0.2	0.4				
10								0.5	1	2.1	1.9	2	2.9	2.6	1	0.7	0.9		1.3		0.3		0.1	0.2				
11										1.5	1.4		2.3	2.1	1	0.3	0.6	3	0.9		0.1							
12									3	0.9	1.0	1	1.7	1.7	1	0.1	0.3		0.6		0.1							
13										0.5	0.7	1	1.2	1.2		0.1	0.2	1	0.4									
14										0.3	0.5	2	0.8	0.9			0.1		0.2									
15										0.1	0.3		0.4	0.6			0.1		0.1									
16										0.1	0.2		0.2	0.4														
17									1		0.1		0.1	0.2														
18												1	0.1	0.1														
Σ	25		25		25		25		25			25			25			25		25		25			25		25	

obs. = observed; Po. = Poisson; n.b. = negative binomial; n.b.* = with maximum likelihood fit.

TABLE VII

STATISTICAL CHARACTERISTICS FOR TABLE VI

	Jan.	Feb.	March	April	May	June	July	August	Sep.	Oct.	Nov.	Dec.
x_m	0.64	1.60	2.44	4.84	7.48	8.84	5.44	6.28	4.72	3.72	1.32	0.52
s^2	0.577	1.500	3.007	5.057	10.676	11.390	7.923	10.543	3.960	5.210	1.560	0.843
χ^2	21.5	22.5	29.6	25.1	(34.2)	30.9	(34.9)	40.2	20.1	(33.6)	28.4	39.0
γ	0.105	−0.063	0.232	0.045	0.427	0.288	0.456	0.679	0.162	0.400	0.182	0.622
k	6.12	−25.00	10.52	108.5	17.51	30.65	11.92	9.25	29.14	9.24	7.25	0.836
C	–	–	–	–	>20	>20	>20	>20	–	>20	–	7.40

The parentheses indicates that the χ^2 value is close to significance, the significant χ^2 is underlined. $\chi^2_{N-1} = (N-1)s^2/x_m$.

for statistical analysis in climatology although very often frequency distributions of climatological data are not Gaussian.
The p.d.f. is:

$$f(x)=[1/(\sigma\sqrt{2\pi})]\,e^{-1/2\left(\frac{x-\bar{x}}{\sigma}\right)^2} \tag{80a}$$

with:

$$F(x)=\int_{-\infty}^{\infty} f(x)\,dx \tag{80b}$$

Parameters are $\bar{x}$ and σ. As previously introduced, $\gamma_1=\gamma_2=0$ (see eq. 28c).
Estimation is simple because:

$$\bar{x}=x_{\mathrm{m}} \tag{81a}$$

and:

$$\sigma^2=s^2=\sum (x_i-x_{\mathrm{m}})^2/N \tag{81b}$$

In order to obtain the unbiased estimator of σ^2 the summation $\sum (x_i-x_{\mathrm{m}})^2$ is divided by $N-1$ instead of N (see eq. 48a).
The unbiased estimator for s is:

$$\hat{S}=C_{\mathrm{N}}s \tag{81c}$$

(see eq. 48b).
The choice of $s=\sqrt{s^2}$ or $s=\hat{S}$ as the estimator depends on the goal of estimation. In point estimation we may want an estimator for the variance s^2 or for the standard deviation s.
The Gaussian distribution has many important properties. Tabulation can be normalized by the transformation:

$$t=(x-x)/\sigma \tag{82}$$

and knowledge of σ is sufficient to recompute any p.d.f. with reference to the mean. This transformation is the basis of many tables (e.g., BURINGTON and MAY, 1953; FISHER and YATES, 1963; BEYER, 1966) in which $f(x)$ or $F(x)$ is listed (see also ESSENWANGER, 1976).
The normal distribution has a central hump with the median being the mode and the mean.

$$x_{\mathrm{med}}=x_{\mathrm{mo}}=\bar{x} \tag{83a}$$

The mode is:

$$f(x_{\mathrm{mo}})=w/(\sigma\sqrt{2\pi})=A \tag{83b}$$

where the class width w is usually assumed to be unity.
Because $\gamma_1=\gamma_2=0$ the skewness and kurtosis of a frequency distribution can be used to test whether a frequency distribution is approximately Gaussian (see standard error, p. 245). The third and fourth moments are:

$$\nu_3=0 \tag{84a}$$

$$\nu_4=3\sigma^4 \tag{84b}$$

The c.d.f. is usually transformed to:

$$F(x)=A\int_{-\infty}^{x} e^{-t^2/2}\,dt \tag{80c}$$

with A being the mode (eq. 83b). For graphical solutions a so-called probability paper exists. In a diagram the right hand side of eq. 80c is used as the ordinate and $x(t)$ as the abscissa. In these coordinate scales the Gaussian model is a straight line (see ESSENWANGER, 1976, p. 162).

The Gaussian distribution is important, but heterogeneous climatological data may not follow the Gaussian distribution. Thus, tests are appropriate before application.

The Gaussian distribution is usually applied to temperature and pressure data, but CEHAK (1967) demonstrated that the p.d.f. of temperature, pressure and relative humidity in the upper air (up to 30 km) over Vienna appeared to be mostly non-Gaussian.

A further important application is the central limit theorem. The variable:

$$\sqrt{n}(\bar{X}-\mu_1)/\sigma=\left(\sum_1^n X_i-n\mu_1\right)\Big/\sigma\sqrt{n} \tag{85}$$

is Gaussian distributed even for data for which the random variate X is not Gaussian distributed. It implies that the distribution of the sample means tends toward the Gaussian model as n increases. According to BRADLEY (1973), this approximation is very slow for non-symmetric distributions of the original variate (e.g., daily rainfall sums).

The multidimensional case such as the bivariate normal distribution has been discussed in a separate text (ESSENWANGER, 1976) and can also be found in KENDALL and STUART (1958), or in BROOKS and CARRUTHERS (1953). The methodology of separating frequency distributions into partial components which have a Gaussian distribution is treated in the author's text (ESSENWANGER, 1976, p. 143). The utilization of the Gaussian distribution as a basis for tests of significance is described on p. 248.

Numerous tables of the Gaussian distribution exist. Following is a simple scheme of calculating the Gaussian p.d.f. by differences. It is easy to apply in electronic data processing although very often sophisticated formulae are utilized (e.g., KERRIDGE and COOK, 1976).

The following equations are derived:

$$\ln f(z)=\ln A-\tfrac{1}{2}\left(\frac{x-\bar{x}}{\sigma}\right)^2 \tag{86a}$$

$$\log f(x)=\log A-\frac{\text{mod}}{2}\left(\frac{x-\bar{x}}{\sigma}\right)^2 \tag{86b}$$

where mod represents the modulus log e, and A denotes the mode (eq. 83b).

$$\frac{\partial(\log f(x))}{\partial x}=-(x-\bar{x})\,\text{mod}/\sigma^2=\Delta(x) \tag{86c}$$

and:

$$\frac{\partial^2(\log f(x))}{\partial x^2}=-\text{mod}/\sigma^2=D \tag{86d}$$

For $\ln f(x)$ set mod $=1.0$.

It is evident that the second differences are constant and equal to D. We compute the starting points $f(x_c)$ and $f(x_{c+1})$, $x_c \leq x_m < x_{c+1}$. x_c and x_{c+1} are the central class values next to the mean. The starting points are:

$$\log f(x_c) = \log A + \frac{D}{2}(x_c - x_m)^2 \tag{87a}$$

$$\log f(x_{c+1}) = \log A + \frac{D}{2}(x_{c+1} - x_m)^2 \tag{87b}$$

Next we calculate:

$$\Delta_0 = \log f(x_{c+1}) - \log f(x_c) = -D[(x_c - x_m) + 0.5] \quad \text{(computation check)} \tag{87c}$$

$$\Delta_{-1} = \Delta_0 - D \tag{87d}$$

$$\Delta_{-2} = \Delta_{-1} - D \text{ etc.} \tag{87e}$$

The difference Δ changes the sign because the point of reference is the mode. Therefore:

$$\Delta_{+1} = \Delta_0 + D \tag{88a}$$

$$\Delta_{+2} = \Delta_1 + D \text{ etc.} \tag{88b}$$

As introduced, the mode is:

$A = 1/\sigma\sqrt{2\pi}$ (see eq. 83b)

and:

$$\log A = -(\log \sigma + \log\sqrt{2\pi}) = -(\log \sigma + 0.39909) \tag{89a}$$

$$D = -\text{mod}/\sigma^2 = -0.43\,429\,448/\sigma^2 \tag{89b}$$

$$\log f(x_{ci}) = \log f(x_{ci-1}) - \Delta_i \tag{89c}$$

The process is illustrated in Table VIII. The five columns of Table VIII exhibit the individual steps. The computation starts in the center of the frequency around the mode. A numerical example follows.

TABLE VIII

SCHEME TO COMPUTE THE NORMAL DISTRIBUTION FROM DIFFERENCES

D	Δ	$\log f(x)$	$f(x)$	n_i
		$\log f(x_{c-1})$		
	Δ_{-1}			
$-D$		$\log f(x_c)$	etc.	etc.
	Δ_0	x_m		
$+D$		$\log f(x_{c+1})$	etc.	etc.
	Δ_{+1}			

Example 9. Computation of a normal distribution for the data of Table II. From the grouped data (Example 3) we adopt:

$x_m = 59.24$, $s^2 = 37.073$ and $s = 6.090$ (adjusted to $N-1$, with Sheppards correction)

To simplify the computation we convert the two-degree class units of Table II by introducing an x-scale of unit classes. First:

$(x_c - x_m) = \frac{1}{2}(58.95 - 59.24) = -0.145$

The standard deviation for unit classes $s_1 = s/2$.

$$s_1 = 3.045 \text{ and } s_1^2 = 9.2720;\ D = \frac{0.43429448}{9.2720} = -0.04684;\ \frac{D}{2} = -0.02342$$

$\log A = 0.11733 - 1$; $A = 13.10\%$

$\log f(x_c) = 0.11733 - 1 - 0.02342(-0.145)^2$

$= 0.11733 - 1 - 0.0049 = 0.11684 - 1$; $f(x_c) = 13.09\%$

$\log f(x_{c+1}) = 0.11733 - 1 - 0.02342(0.855)^2$

$= 0.11733 - 1 - 0.01712 = 0.10021 - 1$; $f(x_{c+1}) = 12.60\%$

check $\Delta_0 = -0.04684(-0.145 + 0.5) = -0.04684(0.355) = -0.01663$ as $0.10021 - 0.11684$

$\Delta_{-1} = +0.01663 + 0.04684 = +0.03021$

$\Delta_1 = -0.01663 - 0.04684 = -0.06347$.

The frequency distribution is displayed in Table IX.

The incomplete gamma function

It is known from advanced calculus that:

$$\Gamma(\alpha) = \int_0^\infty y^{\alpha-1} e^{-y}\, dy = (\alpha - 1)\,\Gamma(\alpha - 1) \tag{90a}$$

and:

$$\Gamma(\alpha) = (\alpha - 1)! \tag{90b}$$

(for approximations see eq. 98a and b).
The function defined in eq. 90a is called the gamma function. We can introduce $y = x/\beta$ and write:

$$F(x) = \frac{1}{\beta^\alpha \Gamma(\alpha)} \int_0^x x^{\alpha-1} e^{-x/\beta}\, dx \tag{91}$$

with $\alpha > 0$, $\beta > 0$ and $\Gamma(\alpha) > 0$. Since $F(x)$ goes to 1 for $x \to \infty$, we have a c.p.f. The integration in eq. 91 is performed from 0 to x instead of 0 to ∞. Therefore the function has been called the incomplete gamma function. In various sources, however, it is simply referred to as gamma function. $F(x)$ is continuous. The p.d.f. is:

$$f(x) = \frac{1}{\beta^\alpha \Gamma(\alpha)} x^{\alpha-1} e^{-x/\beta} \quad \begin{cases} \text{for } 0 < x < \infty \\ 0 \text{ elsewhere} \end{cases} \tag{92}$$

The moments of the function are:

$$\bar{x} = \alpha\beta \tag{93a}$$

TABLE IX

COMPUTATION OF NORMAL DISTRIBUTION FOR DATA OF TABLE II

D	Δ_i	$\log(f(x_i))$	$f(x_i)$	n_i	Observed	Class
		0.20833–4	0.0002	0.03	0	36.0–37.9
	0.49861					
		0.70694–4	0.0005	0.14	0	38.0–39.9
	0.45177					
		0.15871–3	0.0015	0.42	0	40.0–41.9
	0.40493					
		0.56364–3	0.0037	1.04	1	42.0–43.9
	0.35809					
		0.92173–3	0.0084	2.35	6	44.0–45.9
	0.31125					
		0.23298–2	0.0171	4.79	3	46.0–47.9
	0.26441					
		0.49739–2	0.0314	8.79	9	48.0–49.9
	0.21757					
		0.71496–2	0.0519	14.53	10	50.0–51.9
	0.17073					
		0.88569–2	0.0769	21.53	22	52.0–53.9
	0.12389					
etc.		0.00958–1	0.1022	28.62	30	54.0–55.9
	0.07705					
+0.04684		0.08663–1	0.1221	34.19	37	56.0–57.9
	+0.03021					
		0.11684–1	0.1309	36.65	36	58.0–59.9
	−0.01663					
−0.04684		0.10021–1	0.1260	35.28	35	60.0–61.9
	−0.06347					
etc.		0.03674–1	0.1088	30.47	33	62.0–63.9
	−0.11031					
		0.92643–2	0.0844	23.63	22	64.0–65.9
	−0.15715					
		0.76928–2	0.0588	16.46	10	66.0–67.9
	−0.20399					
		0.56529–2	0.0367	10.28	12	68.0–69.9
	−0.25083					
		0.31446–2	0.0206	5.77	9	70.0–71.9
	−0.29767					
		0.01679–2	0.0104	2.91	4	72.0–73.9
	−0.34451					
		0.67228–3	0.0047	1.32	1	74.0–75.9
	−0.39135					
		0.28093–3	0.0019	0.53	0	76.0–77.9
	−0.43819					
		0.84274–4	0.0007	0.20	0	78.0–79.9
	−0.48503					
		0.35771–4	0.0002	0.03	0	80.0–81.9
	−0.53187					
			1.0000		280	

$$\sigma^2 = \alpha\beta^2 = \bar{x}\beta \tag{93b}$$

$$\nu_3 = 2\alpha\beta^3 = 2\sigma^2\beta \tag{93c}$$

$$\nu_4 = 3(\alpha + 2)\alpha\beta^4 \tag{93d}$$

$$\gamma_1 = 2/\sqrt{\alpha} \tag{93e}$$

$$\gamma_2 = 6/\alpha \tag{93f}$$

The variate x in eq. 91 starts with reference point 0, but sometimes $x-\gamma$ is introduced. $F(x)$ is then defined between $\gamma \leq x < \infty$. Another expansion is the hypergamma function (see eq. 106). The mode of the two-parameter model is:

$$x_{\text{mode}} = \beta(\alpha - 1) \text{ for } \alpha > 1 \tag{94a}$$

and:

$$x_{\text{mode}} = 0 \text{ for } 0 < \alpha \leq 1.0 \tag{94b}$$

The gamma function was tabulated by PEARSON (1957) for the parameters u and p which relate the symbols used in this text:

$$u = x/\sigma = x/\beta\sqrt{\alpha} \tag{95a}$$

$$p = \alpha - 1 \tag{95b}$$

The gamma function is applicable to zero bound continuous variables with shapes of the p.d.f. similar to the binomial types. It is often utilized for precipitation data (see p. 347) although precipitation sums for less than five days may be influenced by persistence that can cause significant departures between the observed and computed frequency. The moments fit has a poor efficiency and thus the maximum-likelihood fit is recommended. The latter is relatively easy for a two-parameter model. $f(x)=0$ for $x=0$. Therefore, the dry days must either be treated as occurring for $0 < x < 0.5$, or better, they must be separated. A mixed distribution is sometimes used (THOM, 1968):

$$G(x) = p + qF(x) \tag{96}$$

where p represents the probability of dry days (or zero precipitation) and $q = 1 - p$ denotes the probability (frequency) of precipitations.
If we set $\alpha = c$ and $\beta = 2$, we obtain the χ^2 distribution, which is discussed with eq. 645.
Moments estimators:

$$\alpha = (x_{\text{m}}/s)^2 \tag{97a}$$

$$\beta = s^2/x_{\text{m}} = x_{\text{m}}/\alpha \tag{97b}$$

The calculation of $\Gamma(\alpha)$ for non-integer values of α may create some problems. RAFF (1970) gave an approximation by:

$$\Gamma(n+\varepsilon) = n![(n+\varepsilon/2)^2 + \varepsilon(2-\varepsilon)/12]^{(\varepsilon-1)/2} \tag{98a}$$

where $n \geq 2$...are integers and $0 \leq \varepsilon \leq 1$. For values $\Gamma(\alpha)$ with $\alpha = 1 + \varepsilon$ and $1 \leq \alpha \leq 2$ he suggested:

$$\Gamma(1+\varepsilon) = \Gamma(2+\varepsilon)/\Gamma(1+\varepsilon) \tag{98b}$$

The error for $\Gamma(\alpha)$ in eq. 98a is never more than 1/13000, and decreases with n. Furthermore:

$$\Gamma(\alpha+1) = \alpha\Gamma(\alpha) \tag{98c}$$

Maximum-likelihood estimators

Maximum-likelihood estimators are (after THOM, 1957a):

$$\hat{\alpha}_T = (1+\sqrt{1+4A/3})/(4A) \tag{99a}$$

$$A = \ln X_m - \frac{1}{N}\sum \ln X_i \tag{99b}$$

This approximation is accurate to about 1% for small $\hat{\alpha}_T$. The maximum-likelihood estimator $\hat{\alpha}$ is biased, however. BOWMAN and SHENTON (1968) and SHENTON and BOWMAN (1970a, b, 1973) investigated this bias. By neglecting terms which are divided by higher order of N the expected bias is:

$$E(\hat{\alpha}-\alpha) = \alpha_B \sim [3\alpha - 2/3 + 1/(9\alpha) + 13/(405\,\alpha^3)]/(N-3) \text{ for } N \geq 4 \tag{99c}$$

Therefore BRIDGES and HAAN (1972) recommend a correction. For $\alpha \geq 1$ the first term dominates and:

$$\alpha \sim \hat{\alpha}(N-3)/N \sim \hat{\alpha}_T(N-3)/N \tag{99d}$$

The bias for larger N is only important for $\alpha \leq 0.25$. Then the last term is non-negligible and:

$$\alpha \sim [13(N-3)/(405\hat{\alpha})]^{1/3} \text{ for } \alpha \leq 0.25 \tag{99e}$$

It can be readily checked whether this second case is applicable because α calculated by eq. 99e must be less than or equal to 0.25.
The next step is the calculation of $\hat{\beta}$ from:

$$\hat{\beta} \cdot \hat{\alpha} = x_m \tag{99f}$$

In addition to the approximation of eq. 99a by Thom, an iteration for the calculation of maximum-likelihood estimators can be used (MIELKE, 1976). This procedure is not an approximation. Mielke found:

$$\hat{\alpha}_k = 1 + \frac{\ln\left[\dfrac{\alpha_{k-1}(r+0.5)}{r+\alpha_{k-1}-0.5}\right] + C_E - A_M}{\sum_{j=1}^{r} 1/[j(j+\alpha_{k-1}-1)]} \tag{100a}$$

and again:

$$\hat{\beta}_k = x_m/\hat{\alpha}_k \tag{100b}$$

where $C_E = 0.577215665$ (i.e., Euler's constant), and:

$$A_M = \ln x_M - \left(\sum_{i=1}^{n_1} \ln x_{1i} + \sum_{i=1}^{n_2} \ln x_{2i}\right)\Big/ N = \ln x_M - \sum \ln x_i/N \tag{100c}$$

$$x_M = \left(\sum_{i=1}^{n_1} x_{1i} + \sum_{i=1}^{n_2} x_{2i}\right)\Big/ N = \sum x_i/N = x_m \tag{100d}$$

The integer r is a positive number which is somewhat arbitrary and comes from an approximation of the digamma function. It signifies the number of terms which are necessary for a good approximation of the digamma function.

Mielke's method is based on previous work by SCHICKEDANZ and KRAUSE (1970). They tested the hypothesis that $\beta_1=\beta_2=\beta$ for two given data samples against the assumption that $\beta_1 \neq \beta_2$, given $\alpha_1=\alpha_2=\alpha$. Consequently, the set of data $x_1, x_2, \ldots, x_N$ is split into two groups (e.g., by placing all odd number observations into one and all even number observations into a second group). Thus, the two sets $x_{11}, x_{12}, \ldots, x_{1N_1}$ and $x_{21}, x_{22}, \ldots, x_{2N_2}$ are generated, for which we should expect $\beta_1=\beta_2=\beta$. The iterative process (eq. 100a) can be terminated after $\alpha_{k+1}-\alpha_k \leq \varepsilon$ which is a small but arbitrary number depending on desired precision.

Straight-line fitting

Recently a different approach to the calculation of estimators has been suggested by TAKEUCHI and CHEN (1979). From eq. 92 we derive:

$$f(x)x^{-(\alpha-1)}=[\beta^{\alpha}\Gamma(x)]^{-1}\exp(-x/\beta) \tag{101a}$$

which can be transformed to:

$$Y(x)=\ln f(x)-(\alpha-1)\ln x=\ln(1/C_{\alpha})-x/\beta \tag{101b}$$

where $C_{\alpha}=\beta^{\alpha}\Gamma(\alpha)$. $Y(x)$ represents a straight line in a coordinate system where the ordinate is $\ln[f(x)/x^{\alpha-1}]$ and the abscissa is x with the slope depending on β. It leads to:

$$\varepsilon_Y^2=(S_Y^2-S_{xY}^2/S_x^2)/(n-2) \tag{102a}$$

where $S_Y^2=\sum(Y_i-\bar{Y})^2$, $S_x^2=\sum(x_i-\bar{x})^2$, $S_{xY}=\sum(Y_i-\bar{Y})(x_i-\bar{x})$, and $Y_i=\ln f(x_i)-(\alpha-1)\ln x_i$. Furthermore, $\bar{Y}=\sum Y_i/n$ and $\bar{x}=\sum x_i/n$, where n denotes the number of classes.
Under the postulation that the data follow the gamma distribution ε_Y^2 will have a minimum at the estimator $\tilde{\alpha}$. After $\tilde{\alpha}$ is found:

$$\tilde{\beta}=-S_x^2/S_{xY} \tag{102b}$$

Evidently S_Y^2 and S_{xY} are functions of α.
Takeuchi and Chen listed the variances of $\tilde{\alpha}$ and $\tilde{\beta}$:

$$\mathrm{Var}(\tilde{\alpha})=\varepsilon_Y^2/\sum(\ln x_i-\overline{\ln x})^2 \tag{103a}$$

and:

$$\mathrm{Var}(1/\tilde{\beta})=\varepsilon_Y^2/S_x^2 \tag{103b}$$

For more details see Example 10.
CRUTCHER et al. (1973, 1977 and 1980) and CRUTCHER and JOINER (1978, 1980) established detailed reports on the use of the gamma function in electronic data processing and the production of graphs on the computer.
The gamma function (eqs. 91, 92) is a two-parameter model. An expansion to three parameters was recommended by Suzuki (see eq. 106). Another three-parameter model is possible, however. We substitute into eq. 94 $x=u-\gamma$, which introduces a location parameter. Estimators must be obtained by iteration. Because application of the gamma function in atmospheric science is found primarily for distributions which have a zero boundary (such as precipitation) $\gamma=0$. Then the two-parameter model of eq. 92 is sufficient. The expanded model is described in the author's 1976 text and by eq. 106.

Example 10. A gamma function is fitted to weekly precipitation sums of Kwajalein, Marshalll Islands, for the 13 weeks in summer during the 10-year period 1949–1958. The frequency distribution of the observed values is given in the first column of Table X.
The maximum-likelihood estimators can be obtained from $x_m = 2.308$, $\sigma^2 = 2.929$, $A = 0.8363 - 0.5406 = 0.2957$. $\hat{\alpha}_T = 1.844$, $\hat{\beta}_T = 1.252$. Notice that $\alpha \cdot \beta^2 = 2.89$ which is close to σ_x^2. The bias correction factor is $127/130 = 0.977$, which reduces $\hat{\alpha}_T$ to 1.802 and changes $\hat{\beta}_T$ to 1.281 (see eq. 99d). For the straight line fit (TAKEUCHI and CHEN, 1979) we reformulate eq. 101b:

$$Y(x) = y - \alpha_1 z = a_0 + a_1 x \qquad (101c)$$

where $a_1 = -1/\beta$, $a_0 = -\ln C_\alpha$, and $y = \ln (n_i/N)$, $z = \ln x$. We must minimize:

$$S_Y^2 = S_{xY}^2 / S_x^2 \qquad (104a)$$

or:

$$\sum (Y - \bar{Y})^2 - [\sum (Y - \bar{Y})(x - \bar{x})]^2 / S_x^2 \qquad (104b)$$

is a minimum. In brief:

$$\frac{\partial}{\partial_{\alpha_1}} \text{ of } [A_{y^2} - 2\alpha_1 A_{yz} + \alpha_1^2 A_{z^2} - (A_{xy}^2 - 2\alpha_1 A_{yx} A_{zx} + \alpha_1^2 A_{zx}^2)/S_x^2] = 0$$

Consequently:

$$\alpha_1 = (A_{yz} - A_{xy} A_{xz}/S_x^2)/(A_{z^2} - A_{xz}^2/S_x^2) \qquad (104c)$$

where A_{xy}, A_{xz}, A_{yz} are the cross products (e.g., $A_{xy} = \sum (x - \bar{x})(y - \bar{y})$, etc.) Similarly, $A_{z^2} = \sum (z - \bar{z})^2$. (For S_y^2, S_x^2 see eq. 102a.)

TABLE X

COMPARISON OF ANALYTICAL $f(x)$ WITH OBSERVED PRECIPITATION DATA

x	Precipitation interval (units of 0.01 inch)	n_i	n_i/N	$N_e(x)$ max. 1 (eq. 105a)	$N_e(x)$ (eq. 105b)	$N_e(x)$ (eq. 105c)
0.25	0–50	8	6.2%	11.4	13.6	15.3
0.75	51–100	25	19.2	19.4	17.8	20.3
1.25	101–150	21	16.2	20.0	17.3	19.1
1.75	151–200	15	11.5	17.8	15.3	16.3
2.25	201–250	18	13.8	14.8	13.2	13.4
2.75	251–300	9	6.9	11.8	10.9	10.7
3.25	301–350	8	6.2	9.1	8.9	8.4
3.75	351–400	6	4.6	6.9	7.2	6.5
4.25	401–450	5	3.8	5.2	5.8	5.0
4.75	451–500	4	3.1	3.8	4.6	3.8
5.25	501–550	3	2.3	2.8	3.6	2.9
5.75	551–600	1	0.8	2.0	2.8	2.2
6.25	601–650	1	0.8	1.5	2.2	1.6
6.75	651–700	1	0.8	1.1	1.7	1.2
7.25	701–750	2	1.5	0.7	1.3	0.9
7.75	751–800	2	1.5	0.5	1.0	0.7
8.25	801–850	1	0.8	0.4	0.8	0.5
8.75	851–900	0	–	0.3	0.6	0.4
9.25	901–950	0	–	0.2	0.5	0.3
9.75	951–1000			0.1	0.4	0.2
10.25	1001–1050			0.1	0.3	0.1
		130	100.0	129.9	129.8	129.8

From the data we find: $A_{xy}=41.22$, $A_{xz}=34.56$, $A_{yz}=-12.70$, $A_{z^2}=14.20$. $S_x^2=102$. $\tilde{\alpha}_1=0.505$, $\tilde{\alpha}=1.505$, $S_{xY}=A_{xy}-\tilde{\alpha}_1 A_{xz}=-58.68$, $\tilde{\beta}_1=102/58.68=1.738$. $\tilde{\beta}_2=x_m/\tilde{\alpha}_1=2.308/1.505=1.528$. From curve fitting we have $a_0=\bar{Y}-a_1\bar{x}$. Thus, $a_0=\ln C_\alpha+\varepsilon_C$. Although ε_C is zero if the data sample is a precise gamma distribution, ε_C may not be zero for empirical data samples. This has a significant consequence. From eq. 92 we can conclude that $\sum x^{\alpha-1}\,e^{-x/\beta}=\beta^\alpha\Gamma(\alpha)=C_\alpha$. If $a_0\neq\ln C_\alpha$ then $\sum f(x)\neq 1$, i.e., $\sum f(x)=e^{\varepsilon_C}$. An adjustment must be made to bring $\sum f(x)$ to 1.0. Note that in Example 10 the class units are $\Delta x=0.5$. These smaller steps provide a better approximation of the incomplete gamma function if calculated by eq. 92. It is self-evident that for $\Delta x=0.5$ the sum of $f(x)$ would be 2, which requires an adjustment by using $f(x)/2$ (see eq. 105a, b, c). $f(x)$ is omitted in Table X for the three models. The columns in Table X exhibit $N_e=N\cdot f(x)$.
Three equations have been used:
Maximum-likelihood method:

$$\ln f(x)=y=0.801\cdot\ln x-0.375-0.781x \qquad (105a)$$

Straight-line method (eq. 102a and b):

$$y=0.505\ln x-0.816-0.575x \qquad (105b)$$

Straight-line method (eqs. 102a and 93a):

$$y=0.505\ln x-0.518-0.654x \qquad (105c)$$

$a_0=-0.375$ and -0.518, which are numerical values for $\ln C_\alpha$ with $\varepsilon_C=0$, $\varepsilon_C=-0.104$ for $a_0=-0.816$. In the latter case $\sum f(x)=\varepsilon^{\varepsilon C}=0.901$. An adjustment has been made in Table X. (Note, that for utilizing $x=0.5$ a correction of -0.693 must be added to the constants -0.375, etc.).
Fig. 2 discloses that apparently the straight line (eq. 105b) provides the best fit of Y and leads to a minimum of the squared deviations from Y. The corresponding lines for the maximum-likelihood estimators and the combination eq. 105c give the impression of an apparent bias. We must consider, however, that we are not interested in a good fit of Y but a good representation of n_i. Table X discloses that eqs. 105a and 105c provide a smaller difference for N_e-n_i than eq. 105b. This is not a discrepancy because $Y=\ln f(x)-(\alpha-1)\ln x$ or $f(x)=Y=a_0+a_1x+(\alpha-1)\ln x$, the latter is not a straight line. Consequently, the diagram Fig. 2 does not reflect the true magnitude of the deviations $\sum(N_{e_i}-n_i)^2$.
The differences between the models should be evaluated by statistical tests of significance. They are introduced on p. 302ff.

The hypergamma function

The hypergamma function (SUZUKI, 1964, 1980) is found as a derivation from the 4-parameter Weibull model (see ESSENWANGER, 1976):

$$f(x)=\frac{a}{\beta^{\alpha/a}\Gamma(\alpha/a)}\,x^{\alpha-1}\exp(-x^a/\beta)\left\}\begin{array}{l}\text{for } 0<x<\infty\\ \hline 0 \text{ elsewhere}\end{array}\right. \qquad (106)$$

where $b=1/\beta$ and a is a third parameter. The moments are not trivial and the maximum-likelihood estimators can be obtained by iteration.
The moments of the hypergamma distribution can be computed from:

$$\mu_k=\Gamma[(k+\alpha)/a]/[\Gamma(\alpha/a)\cdot b^{k/a}] \qquad (107a)$$

Hence:

$$\mu_1=\Gamma[(1+\alpha)/a]/[\Gamma(\alpha/a)\cdot b^{1/a}]=\bar{x} \qquad (107b)$$

$$\mu_2=\Gamma[(2+\alpha)/a]/[\Gamma(\alpha/a)\cdot b^{2/a}]=\sigma^2+\bar{x}^2 \qquad (107c)$$

$$\mu_3=\Gamma[(3+\alpha)/a]/[\Gamma(\alpha/a)b^{3/a}] \qquad (107d)$$

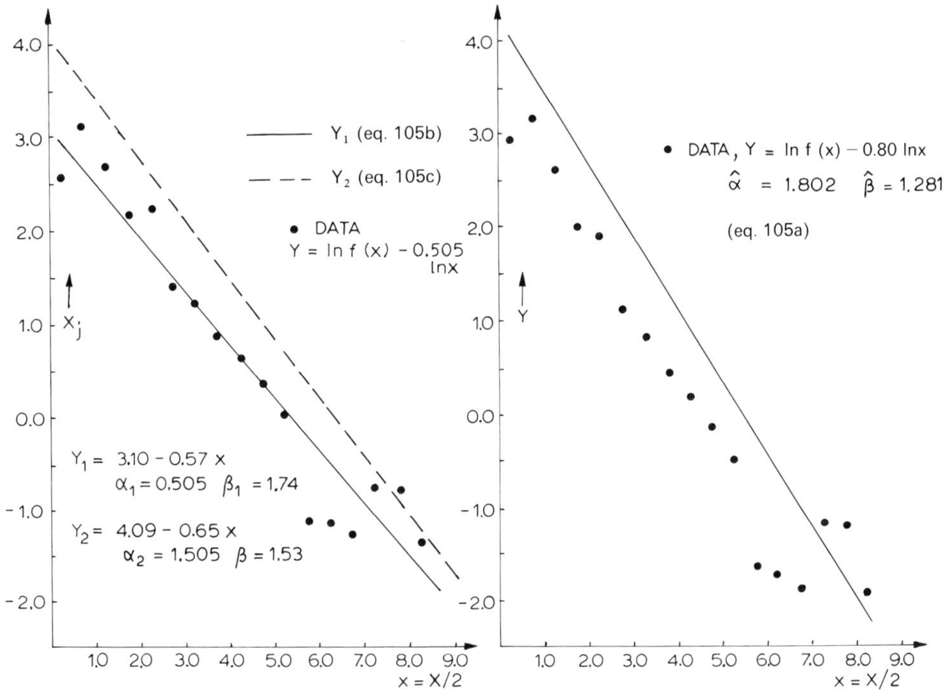

Fig. 2. Comparison of empirical precipitation data fitted by three different methods (eq. 105a, b, c).

These moments lead to the following relationship:

$$\bar{x}^2/(\bar{x}^2+\sigma^2)=\Gamma^2[(\alpha+1)/a]/[\Gamma(\alpha/a)\cdot\Gamma[(\alpha+2)/a]] \quad (108a)$$

$$\bar{x}^3/\mu_3=\Gamma^3[(\alpha+1)/a]/[\Gamma^2(\alpha/a)\Gamma[(\alpha+3)/a]] \quad (108b)$$

$$a\cdot b^a=\Gamma[(\alpha+1)/a]/\Gamma(\alpha/a) \quad (108c)$$

SUZUKI (1964) has given graphical solutions for the parameters a, b, and α. Solutions by electronic data processing are not trivial.

The maximum-likelihood estimators can be found from the following expressions:

$$a \ln x_g-\psi\left(\frac{\alpha}{a}\right)+\ln b=0 \quad (109a)$$

$$ab\sum x_i^a-N\alpha=0 \quad (109b)$$

$$ab\sum x_i^a \ln x_i-N-N\alpha \ln x_g=0 \quad (109c)$$

where:

$$\ln x_g=(\sum \ln x_i)/N \quad (109d)$$

and $\psi(\alpha/a)$ denotes the digamma function (ABRAMOVITZ and STEGUN, 1964).

Suzuki suggests an iterative procedure by the Newton-Raphson method, with initial guesses $\hat{a}_0$, $\hat{b}_0$ and $\hat{\alpha}_0$ and i-th approximation $a_i=a_{i-1}+h_i$, (see ESSENWANGER, 1976) $b_i=b_{i-1}+k_i$, and $\alpha_i=\alpha_{i-1}+l_i$.

The corrections h_i, k_i, and l_i can be computed from the matrix equation (109e):

$$\begin{bmatrix} h_i \\ k_i \\ l_i \end{bmatrix} = \begin{bmatrix} \ln x_g + (\alpha/a^2)\psi'(\alpha/a) & b^{-1} & -(1/a)\psi'(\alpha/a) \\ b\sum x_i^a + ab\sum x_i^a \ln x_i & a\sum x_i^a & -N \\ b\sum x_i^a \ln x_i + ab\sum x_i^a(\ln x_i)^2 & a\sum x_i^a \ln x_i & -N\ln x_g \end{bmatrix}_{i-1}$$

$$\begin{bmatrix} -a\ln x_g + \psi(\alpha/a) - \ln b \\ N - a\sum x_i^a \\ N + N\alpha \ln x_g - ab\sum x_i^a \ln x_i \end{bmatrix}_{i-1} \qquad (109e)$$

The suffixes $i-1$ to the matrix symbolize $a=a_{i-1}$, $b=b_{i-1}$ and $\alpha=\alpha_{i-1}$ for all elements of the matrix. Furthermore, $\psi'(\alpha/a)$ is the trigamma function (ABRAMOVITZ and STEGUN, 1964).
If $a=2/3$ and $\alpha=1/3$, we have:

$$f(x) = \frac{2}{3}\frac{b^{1/2}}{3\Gamma(\frac{1}{2})} e^{-bx^{2/3}} x^{-2/3} \qquad (110a)$$

This is known as a cube root semi-normal type.
For $a=2$, $\alpha=1$ we obtain the semi-normal type:

$$f(x) = \frac{2b^{1/2}}{\Gamma(\frac{1}{2})} e^{-bx^2} \qquad (110b)$$

The Weibull distribution

The distribution models which were previously introduced have in common that their cumulative distribution $F(x)$ is obtained by stepwise integration or by replacing the distribution function by a series of mathematical terms. Although this procedure is no longer a handicap today because electronic data processing gives quick answers, it may sometimes be desirable to utilize a function with a simple analytical expression for the c.d.f. which permits us to calculate percentiles directly. The subsequent function possesses this property. In addition, it shows considerable flexibility in shape and form and may even be used to approximate a Gaussian distribution.
The model is related to the Fisher-Tippett II distribution which is an extreme value distribution and will be discussed later (eq. 207a), but the function has found independent introduction by WEIBULL (1951) in life-testing of material. It is now referenced in the statistical literature as the Weibull distribution.
The four-parameter model was discussed by the author in a previous text (ESSENWANGER, 1976):

$$f(x) = \frac{\delta}{\beta^{\alpha+1}\Gamma(\alpha+1)}(x-\gamma)^{\delta(\alpha+1)-1}\exp[-(x-\gamma)^\delta/\beta] \qquad (111a)$$

We now set $\alpha=0$ and $\beta=\theta^\delta$. Then:

$$f(x) = \frac{\delta}{\theta}\left(\frac{x-\gamma}{\theta}\right)^{\delta-1} \exp\left[-\left(\frac{x-\gamma}{\theta}\right)^\delta\right] \qquad (111b)$$

This p.d.f. has a simple c.p.f.:

$$F(x)=1-\exp\left[-\left(\frac{x-\gamma}{\theta}\right)^{\delta}\right] \begin{cases} =F(x) \text{ for } x>\gamma \\ 0 \text{ for } x<\gamma \end{cases} \qquad (111c)$$

where $\theta>0$, $\delta>0$ and $x\geq\gamma$. Eqs. 111b and c are known as the Weibull model. Its distribution transforms into the Rayleigh distribution for $\delta=2$, $\gamma=0$ and $\theta=1/\sqrt{a}$; and into the exponential distribution for $\delta=1$. For more details see ESSENWANGER (1976).
For any threshold X_{th} the associated cumulative probability can be easily computed and vice versa:

$$X_{\text{th}}=\theta\{-\ln[1-F(x)]\}^{1/\delta}+\gamma \qquad (112)$$

In comparison with other distribution types one disadvantage of the Weibull model is the derivation of estimators for the parameters of the model. This may be one reason why the distribution has not found more widespread use until very recently, when electronic data processing became available.
The moments are:

$$\bar{x}=\mu_1=\theta a+\gamma \qquad (113a)$$

$$\sigma^2=\nu_2=\theta^2(b-a^2) \qquad (113b)$$

$$\nu_3=\theta^3(c-3ba+2a^3) \qquad (113c)$$

$$\nu_4=\theta^4(d-4ca+6a^2b-3a^4) \qquad (113d)$$

with:

$$\gamma_1=\frac{c-3ba+2a^3}{(b-a^2)^{3/2}}=\frac{M_3}{s^3} \qquad (113e)$$

and:

$$\gamma_2=\frac{(d-4ca+6a^2b-3a^4)}{(b-a^2)^2}-3 \qquad (113f)$$

The following replacements have been made:

$$a=\Gamma(1+1/\delta) \qquad (114a)$$

$$b=\Gamma(1+2/\delta) \qquad (114b)$$

$$c=\Gamma(1+3/\delta) \qquad (114c)$$

$$d=\Gamma(1+4/\delta) \qquad (114d)$$

Moments estimators

We notice that γ_1 or γ_2 are free of θ and γ and depend on δ only. Thus eq. 113e can be used to calculate moments estimators. With δ known, the other parameters result from:

$$\theta^2=\frac{s^2}{(b-a^2)} \qquad (115a)$$

$$\gamma = X_m - \theta a \tag{115b}$$

The determination of δ from eq. 113e is no problem by electronic data processing. Table XI gives a quick approximation when only a desk calculator is available.

Maximum-likelihood estimation

The maximum-likelihood equations are equally difficult. This was recently reconfirmed by ROCKETTE et al. (1974):

$$-\frac{N}{\theta^\delta} + \frac{1}{\delta^2}\sum_1^N (X_i - \gamma)^\delta = 0 \tag{116a}$$

$$\frac{N}{\delta} - \frac{1}{\theta^\delta}\sum_1^N (X_i - \gamma)^\delta \ln (X_i - \gamma) + \sum_1^N \ln (X_i - \gamma) = 0 \tag{116b}$$

$$\sum_1^N \left(\frac{1-\delta}{X_i - \gamma}\right) + \frac{\delta}{\theta^\delta}\sum_1^N (X_i - \gamma)^{\delta - 1} = 0 \tag{116c}$$

Since γ cannot be made available explicitly, a simultaneous solution of δ and γ from any two of the three equations must be found. One can use the moments estimators as a first approach, but the equations cannot readily be solved without electronic data processing, and the solution is not trivial.

If an assumption as to γ can be made, i.e., γ is known, then the solution is greatly simplified, and $\hat{\theta}$ and $\hat{\delta}$ exist (MCCOOL, 1970). The minimum of X_i in meteorological data

TABLE XI

AUXILIARY NUMERICAL VALUES FOR THE CALCULATION OF MOMENTS ESTIMATORS OF THE WEIBULL DISTRIBUTION

δ	γ_1	$b - a^2$	a
0.1	$699.00 \cdot 10^2$	$0.2433 \cdot 10^{19}$	$0.3629 \cdot 10^7$
0.25	60.09	$0.3974 \cdot 10^5$	24.0
0.50	6.62	20.0	2.0
0.75	3.12	2.595	1.191
1.0	2.0	1.0	1.0
1.25	1.430	0.5621	0.9314
1.5	1.072	0.3757	0.9027
1.75	0.8207	0.2759	0.8906
2.0	0.6311	0.2146	0.8862
2.5	0.3586	0.1441	0.8873
3.0	0.1681	0.1053	0.8930
3.5	0.02511	0.08107	0.8997
3.6	0.00056	0.07730	0.9011
4.0	−0.08723	0.06466	0.9064
4.5	−0.1783	0.05294	0.9126
5.0	−0.2540	0.04423	0.9182
5.5	−0.3181	0.03756	0.9232
6.0	−0.3732	0.03232	0.9277
6.5	−0.4212	0.02812	0.9318
7.0	−0.4634	0.02470	0.9354
7.5	−0.5008	0.02188	0.9387
8.0	−0.5342	0.01952	0.9417

samples, however, cannot automatically be assumed to correspond to γ. Compare also the case where $\bar{\gamma}=0$. When δ is known the maximum-likelihood estimates are unique (ROCKETTE et al., 1974).

An iterative procedure for the two-parameter Weibull model was suggested by WONG (1977). TACKLE and BROWN (1978) developed a graphical method which is an approximation to the maximum-likelihood estimators. According to their investigation their estimators stay within a few percent of values obtained from maximum-likelihood estimation.

Estimation by utilization of Gumbel's distribution

DOWNTON (1966) outlined a simple solution for obtaining estimators when $\gamma=0$. This two-parameter Weibull model can be related to Gumbel's extreme value distribution (see eq. 180). We introduce $Y=\ln x$, where x has a Weibull distribution. Then:

$$u=\bar{Y}\pm\bar{Z}/a \quad (117a)$$

$$\sigma^2=\sigma_Z^2/\sigma_Y^2 \quad (117b)$$

where $\bar{Z}=0.57721$ and $\alpha_Z^2=\pi^2/6$ (see eq. 184a, b). The parameters a and u can be determined by the calculation of $\bar{Y}=E(\ln x)$ and $\sigma_Y^2=\text{Var}(\ln x)$. The association with the parameters is simple:

$$\delta=a \quad (117c)$$

$$\theta=e^u \quad (117d)$$

In other words, estimators for the two-parameter Weibull distribution can be easily calculated by determining mean and variance of the transformed variable whose original variate has a Weibull distribution.

Straight-line fit estimators

An application to the long-term wave height distribution was investigated by BATTJES (1972). His solution was based on a graphical method by straight-line fitting. However, the cumulative distribution renders only a straight line in transformed logarithmic coordinates when γ is known or zero (see also BERRETTONI, 1964). We transform:

$$y=\ln[-\ln(1-F(z)]=\delta\ln(1/\theta)+\delta\ln z \quad (118a)$$

with $z=x-\gamma$. We now set $Z=\ln z=\ln(x-\gamma)$:

$$Y_i=a_0+a_1Z_i \quad (118b)$$

With known γ or $\gamma=0$ we have $F(z)\equiv F(x-\gamma)$, and a and b are readily obtained from the fitting of a straight line through y (calculation of coefficients see p. 105). Then:

$$\delta=a_1 \quad (118c)$$

$$\theta=\exp(-a_0/a_1) \quad (118d)$$

JUSTUS et al. (1978) have applied the Weibull distribution in this form for estimating wind speed frequency distributions. The technique is suitable for the two-parameter model or when γ is known. In the case that γ is unknown we must assume:

$$Z_\xi = (x - \xi) \tag{119}$$

and $F(z_\xi) \neq F(z)$ unless $\xi = \gamma$. It implies that y does not produce a straight line between y and Z (unless $\xi \equiv \gamma$, see ESSENWANGER, 1976, p. 189). Consequently:

$$y_i = a_0 + a_1 Z_i + a_2 Z_i^2 + \ldots + a_k Z_i^k \tag{120a}$$

The coefficients can be calculated via a matrix (see eq. 271a). It is simpler, however, to work with an orthogonal system (see p. 134ff):

$$y_i = A_0 + A, \ \phi_{1i} + A_2 \phi_{2i} + \ \ldots \ + A_k \phi_k \tag{120b}$$

where $i = 1, \ldots, k$.
It is evident that y is a straight line if and only if all coefficients A_j, $j \geq 2$ disappear. Consequently, if $A_2 = 0$ and the coefficients A_j for $j \geq 3$ are not simultaneously zero or negligible, the Weibull distribution is not the appropriate model for the data sample. Thus, we may concentrate on finding a solution with $A_2 = 0$ at $\xi = \gamma$, i.e., we search for $z_\xi = x - \gamma$. BERRETTONI (1964) has suggested a graphical approach by trial and error. The author recommends an iterative method by electronic data processing (see STEWART and ESSENWANGER, 1978). We produce:

$$Y_i(\xi) = \ln\left[-\ln\left(1 - F(z_\xi)\right]\right. \tag{121a}$$

and calculate A_2:

$$A_2(\xi) = |(1/\phi_2^2) \sum_{i=1}^{k} Y_i \phi_{2i}| \leq |\varepsilon| \sim 0 \tag{121b}$$

where $\phi_2^2 = \sum_{i=1}^{k} \phi_{2i}^2$ (see eq. 369). For checking purpose we may add:

$$A_j(\xi) = (1/\phi_j^2) \sum_{i=1}^{k} Y_i \phi_{ji} \tag{121c}$$

for any $j \geq 3$ and we must decide that A_j is either zero, negligible, or the Weibull model is not suitable (see p. 302ff). After $\xi = \gamma$ has been found eqs. 113b, c, d can be utilized to determine δ and θ.
Although the sequence of z_i and the distance Δz_i between z_{i+1} and z_i are arbitrary choices, a system where $\Delta z_i = \Delta z = \text{constant}$ and $z_i < z_{i+1}$ simplifies the mathematical procedure, and is necessary for the application of eq. 120b. We may select:

$$Z_{\xi_i} = z_0 + i\Delta z \tag{121d}$$

where Δz is constant, $i = 0, \ldots, k-1$ and z_0 is a selected minimum $z_0 \geq \xi$, with $F(z_{\xi_0}) > 0$. Notice that $F(z_{\xi_k}) < 1.0$. The efficiency of the estimators has not been studied in detail up to now but should be at least as good as the efficiency of the moments estimators.

Estimation by order statistics

MURTHY and SWARTZ (1975) developed formulae for the estimation of parameters by order statistics in the two-parameter model:

$$1/\hat{\delta}=(\ln F_t-\ln F_s)B(N,s,t) \tag{122}$$

where θ can be determined from eq. 115a after δ is known. B is a function to unbias the estimator for δ.

$$B(N,s,t)=1/2\;E_y \tag{123a}$$

with:

$$E_y=2A\sum_{i=0}^{s-1}\sum_{j=0}^{t-s-1}(C_{ij}/4\rho_j b_{ij}^2)\ln(\rho_j+1)/\rho_j \tag{123b}$$

$$A=N!/[(s-1)!(t-s-1)!(N-t)!] \tag{123c}$$

$$b_{ij}=t-s+i-j \tag{123d}$$

$$C_{ij}=(-1)^{i+j}\binom{s-1}{i}\binom{t-s-1}{j},\quad 0<s<t\leq N \tag{123e}$$

$$\rho_j=(N+j-t+1)/b_{ij} \tag{123f}$$

Murthy and Swartz deduced the variance of the estimator:

$$\mathrm{Var}\,(1/\hat{\delta})=(1/\delta)^2 g^2(N,s,t) \tag{124a}$$

where $1/\delta$ is the population parameter.

$$g^2(N,s,t)=E_{y^2}/E_y^2-1 \tag{124b}$$

$$E_{y^2}=2A\sum_{i=0}^{s-1}\sum_{j=0}^{t-s-1}(C_{ij}/8\rho_j b_{ij}^2)[\ln^2[(\rho_j+1)/\rho_j]+2g_t(1+\rho_j)] \tag{124c}$$

and:

$$g_t=\sum_{m=1}^{\infty}1/(m^2t^2) \tag{124d}$$

It is evident that the many summations need electronic data processing but Murthy and Swartz have given $B(N,s,t)$ for $N\leq 26$. They also recommended which of two order statistics for a sample size up to $N=26$ provides the optimum estimator for δ. The use of an order statistic has the advantage that it can be applied to truncated (censored) samples as long as N is known.

Miscellaneous estimators

JUSTUS et al. (1978) suggested various techniques for calculating estimators of the two-parameter model ($\gamma=0$) primarily applicable to surface wind speed distributions. Their use of a straight line estimation was mentioned on p. 53.
One of their procedures is an order statistics based on quartiles and the median.

$$\delta=1.57253/\ln(x_{25}/x_{75}) \tag{125a}$$

$$\theta = x_{50}/(\ln 2)^{1/\delta} \tag{125b}$$

where x_{25}, x_{75} are the quartiles, x_{50} the median.
Another method is the use of the mean and variance:

$$\delta = (\sigma/x_m)^{-1.086} \tag{126a}$$

$$\theta = x_m/\Gamma(1+1/\delta) \tag{126b}$$

(see eqs. 113a and b).
Justus et al. also recommend the use of the maximum x_{max} and $\bar{x}$. We find:

$$\ln[-\ln(1-F_{max})] = \delta[\ln x_{max} + \ln\Gamma(1+1/\delta) - \ln x_m] \tag{127}$$

This equation does not lead to an explicit expression for δ, and $F_{max} < 1.0$ but is unknown. (Notice, $F_{max} = 1.0$ creates ln 0.) In the special case of the surface wind speed distributions, Justus et al. recommend the approximation $\Gamma(1+1/\delta) \sim 0.9$ and a substitution $(1-F_{max}) = 24\, V_{max} \cdot d_m$ where V_{max} is the fastest mile (i.e., the average speed associated with the most rapid 1 mile run of the wind) and d_m is the number of days per month.
Justus et al. also derived another special formula for the calculation of δ from the 90 and 10 percentiles and the mean.
TACKLE and BROWN (1978) correctly pointed out that the two-parameter Weibull model may be deficient because it does not properly account for calms. They suggested a mixed model (see eq. 96, where $F(x)$ is now the Weibull distribution).

Example 11. Assume that we are interested in the distribution of the number of hours below a certain temperature threshold t_{th}. This problem could be solved by computing the number of runs of consecutive hours below t_{th}. This approach splits the data into two groups and the binomial distribution can be applied (eq. 59a). For a data set which has been observed for a short time and a temperature threshold (high or low) towards either extreme we expect very few runs. The empirical frequency distribution is then unbalanced. Customarily a smoothing of the data is applied. The

TABLE XII

COMPARISON OF THE WEIBULL DISTRIBUTION WITH THE OBSERVED HOURS (Example 11)

Cumulative percentage	Weibull (h)	Observed (h)
100	–	69.0
99.5	76.0	–
99.0	64.5	–
96.77	45.8	43.5
95.0	39.1	–
93.5	35.3	25.5
90.3	29.4	22.5
83.9	22.2	19.5
80.6	19.7	16.5
67.7	13.0	13.5
54.8	8.9	10.5
51.6	8.1	7.5
25.8	3.5	4.5
10.0	1.8	–
1.0	1.1	–

TABLE XIII

COMPARISON BETWEEN WEIBULL AND GAUSSIAN DISTRIBUTION

Classes (°F)	x_c	Observ. n_i	N_e Weibull	N_e Gaussian	n_i/N (%)	f_w (%)	f_g (%)
<4.5	2.0	29	36	66	0.6	0.8	1.4
4.6–9.5	7.0	265	224	225	5.6	4.7	4.7
9.6–14.5	12.0	529	591	600	11.1	12.4	12.7
19.5	17.0	990	997	1052	20.9	21.0	22.2
24.5	22.0	1268	1177	1217	26.7	24.8	25.7
29.5	27.0	892	966	927	18.8	20.4	19.5
34.5	32.0	536	530	465	11.3	11.2	9.8
39.5	37.0	200	183	154	4.2	3.8	3.2
44.6	42.0	33	37	33	0.7	0.8	0.7
>44.6	47.0	3	4	6	0.1	0.1	0.1
N		4745	4745	4745			

Weibull distribution may be used for this purpose, but it is only one of the applications of the Weibull distributions (Table XII).
For the Februaries 1949–1958 at Vilynysk (U.S.S.R.), 31 cases of temperatures below −40°F were observed with a mean of 12.39 h, $\sigma_x = 13.50$ and $\gamma_1 = 2.64$. The following Weibull parameters are derived: $\delta = 0.84$; eq. 115a provides $\theta = 10.29$ and eq. 115b results in $\gamma = 1.11$.

Example 12. Approximation of a Gaussian distribution. Table XIII provides a comparison between the fitting of the observed frequency by a Gaussian and a Weibull distribution. The data sample*[1] illustrates the observed distribution of the daily temperature range ($T_{max} - T_{min}$) for Huntsville, Alabama from January 1959 through December 1971; $N = 4745$, $x_m = 21.74°$, $s_x = 7.61$, $M_3 = 21.44$ Weibull distribution (moments estimators): $\gamma = -1.73$, $\theta = 26.13$, $\delta = 3.41$. The testing of the goodness-of-fit is postponed until p. 302.

The kappa distribution

A variety of frequency models has been introduced in this chapter. MIELKE (1973) and JOHNSON and MIELKE (1973) have investigated a family of frequency distributions which is based on the beta function and which Mielke has termed as kappa distribution. It was intended to approximate certain frequencies of precipitation better than the incomplete gamma distribution. In a later article MIELKE and JOHNSON (1973) concluded, however, that only a three-parameter model performs quite well. This three-parameter model was presented in the author's previous text (ESSENWANGER, 1976). Some basic concepts of this family of frequency distributions are described here.
The kappa distribution can be stated in the form of a three-parameter model:

$$F(x) = [\xi^a/(\alpha + \xi^a)]^{1/\alpha} \quad \begin{cases} \text{for } x \geq 0 \\ = 0 \text{ for } x \leq 0 \end{cases} \tag{128a}$$

$$f(x) = c\xi^{\theta-1}[\alpha + \xi^a]^{-b} \quad \begin{cases} \text{for } x > 0 \\ = 0 \text{ for } x \leq 0. \end{cases} \tag{128b}$$

*[1] The author's thanks go to Mr. H. P. Dudel (Army Missile Command, Huntsville, Alabama) who generously made his computations available for inclusion.

The following abbreviations have been employed:

$$\xi = x/\beta \qquad (128c)$$

$$a = \alpha\theta \qquad (128d)$$

$$b = 1 + 1/\alpha \qquad (128e)$$

$$c = \alpha\theta/\beta \qquad (128f)$$

All three parameters α, β, θ must be >0.
Setting $\theta = 1$ a two-parameter model remains with:

$$F(x) = [\xi^{\alpha}/(\alpha + \xi^{\alpha})]^{1/\alpha} \quad \text{for } x \geq 0 \qquad (129a)$$

$$f(x) = (\alpha/\beta)[\alpha + \xi^{\alpha}]^{-b} \quad \text{for } x \geq 0 \qquad (129b)$$

The conditions for x and parameters α and β follow the general principle of the three-parameter model.
The presented form of the frequency distribution is one version of the beta function, and the moments can be stated as:

$$\mu_r = \beta^r \alpha^{-w} B(z,w) \qquad (130a)$$

where:

$$z = (\theta + r)/\alpha\theta \qquad (130b)$$

$$w = (\alpha\theta - r)/\alpha\theta \qquad (130c)$$

The beta function B is defined by:

$$B(m,n) = \Gamma(m)\Gamma(n)/\Gamma(m+n) \qquad (130d)$$

where Γ has been introduced (eq. 90b). For $\theta = 1$, z and w transform to:

$$z = (1 + r)/\alpha \qquad (130e)$$

$$w = (\alpha - r)/\alpha \qquad (130f)$$

and the moments exist only when $w > 0$ or $\alpha > r$.
By introduction of z and w into eq. 130a we find the first two moments (with $\alpha > 2$):

$$\bar{x} = \beta\alpha^{-w_1} B(z_1,w_1) \qquad (131a)$$

$$\mu_2 = \beta^2 \alpha^{-w_2} B(z_2,w_2) \qquad (131b)$$

where:

$$z_1 = 2/\alpha \qquad (131c)$$

$$z_2 = 3/\alpha \qquad (131d)$$

$$w_1 = (\alpha - 1)/\alpha \qquad (131e)$$

$$w_2 = (\alpha - 2)/\alpha \qquad (131f)$$

Moments estimators can be obtained from:

$$g(\alpha) = \mu_2/\bar{x}^2 = \alpha B(z_2,w_2)/B^2(z_1,w_1) \qquad (132a)$$

$$h(\alpha)=\beta/\bar{x}=\alpha^{w_1}/B(z_1,w_1) \tag{132b}$$

where $\bar{x}$ and μ_2 as usually are replaced by the moments from the observational data, namely x_m and $m^2=s^2+x_m^2$.

The functions $g(\alpha)$ and $h(\alpha)$ are difficult to solve without electronic data processing. MIELKE (1973) has given a table (Table XIV) which is reproduced below by permission. First, α is determined from $g(\alpha)$, and then $\beta=x_m h(\alpha)$.

The maximum-likelihood estimates are not readily calculated. An iterative procedure, based on the Newton-Raphson method, and starting with α_0 and β_0, was described by MIELKE (1973):

$$\alpha_{i+1}=\alpha_i-g_1(\alpha_i,\beta_i)/g_2(\alpha_i,\beta_i) \tag{133a}$$

$$\beta_{i+1}=\beta_i-g_3(\alpha_i,\beta_i)/g_2(\alpha_i,\beta_i) \tag{133b}$$

The first α_0,β_0 values may be taken from the moments estimators. According to Mielke, the iterative process converges. The following notation has been utilized:

$$g_1(\alpha_i,\beta_i)=G_1G_{22}-G_2G_{12} \tag{134a}$$

$$g_2(\alpha_i,\beta_i)=G_{11}G_{22}-G_{12}^2 \tag{134b}$$

$$g_3(\alpha_i,\beta_i)=G_2G_{11}-G_1G_{12} \tag{134c}$$

where the G's are functions of α, β, i.e. $G_i(\alpha,\beta)$. In detail:

$$G_1(\alpha,\beta)=\frac{1}{\alpha^2}\sum_{i=1}^{n}\ln\left[\alpha+(x_i/\beta)^\alpha\right]+\frac{n}{\alpha}\frac{\alpha+1}{\alpha}\sum_{i=1}^{n}\frac{1+(x_i/\beta)^\alpha\ln(x_i/\beta)}{\alpha+(x_i/\beta)^\alpha} \tag{135a}$$

$$G_2(\alpha,\beta)=\frac{\alpha+1}{\beta}\sum_{i=1}^{n}\frac{(x_i/\beta)^\alpha}{\alpha+(x_i/\beta)^\alpha}\frac{n}{\beta} \tag{135b}$$

TABLE XIV

FUNCTIONS $g(\alpha)$ AND $h(\alpha)$

α	$g(\alpha)$	$h(\alpha)$	α	$g(\alpha)$	$h(\alpha)$
2.1	11.0863	0.7489	8.0	1.4022	1.4705
2.2	6.0929	0.7875	9.0	1.3872	1.5085
2.3	4.4324	0.8231	10.0	1.3767	1.5404
2.4	3.6049	0.8561	12.0	1.3633	1.5911
2.5	3.1105	0.8868	14.0	1.3553	1.6301
2.6	2.7824	0.9154	16.0	1.3501	1.6612
2.8	2.3756	0.9673	18.0	1.3466	1.6867
3.0	2.1345	1.0130	20.0	1.3441	1.7082
3.5	1.8203	1.1070	25.0	1.3402	1.7494
4.0	1.6693	1.1803	30.0	1.3381	1.7793
4.5	1.5823	1.2395	40.0	1.3360	1.8201
5.0	1.5266	1.2884	60.0	1.3345	1.8664
6.0	1.4610	1.3655	80.0	1.3340	1.8924
7.0	1.4246	1.4241	100.0	1.3338	1.9094

$$G_{11}(\alpha,\beta) = -\frac{2}{\alpha^3}\sum_{i=1}^{n} \ln\left[\alpha + (x_i/\beta)^\alpha\right] - \frac{n}{\alpha^2} + \frac{2}{\alpha^2}\sum_{i=1}^{n} \frac{1 + (x_i/\beta)^\alpha \ln(x_i/\beta)}{\alpha + (x_i/\beta)^\alpha}$$

$$-\frac{\alpha+1}{\alpha}\sum_{i=1}^{n} \frac{(x_i/\beta)^\alpha[\ln(x_i/\beta)]^2}{\alpha + (x_i/\beta)^\alpha} + \frac{\alpha+1}{\alpha}\sum_{i=1}^{n}\left[\frac{1 + (x_i/\beta)^\alpha \ln(x_i/\beta)}{\alpha + (x_i/\beta)^\alpha}\right]^2 \quad (135c)$$

$$G_{22}(\alpha,\beta) = \frac{\alpha(\alpha+1)}{\beta^2}\sum_{i=1}^{n}\left[\frac{(x_i/\beta)^\alpha}{\alpha + (x_i/\beta)^\alpha}\right]^2 + \frac{n}{\beta^2} - \frac{(\alpha+1)^2}{\beta^2}\sum_{i=1}^{n} \frac{(x_i/\beta)^\alpha}{\alpha + (x_i/\beta)^\alpha} \quad (135d)$$

$$G_{12}(\alpha,\beta) = \frac{1}{\beta}\sum_{i=1}^{n} \frac{(x_i/\beta)^\alpha}{\alpha + (x_i/\beta)^\alpha} + \frac{\alpha+1}{\beta}\sum_{i=1}^{n} \frac{(x_i/\beta)^\alpha \ln(x_i/\beta)}{\alpha + (x_i/\beta)^\alpha}$$

$$-\frac{\alpha+1}{\beta}\sum_{i=1}^{n} \frac{(x_i/\beta)^\alpha[1 + (x_i/\beta)^\alpha \ln(x_i/\beta)]}{[\alpha + (x_i/\beta)^\alpha]^2} \quad (135e)$$

The three-parameter model has more flexibility and provides a closer approximation of the empirical data. The moments follow from eq. 130a. A detailed description and tables for the calculation of moments estimators can be found in Essenwanger (1976). One advantage of the kappa distribution is its closed form for $F(x)$.

The logarithmic series distribution

Bowman and Shenton (1970) found a useful model for frequencies of the duration of storms. The density function can be written:

$$f(x) = \alpha\theta^x/x \quad (136a)$$

with $0 < \theta < 1$ and $x = 1, 2 \ldots n$.
The α is a function of θ and as such is not a new parameter, namely:

$$1/\alpha = -\ln(1-\theta) = \ln[1/(1-\theta)] \quad (136b)$$

The distribution has the following moments:

$$\bar{x} = \alpha\theta/(1-\theta) \quad (137a)$$

$$\mu_2 = \bar{x}/(1-\theta) \quad (137b)$$

$$\sigma^2 = \alpha\theta(1-\alpha\theta)/(1-\theta)^2 = \bar{x}(1-\alpha\theta)/(1-\theta) \quad (137c)$$

$$\mu_3 = \mu_2(1+\theta)/(1-\theta) \quad \text{(reference zero)} \quad (137d)$$

$$\mu_4 = \mu_3[(1+\theta) + 2\theta/(1+\theta)]/(1-\theta) \quad \text{(reference zero)} \quad (137e)$$

The maximum-likelihood estimator for θ can be obtained from:

$$\hat{\theta}/[(1-\hat{\theta})\ln(1/(1-\hat{\theta})] = \bar{x} \quad (138)$$

Patil (1962) has stated that an asymptotic variance of $\hat{\theta}$ is:

$$\sigma_{\hat{\theta}}^2 = \theta^2/(N \cdot \sigma^2) \quad (139a)$$

Patil has prepared a table to solve eq. 138. The entry in the table is the mean. Otherwise an iterative method is needed.
Other estimators are:

$$\hat{\theta}_1 = 1 - f_1/\bar{x} \tag{139b}$$

$$\hat{\theta}_2 = 1 - \bar{x}/\mu_2 \tag{139c}$$

$$\hat{\theta}_3 = \sum_{x=2}^{\infty} f(x,\theta)\cdot x/(x-1) \tag{139d}$$

where f_1 represents the first-class frequency (n_1/N), and $f(x,\theta)$ the frequency density. Patil found that $\hat{\theta}_2$ and $\hat{\theta}_3$ have a poor efficiency, while $\hat{\theta}_1$ is reasonably efficient.

The logarithmic negative mixture distribution

Another possible frequency model has been suggested by SHENTON and SKEES (1970). It is primarily applicable to precipitation and is called the logarithmic negative mixture.

$$F(x) = \sum_{y=1}^{x} f(y) = 1 - a\theta^2/(x+b) \quad \text{for } a>0,\ b>-1,\ 0<\theta<1 \tag{140a}$$

$$F(0) = 0 \tag{140b}$$

$$F(1) = 1 - a\theta/(1+b) \tag{140c}$$

$$f(x) = a\theta^{x-1}[1/(x+b-1) = \theta/(x+b)] \quad (\text{for } x \geq 2) \tag{141a}$$

Furthermore:

$$f(x) = F(x) - F(x-1) \tag{141b}$$

$$f(1) \equiv F(1) \tag{141c}$$

The mean has limited value for estimating the parameters because:

$$\bar{x} = 1 + a\sum_{i=1}^{\infty} \theta^i/(b+i) \tag{142}$$

Recall that x denotes the upper class boundary for the use of $F(x)$ and not the central class value (see Example 13, p. 65).
The estimation of the parameters a, b and θ is not trivial. BURR (1942) suggested employing three frequency intervals for this type of function. In our case, this procedure appears as the simplest technique although it requires costly computations.
Assume we take n_i, n_j and n_k as the three frequency intervals which correspond to the relative frequency f_i, f_j and f_k ($i \neq j \neq k$). We establish the (complementary) cumulative frequency:

$$F'_i = 1 - \sum_{1}^{i} f_m = 1 - F_{(i)} \tag{143}$$

Correspondingly, F'_j and F'_k are calculated. Then $\tilde{b}$ must be determined from:

$$\left(\frac{F'_i}{F'_j}\cdot\frac{\tilde{b}+i}{\tilde{b}+j}\right)^{1/(i-j)} = \left(\frac{F'_i}{F'_k}\cdot\frac{\tilde{b}+i}{\tilde{b}+k}\right)^{1/(i-k)} \tag{144a}$$

After $\tilde{b}$ has been found, the remaining estimators follow easily from:

$$\tilde{\theta}=\left(\frac{F'_i}{F'_j}\cdot\frac{\tilde{b}+i}{\tilde{b}+j}\right)^{1/(i-j)} \tag{144b}$$

$$\tilde{a}=(\tilde{b}+i)F'_i/\tilde{\theta}^i \tag{144c}$$

This procedure is repeated for other combinations of F'_i, F'_j and F'_k. The one set of estimators which minimizes chi-square (see eq. 645) is finally adopted.

It is evident that the determination of estimators is somewhat lengthy, especially when i, j and k are not sequential numbers. For $j=i+1$, $k=i+2$ we can simplify eq. 144a, and obtain an explicit expression for $\tilde{b}$:

$$\tilde{b}=-[A_F^2(i+k)-2jB_F]/[2(A_F^2-B_F)]\pm A_F/(A_F^2-B_F)^{1/2} \tag{145a}$$

This equation has a real solution for $A_F^2>B_F$. Otherwise we must select other combinations (permutations) of frequency intervals and/or go back to eq. 144b. The following symbols have been substituted:

$$A_F=F'_i/F'_j \tag{145b}$$

$$B_F=F'_i/F'_k \tag{145c}$$

It should be reiterated that $\tilde{b}>-1$.

Moments estimators

Moments estimators are best based on the factorial moments ϕ_i. These are defined as:

$$\phi_r=\sum_{j=-\infty}^{\infty}(x_j-c)^{[r]}\cdot f(x_j) \tag{146}$$

where c denotes an arbitrary origin and $[r]$, the exponent, designates the operation:

$$x^{[r]}=x(x-h)(x-2h)\ldots(x-[r-1]h) \tag{147}$$

The parameter h is the width of the class interval of the grouped data (e.g., classes of 2 mm or 3 h of precipitation, etc.). For $c=0$ and $h=1$ we find:

$$\phi_1=\sum_{j-=\infty}^{\infty}x_jf(x_j) \tag{148a}$$

$$\phi_2=\sum x_j(x_j-1)f(x_j) \tag{148b}$$

The factorial moments relate to the ordinary moments μ:

$$\phi_1=\mu_1=\bar{x} \tag{149a}$$

$$\phi_2=\mu_2-h\mu_1 \tag{149b}$$

$$\phi_3=\mu_3-3h\mu_2+2h^2\mu_1 \tag{149c}$$

$$\phi_4=\mu_4-6h\mu_3+11h^2\mu_2-6h^3\mu_1 \tag{149d}$$

Conversely we can write:

$$\mu_2=\phi_2+h\phi_1 \tag{150a}$$

$$\mu_3 = \phi_3 + 3h\phi_2 + h^2\phi_1 \quad (150b)$$

$$\mu_4 = \phi_4 + 6h\phi_3 + 7h^2\phi_2 + h^3\phi_1 \quad (150c)$$

or:

$$\mu_3 = \phi_3 + 3h\mu_2 - 2h^2\bar{x} \quad (150d)$$

$$\mu_4 = \phi_4 + 6h\mu_3 - 11h^2\mu_2 + 6h^3\bar{x} \quad (150e)$$

When μ_i is given, ν_i can be computed (see eqs. 26d and 29a–d. For $h=1$ we obtain:

$$\nu_2 = \phi_2 - \bar{x}(\bar{x}-1) \quad (151a)$$

$$\nu_3 = \phi_3 - 3(x-1)\phi_2 + x(\bar{x}-1)(2\bar{x}-1) \quad (151b)$$

$$\nu_4 = \phi_4 - 2(2\bar{x}-3)\phi_3 + [6(\bar{x}-1)^2 + 1]\phi_2 - \bar{x}(\bar{x}-1)^3 + \bar{x}^2(\bar{x}-1) \quad (151c)$$

After this digression we return to the logarithmic negative mixture distribution which has the following factorial moments:

$\phi_1 = \mu_1 = \bar{x}$ (see eq. 149a)

$$\phi_2 = 2a[\theta/(1-\theta) + b(1-\bar{x})/a] \quad (152a)$$

$$\phi_3 = 3a \sum_{s=1}^{\infty} s(s-1)\theta^s/(b+s) \quad (152b)$$

generally:

$$\phi_r = ra \sum_{s=1}^{\infty} s(s-1) \ldots (s-r+2)\theta^2/(b+s) \text{ for } r \geq 2 \quad (153)$$

The higher factorial moments can also be expressed by the relationship:

$$\phi_r = r\phi_r' \quad (154a)$$

where:

$$\phi_{r+1}' = -(r+b-1)\phi_r' + \frac{a(r-1)!}{\theta}\left(\frac{\theta}{1-\theta}\right)^r \text{ for } r \geq 2 \quad (154b)$$

This leads to:

$$\phi_3' = -(b+1)\phi_2/2 + a\theta/(1-\theta)^2 \quad (155a)$$

$$\phi_4' = -(b+2)\phi_3/3 + 2a\theta^2/(1-\theta)^3 \quad (155b)$$

For a known or calculated ϕ_i or ϕ_i' (see eq. 146) estimators for b, a and θ can be computed although often by lengthy calculations.
The summation in eq. 142 limits an explicit solution for θ to cases of $b=0$ (see eq. 155a). Thus, the mean is of little value for estimation. Consequently, an estimator for θ must be based on ϕ_2 through ϕ_4. From a quadratic equation the following estimator can be found:

$$\tilde{\theta}_{1,2} = (-B \pm \sqrt{B^2 - 4AC})/(2A) \text{ with } 0 < \tilde{\theta} < 1.0 \quad (156a)$$

where:

$$A = \phi_3'(\phi_2' - \phi_3') + \phi_2'\phi_4' \quad (156b)$$

$$-B=\phi'_3(3\phi'_2-2\phi'_3)+2\phi'_2(\phi'_2+\phi'_4)+(1-\bar{x})(4\phi'_3+\phi'_4+2\phi'_2) \tag{156c}$$

$$C=\phi'_2\phi'_4-\phi'_3(\phi'_3-2\phi'_2)+(1-\bar{x})(2\phi'_3+\phi'_4) \tag{156d}$$

(The sign of B has been adjusted to fit eq. 156a.)
Afterwards an estimator for b can be calculated from either:

$$\tilde{b}=[\theta\phi'_2-(1-\theta)\phi'_3]/[(1-\bar{x})+(1-\theta)\phi'_2] \tag{157a}$$

or:

$$\tilde{b}=[2\phi'_3(2\theta-1)-(1-\theta)\phi'_4+2\theta\phi'_2]/[(1-\theta)\phi'_3-2\theta\phi'_2] \tag{157b}$$

Finally an estimator of a is:

$$\tilde{a}=(\bar{x}-1)/\left[\sum_{i=1}^{\infty}\theta^i/(b+i)\right] \tag{157c}$$

or:

$$\tilde{a}=(1-\theta)[\phi'_2-b(1-\bar{x})]/\theta \tag{157d}$$

Eq. 156a does not contain a summation term such as eq. 157c but eq. 157d serves as an independent check.
In the calculation of moments estimators we may not need a criterion for selection such as the minimum χ^2 because the quadratic solution leads to two choices, and $0<\theta<1$. The author has found, however, that for numerous samples both estimates of θ could fall within the specified boundaries. One of the estimators for θ must then be eliminated by a judgment of $\tilde{a}$ and $\tilde{b}$. If $\tilde{a}$ and $\tilde{b}$ do not permit a decision because they also stay within the specificd boundaries (see eq. 140a), a decision can be made by adopting the triplet with the minimum χ^2.
In eq. 156a the estimator for θ was procured first. We could reverse the sequence and calculate an estimate for b first, then obtain $\tilde{\theta}$ and $\tilde{a}$. It requires the following steps:

$$\tilde{b}_{1,2}=(-B\pm\sqrt{B^2-4AC})/(2A) \tag{158a}$$

where:

$$A=(1-\bar{x})(2\phi'_2+\phi'_3)+2(\phi'_2)^2 \tag{158b}$$

$$B=(1-\bar{x})(2\phi'_2+4\phi'_3)+\phi'_2(2\phi'_2+3\phi'_3) \tag{158c}$$

$$C=2(\phi_3)^2-\phi'_2\phi'_4 \tag{158d}$$

Subsequently:

$$\tilde{\theta}=[b(1-\bar{x}+\phi'_2)+\phi'_3]/[b\phi'_2+\phi'_2+\phi'_3] \tag{158e}$$

or:

$$\tilde{\theta}=[b\phi'_3+2\phi'_3+\phi'_4]/[b(2\phi'_2+\phi'_3)+2\phi'_2+4\phi'_3+\phi'_4] \tag{158f}$$

The estimator of $\tilde{a}$ follows from eqs. 157c and d.
The moments estimators necessitate the computation of four factorial moments and probably lack efficiency, as most moments estimators do. The decision regarding which type of estimators should be obtained may not only depend on statistical theory but on the

availability of funds for electronic data processing and the number of samples in a particular study. Virtually all possible permutations must be tried in the calculation of estimation by the frequency method (eqs. 144, 145). Thus the procedure can be time-consuming and very costly but it can provide a better approximation of the observed frequency than the one gained from the moments estimators.

Example 13. Logarithmic negative mixture. Let us first consider an assumed sample where $\theta = 0.25$; $b=0$ and $a=1$. In this case an analytical solution for θ exists from a similarity with eq. 136a because $\bar{x}=1-\ln(1-\theta)=1-\ln(0.75)=1.28768$. The short series for $f(x)$ makes it possible to demonstrate the calculation of permutations for the frequency estimators (see Table XV, b).
Table XV, a lists the frequency $f(x)$ and cumulative $F(x)$ obtained from the given parameters in the first two columns (notice that x is the upper class limit). The factorial moments are shown for the given parameters and calculated from $f(x)$ (8 digit precision; see Table XVI, a). It is evident that the accuracy of ϕ_r decreases with increasing order of r. This comparison illustrates one difficulty in the use of the logarithmic series. Most frequencies of empirical data samples show random fluctuations. Thus, the factorial moments can only be determined to a limited degree of accuracy. Because random fluctuations enter into the error of moments estimators the solution may not be very robust. The departure of the moment estimators from the correct parameter is illustrated in Table XVI, b. We learn that in this case no decision can be made which triplet should be eliminated. Both θ_1 and θ_2 stay within defined bounds (see eq. 140a). The set of estimators to be rejected can be found from $\tilde{b}$ and $\tilde{a}$ which are out of bounds for one set.
The frequency density derived from the accepted set of moments estimators is displayed under the heading $f_M(x)$ in Table XV, a.
The differences between $f(x)$ and $f_M(x)$ are small despite the deviation from the parameters which the estimators show. This indicates that judgment about the discrepancies in the p.d.f. cannot be made

TABLE XV

LOGARITHMIC NEGATIVE MIXTURE ($\theta=0.25$, $a=1.0$, $b=0$)

(*a*) Frequency distribution

x	$f(x)$	$F(x)$	$f'(x)$	$f_M(x)$	$f_F(x)$
1	0.7500	0.7500	0.2500	0.7506	0.7500
2	0.2188	0.9688	0.0312	0.2174	0.2188
3	0.0260	0.9648	0.0052	0.0269	0.0260
4	0.0042	0.9990	0.0010	0.0042	0.0042
5	0.0008	0.9998	0.0020	0.0007	0.0008
6	0.0002	1.0000	0	0.0001	0.0002

(*b*) Calculation of estimators (eq. 144, a–c)

Combination: i_1	j_2	k_3	θ_1	b	a	θ_2	b	a
1	2	3	0.2502	−0.0045	0.9949	0.0831	−4.00	−9.01
1	2	4	0.2543	−0.0362	0.9476	–	–	–
1	2	5	0.2526	−0.0238	0.966	–	–	–
1	3	4	0.2585	−0.0963	0.8739	–	–	–
1	3	5	0.2540	−0.0485	0.9365	–	–	–
1	4	5	0.2495	+0.0410	1.0432	–	–	–
2	3	4	0.2625	−0.2610	0.7871	0.1221	−5.74	−7.83
2	3	5	0.2552	−0.1185	0.9010	–	–	–
2	4	5	0.2478	0.1839	1.1097	–	–	–
3	4	5	0.2392	1.0990	1.5569	0.1608	−9.10	−7.63

TABLE XVI

FACTORIAL MOMENTS AND ESTIMATORS FOR LOGARITHMIC NEGATIVE MIXTURE

(*a*) Factorial moments

	Postulated	Calculated (from p.d.f)
$\bar{x}$	1.28768	1.28760
ϕ_2	2/3	0.66600
ϕ_3	1/3	0.32880
ϕ_4	8/27 (0.29630)	0.26880

(*b*) Estimators from factorial moments

	Postulated	Eq. 156		Eq. 158	
		first	second	first	second
θ	0.25	0.2287	0.0924	0.2287	0.0924
b	0	0.2698	(−4.69)	0.2729	(−4.70)
a	1.0	1.3836	(−10.00)	1.3877	(−10.00)

Outside definition boundaries between brackets (see eq. 140a).

only from the comparison of estimators for parameters because the estimators are not independent of each other.

The last section (Table XV, b) contains the frequency fit (see eq. 144a). Again, the deviations from the true value are caused by the inaccuracy of the relative frequency. The best fit (judged by the χ^2 test) was obtained for the combination $x_1=1$, $x_2=2$, $x_3=3$. This is no surprise because these are the frequencies with the smallest precision error, however, in data samples from observations this permutation may not lead to the best fit. The recalculated $f_F(x)$ is listed in the last column of Table XV, a.

Attention is called to a restriction. Because $F'(x=6)=0$ it cannot be utilized in eq. 144a. The permutation of frequencies goes to $k=n-1$, where n denotes the number of classes. If we select $j=i+1$ and $k=i+2$ we can utilize eq. 145a. Here the smallest $\bar{b}$ was accepted. In this particular case it appeared as a reasonable choice and reduced the costs of data processing instead of going through the permutations.

Example 14. Storm data for Athens (Georgia), moments and frequency estimators; logarithmic negative mixture distributions.

The difference between estimators from factorial moments and frequency estimators is now demonstrated with an example from observed data. SHENTON and SKEES (1970) have compiled storm data for several stations. Athens (Georgia) with hourly observations for the period 1955–1964 (one hour between new storm counts) was selected. The observations are given in Table XVII (column n_x, where x designates the duration of the storms).

Three cases were studied. In Case A the 16 chosen classes with the observed frequencies n_x Table XVII) were utilized. Case B comprises an expansion to 24 classes (i.e., up to 24h duration) where n_{24} sums all storms >24h. Case C is based on the entire material with the maximum of 30 classes.

The statistical characteristics for these three cases are depicted in Table XVIII. While the moments up to order two differ little, the higher moments show an increase with a decrease of truncation. This effect is also well reflected in γ_1 and γ_2.

In Case A eq. 156a leads to a negative square root. Cases B and C render estimators for θ, a and b. These estimators differ significantly from those of the frequency method (see Table XVIII). It was pointed out in Example 13 that this alone would not be a reason for special concern. However,

TABLE XVII

OBSERVED AND FITTED STORM DATA FOR ATHENS, GEORGIA

(1 dry hour between storms; period 1955–1964 (compiled by SHENTON and SKEES, 1970)

x (h)	n_x	$f(x)$	$F'(x)$	Frequency fit, n_i	Moments fit, n_i	Continued from col. 1 and 2 x (h)	n_x
1	363	0.3262	0.6738	363.6	495.2	16	4
2	291	0.2614	0.4124	275.6	144.5	17	1
3	142	0.1276	0.2848	142.3	108.8	18	3
4	71	0.0638	0.2210	85.7	82.5	19	0
5	51	0.0458	0.1752	56.6	63.0	20	3
6	38	0.0341	0.1411	39.7	48.3	21	3
7	32	0.0288	0.1123	29.1	37.2	22	1
8	25	0.0225	0.0898	22.0	28.8	23	2
9	16	0.0143	0.0755	17.0	22.4	24	1
10	16	0.0144	0.0611	13.4	17.4	25	0
11	12	0.0108	0.0503	10.7	13.6	26	1
12	14	0.0126	0.0377	8.7	10.7	27	1
13	10	0.0090	0.0287	7.2	8.4	28	0
14	8	0.0071	0.0216	5.9	6.6	29	0
15	3	0.0027	0.0189	4.9	5.2	30	1
≥ 16	21	0.0189	0	30.6	20.4		
	1113						21

TABLE XVIII

STATISTICAL CHARACTERISTICS FOR THE COMPUTATION OF MOMENTS AND FREQUENCY ESTIMATORS FOR DATA OF TABLE XVII

Parameter	Estimators from factorial moments			Frequency fit
	Case A	Case B	Case C	
$\bar{x}$	3.40	3.48	3.49	3.64
σ	3.35	3.70	3.76	4.46
ϕ_2	19.44	22.31	22.82	29.55
ϕ_3	169.47	246.00	264.94	552.41
ϕ_4	1671.27	3410.11	4014.47	16805.37
ν_3	76.80	131.45	146.45	370.60
ν_4	864.87	2074.21	2540.88	12264.66
μ_2	22.84	35.79	26.31	33.14
μ_3	231.19	316.40	336.88	644.70
μ_4	2827.58	5045.75	5767.30	20330.32
a	–	14.6	8.62	1.63
θ	root negative	0.808	0.826	0.917
b	–	20.19	11.82	1.22
γ_1	2.04	2.76	2.76	4.18
γ_2	3.83	8.10	9.75	28.00

observed and analytical frequencies show major differences (see Table XVII). As displayed in Table XVII, the first three classes differ significantly from the observations if the moments estimators are used. The explanation is the truncation of data, not only in Case A or B but possibly the data sample.

Let us now turn our attention to the frequency fit. Table XVIII illustrates the combination of classes for calculating estimators up to $k=15$ for $j=2$, 3 and 4 with i denoting the first frequency class. As expected for the frequency fit the truncation causes no problem. Table XIX discloses the fluctuations associated with estimators from empirical data.
The adoption of a set of estimators in the frequency method depends on the outcome of the χ^2 test. The estimators with the minimum χ^2 are selected. SHENTON and SKEES (1970) have found the best results for $i=1, j=4, k=10$. This permutation was adopted in this text. The frequency density for this set of estimators is given in Table XVII under the column "frequency fit". The estimators here differ slightly from results by Shenton and Skees because they or the author may have used more precision for the calculations.
At first glance, it may seem that no significant deviation between empirical and analytical frequency can be discovered because the set of estimators with the smallest χ^2 was accepted. This is no

TABLE XIX

ESTIMATORS OF THE LOG-NEGATIVE MIXTURE DISTRIBUTION FOR VARIOUS COMBINATIONS (data table XVII)

i	j	k	$\tilde{b}$	$\tilde{A}$	$\tilde{a}$
1	2	3	0.964	0.924	1.43
		4	0.747	0.962	1.22
		5	0.753	0.961	1.23
		6	0.781	0.956	1.26
		7	0.841	0.944	1.31
		8	0.893	0.935	1.36
		9	0.894	0.935	1.36
		10	0.934	0.928	1.40
		11	0.959	0.924	1.43
		12	1.050	0.910	1.51
		13	1.122	0.900	1.59
		14	1.198	0.890	1.66
		15	1.170	0.894	1.64
1	3	4	0.464	0.999	0.99
		5	0.576	0.979	1.08
		6	0.655	0.966	1.15
		7	0.764	0.950	1.25
		8	0.851	0.938	1.33
		9	0.856	0.937	1.33
		10	0.919	0.929	1.39
		11	0.956	0.925	1.42
		12	1.095	0.909	1.55
		13	1.202	0.898	1.65
		14	1.318	0.887	1.76
		15	1.271	0.892	1.72
1	4	5	0.781	0.958	1.25
		6	0.870	0.949	1.33
		7	1.039	0.932	1.47
		8	1.164	0.922	1.58
		9	1.134	0.924	1.56
		10	1.223*	0.917*	1.63*
		11	1.268	0.913	1.67
		12	1.500	0.897	1.88
		13	1.679	0.886	2.04
		14	1.874	0.875	2.21
		15	1.765	0.881	2.12

*Selected combination for frequency fit (see SHENTON and SKEES, 1970).

necessity. The frequency distribution with the smallest χ^2 could still show significant deviations. In our case the Kolmogorov-Smirnov test (eq. 694a, b) also indicates that the differences are insignificant.
It is reiterated that the observations at the tail end of the frequency distribution contribute heavily to the magnitude of the higher order factorial moments. The possibility of truncation (or censoring) should always be considered for one-sided distributions with a drawn-out tail. The poor agreement between the analytical and observed frequency in our example is attributed to this deficiency. This effect may not be as strong in other data samples and the truncation may have been overemphasized in this particular example. The author's goal was to caution the reader of the pitfalls which may be encountered in calculating estimators from factorial moments for the logarithmic negative series.

The circular normal distribution

The wind direction is a circular variate. In most cases ordinary models of frequency distributions which are suitable for a linear variate are inappropriate. This fact was already recognized by VON MISES (1918) who introduced a circular distribution which takes the periodic character of a circular variate into account. Later GUMBEL (1954) applied the circular distribution to the study of special periodicities such as the annual or the daily cycle where the period of repetition is known a priori. GUMBEL et al. (1953) have called it the circular normal distribution.
Recently, SNEYERS and VAN ISACKER (1980) generalized this circular model which thus has become a distribution of great flexibility. It offers an interesting approach to the presentation of distributions for circular variates and phenomena of known periodicity but in these cases the Fourier series is also available as a tool. In fact, the generalized circular distribution is the Fourier series for the logarithm of the frequency distribution. The model is introduced here in its generalized form by Sneyers, and we elaborate later on the special case (Gumbel's model). We may write:

$$f(\alpha)=C^{-1}\exp[\sum A_j\cos(\alpha-\beta_j)] \qquad (159a)$$

where C is a constant to force $\sum f(\alpha)=1.0$, α designates an angular variate, and A_j, β_j are parameters. Gumbel's model is the limitation to the first term:

$$f(\alpha)=C^{-1}\exp[A_1\cos(\alpha-\beta_1)]. \qquad (159b)$$

This model was derived by Von Mises from the consideration of the likelihood function. An example of an application to wind direction data was given by HIROH and ITOH (1983).

Gumbel's model

In frequency distribution models for a linear variate the mean is the most likely value. This principle was applied by VON MISES (1918) to a circular variate, resulting in eq. 159b. Let the rectangular coordinates (x = abscissa, y = ordinate) be $x_i=\cos\alpha_i$ and $y_i=\sin\alpha_i$. Then:

$$N\bar{x}=\sum x_i=\sum_1^N \cos\alpha_i \qquad (160a)$$

and:

$$N\bar{y}=\sum y_i=\sum_1^N \sin\alpha_i \qquad (160b)$$

Because:

$\bar{x}=r\cos\gamma_1$ and $\bar{y}=r\sin\gamma_1$, we have:

$$r^2=\bar{x}^2+\bar{y}^2 \tag{161a}$$

$$\tan\gamma_1=\bar{y}/\bar{x}\equiv\tan\beta_1 \tag{161b}$$

which has a unique solution unless $\bar{y}=\bar{x}=0$. The latter case is the rectangular distribution (see ESSENWANGER, 1976), i.e., $f(\alpha)$ has the same expectation for every α.
$\sum f(\alpha)=1$ is a requirement for frequency distributions. Consequently:

$$C=\sum\exp[A_1\cos(\alpha-\beta_1)] \qquad 0\leq\alpha<2\pi \tag{162a}$$

or:

$$C=\int_0^{2\pi} e^{A_1\cos(\alpha-\beta_1)}=2\pi I_0(A_1) \tag{162b}$$

where $I_0(A_1)$ is called the hyperbolic Bessel function (see WEAST et al., 1964), or the modified Bessel function (ABRAMOWITZ and STEGUN, 1964). GUMBEL et al. (1953) have compiled a table, listing A_1 (i.e., k in their notation) as function of r (i.e., $\bar{a}$) based on the relationship:

$$r=I_0'(A_1)/I_0(A_1) \tag{163}$$

from which A_1 can be obtained.
Observations may sometimes become available only as grouped data (e.g., the wind direction in form of the 16 points of the compass, or the 12 months, see GUMBEL, 1954), or they can be grouped into classes. In this case eq. 160a, b must be modified. Let k denote the number of classes. Then:

$$\bar{x}=\sum_1^k f(\alpha_i)\cos\alpha_i/k \tag{164a}$$

$$\bar{y}=\sum_1^k f(\alpha_i)\sin\alpha_i/k \tag{164b}$$

In this case:

$$C=kI_0(A_1) \tag{164c}$$

with A_1 and γ_1 as previously designated.

Gumbel's table may not always be readily available. Then estimators can be derived from the Fourier series (see eq. 166a, b). After A_1 and γ_1 are known C can be obtained by the summation:

$$NC=\sum_1^k\exp[A_1\cos(\alpha-\gamma_1)] \tag{165}$$

If the frequencies have been converted to unity (i.e., $f(\alpha_i)=n_i/N$) then $N=1.0$ in eq. 165. The case where γ_1 and β_1 are different is explained on p. 71.

The generalized circular distribution

Gumbel's model requires symmetry around γ_1 and is unimodal. These two conditions can be waived for the generalized model. One difficulty may be the derivation of estimators.

Let us transform eq. 159a by taking the logarithm:

$$\ln f(\alpha) = -\ln C + \sum A_j \cos(j\alpha - \beta_j) \quad (166a)$$

or:

$$z(\alpha) = A_0 + \sum A_j \cos(j\alpha - \beta_j) \quad (166b)$$

The reader can recognize this transformed model as the Fourier series applied to the logarithm of the frequencies. In eq. 384a we use $\sin(\alpha + \beta)$ as the basis for the Fourier series but here we have:

$$A_j \cos(j\alpha - \beta_j) = A_j \sin \beta_j \sin j\alpha + A_j \cos \beta_j \cos j\alpha \quad (167a)$$

or:

$$A_j \cos(j\alpha - \beta_j) = a_j \sin j\alpha + b_j \cos j\alpha \quad (167b)$$

which leads to:

$$a_j = (2/k) \sum_1^k \ln f(\alpha) \sin j\alpha \quad (168a)$$

$$b_j = (2/k) \sum_1^k \ln f(\alpha) \cos j\alpha \quad (168b)$$

$$A_j^2 = a_j^2 + b_j^2 \quad (169a)$$

and:

$$\tan \beta_j = a_j / b_j \quad (169b)$$

with:

$$C = \sum_1^k \exp[\sum A_j \cos(j\alpha + \beta_j)] \quad (169c)$$

Unless $z_a(\alpha) \equiv \ln f(\alpha)$ for all α values ($z_a(\alpha)$ stands for the recalculated analytical value) the sum $\sum f_a(\alpha)$ utilizing $z_a(\alpha)$ may not add up to unity because $f(\alpha) = f_a(\alpha) + \varepsilon(\ln f)$. In that case $\ln C$ from eq. 169c and $\sum \ln f(\alpha)$ from the data will not be identical. This discrepancy does not affect the numerical value of the estimators a_j and b_j by eq. 168a, b, but C must be adjusted.

It was silently assumed that $\gamma_1 \equiv \beta_1$. We check this postulation now. We expand the definition in eq. 160a, b:

$$\bar{x}_j = \sum f(\alpha) \cos j\alpha = r_j \cos \beta_j \quad (170a)$$

$$\bar{y}_j = \sum f(\alpha) \sin j\alpha = r_j \sin \beta_j \quad (170b)$$

Now let us assume that $f(\alpha) = C \exp \sum A_j \cos(j\alpha - \gamma_j)$. Then:

$$\bar{x}_j = \sum [C \exp \sum A_j \cos(j\alpha - \gamma_j)] \cos j\alpha = r_j \cos \beta_j \quad (171a)$$

$$\bar{y}_j = \sum [C \exp \sum A_j \cos(j\alpha - \gamma_j)] \sin j\alpha = r_j \sin \beta_j \quad (171b)$$

In this case β_j and γ_j do not show a simple relationship and identity. However, in the Fourier series γ_j and β_j would be identical:

$$a_j = \sum \ln f(x) \sin j\alpha \quad (172a)$$

or:

$$a_j = \sum_{i=1}^{N} [\ln C + \sum_{j=1}^{n_j} A_j \cos(j\alpha_i - \gamma_j)] \sin j\alpha_i = A_j \sin \beta_j \tag{172b}$$

necessitates $\gamma_j \equiv \beta_j$ because of orthogonality. For a specified j only one angular parameter is left, i.e., γ_j. Similarly an equation for b_j is valid, and $\tan \beta_j \equiv \tan \gamma_j$.
Gumbel's model has one angular parameter:

$$\bar{x}_1 = \sum C \exp A_1 \cos(\alpha - \gamma_1) \cos \alpha = r \cos \beta_1 \tag{173}$$

where $\gamma_1 \equiv \beta_1$ (by definition of $f(\alpha)$ and $\bar{x}/\bar{y}$).
We can illustrate the agreement between γ_1 and β_1 differently. Assume that:

$$f(\alpha) = f_G(\alpha) + \Delta f(\alpha) \tag{174}$$

where the frequency distribution comprises $f_G(\alpha)$, the contribution by Gumbel's model (i.e., the first Fourier term) and an (undetermined) remainder. Then:

$$\tan \psi = [\sum f_G(\alpha) \sin \alpha + \sum \Delta f(\alpha) \sin \alpha] / [\sum f_G(\alpha) \cos \alpha + \sum \Delta f(\alpha) \cos \alpha] \tag{175a}$$

or:

$$\tan \psi = (\bar{y} + \sum \ldots)/(\bar{x} + \sum \ldots) \tag{175b}$$

Because $\tan \gamma_1 = \bar{x}/\bar{y}$ the value ψ is identical with γ_1 only if the second terms with $\Delta f(\alpha)$ disappear. This is expected to be the case for a true circular normal distribution (i.e., Gumbel's model) but it is not a necessity of the generalized model. Thus, γ_1 and β_1 may disagree unless the frequency density approximately follows Gumbel's model (see Examples 15 and 16).
The difference $\Delta\psi = \gamma_1 - \beta_1$ can be used as a test whether the generalized model is more suitable for the observed data than Gumbel's model. If the difference $\Delta\psi$ is significant the generalized form should be used but $\gamma_1 \sim \beta_1$ does not imply that the generalized model (see Example 16) is invalid. Similarly, equations can be developed which show that γ_j and β_j need not be identical (see also Example 16).

Estimation by the method of steepest descent

SNEYERS and VAN ISACKER (1980) recommend estimation by the method of steepest descent. We first assume a given set of estimators u_j, v_j, $j = 1, \ldots, n_k$ for a vector θ. Let us designate the components of θ by θ_s, i.e., $\theta_1 = u_1$, $\theta_2 = v_1$, $\theta_3 = u_2$, etc., $s = 1, 2, \ldots, 2n_k$. Sneyers and Van Isacker start with the likelihood function:

$$L = C^{-n} \exp \sum_{1}^{n_k} (u_j \bar{x}_j N + v_j \bar{y}_j N) \tag{176a}$$

$$\hat{\theta}^2 = \sum_{1}^{2n_k} \theta_s^2 = \sum_{1}^{n_k} (u_j^2 + v_j^2) \tag{176b}$$

and:

$$U_j = u_j/\theta, \; V_j = v_j/\theta \tag{176c}$$

Now:

$$g(\alpha)=\sum [U_j (\cos j\alpha-\bar{x}_j)+V_j(\sin j\alpha-\bar{y}_j)] \tag{177a}$$

and:

$$L^{-1/N}=I(\theta)=\int_0^{2\pi} \exp[\theta g(\alpha)]\,\mathrm{d}\alpha \tag{177b}$$

The method of steepest descent requires the following steps:

$$I_h=I(\theta_{h-1}+\lambda_h w_j)<I(\theta_{h-1}) \quad h=1, 2, \ldots \tag{178a}$$

If this inequality holds a new step is necessary: $\theta_h=\theta_{h-1}+\lambda_h w_j$.
We calculate $I_{h+1}=I(\theta_h+\lambda_{h+1}w_j)$ and determine λ from:

$$\lambda_h=\sum w_j^2/\sum\sum w_j w_k(\partial^2 I/\partial\theta_j\partial\theta_k)_\theta>0 \tag{178b}$$

which is a minimum for the limited Taylor expansion:

$$I\approx I(\theta)-\sum w_j^2\lambda+0.5\sum\sum w_j w_k(\partial^2 I/\partial\theta_j\partial\theta_k)_\theta\cdot\lambda^2 \tag{178c}$$

The derivatives are:

$$w_j=-(\partial I/\partial\theta_j)_\theta \tag{179a}$$

$$\partial I/\partial\lambda=\sum w_j(\partial I/\partial\theta_j) \tag{179b}$$

$$\partial I/\partial\lambda^2=\sum\sum w_j(\partial^2 I/\partial\theta_j\partial\theta_k)w_k>0 \tag{179c}$$

Example 15. Comparison of Gumbel's model with the generalized model. Table XX displays the frequency density for twelve classes of the following generalized distribution:

$$f(\alpha)=56.385 \exp[0.5 \sin \alpha+0.8 \cos \alpha-0.5 \sin 2\alpha+\sqrt{0.55} \cos 2\alpha]$$

or

$$f(\alpha)=56.385 \exp[0.943 \cos(\alpha-32.0)+0.894 \cos(2\alpha+34.0)]$$

Table XX, a illustrates the calculation of the coefficients via eq. 166. It is evident that γ_1 and γ_2 do not coincide with β_1 and β_2 for two terms (generalized model) while $\gamma_1\equiv\beta_1$ in Gumbel's model (see Table XX, b). Consequently, β_1 and β_2 cannot be obtained from utilizations of $\bar{x}_j$, $\bar{y}_j$, i.e., $\sum f(\alpha)\sin\alpha$, etc. because the distribution follows the general model. Gumbel's table (for $\bar{a}$ and k) provides rough estimates of A_j. E.g., $r_1^2=\bar{x}_1^2+\bar{y}_1^2=(0.0723)^2+(0.4315)^2=0.1914$ or $r_1=0.438$. From Gumbel's table we find $k_1\sim 0.975$. This compares to $A_1=0.943$. Moreover, $r_2^2=(0.1484)^2+(0.3784)^2=0.1652$; $r_2=0.406$, $k_2=0.890$ versus $A_2=0.894$.

Example 16. This example elucidates the application of the generalized model to wind direction data. Given is the frequency density (in ‰) for a 25-year period of record in June, 06h a.m. local time, at 500 m altitude, Washington, D.C., $N=750$ (Table XXI, a). The estimators are provided in Table XXI, b. The first analytical frequency density is Gumbel's model. As anticipated the χ^2 as a measure of agreement (disagreement) between observed and analytical frequency density exceeds the significant threshold χ^2_{th} (95% level, 13 degrees of freedom, $\chi^2_{\mathrm{th}}=22.4$; see eq. 645). The observed distribution is neither symmetrical nor unimodal. For these reasons it has been selected to illustrate the application of the generalized model. Adding the second term did not reduce χ^2 considerably but including the third term achieves the goal. Now $\chi^2=12.4$ which is smaller than the threshold $\chi^2_{\mathrm{th}}=16.9$ for the 95% level and 9 degrees of freedom. Thus, we may stop after three terms and consider the three-term generalized model as a fair representation of the observed data.
We recognize that the analytical model emerges with a secondary maximum at NW. The sharp rise of the frequency density for the observations at SW, however, is not reflected in the analytical

TABLE XX

COMPARISON BETWEEN GUMBEL'S CIRCULAR NORMAL DISTRIBUTION AND THE GENERALIZED MODEL

(*a*) Generalized model

General $f(\alpha)$	α	$f(d)$ sin α	$f(d)$ cos α	$f(d)$ sin 2α	$f(d)$ cos 2α	ln $f(d)$ sin α	ln $f(d)$ cos α	ln $f(d)$ sin 2α	ln $f(d)$ cos 2α
263.44	0	0	263.4	0	263.4	0	5.574	0	5.574
136.02	30	68.0	117.8	117.8	68.0	2.456	4.255	4.255	2.456
58.05	60	50.3	29.0	50.3	−29.0	3.517	2.031	3.517	−2.031
44.28	90	44.3	0	0	−44.3	3.791	0	0	−3.791
62.02	120	53.7	−31.0	−53.7	−31.0	3.574	−2.064	−3.574	−2.064
80.90	150	40.5	−70.0	−70.0	40.5	2.197	−3.805	−3.805	+2.197
53.19	180		−53.2	0	53.2	0	−3.974	0	3.974
20.64	210	−10.3	−17.9	+17.9	10.3	−1.514	−2.622	2.622	1.514
10.97	240	−9.5	−5.5	+9.5	−5.5	−2.074	−1.198	2.074	−1.198
16.29	270	−16.3	0	0	−16.3	−2.791	0	0	−2.791
58.05	300	−50.3	29.0	−50.3	−29.0	−3.517	2.031	−3.517	−2.031
196.14	330	−98.1	169.9	−169.9	98.1	−2.639	4.572	−4.572	2.639
		$\sum=72.3$	431.5	−148.4	378.4	3.001	4.8	−3.000	4.448
						0.5	0.8	−0.5	0.741
		tan $\gamma_j=0.1676$		−0.3922		tan $\beta_j=0.625$		0.674	
		$\gamma_j=9.5$		−21.4		$\beta_j=32.0$		−34.0	
						$A_j=0.943$		0.894	

(*b*) Gumbel's model

Gumbel $f(\alpha)$	α	$f(\alpha)$sin α	$f(\alpha)$cos α	ln $f(\alpha)$sin α	ln $f(\alpha)$cos α
150.15	0	0	150.2	0	5.012
173.20	30	86.6	150.0	2.577	4.464
155.19	60	134.4	77.6	4.369	2.522
111.23	90	111.2	0	4.712	0
69.73	120	60.4	−34.9	3.676	−2.122
43.33	150	21.7	−37.5	1.884	−3.264
30.31	180	0	−30.3	0	−3.412
26.28	210	−13.1	−22.8	−1.634	−2.831
29.33	240	−25.4	−14.6	−2.926	−1.689
40.92	270	−40.9	0	−3.712	0
65.28	300	−56.5	32.6	−3.619	2.089
105.05	330	−52.5	91.0	−2.327	4.031
1000.00		225.9	361.3	3.000	4.800
				0.5	0.8
		tan $\gamma_1=0.625$		tan $\beta_1=0.625$	
		$\gamma_1=32.0$		$\beta_1=32.0$	

frequency. The sharp peak could be a product of sampling fluctuations. The reader will also notice that γ_1 is close to β_1, but γ_2 and γ_3 are much different from β_2 and β_3. This example illustrates that an agreement between γ_1 and β_1 is necessary for Gumbel's model but is not an exclusive condition. The example also shows the closeness between A_j and k_j.

The summation of ln $f(\alpha)$ leads to $C=55.42$. The calculation of $f(\alpha)$ with this C makes $\sum f_a(\alpha)=0.9808$. This is somewhat short of unity. An adjustment was made and $C=56.51$ as given in the last column, third row of Table XXI, b.

TABLE XXI

WIND DIRECTION DISTRIBUTION, WASHINGTON, D.C., FOR JUNE 1949–1973, 06 A.M. LOCAL TIME AT 500 m ALTITUDE ($N = 750$)

(*a*) Frequency distribution

	α	n_i/N observed (‰)	$\ln f(\alpha)$	Gumbel		Δ	General (3 terms)		Δ
				$\ln f_a(\alpha)$	$f_a(\alpha)$		$\ln f_a(\alpha)$	$f_a(\alpha)$	
N	0	53	3.97	4.01	55.1	−2.1	4.10	60.5	−7.5
NNE	22.5	40	3.69	3.80	44.9	−4.9	3.61	37.0	3.0
NE	45	33	3.50	3.64	38.1	−5.1	3.42	30.6	2.4
ENE	67.5	30	3.40	3.54	34.4	−4.4	3.52	33.8	−3.8
E	90	33	3.50	3.52	33.6	−0.6	3.61	37.0	−4.0
ESE	112.5	36	3.58	3.58	35.8	0.2	3.53	34.1	1.9
SE	135	38	3.64	3.71	40.9	−2.9	3.46	31.8	6.2
SSE	157.5	30	3.40	3.90	49.5	−19.5	3.69	40.1	−10.1
S	180	69	4.23	4.11	61.2	7.8	4.20	66.8	2.2
SSW	202.5	103	4.63	4.32	75.1	27.9	4.62	101.4	1.6
SW	225	115	4.75	4.48	88.6	26.4	4.64	103.4	11.6
WSW	247.5	67	4.21	4.58	98.0	−31.0	4.37	79.4	−12.4
W	270	62	4.13	4.61	100.2	−38.2	4.22	68.1	−6.1
WNW	292.5	93	4.53	4.54	94.1	−1.1	4.38	79.9	13.1
NW	315	97	4.57	4.41	82.3	14.7	4.62	101.4	−4.4
NNW	337.5	91	4.51	4.22	68.1	22.9	4.55	94.6	−3.6
		$\sum = 1000$	64.24		999.9 ($\chi^2 = 75.4$)			999.9 ($\chi^2 = 12.44$)	

(*b*) Estimators and statistics

j	$\bar{x}_j$	$\bar{y}_j$	γ_j	a_j	b_j	β_j	A_j	r	k_j	C_j (‰)
1	−0.0253	−0.2630	185.5°	−0.5727	−0.0346	183.5	0.5737	0.264	0.548	58.02
2	0.0059	0.0539	6.3	−0.0051	0.1180	92.5	0.1181	0.054	0.109	
3	−0.1481	−0.0190	262.7	−0.2679	−0.0145	183.1	0.2683	0.149	0.302	(56.51)

The χ^2 has been calculated from $\sum \Delta^2/f(\alpha)$, where $\Delta = n_i/N - f(\alpha)$. The analytical generalized model is now:

$$f_a(\alpha) = 56.51 \exp[0.574 \cos(\alpha - 183.5) + 0.118 \cos(2\alpha - 92.5) + 0.268 \cos(3\alpha - 183.1)]$$

Extreme value distributions

Up to now we have dealt with elements X of a set A without further specification of X except that it should be a random variable. Previously introduced frequency distributions describe the behavior of some random variables X. Assume now that the random variable is especially selected to represent extreme events only. We may be interested in the distribution of such extreme events designated by x for a certain time period such as a monthly or weekly extreme value.

FISHER and TIPPETT (1928) found three types of distributions which are applicable irrespective of the distribution form for the set of random variables X from which the extreme values x are extracted. For a standardized variate Z these three types are:

I. $F(Z)=\exp[-\exp(-Z)]$ (180)

II. $F(Z)=\exp[-Z^{-\delta}]$ (181)

III. $F(Z)=\exp[-(-Z)^{\delta}]$ (182)

Type I is the limiting distribution from type II or III, i.e., $\delta=1/\omega$ for $\omega=0$, and has been thoroughly explored by GUMBEL (1958) who derived the distribution from the m-th distribution (see eq. 217). Hence, it is sometimes referred to as Gumbel's law.
Types II and III differ only in the signs of Z and δ. For Type II, $\omega<0$; for Type III, $\omega>0$. Thus, the three types comprise the entire range of ω. We notice further that Types II and III are bound by 0, while Type I is unbounded (in the finite space) at both ends.
We find examples from atmospheric data for all three types. The discussion in the following pages elaborates on Types I and II as the most important models.

The Fisher-Tippett Type I or Gumbel's law

Gumbel's law has very widespread application in climatology.

$$F(Z)=\exp[-\exp(-Z)] \quad (183a)$$

hence:

$$f(Z)=\mathrm{d}F(Z)=\exp[-Z-\exp(-Z)]\mathrm{d}Z \quad (183b)$$

or:

$$Z=-\ln[-\ln F(Z)] \quad (183c)$$

Moments have been derived as:

$$\mu_1=\bar{Z}=0.57721 \quad \text{(Euler's constant, for } N\to\infty) \quad (184a)$$

$$\nu_2=\sigma_Z^2=\pi^2/6 \quad (184b)$$

and:

$$\sigma_Z=\pi/\sqrt{6}=1.28254 \quad (184c)$$

$$\nu_3=2.40411 \quad (185a)$$

$$\gamma_1=1.1396 \quad (185b)$$

$$\nu_4=3\pi^4/20=14.6114 \quad (185c)$$

$$\gamma_2=5.4-3.0=2.4 \quad (185d)$$

Eq. 183a is written for Z, the standardized variable. The transformation into x, the observed extreme values, is governed by:

$$(Z-\bar{Z})/\sigma_Z=(x-\bar{x})/\sigma_x \quad (186a)$$

Hence:

$$Z=(\sigma_Z/\sigma_x)(x-\bar{x})+\bar{Z} \quad (186b)$$

or introducing:

$$a = \sigma_Z/\sigma_x = 1.28254/\sigma_x \tag{186c}$$

$$1/a = 0.77970 \cdot \sigma_x \tag{187a}$$

$$u = \bar{x} \mp \bar{Z}/a = \bar{x} \mp \sigma_x \cdot 0.45005 \tag{187b}$$

where u is counted from a reference point $\bar{x}$ which is the mode at the same time. Now:

$$Z = a(x - u) \tag{188a}$$

and:

$$x = Z/a \pm u \tag{188b}$$

$$\mathrm{d}Z = a \,\mathrm{d}x \tag{188c}$$

The upper sign is valid for maxima, the lower for minima in eq. 187b and eq. 188b.
The derivation of estimators from the moments of the distribution is based on eqs. 186 and 187 but the moments estimators have poor efficiency. Maximum-likelihood estimators are obtained from:

$$N = [\exp(au)][\sum \exp(-ax)] \tag{189a}$$

$$1/a - \bar{x} = -[\sum X \exp(-ax)]/[\sum \exp(-ax)] \tag{189b}$$

The summation is carried out from 1 through N.
If we assume that the best estimate for $\bar{x}$ is the mean, x_m, then eq. 189b contains only the unknown parameter a, from which an estimator $\hat{a}$ can be found, and $\hat{u}$ can be computed from eq. 189a:

$$\hat{u} = \ln N/[\hat{a} \ln \sum \exp(-\hat{a}x)] \tag{189c}$$

Several approximations to solve eq. 189b for a have been discussed in the literature (LIEBLEIN, 1954; GUMBEL, 1958; ESSENWANGER, 1972). Today the availability of computers permits iterative procedures to solve eq. 189b without difficulties. In Example 17 eq. 189b has been solved by an iteration process.
LIEBLEIN (1954) derived an optimum minimum variance estimator, largely for small samples.

$$u^* = \sum_{j=1}^{m} \omega_j s_j/k \tag{190a}$$

and:

$$1/\alpha^* = \sum_{j=1}^{m} w_j s_j/k \tag{190b}$$

where ω_j and w_j are tabulated weighting factors up to $m = 6$ (LIEBLEIN, 1954). The data are broken into an array of $m \cdot k = N$ elements and s_j stands for the column sums. Incomplete rows must be adjusted. Difficulties are encountered in this method when N is a prime number > 6.
An approximation of the maximum-likelihood estimator has been suggested by the author

(ESSENWANGER, 1972). Instead of solving eq. 189a, b the following equation can be utilized:

$$1-\hat{a}_2\bar{x}-\hat{a}_2\sum x\,e^{-Z}=0 \tag{191a}$$

or:

$$\hat{a}_2=1/[\bar{x}-\sum x_i\exp(-Z)] \tag{191b}$$

This equation contains a mixture between the observed and theoretical observations X and Z, respectively. Since:

$$Z=\ln[-\ln F(x)] \tag{192}$$

and $F(x)$ is the order of X in the cumulative distribution, the summation term in eq. 191b is calculated only once, and $\hat{a}_2$ has an explicit solution in contrast to eq. 189a, b. This reduces the computer costs considerably for the iterative procedure. The author (ESSENWANGER, 1972) showed that the deviation $\hat{a}-\hat{a}_2$ stayed within 2% of $\hat{a}$ obtained from eq. 189a, b for upper-air extreme wind speed data. The deviations $\hat{a}-a^*$ (from eq. 190b) were generally larger than 2% of $\hat{a}$. Because of the small sample size it usually cannot be proven that $\hat{a}\neq\hat{a}_2$ or $\hat{a}\neq a^*$. For large samples, however, $\hat{a}_2\rightarrow\hat{a}$.
The author also found that Gumbel's law was more suitable for the upper-air extreme values of wind speed, density and temperature than the Fisher-Tippett Model II (two-parameter) because the χ^2 values between analytical and observed distribution were smaller for Gumbel's law. In addition, the Kolmogorov-Smirnov test led to smaller values. (See also Example 19, p. 88.)
Another order statistic has been recommended by DOWNTON (1966) who dislikes that Lieblein's optimum variance estimation requires the arrangement of data sets with $m\leq 6$. Downton's (linear) estimators are based on the entire ordered data, say $x_{k_1}<x_{k_2}<x_{k_3}\ldots$. Then:

$$u_D^*=\frac{(N-1)\ln 2-\bar{Z}(N+1)}{N(N-1)\ln 2}\,\omega_1+\frac{2\bar{Z}}{N(N-1)\ln 2}\,\omega_2 \tag{193a}$$

$$1/a_D^*=-\frac{N+1}{N(N-1)\ln 2}\,\omega_1+\frac{2}{N(N-1)\ln 2}\,\omega_2 \tag{193b}$$

where:

$$\omega_j=\sum_{k=1}^{N}(k^{j-1})x_k,\quad j>0 \tag{193c}$$

Note that x_k designates the ordered extreme value data. The above formulae have been tailored to the distribution of the minima (i.e., $F(Z)=\exp(-\exp Z)$). For maxima some adjustment of the sign for Z must be made (see eq. 180).
One advantage of these estimators is the easy calculation of their variances:

$$\operatorname{Var}(u_D^*)=\sigma^2(1.112825N-0.906557)/[N(N-1)] \tag{194a}$$

$$\operatorname{Var}(a_D^*)=\sigma^2(0.804621N-0.185527)/[N(N-1)] \tag{194b}$$

$$\operatorname{Cov}(u_D^*,a_D^*)=-\sigma^2(0.228707N-0.586058)/[N(N-1)] \tag{194c}$$

Downton has also developed estimators by utilization of polynomial coefficients. The reader is referred to DOWNTON (1966) for details.

Sneyers and Van Isacker (1972) recommend that the percentage value of x should be calculated from:

$$x_p = \hat{\gamma} + \hat{S} Z_p \quad (195a)$$

where:

$$\hat{S} = \sum x_i (1 + \ln F_i)/N = \hat{x}_m + \sum x_i \ln F_i/N \quad (195b)$$

and:

$$\hat{\gamma} = \hat{x}_m - \hat{\gamma}_E S \quad (195c)$$

$\gamma_E = \bar{Z}$ (see eq. 184a).
Notice, the set of x_i designates ordered observations, i.e., $x_i \leq x_{i+1}$. Kimball (1956) replaced $\ln F_i$ in eq. 195b by X_{L_i} where:

$$X_{L_i} = E(\ln F_i) = -\sum_{j=i}^{N} 1/j \quad (196a)$$

then:

$$\hat{S} = [X_m + \sum X_{L_i} X_i/N]/S_B \quad (196b)$$

where S_B is a correction for the bias (Kimball, 1956).

$$S_{B_j} = S_{B_{j-1}} + \sum_{j=2}^{N} [j(j-1)]^{-1} \sum_{i=1}^{j-1} (-1)^{i+1} (\Delta^i \ln|) \quad (197a)$$

where:

$$\Delta^n \ln| = (-1)^n \int_0^1 t^n \, dt/[\ln(1-t)] \quad (197b)$$

and $S_{B_1} = 0$. Kimball (1956) and Sneyers and Van Isacker (1972) have published a table for the bias factor S_{B_j}, up to $N = 500$ in the latter article.
The error variance of x_p is:

$$\varepsilon_{x_p}^2 = \mathrm{Var}\, \hat{x}_m + 2Z_p \,\mathrm{Cov}\,(\hat{x}, \hat{S}) + Z_p^2 \,\mathrm{Var}\,(\hat{S}) \quad (198a)$$

or:

$$\varepsilon_{x_p}^2 = (1.10866 + 2Z_p\, 0.25702 + Z_p^2\, 0.60793) \cdot \hat{S}^2/N \quad (198b)$$

For precipitation data Sneyers (1977, 1979b) suggested:

$$Z_p = (\ln y - \hat{\gamma})/\sigma \quad (199)$$

In this case $\hat{\gamma} = \sum \ln y/N$, $\sigma = \hat{s}$ is calculated from eq. 195b with $x_i = \ln y$, y is the precipitation amount. Thus, $\hat{\gamma} = \sum \ln y/N$ is the logarithmic mean of y.

The return period

In most cases it is of interest to know how frequently an extreme value recurs. This is called the return period for a given extreme:

$$T(Z) = 1.0/[1.0 - F(Z)] \quad (200)$$

where:

$T(Z) > 1.0$, since $F(Z) \leq 1.0$, e.g., $Z = Z_p$ (see eq. 199)

Although an event with a cumulative probability threshold of 90% (i.e., $F(Z) = 0.9$) returns in the average every 10th time unit (e.g., year or month, etc.) the probability of risk may be different (see eq. 239a on the time interval distribution and eq. 201a).
Sometimes the empirical value $F(x)$ is utilized and replaces $F(Z)$ in eq. 200. There are two reasons, however, to employ $F(Z)$ or the analytical distribution. First, the maximum likelihood principle is more appropriate for predictions. Second, $F(x)$ and $F(Z)$ may differ because an analytical expression includes a smoothing effect that balances random and irregular fluctuations from data sampling. In Example 17 differences between return periods deduced from $F(Z)$ and $F(x)$ are demonstrated.

Risk of occurrence

HERSHFIELD (1973) pointed out that in many problems the risk of occurrence is important. The risk that x (or Z) will occur is simply the reverse of the return period:

$$P_r = 1 - F(x) = 1/T(Z) \tag{201a}$$

The chances that the event x will not occur in the next year is:

$$Q = F(x) = 1 - 1/T(Z) \tag{201b}$$

This equation can be expanded to provide an answer that the event will occur for the first time in the n-th year:

$$P_{r_n} = [F(x)]^{n-1}[1 - F(x)] = (1 - 1/T)^{n-1} \cdot 1/T \tag{202a}$$

Then the probability that the event x will occur at least once in the next n years is:

$$P_r(1,n) = 1 - (1 - 1/T)^n = 1 - Q^n \tag{202b}$$

Furthermore, $P_r(1,n)$ is also the risk that the event will occur within the initial known period. Let us assume that we want to take a risk of 1% that the event x will occur in the next 100 years. Then:

$$0.01 = 1 - (1 - 1/T)^{100}$$

and $0.9999 = 1 - 1/T$, or $T \sim 10^4$. In other words: we should design for a return period of 10^4 years and not 10^2 years. From eq. 200 we derive $F(Z) = 0.9999$ from which $X = Z_{0.9999}/a + u$ can be calculated.
The formulae for the return period can be utilized with other types of extreme value distribution models than Gumbel's law.

Return period from time series

Let us assume that a set of extreme values is given such as $x_1, x_2 \ldots x_N$ which are ordered ($X_i \leq X_{i+1}$, $i = 1, \ldots, N-1$). We find that the probability for X_{N+1} is the conditional probability density:

$$f(X_{N+1}|X_1, \ldots, X_N) = f(X_{N+1})/[1 - F(X_N)] \tag{203}$$

Mean and variance of X_{N+1} cannot always be expressed in explicit form for eq. 203. Consequently, some approximations have been suggested. E.g.:

$$E(X_{N+1}|X_1, \ldots, X_N) = X_N + 1/[(N+1)f(X_N)] \quad (204a)$$

or:

$$E[X_{N+t}|X_1, \ldots, X_N] = X_{N+t-1} + 1/[(N+t)f(X_{N+t-1})] \quad (204b)$$

Suzuki et al. (1980a) pointed out, however, that this approximation is not very accurate. They began with a prediction of the next observation from the past:

$$T(X_{i+1}) = A(X_i)T(X_i) + \varepsilon_T \quad (205a)$$

A similar equation can be cast for the past observations:

$$y(X_i) = C \cdot T(X_i) + \varepsilon_y \quad (205b)$$

A and C are coefficients and ε designates a random error depending on X_i.
Now the terms in eq. 205a are rearranged and ε_T is neglected:

$$A(X_i) = T(X_{i+1})/T(X_i) \quad (206a)$$

Suzuki et al. postulated:

$$A(X_i) = aA(X_{i-1}) + b(X_i - X_{i-1}) + \varepsilon_A \quad (206b)$$

This leads to a recurrence formula:

$$T(X_{N+1}) = A(X_N) \cdot T(X_N) \quad (206c)$$

For more details the reader is referred to Suzuki et al. Estimating the recurrence of weather events has also been studied by Lund and Grantham (1979).

Example 17. Given are the annual extreme daily minimum temperatures (in °F) at Oklahoma City for the period 1918–1948 (see Table XXII).

TABLE XXII

ANNUAL MINIMUM TEMPERATURES AT OKLAHOMA CITY

Year	°F	Day	Year	°F	Day
1918	−7	Jan.11	1934	11	Feb. 26
1919	1	Jan. 3	1935	−2	Jan. 21
1920	7	Mar. 7	1936	−1	Feb. 8
1921	10	Dec. 24	1937	7	Jan. 8
1922	6	Mar. 2	1938	9	Jan. 31
1923	7	Dec. 31	1939	9	Feb. 21
1924	−2	Dec. 19	1940	2	Jan. 18
1925	5	Jan. 27	1941	19	Jan. 18
1926	6	Dec. 15	1942	2	Jan. 5
1927	1	Dec. 31	1943	−2	Jan. 19
1928	2	Jan. 1	1944	5	Jan. 9
1929	0	Feb. 9	1945	7	Dec. 19
1930	−9	Jan. 17	1946	8	Dec. 30
1931	15	Jan. 14	1947	−7	Jan. 4
1932	6	Dec. 12	1948	1	Mar. 11
1933	−5	Feb. 7			

TABLE XXIII

COMPARISON BETWEEN OBSERVED AND ANNUAL EXTREME DAILY MINIMUM TEMPERATURE (°F) AT OKLAHOMA CITY, 1918–1948

x_c extreme values	Z_c derived variable	Observed	$F(Z)$ accumulated frequency (%)	$f(Z)$ density function (%)	$N \cdot f(Z)$ frequency
20	−2.78		0.00		
		1		0.09	0.0
16	−1.96		0.09		
		1		4.30	1.3
12	−1.14		4.39		
		4		20.50	6.4
8	−0.33		24.89		
		10		29.29	9.1
4	0.49		54.18		
		6		22.16	6.9
0	1.31		76.34		
		5		12.33	3.8
−4	2.12		88.67		
		3		6.18	1.9
−8	2.94		94.85		
		1		2.83	0.9
−12	3.76		97.68		
		0		1.30	0.4
−16	4.58		98.98		
				1.02	0.3

The following data can be computed:

$$x_m = \frac{111}{31} = 3.5806$$

$$S_x = \sqrt{39.4047} = 6.2774$$

$$1/a = 0.77970 \cdot S_x = 4.8945$$

$$a = 0.20431$$

$$u = 3.5806 + 2.8251 = 6.4057$$

(Note the plus sign, because we deal with minimum temperatures.)

$$x = 6.4057 - 4.8945 \cdot Z$$

or:

$$Z = (6.4057 - x) \cdot 0.20431$$

The moments estimators lead to the frequency distributions of Table XXIII which displays empirical and analytical frequency densities and cumulative distributions.
The estimators by Downton (eq. 193a, b) provide $u_D^* = 6.5982$, and $1/a_D^* = 5.2278$. These are approximately of the same numerical value as the estimators above. The cumulative frequency is similar to the one calculated with the moments estimators and has been omitted in Table XXIII.
The maximum-likelihood estimators result in a slightly different numerical value for a and u:

$$\hat{a} = 0.1575$$

$$x_m = 3.5806$$

TABLE XXIV

SAME AS TABLE XXIII FOR MAXIMUM-LIKELIHOOD ESTIMATORS

x_c extreme values	Z_c transformed variable	Observed	$F(Z)$ cumulative (%)	$f(Z)$ p.d.f. (%)	$N \cdot f(Z)$
20	−2.01		0.06		
		1		1.83	0.6
16	−1.38		1.89		
		1		10.18	3.1
12	−0.75		12.07		
		4		20.36	6.3
8	−0.12		32.43		
		10		22.46	7.0
4	0.50		54.89		
		6		17.76	5.5
0	1.13		72.65		
		5		11.70	3.6
−4	1.76		84.35		
		3		6.99	2.2
−8	2.39		91.34		
		1		3.95	1.2
−12	3.02		95.29		
				2.17	0.7
−16	3.65		97.46		
				1.18	0.4
−20			98.64		
				1.36	0.4

$S_x = 8.1431$

$\hat{u} = 3.5806 + 3.6648 = 7.2454$

Table XXIV discloses the result for the frequency distributions. Notice that the 90% threshold from moments, Downton, and maximum-likelihood estimators is −4.61, −5.17 and −7.04, respectively. This implies that temperatures of −4°F or below are expected more often according to the maximum-likelihood estimation. Consequently, the return period is 8.9, 8.1 and 6.4, respectively, i.e., the maximum-likelihood estimators indicate that extreme temperatures of −4°F or below could be expected every 6th or 7th year while from the moments estimate we would deduce that extreme temperatures of −4° or below can be expected only every 9th year. From $F(x)$ the return period is 7.8 years, which is somewhat between the bounds of the lowest and the highest estimates.

Fisher-Tippett Type II

Distribution, moments and estimators

The cumulative frequency distribution of Type II (eq. 181) has the form:

$$F(Z) = \exp[-Z^{-\delta}] \quad Z \geq 0; \qquad F(Z) = 0 \quad Z < 0; \qquad 0 < \delta < \infty \tag{207a}$$

from which the probability density function is:

$$f(Z) = (\delta/\beta) \cdot Z^{-(\delta+1)} \exp[-Z^{-\delta}] \text{ for } Z \geq 0 \text{ and } \beta > 0 \tag{207b}$$

This is an exponential function and the user is cautioned that the probability density function must be prepared for a sufficient number of classes, otherwise $\sum f(Z) \neq 1.0$. This pitfall can be avoided in most cases by grouping x into classes derived from $F(x)$.
The transformation to x is simple, namely:

$$Z = x/\beta \tag{208a}$$

since $Z \geq 0$, $x \geq 0$.
If we use instead of eq. 208a the transformation:

$$Z = (x - x_0)/\beta \tag{208b}$$

the cumulative distribution of eq. 207a (with negative δ) becomes the Weibull distribution with $\gamma = 0$ (see eq. 111b).
The moments of the Type II distribution exist for $\delta > \kappa$, where κ designates the order of the moments.*[1] This can be seen from the following:

$$\bar{x} = \beta a \tag{209a}$$

$$\sigma^2 = \beta^2(b - a^2) \tag{209b}$$

$$\gamma_1 = \pm \frac{c - 3ba + 2a^3}{(b - a^2)^{3/2}} \tag{209c}$$

$$\gamma_2 = \frac{d - 4ca + 6a^2b - 3a^4}{(b - a^2)^2} - 3 \tag{209d}$$

The following abbreviations are used:

$$a = \Gamma(1 - 1/\delta) \tag{210a}$$

$$b = \Gamma(1 - 2/\delta) \tag{210b}$$

$$c = \Gamma(1 - 3/\delta) \tag{210c}$$

$$d = \Gamma(1 - 4/\delta) \tag{210d}$$

Moments estimators can be obtained by solving for δ in the right hand side of the equation:

$$s^2/x_m^2 + 1 = b/a^2 = [\Gamma(1 - 2/\delta)]/[\Gamma^2(1 - 1/\delta)] \tag{211a}$$

with:

$$\beta = x_m/\Gamma(1 - 1/\delta) \tag{211b}$$

Table XXV is self-explanatory and aids in finding a solution without electronic data processing.
The maximum-likelihood method is based on solving the following:

$$\ln \beta = [\ln N - \ln (\textstyle\sum x^{-\delta})]/\delta = 0 \tag{212a}$$

*[1] Although $\Gamma(-n)$ can be computed for certain n, it assumes ∞ for whole numbers and therefore in our special case n is limited to positive numbers > 0.

TABLE XXV

RELATIONSHIP BETWEEN δ AND RATIO b/a^2 OF EQ. 211a

δ	b/a^2	$a=\Gamma(1-1/\delta)$	$b=\Gamma(1-2/\delta)$	$b-a^2$
2.05	13.496	1.73	40.45	37.45
2.25	3.326	1.60	8.52	5.96
2.50	2.070	1.49	4.59	2.37
2.75	1.660	1.41	3.31	1.32
3.00	1.461	1.35	2.68	0.85
3.5	1.270	1.27	2.08	0.44
4.0	1.180	1.22	1.77	0.27
4.5	1.130	1.19	1.60	0.184
5.0	1.099	1.16	1.49	0.134
6.0	1.063	1.13	1.35	0.080
7.0	1.043	1.11	1.28	0.053
8.0	1.032	1.09	1.23	0.0380
9.0	1.023	1.08	1.19	0.0285
10.0	1.019	1.07	1.16	0.0222
12.0	1.013	1.06	1.13	0.0146
14.0	1.009	1.05	1.11	0.0103
16.0	1.0071	1.040	1.090	0.0076
18.0	1.0055	1.035	1.078	0.0059
20.0	1.0044	1.031	1.069	0.0047
25.0	1.0028	1.025	1.053	0.0029
30.0	1.0019	1.020	1.043	0.0020
35.0	1.0014	1.017	1.036	0.0014
40.0	1.0011	1.015	1.031	0.0011

and:

$$N/\delta-\sum \ln x+[N\sum x^{-\delta}\ln x]/\sum x^{-\delta}=0 \qquad (212b)$$

The latter equation is free of β and can be solved for δ by iteration. Then β can be determined from eq. 212a. Since no analytical expression exists for solving eq. 212b, it is understandable that the model Fisher-Tippett Type II was seldom used in climatology prior to the availability of electronic data processing.

The model of Type II is zero-bounded. One should expect some application to zero-bounded elements in meteorology such as the wind. THOM (1954) has outlined its use for surface winds. ESSENWANGER (1972) has pointed out, however, that for upper air data no special advantage is obtained by employing Type II instead of Gumbel's law. This was already anticipated by GUMBEL (1958). Further discussion is reserved to Example 19.

One word of caution is appropriate. The maximum-likelihood estimators usually lead to much higher extremes than observed (e.g., Example 18). The short time period where reliable records of upper air observations are available may limit the occurrence of extremes. In addition, the well-known truncation of wind speed observations on the side of strong winds in the regions of the jet stream may further contribute a truncation of the tail-end. The observed extreme values which can be expected may nevertheless be considerably lower than some of the predictions from the analytical results of Type II (see Table XXVII and discussion in Example 19).

Example 18. Computation of a Fisher-Tippett II distribution for monthly extreme wind speeds at Montgomery, Alabama, January–March, 1957–1964 at 22 km altitude (Table XXVI).

TABLE XXVI

EXTREME WIND SPEEDS ($m\ s^{-1}$), MONTGOMERY, ALABAMA

Year	Month	Wind speed	Wind speed v (ranked)	ln v	$v^{-\delta}$ $\delta=3.21$	$v^{-\delta}$ ln v
1957	1	37.0	43.0	3.761	$3.86 \cdot 10^{-6}$	$14.52 \cdot 10^{-6}$
	2	16.0	42.0	3.738	4.24	15.85
	3	34.0	40.0	3.689	4.98	18.37
1958	1	27.0	37.0	3.611	6.45	23.29
	2	31.0	34.0	3.526	8.53	30.08
	3	40.0	31.0	3.434	11.58	39.76
1959	1	42.0	31.0	3.434	11.58	39.76
	2	17.0	27.0	3.296	18.29	60.28
	3	43.0	25.0	3.219	23.59	75.93
1960	1	14.0	24.0	3.178	27.01	85.84
	2	18.0	23.0	3.135	31.09	97.48
	3	31.0	21.0	3.044	36.73	111.83
1961	1	24.0	20.0	2.996	49.38	147.93
	2	16.0	20.0	2.996	49.38	147.93
	3	19.0	19.0	2.944	58.52	172.31
1962	1	20.0	19.0	2.944	58.52	172.31
	2	19.0	18.0	2.890	69.99	202.30
	3	18.0	18.0	2.890	69.99	202.30
1963	1	14.0	17.0	2.833	84.57	239.60
	2	21.0	16.0	2.772	103.36	286.57
	3	23.0	16.0	2.772	103.36	286.57
1964	1	25.0	14.0	2.639	160.81	424.39
	2	20.0	14.0	2.639	160.81	424.39
	3	12.0	12.0	2.485	267.84	665.56
				$\sum = 74.868$	$1424.46 \cdot 10^{-6}$	$3985.15 \cdot 10^{-6}$

TABLE XXVII

FISHER-TIPPETT II DISTRIBUTION OF MONTHLY EXTREME WIND SPEEDS AT MONTGOMERY, ALABAMA (Example 18)

Percentage	Fisher-Tippett II (max. likelihood)	Moments	Gumbel (max. likelihood)	Observed
100.0	–	–	–	43.0
99.5	98.9 ($m\ s^{-1}$)	67.8	57.9	–
99.0	79.4	57.8	52.9	–
98.0	64.0	49.3	48.0	–
96.0	51.4	42.0	42.9	–
95.833	50.7	41.6	42.6	42.0
95.0	47.9	39.8	41.3	–
91.667	40.6	35.3	37.5	40.0
90.0	38.3	33.8	36.2	–
87.5	35.6	32.0	34.5	37.0
75.0	28.0	26.8	29.0	31.0
62.5	24.0	24.0	25.5	24.0
50.0	21.3	22.0	22.7	20.0
37.5	19.1	20.3	20.2	19.0
25.0	17.1	18.7	17.7	17.0
12.5	15.1	17.0	14.9	14.0

Eq. 212b renders for $\delta=3.21$:

$$[24/3.21-74.868+24(3985.15\cdot 10^{-6})]/(1424.46)\cdot 10^{-6}=-0.247$$

The more precise solution with electronic data processing is closer to zero, i.e., -0.072 for $\delta=3.21$. The remainder is 0.326 for $\delta=3.22$. Consequently, the value of δ is closer to $\delta=3.21$. Then:

$$\ln \beta=(3.178+6.554)/3.21=9.732/3.21=3.033$$

and $\beta=20.75$. A more precise solution rendered $\beta=18.98$, indicating the sensitivity of β to the numerical value of δ. The maximum-likelihood estimates lead to the cumulative distributions as exhibited in Table XXVII. The cumulative frequency from the moments estimators ($\delta=4.37$, $\beta=20.18$) and Gumbel's distribution ($a=0.140$, $u=20.08$) is included into Table XXVII for comparison.

Test for suitability of Type I or Type II model

Example 18 illustrates the differences in the tail-ends for the Type I and Type II models. Consequently, in practical applications it is important to determine which of the two models is more suitable. Let us designate Type I by F_1 and Type II by F_2.
We modify eq. 207a by substituting $y=\delta(Z-1)$. Then:

$$F_2(y)=\exp[-(1+y/\delta)^{-\delta}] \tag{213}$$

Now we introduce $y=(x-\gamma)/\sigma_x$ which was called the standardized distribution by VAN MONTFORT (1970) for $\gamma=0$ and $\sigma_x=1$ (i.e., if $y\equiv x$).
If x has a distribution following the Type II then:

$$F_1(z)=\exp(-\exp[-\delta(z-\ln \sigma_x)]) \tag{214}$$

has a distribution following Type I for $z=\ln(x-\gamma)$. It implies that Type II can be converted into Type I for known γ and σ_x.
The larger δ the smaller are the differences between F_2 and F_1. We define $t=1/\delta$. Then the case of $t=0$ indicates a Type I distribution for x and $t>0$ implies the use of Type II. Consequently, a test can be constructed, with H_0: $t=0$ and H_1: $t>0$ (details on p. 240). This test is based on the differences of the tail-end for F_2 and F_1.
Van Montfort recommended the computation of a test statistic:

$$Z_F=0.5 \ln[(1+r)/(1-r)] \tag{215}$$

which is Fisher's z-transformation (see eq. 640b) and r is a correlation coefficient between "leaps" y_{L_i} and $u_{L_{i+0.5}}$. This correlation has $r=0$ for $t=1/\delta=0$. The definitions of y_{L_i} and u_{L_i} are:

$$u_{L_i}=-\ln[-\ln[i/(N+1)]] \tag{216a}$$

and:

$$y_{L_i}=(x_{(i+1)}-x_{(i)})/(u_{L_{i+1}}-u_{L_i}),\ (i=1, \ldots, N-1) \tag{216b}$$

Van Montfort calculated the criterion Z_t for the distribution $1/\delta=0$. An excerpt of the threshold Z_t is disclosed in Table XXVIII. H_0 is accepted if $Z_F<Z_t$ at the selected level of significance α, and $Z_F>Z_t$ supports a Type II model.
Later, VAN MONTFORT and OTTEN (1978) expanded the test by inclusion of other applications.

TABLE XXVIII

CRITICAL VALUE OF Z_t
(After VAN MONTFORT, 1970)

N	α: 0.25	0.10	0.05	0.02
10	0.312	0.541	0.632	0.715
25	0.169	0.308	0.371	0.459
50	0.118	0.207	0.272	0.336
100	0.088	0.147	0.185	0.235

Example 19. Testing for the suitability of Type I or Type II model. Example 18 has been prepared to illustrate that the Fisher-Tippett Type II model has a long drawn-out tail. Consequently, the question arises whether the Type I model would have been more suitable for the data of Example 18. This question is pursued by VAN MONTFORT's (1970) test. We have $t=1/\delta=1/3.21$, i.e., $H_0:t=0.31\sim 0$ and $H_1:t=0.31>0$. The calculations for the test are exhibited in Table XXIX. The columns are self-explanatory. $u_{L_i}=-\ln\left[-\ln\left(i/25\right)\right]$ and $y_{L_i}=(x_{i+1}-x_i)/(u_{L_{i+1}}-u_{L_i})$. This leads to

TABLE XXIX

CALCULATION OF THE TEST STATISTIC Z_F (Example 19)

i	x_i	$x_{m_{i+1}}$	u_{L_i}	$u_{L_{i+1}}$	y_{L_i}	$u_{L(i+0.5)}$	$y_{L_i}\cdot u_{L(i+1)}$
1	12	2	−1.1690	0.2425	8.247	−1.0344	−8.531
2	14	0	−0.9265	0.1750	0	−0.8340	0
3	14	2	−0.7515	0.1458	13.716	−0.6761	−9.273
4	16	0	−0.6057	0.1298	0	−0.5393	0
5	16	1	−0.4759	0.1202	8.317	−0.4148	−3.450
6	17	1	−0.3557	0.1143	8.748	−0.2979	−2.606
7	18	0	−0.2413	0.1108	0	−0.1856	0
8	18	1	−0.1305	0.1091	9.165	−0.0759	−0.695
9	19	0	−0.0214	0.1088	0	−0.0330	0
10	19	1	0.0874	0.1098	9.105	0.1421	1.294
11	20	0	0.1973	0.1120	0	0.2529	0
12	20	1	0.3093	0.1155	8.660	0.3665	3.174
13	21	2	0.4248	0.1203	16.628	0.4842	8.051
14	23	1	0.5450	0.1267	7.893	0.6075	4.795
15	24	1	0.6717	0.1351	7.404	0.7381	5.465
16	25	2	0.8068	0.1460	13.699	0.8782	12.031
17	27	4	0.9528	0.1604	24.936	1.0309	25.707
18	31	0	1.1132	0.1798	0	1.2003	0
19	31	3	1.2930	0.2069	14.499	1.3925	20.190
20	34	3	1.4999	0.2467	12.159	1.6172	19.664
21	37	3	1.7467	0.3104	9.666	1.8916	18.285
22	40	2	2.0570	0.4273	4.680	2.2504	10.533
23	42	1	2.4843	0.7142	1.400	2.7826	3.896
24	43		3.1985				
	Σ				178.922	11.5940	108.53
					7.7792	0.5019	4.7187
					$\bar{y}\,\bar{u}$	=	−3.9044
					r	=	0.8143

$r = \text{Cov}/(\sigma_y \sigma_u)$ where $\text{Cov} = \sum_{1}^{N-1} y_{L_i} \cdot u_{L_i+0.5}/(N-1) - \bar{y}_{L_i} \bar{u}_{L_i+0.5} = 0.8143$.

The calculations for σ_y and σ_u have been omitted in Table XXIX. We find: $\sigma_y^2 = 40.4478$ and $\sigma_u^2 = 0.9812$. The correlation coefficient is $r = 0.1293$ which transforms to $Z_F = 0.1300$. For $N = 25$ and a significance level $\alpha = 0.05$ we find from Table XXVIII that $Z_t = 0.371$. Z_t would be slightly higher for $N = 24$ but $Z_F < Z_t$ for 0.371. Consequently the calculation of the precise threshold for $N = 24$ is not necessary because it does not alter $Z_F < Z_t$. H_0 is accepted, i.e., in our case $t = 0.31 \sim 0$ and the Type I distribution model emerges as the more suitable.
Some readers may conclude that the outcome of the test could have been predicted and is no surprise. Inspection of Table XXVII reveals the discrepancies between observed and analytical frequency in the tail-ends, and the calculations of the test were superfluous. However, eyesight is not a valid statistical test and $t = 0.31$ could have been significantly different from $t = 0$. For the moment estimators $t = 0.23$ which calls for Type I, too.
The author intentionally chose this set of data in order to discuss the difficulties which the reader may encounter in the analysis of extreme values. Therefore, the data set of 24 in Table VI has not been supplemented by later data. The remarks about truncation (Example 18) are reiterated. The possibility of a truncation of data is not considered in Van Montfort's test.

The *m*-th value distribution

Although akin to Gumbel's law, there are some differences and therefore a short survey will be given here.
The *m*-th distribution fits a requirement in the design of equipment or in the field of construction. The manufacturer or the engineer may assume a certain risk factor for a particular chosen threshold, above which the equipment would not operate satisfactorily or the established construction could encounter adverse effects by weather elements. Suppose that we are interested in manufacturing an air-conditioning unit with a 90% risk factor, e.g., we are looking for a threshold value in which 9 out of 10 cases the unit provides sufficient cooling, but in one out of 10 cases the unit may be insufficient. This does not necessarily mean that the air-conditioner breaks down completely but the unit may not provide enough cooling power for the customer. The manufacturer may have chosen this risk factor because it could mean a substantial saving in production costs compared to a design for the absolute extreme, and the equipment may be more marketable at the lower price.
We could postulate that a 90% threshold is adopted from the ordinary frequency distributions of daily maxima but this threshold may be too low because this threshold could be exceeded in every individual year. It could mean, e.g., that in a 30-day period the air conditioner would be insufficient on three days (i.e., 10% of 30 days). Although this could be an acceptable risk it is well-known that atmospheric data display persistence, and these three days could occur consecutively. This consecutive deficiency is exactly what the manufacturer wants to avoid, because the customer may tolerate insufficient operation on one individual day but may react unfavorably if it occurs on consecutive days.
In this situation the *m*-th distribution would be the proper statistical approach. We examine the frequency distribution of the 3rd extreme value and take the 90% value of this distribution as the threshold for the risk. Accordingly the threshold would be exceeded on three consecutive days only in one out of ten years but not in every individual year (provided the past records are indicative of the future).

Gumbel's *m*-th distribution

The *m*-th distribution (subscript *m*) resembles Gumbel's law for the p.d.f.:

$$f(Z_m) = \mathrm{d}F(Z_m) = \frac{m^m}{(m-1)!}\exp(-mZ_m - m\,\mathrm{e}^{-Z_m})\,\mathrm{d}Z_m \tag{217}$$

with:

$$\mathrm{d}Z_m = a_m\,\mathrm{d}x_m \tag{218a}$$

and:

$$\pm Z_m = a_m(x - u_m) \tag{218b}$$

$$\bar{x} = u_m \pm \bar{Z}_m/a_m \tag{219a}$$

or:

$$u_m = \bar{x} \mp \bar{Z}_m/a_m = \bar{x} \mp (\bar{Z}_m/\sigma_Z)\cdot\sigma_x \tag{219b}$$

(The upper sign is taken for maxima.)

$$a_m = \sigma_Z/\sigma_x \tag{219c}$$

This is analogous to eqs. 183b and 186b, c. For $m=1$ eq. 217 reverts to Gumbel's law. Observe that x in the above notation stands for the set of data of the *m*-th extreme, i.e., X_{m_i}. The c.f.d. has the following form:

$$F(Z_m) = [\exp(-m\,\mathrm{e}^{-Z_m})]\cdot\sum_{\nu=0}^{m-1}\frac{m^\nu\,\mathrm{e}^{-\nu Z_m}}{\nu!} \tag{220}$$

Again, for $m=1$ we recognize Gumbel's law, but for $m>1$ some additional terms follow. Hence the moments are not simple:

$$\bar{Z}_m = \bar{Z}_1 + \ln m - \sum_{k=1}^{m-1}\frac{1}{k}, \quad m \geq 2 \tag{221}$$

where $\bar{Z}_1 = 0.57721$, Euler's constant.

$$\sigma^2_{Z_m} = \sigma^2_{Z_1} - \sum_{k=1}^{m-1}\frac{1}{k^2}, \quad m \geq 2 \tag{222a}$$

with:

$$\sigma^2_{Z_1} = \pi^2/6 \tag{222b}$$

The higher (central) moments are:

$$\nu_{3,Z_m} = 2S_{3,m} \tag{223a}$$

$$S_{3,m} = S_{3,1} - \sum_{k=1}^{m-1}\frac{1}{k^3} \tag{223b}$$

with:

$$S_{3,1} = \sum_{k=1}^{\infty}\frac{1}{k^3} = 1.20205690 \tag{223c}$$

$$\nu_{4,Z_m} = 6S_{4,m} + 3S^2_{2,m} \tag{224a}$$

with:

$$S_{4,m} = S_{4,1} - \sum_{k=1}^{m-1} \frac{1}{k^4} \tag{224b}$$

and:

$$S_{2,m} = \sigma^2_{Zm} \tag{224c}$$

and:

$$S_{4,1} = \pi^4/90 = 1.08232323 \tag{224d}$$

$$\gamma_1 = 2S_{3,m}/\sigma^3_{Zm} \tag{225a}$$

$$\gamma_2 = 6S_{4,m}/\sigma^4_{Zm} \tag{225b}$$

The mode occurs at ln m. Consequently:

$$Y_m = 0 = Z_m - \ln m \tag{226a}$$

We find the short version for the probability of the mode:

$$F(Z_{\text{mode}}) = e^{-m} \sum_{\nu=0}^{m-1} m^{\nu}/\nu! \tag{226b}$$

The moments estimators can be deduced by the process which was discussed with eq. 183a.

The maximum-likelihood equations are:

$$\sum e^{-Z} = \sum e^{-a\,m(x-u_m)} = N \tag{227a}$$

$$1/a - \bar{x} + (m/N) \sum x\, e^{-a\,m(x-u_m)} = 0 \tag{227b}$$

(Notice, x again is the set of data for the m-th extreme.)

Table XXX displays some of the constants of the m-th distribution.

The maximum-likelihood equations can be rearranged so that the variates are separated. It can be recognized that:

$$\sum \exp[-a(x-u)] = [\exp(+au)] \sum \exp(-ax)$$

Thus u can be eliminated from eq. 227b:

$$1/ma_m - \bar{x} + [\sum x_i \exp(-a_m x_i)]/\sum \exp(-a_m x_i) = 0 \tag{228a}$$

TABLE XXX

SOME CHARACTERISTICS OF THE m-TH DISTRIBUTION ($A_m = m^m/(M-1)!$)

m	$\bar{Z}_m$	σ_{Zm}	A_m	$\bar{Z}_m/\sigma_Z$	γ_1	γ_2
1	0.577216	1.282550	1	0.450053	1.139547	2.400000
2	0.270363	0.803078	4	0.336658	0.780245	1.187526
3	0.175828	0.628438	13.5	0.279786	0.620947	0.762564
4	0.130177	0.532750	42 2/3	0.244349	0.529340	0.556950
5	0.103321	0.470450	130 5/24	0.219622	0.468585	0.437447

TABLE XXXI

CALCULATION OF THE x_{90} THRESHOLD FOR THE m-TH DISTRIBUTION

m	x	σ_x	a	$\bar{Z}_m/a$	u_m	Z_{90}	x_{90}
1	106.40	2.565	0.500	1.154	105.25	2.25	109.75
2	104.85	2.008	0.400	0.676	104.17	1.33	107.50
3	104.05	2.027	0.310	0.567	103.48	1.00	106.71

$x_{90} = Z_{90}/a + u$

Then:

$$u_m = [\ln N - \ln \sum \exp(-a_m x_i)]/a_m \tag{228b}$$

a_m can be obtained by an iterative procedure suggested by STEVENS and LEDUC (1975). In the case of $m = 1$ an explicit solution (see eq. 191b) and an order statistics has been discussed.

Example 20. Assume that we need the 12h (noon) extreme temperature threshold which can be exceeded on three consecutive days of the month once in ten years. The equipment will be designed for a 90% risk factor. This is a typical problem for the application of the m-th distribution.
In order to judge the benefits gained by the m-th distribution the regular frequency distribution is analyzed first. Three days of the month would correspond to the 90% value of the cumulative distribution.*[1] To be overcautious, we would probably adopt the temperature exceeded by three days out of the ten-year period. Because $N = 300$ it would be the 99% value of the ordinary cumulative distribution. In the m-th distribution we select the 3rd extreme and the 90% cumulative threshold of this third extreme value distribution model.
The data set is taken from the 12h (noon) temperatures during July–August 1955–1964 at Yuma, Arizona. $X_m = 98.91°$, standard deviation $S = 4.36$, 90% of the regular distribution $X_{90} = X_m + A_{90} \cdot S = 98.91 + (1.28)(4.36) = 104.49°$F, 99% of the regular distribution $X_{99} = X_m + a_{99} \cdot S = 98.91 + (2.33)(4.36) = 109.07°$F. The comparable threshold for the m-th distribution is found in Table XXXI.
It is obvious that the equipment would not be properly designed based on the 90% threshold of the ordinary frequency distribution. In turn, the equipment would be overdesigned if the 99% threshold of the regular distribution would be taken. We conclude from the extreme value theory that a design for the threshold X_{99} of the ordinary distribution is equivalent to an approximate risk factor of a design for an exceedance of one day every ten years (see $m = 1$).
In this example the differences between design temperatures are not very large but in other cases they could amount to a considerable change in the design threshold.

Cramer's *m*-th distribution

Another distribution of m-th values based on the Laplace distribution has been studied by CRAMER (1946). Let us define the transformation ξ for a set of N observations X:

$$\xi_m = N[1 - F(x_m)] \tag{229a}$$

where x_m designates the m-th extreme of the data set X_i. The frequency density of the distribution is:

$$f(\xi) = [\xi^{m-1} \exp(-\xi)]/\Gamma(m) \tag{229b}$$

*[1] For simplicity assume 30 days in a month. An adjustment can be made for a 31-day month.

The transformation:

$$U_m = -\ln \xi_m \tag{230a}$$

leads to:

$$f(U_m) = (\exp[-mU_m - \exp(-U_m)])\ \mathrm{d}U_m/\Gamma(m) \tag{230b}$$

The mode of U_m is:

$$U_{\text{mode}} = -\ln m \tag{230c}$$

The mode can be used as the reference point by the transformation:

$$V_m = U_m + \ln m \tag{231a}$$

Introducing V_m into eq. 230b produces:

$$f(V_m) = \frac{m^m}{(m-1)!} \exp[-mV_m - m\exp(-V_m)]\ \mathrm{d}V_m \tag{231b}$$

which is identical with eq. 217. Therefore:

$$F(V_m) = [\exp(-m\,\mathrm{e}^{-V_m})] \sum_{\nu=0}^{m=1} (m^\nu\, \mathrm{e}^{-\nu V_m})/\nu! \tag{232a}$$

with:

$$V_m = U_m + \ln m = \ln m - \ln \xi_m \tag{232b}$$

Borgman (1961) based the decision about the m-th extreme on Cramer's model modified for an ordinary distribution. This method is most suitable if a specified threshold is desired and the probability of exceedance is sought.

$$P_r(X > x_{\text{th}}) = 1 - G_{m,N}(x_{\text{th}}) \tag{233}$$

We calculate:

$$\xi_m = N[1 - F(x_{\text{th}})] \tag{234}$$

and for large N the approximation is used:

$$G_{m,N}(\xi) \sim [\exp(-\xi)] \sum_{\nu=0}^{m-1} \xi^\nu/\nu! \tag{235a}$$

This distribution was developed by Borgman from the binomial:

$$G_{m,N}(x) = \sum_{\nu=0}^{m-1} \binom{N}{\nu} [1 - F^k(x)][F(x)]^{N-k} \tag{235b}$$

Another approximation is the incomplete gamma function:

$$G_{m,N}(\xi) = 1 - [1/(m-1)!] \int_0^\xi \mathrm{e}^{-s} s^{m-1}\, \mathrm{d}s \tag{235c}$$

Borgman published tables for the first five extremes and values of N from m to ∞.

Example 21. Let us analyze the same data as in Example 20. It was deduced that X_{90} for the 3rd distribution was 106.7°. The ordinary distribution renders $t = (X - X_m)/S$, i.e., (106.7 − 98.9)/4.36 or

$t = 1.79$. Assuming a Gaussian distribution $F(t) = 0.9633$. Now let us first consider the total period of record, $N = 300$. $\xi_m = 300(1 - 0.9633) = 11.01$. From eq. 235a $G_{m,N} = 0.001$. (Borgman's table lists $P_r = 0.005$ for $\xi = 9.16$ as the last entry.) Thus, $P_r(\xi) = 1 - 0.001 = 0.999$ which implies that in the 10-year period a 0.1% probability exists that 106.7 is not exceeded on 3 consecutive days. This result agrees with the 10% risk of the 3rd extreme.
Assume now that we are interested that 106.7 is exceeded within a 30-day period. Then $\xi = 1.10$ because $\bar{X} = 98.9$ and $S = 4.36$ remain. Now $G_{m,N} = 0.90$, and $P_r(106.7) = 0.10$. This confirms the result from the m-th distribution, where the value was derived for a 10% exceedance risk within a month. Thus we may conclude that eq. 233 provides the chances of exceedance without going through the calculations of extreme value data for a specified threshold and a known frequency model of the data.
The respective probability for the second extreme is $P_r \sim 0.17$ from $F(107.5) = 0.976$, $\xi = 0.732$ for 30 days. It would indicate a somewhat larger risk factor than from the m-th distribution. For $F(109.8) = 0.9936$, $\xi = 0.192$ for 30 days. $P_r \sim 0.18$, which is also higher than the 10% risk deduced from the m-th distribution. Two apparent explanations can be given for the discrepancies. First, the risk factors from eq. 233 are derived from different statistical backgrounds. Thus, they need not be identical. A second cause for the difference may be the short period of record which provides $N = 10$ for the m-th distribution. The data set for the ordinary frequency distribution is much larger ($N = 300$). Therefore, a bias could exist in the small data sample of the 2nd and 1st extreme. Some of the larger extremes which we would expect based on the distribution of the ordinary data sample may be missing in the small data set of 10 from the short period of record.

Other extreme value distributions

Analysis of individual data will often reveal that the simple models do not always apply. E.g., SNEYERS (1960) commenced from the general model:

$$F(Z) = \exp[-\exp(-Z)] \qquad (236a)$$

In our notation (see eq. 188a):

$$Z = AX + b \qquad (236b)$$

Sneyers found this assumption unsuitable for maximum rainfalls in Belgium. He suggested a relationship:

$$Z = aX + b \pm \sqrt{c^2(X-d)^2 + e^2} \qquad (236c)$$

which is a branch of a hyperbola. The reader is referred to SNEYERS (1960, 1979) for more details.
MARITZ and MUNRO (1967) discussed a generalized extreme value distribution. They define:

$$[F(X)]^k = \exp[-\exp(-Y + \ln K)] \qquad (237a)$$

where:

$$Y = (X - \gamma)/\beta \qquad (237b)$$

and:

$$Z_k = Y - \ln K = \ln(-\ln [F(X)]^k \qquad (237c)$$

This can be expanded to an arbitrary function $f(X)$:

$$F(X) = \exp(-\exp[-f(X)]) \qquad (238a)$$

Finally a generalized formula is:

$$F(X)=\exp\left(-\left[1-\frac{\delta(X-\alpha)}{\beta}\right]^{1/\delta}\right) \tag{238b}$$

Estimators are not very simple to obtain and usually are calculated with the aid of matrices. The detailed discussion would exceed the frame of this section.
An expansion of the extreme value theory in bivariate samples has been attempted by POSNER et al. (1969) and CAMPBELL and TSOKOS (1973). An application to rainfall rates has been delineated by LIN (1976b) (see p. 374).
OLIVEIRA (1983) based an exceedance model on the binomial distribution and discussed the asymptotic distribution of extremes, including the Weibull distribution. Another approach was taken by SNEYERS and VANDIEPENBEECK (1983) by utilizing the two parameter exponential distribution for exceedances. BUISHAND (1983) modified the extreme value theory to include dependent data and provided an example for rainfall data.

The time interval distribution

Design of drainage systems require data on the recurrence of high intensity rainfall. It is customary to prepare design criteria by Gumbel's extreme value distribution (eq. 183a), the m-th distribution (eq. 217), or the return period (eq. 200). The return period was defined as the occurrence of a certain threshold x_{th} per time interval, e.g., a number of years N_y. Let us assume we have a 30-year period ($N=30$), and a certain threshold x_{th} has been exceeded twice ($n=2$). The (mean) return period is $N_y/n=15$ years.
The return period as discussed above does not include any time sequence after which the event x_{th} (e.g., high intensity rainfall) is likely to recur. It is merely stated that two events $\geq x_{\mathrm{th}}$ have been observed or will occur in 30 years, but the two events may have taken place in two consecutive years. Had the engineer designed the drainage system during the first year of the occurrence, the next year would have brought the second event, and the designer may have questioned the validity of the data provided to him or the method of design.
THOM (1959) suggested a solution to this dilemma by finding a probability distribution for the "time interval between such excessive events." Instead of averaging the time interval as in the return period, we provide the probabilities for the time interval t between events exceeding x_{th}. This distribution exists and was presented by Thom as:

$$F(T)=a\int_0^T \mathrm{e}^{-at}\,\mathrm{d}t \tag{239a}$$

which is a special type of the exponential distribution (see ESSENWANGER, 1976, p. 113). The frequency density is:

$$f(t)=a\mathrm{e}^{-at}\,(\mathrm{d}t) \tag{239b}$$

It is also called the Poisson time interval distribution. The mean occurrence is $1/a$. It can be shown (THOM, 1959) that the relation between a and the return period T_r is:

$$T_r=1/a \tag{240a}$$

Since $T_r = N_y/n_x$, the estimator a for the time distribution function is:

$$a = n_X/N_y \tag{240b}$$

Eq. 239a can be integrated and solved for a, namely:

$$a = T^{-1} \ln [1/(1-F(T))] \tag{241a}$$

or as a function of $F(T)$ we can write:

$$F(T) = 1 - e^{-aT} \tag{241b}$$

Commonly we can assume $T \geq 1.0$, which implies that the time unit of the recurring event is equal to or smaller than the time period for which design data are desired. The probability that a certain event ($\geq x_{th}$) does not occur within a specified time interval is then:

$$P_{x_{th}} = 1 - F(T) = e^{-aT} \tag{241c}$$

Example 22 should clarify the use of the equations. Assume that the engineer would like to have a 95% risk probability that the event does not occur in the next year. Then $P_{x_{th}} = 0.95$, or $F(T) = 0.05$. For $T = 1.0$ (year) this leads to $a = \ln(1/0.95) = 0.0513$. Now we enter eq. 240b with:

$$n_x = N_y \cdot a \tag{242}$$

For 30 years we obtain $n_x = 30 \cdot (0.0513) = 1.539$. Since observations do not occur in fractions but in integers, we would look for the threshold x_{th} which has occurred once in that 30-year period (i.e., the extreme) or a threshold corresponding to about the mean between the amount of precipitation observed once and twice in 30 years. The ordinary threshold, x_{th} occurring once in 15 years (i.e., maximum x_{max}) would not necessarily lead to the same design threshold because more than one value could be higher in the second 15 years than x_{max} of the first 15 years.
For comparison, we ask for the number of years which are required that $n_x = 1$. This leads to $N_y = 19.5$ (or in integers 20 years).
Since a and $F(T)$ are not greatly different, the example does not convincingly demonstrate the real merits of the time function. Therefore we expand the example to include the 95% risk for a 2-year period. Then $T = 2$ which leads to $N_y = 39$ years. In other words, we need a threshold value which has been observed once in a set of data from a period of 39 years. This result is quite different from the customary concept of a 5% exceedance in 20 years.
Returning to our earlier assumption of two cases out of 30 years we find $a = 0.067$. This leads to $F(1) = 0.065$, or the risk is 93.5% which is slightly less than the preselected 95% risk criterion. For $T = 2$ we obtain $F(2) = 1 - 0.875 = 0.125$. The risk is 87.5% which would not satisfy a 90% risk factor. The risk factor of the time interval distribution includes more than the consideration of the return period alone.
After what time period does the event occur with 50% or more chance? Assume the first example, $a = 0.0513$ and $N_y = 19.5$. Then $T_{50\%} = a^{-1} \ln(1/0.50) = 13.5$ years. This is smaller than the average N_y of 19.5 years. For $N_y = 39$ years and a 2-year period we calculate $a = 0.0256$, or $T_{50\%} = 27$ years. Although we would design for a value which was observed once in 39 years, the chances are 50% or higher that the extreme would already occur after 27 years. This is a much shorter time period than given by the return period alone (see risk of occurrence, eq. 201a).

The generalized extreme value distribution

Three models of extreme value distributions were introduced. These were derived by Fisher and Tippett (1928), and a test procedure for the suitability of Type I or II was discussed (eq. 213). The question of which model is most suitable in a specific application to atmospheric elements is much more fundamental, however. In order to obtain a satisfactory answer Jenkinson (1955) recommended a general equation and solution to the problem, followed by articles in 1969 and 1975a.

Jenkinson's model

Consider the following generalized model:

$$F(X)=\exp-[1-Z/\delta]^{\delta} \qquad (243a)$$

with:

$$Z=(x-\gamma)/\beta \qquad (243b)$$

This is a three-parameter model with δ, γ, and $\beta>0$.
The double exponential model is defined by:

$$F(y)=\exp[-\exp(-y)] \qquad (244a)$$

or:

$$-y=\ln\ln[1/F(y)] \qquad (244b)$$

In order to relate y and x take double logarithms of eq. 243a:

$$\ln\ln[1/F(x)]=\delta\ln[1-Z/\delta] \qquad (245)$$

If we define y to be the left side of eq. 245 then a "reduced variate" y is obtained:

$$-y=\ln\ln[1/F(x)] \qquad (246a)$$

and the relationship between y and Z renders:

$$-y=\delta\ln[1-Z/\delta] \qquad (246b)$$

or:

$$Z=\delta[1-\exp(-y/\delta)] \qquad (246c)$$

and:

$$x=\gamma+\beta\delta[1-\exp(-y/\delta)] \qquad (246d)$$

We set $\delta=1/\omega$ (p. 76). The association with the three Fisher-Tippett models is now evident. We have for ω = positive, 0, and negative the Types III, I, and II, respectively. For Gumbel's model (Type I) with $\omega=0$ the relationship between y and x (eq. 246d) reduces to:

$$x=\gamma+\beta y \qquad (246e)$$

This leads to a straight line, i.e., $y=Z$, between x and y with slope β and location γ, while for the other types we have curved lines. The task is now to find appropriate estimators. Jenkinson (1955) demonstrated that eq. 246d is a general solution of the Fisher-Tippett functional equation:

$$P^{s}(X)=P(a_sX+b_s) \qquad (247a)$$

where a_s and b_s are functions of s with:

$$P=\exp[-\exp(-y)]=F(X) \qquad (247b)$$

Although eq.247b looks like Gumbel's law, the reader will observe that the difference lies in the definition of Z by eq. 186b for Gumbel and eq. 243b for the generalized model. The latter is in line with the suggestion by SNEYERS and VAN ISACKER (1972) as given by eq. 195a.

JENKINSON (1955, 1975a) showed that the relationship between y and the return period T is approximately:

$$y = \ln T \tag{248}$$

Maximum-likelihood estimates

The likelihood function can be derived:

$$-L = N \ln|\beta| + (1 - 1/\delta)\sum y + \sum \exp(-y) \tag{249}$$

The summation takes place over all $X_1, X_2, \ldots, X_N$ ordered extremes. From the derivatives JENKINSON (1969, 1975a) suggested an iterative procedure for the calculation of likelihood estimators $\hat{\beta}$, $\hat{\delta}$ and γ. The joint corrections may have the form:

$$\hat{\beta}_{i+1} = \hat{\beta}_i + \Delta\beta_i;\ \hat{\gamma}_{i+1} = \hat{\gamma}_i + \Delta\gamma_i,\ \hat{\omega}_{i+1} = \hat{\omega}_i + \Delta\omega_i \tag{250}$$

with $\omega = 1/\delta$. The solution can be found by solving the matrix equation:

$$\begin{bmatrix} \Delta\beta_i/\beta_i \\ \Delta\gamma_i/\gamma_i \\ \Delta\omega_i \end{bmatrix} = \begin{bmatrix} a(\omega) & d(\omega) & e(\omega) \\ d(\omega) & b(\omega) & f(\omega) \\ e(\omega) & f(\omega) & c(\omega) \end{bmatrix} \begin{bmatrix} -U(y_1,\omega) \\ -V(y_i,\omega) \\ W(y_i,\omega) \end{bmatrix} \tag{251}$$

Jenkinson calculated the elements a–f of the matrix as provided in Table XXXII. An empirical equation for the calculation of a through f is given by eq. 256. The other entries in eq. 251 are:

$$\left.\begin{aligned} &U = (V + P)/\omega \\ &V = \sum \exp(-y + \omega y)/N - (1-\omega)\sum e^{\omega y}/N \\ &W = (U - R)/\omega \\ &\text{with:} \\ &P = 1 - \sum e^{-y}/N \\ &R = 1 - \sum y/N + \sum y\,e^{-y}/N \end{aligned}\right| \tag{252}$$

Jenkinson recommended to find a solution for the two parameters β, γ first and assume that $\omega = 0$. For $\omega \to 0$ we find $-U \to -R$; $V \to P$ and $V \to \sum (y + 0.5y^2\,e^{-y} - 0.5y^2)/N$.

From initial values β_0 and γ_0 (see following section on initial estimators) we deduce:

$$\Delta\beta_0/\beta_0 = -0.6079R + 0.2570P \tag{253a}$$

$$\Delta\gamma_0/\gamma_0 = -0.2570R + 1.1087P \tag{253b}$$

The standard error of x with a return period T is given by:

$$S(x) = (\beta/\sqrt{N})[1 + 0.6079(y_T + 0.4228)^2] \tag{253c}$$

TABLE XXXII

ENTRIES FOR MATRIX EQ. 251
(From JENKINSON, 1975a)

ω	a	b	c	d	e	f
−0.6	1.367	1.289	1.048	−0.250	1.019	0.233
−0.4	1.046	1.291	0.835	0.089	0.799	0.264
−0.2	0.806	1.278	0.645	0.045	0.571	0.273
0	0.653	1.249	0.477	0.147	0.337	0.258
0.2	0.584	1.202	0.330	0.214	0.092	0.220
0.4	0.595	1.141	0.206	0.242	−0.164	0.162
0.6	0.679	1.077	0.104	0.225	−0.433	0.094

where:

$$y_T = \ln \ln [T/(T-1)] \tag{253d}$$

and:

$$x = \gamma_0 + \beta_0 y_T \tag{253e}$$

The initial values for the three-parameter solution are $\hat{\beta}_1$, $\hat{\gamma}_1$ and $\omega = 0$. (β_1 and γ_1 by eqs. 251 and 250). Now:

$$\beta_2 = \beta_1 + 0.147 S\beta_1 \tag{254a}$$

$$\gamma_2 = \gamma_1 + 0.257 S\gamma_1 \tag{254b}$$

$$\omega_2 = 0.477 S \tag{254c}$$

$$S = \sum y + 0.5 \sum y^2 \exp(-y) - 0.5 \sum y^2 \tag{254d}$$

If further iterations are necessary the set of eq. 251 can be used with $i \geq 2$.

Initial estimators

JENKINSON (1975a) pointed out that initial estimators may be obtained from mean quartiles. Let us denote these by $y_{12.5}$, $y_{37.5}$, $y_{62.5}$ and $y_{87.5}$. The corresponding values are −0.73, +0.02, 0.76 and 2.01 from eq. 244b. (Jenkinson suggested y_{10} and y_{90} instead of $y_{12.5}$ and $y_{87.5}$, with $y_{10} = 0.80$ and $y_{90} = 2.32$.) An approximation can be made from the return period. We select y_1 for x_1 which occurs twice, y_2 for x_2 which appears once in a year. Other values are y_3 for x_3 every second year and y_4 for x_4 every fifth year. The corresponding y values for $i = 1, \ldots, 4$ would be −0.69, 0, 0.37, and 1.50. We may add $y_5 = 2.25$ for a return period of ten years. From these one can derive the necessary equations for initial β_0 and γ_0 estimators.
JENKINSON (1975a) derived:

$$\beta_0 = (x_3 - x_1)/1.57 \tag{255a}$$

$$\gamma_0 = x_2 \tag{255b}$$

In Jenkinson's opinion the two-parameter model (Gumbel's law) is sufficient if $|\omega| \leq 0.025$.

The entries a through f in the matrix eq. 251 can be calculated from the following (empirical) formulae:

$$\left.\begin{aligned}
a&=0.6528-0.5547\omega+1.0634\omega^2-0.0521\omega^3-0.0971\omega^4\\
b&=1.2489-0.1943\omega-0.2239\omega^2+0.0486\omega^3+0.1136\omega^4\\
c&=0.4768-0.7866\omega+0.2705\omega^2\\
d&=0.1470+0.4772\omega-0.4389\omega^2-0.0868\omega^3-0.0118\omega^4\\
e&=0.3366-1.1976\omega+0.1193\omega^2-0.0347\omega^3-0.0047\omega^4\\
f&=0.2581-0.1359\omega-0.2970\omega^2+0.0556\omega^3+0.0947\omega^4
\end{aligned}\right| \qquad (256)$$

A word of caution is appropriate. Jenkinson stated that the iteration usually can be stopped after 8 steps. However, difficulties may arise for small samples, e.g., $N<10$. Diverging from a solution can be avoided by requiring that only half of the corrections such as $\Delta\beta/2$, etc. are made when W has changed the sign from i to $i+1$.
In agreement with SNEYERS and VAN ISACKER (1972) Jenkinson recommended utilization of $\ln x$ for the extreme values of precipitations.
JENKINSON (1955) deduced a solution of the maximum-likelihood equations by entering the average and standard deviation of the greatest member in a data set of annual maxima and minima. In Jenkinson's article the reader can also find a table of y in steps of 1% for P (see eq. 247b).

The Pareto distribution

HURST et al. (1977), COROTIS et al. (1978) and EDWARDS (1980) have suggested that the duration of runs of the surface wind speed up to several hours (except for long durations) is well-fitted by:

$$F(t)=1-(t/t_0)^{1-c} \qquad (257)$$

which is a Pareto distribution where t_0 designates the resolution (e.g., 50 s), $t>t_0$. HARRIS (1968) has demonstrated that the Pareto distribution can be explained as a mixture of an exponential distribution $\exp(-x/\theta)$ where the parameter θ^{-1} has a gamma distribution. It is a special form of Pearson Type VI (see ESSENWANGER, 1976, p. 60).
Three kinds of the Pareto distribution exist, but the second kind is used most commonly:

$$F(x)=1-k/(x+C)^a \qquad (258a)$$

for which C is a reference constant and:

$$f(x)=ak^a/x^{a+1};\ x\geq k\geq 0;\ a>0 \qquad (258b)$$

For $C=0$ and $k=k_1^a$ we obtain the first kind:

$$F(x)=1-(k_1/x)^a \qquad (259)$$

The moments for the second kind are:

$$\mu_r=ak^r/(a-r) \qquad (260)$$

This provides the mean:

$$\bar{x}=\mu_1=ak/(a-1) \quad (261a)$$

and the variance:

$$\sigma^2=ak^2(a-1)^{-1}(a-2)^{-1}=\bar{x}k(a-2)^{-1} \quad (261b)$$

QUANDT (1966) elaborated on a variety of estimators. Maximum-likelihood estimators are:

$$\hat{k}=x_{min} \quad (262a)$$

$$\hat{a}=n\left[\sum_{i=1}^{n} \ln (x_i/\hat{k})\right]^{-1} \quad (262b)$$

Moment estimators according to Quandt are:

$$a=(n\bar{x}-x_{min})/[n(\bar{x}-x_{min})] \quad (263a)$$

$$k=(an-1)x_{min}/(an) \quad (263b)$$

These are simpler to solve than $\sigma^2/\bar{x}^2=(a-1)/[a(a-2)]$.
Estimators for the Pareto distribution can also be found from the quantiles. Let us assume that $Q_1=F(x_1)$ and $Q_2=F(x_2)$ are two quantile values. Then:

$$a=\ln [(1-Q_1)/(1-Q_2)]/\ln (x_1/x_2) \quad (264a)$$

and k can be obtained from:

$$Q_j=1-(k/x_j)^a \quad (264b)$$

$$k=(1-Q_j)^{-a}x_j \quad (264c)$$

EDWARDS (1980) later recommended a modified form for longer runs of the wind speed:

$$F(t)=1-(t/t_0)^{1-c_1}\exp[-\lambda(t-t_0)] \quad (265)$$

for which:

$$\bar{t}=t_0[(\lambda t_0)^{c_1-2}\Gamma(2-c_1) \quad (266a)$$

An estimator for c_1 can be obtained from shorter runs which have the Pareto distribution, i.e. $x^{-a}=t^{1-c^1}$, or $a-1=c_1$. After c_1 is known λ can be calculated from $\bar{t}$ (eq. 266a) because t_0 is known. We may also obtain c_1 from:

$$(\hat{c}_1-1)^{-1}=\sum^{N} (\ln t_i) (\ln t_i)/N-\ln t_0 \quad (266b)$$

Afterwards λ can again be found from eq. 266a.

Chapter 3

Correlations and Linear Regression

The next two chapters deal with relationships between atmospheric elements and the derivation of mathematical expressions for their time and/or space variations. These techniques may be used to predict either the behavior or occurrence of one atmospheric element from available observations of the same or other elements, or to delineate the relationship between them.

In this chapter various forms of correlations will be introduced. Before details are presented an outline of the general mathematical background is in order.

A myriad of articles on correlation, regression, and related topics can be found in statistical journals and texts. The theoretical background is treated in various excellent texts (e.g., MOOD, 1950; KENNEY and KEEPING, 1954; KENDALL and STUART, 1961; GRAYBILL, 1961; ANDERSON, 1962; HOGG and CRAIG, 1967; and many more). The author's presentation of correlation and regression cannot be comprehensive in the framework of this text. Some topics have been selected which are often found in the literature of climatology and the atmospheric sciences.

The reader has become familiar with the various models of frequency distributions. Correlations and regression analysis can be applied to data irrespective of the model type although the statistical background favors the Gaussian distribution law in data samples. It is self-evident, however, that a poor linear correlation coefficient e.g., can result from incompatible frequency models of the examined atmospheric elements. These discrepancies occasionally will be pointed out later in this text but an elaboration of these problems will not always be possible. Therefore, the reader is cautioned to examine limitations which may affect correlations or other measures of associations, and which could lead to erroneous interpretations.

General regression model

Suppose that we are interested to relate a set of elements (variates) designated as $Y_1, \ldots, Y_n$ with another element Z, or we wish to predict Z from the given sets of Y_j. This task can also be interpreted that Z is the dependent variate or predictand while the set of Y_j represents the independent variables or predictors. A mathematical formulation is:

$$Z = a_0 + a_1 Y_1 + a_2 Y_2 + \ldots + a_n Y_n + \varepsilon \qquad (267a)$$

It is customary to call eq. 267a a linear regression system; linear, because none of the variables Y_j appears in higher order although the general principle can be expanded to include nonlinear terms such as $Y_1 = \ln X_1$ e.g., X is the precipitation amount, or $Y_2 = T^2$, and T is the temperature. The term linear "regression" system is found in widespread use in the statistical literature but GUTTMAN (1977) considered it an example where mathematical statisticians have adopted terminology which the reader can easily misinterpret. In most cases "regression" no longer has any connection with a genetic process for which the method was originally developed and regression equations should be properly called a set of conditional arithmetic means. Let us consider eq. 267a as a system of linear equations (see eq. 267b and CUTTER, 1976) and agree that regression analysis is a mathematical (statistical) terminology.

Usually it is postulated that the system of linear equations is composed of variables whose joint probability density function $f(Y_1, Y_2, \ldots, Y_n)$ follows the multivariate Gaussian distribution, an assumption which is not correct for some atmospheric elements. As stated, the effects of this deviation cannot always be assessed a priori and must be studied for the individual case.

Let us assume that every variate Y_j consists of a set of data Y_{ji}, $i = 1, \ldots, N$, $j = 1, \ldots, n$. Then eq. 267a holds for every corresponding individual value i of the system. Thus we can write i equations:

$$Z_i = a_0 + a_1 Y_{1i} + a_2 Y_{2i} + \ldots + a_n Y_{ni} + \varepsilon_i \qquad (267b)$$

When $N > n$, the system is oversaturated or mathematically overdetermined and has numerous solutions. The coefficients $a_1, \ldots, a_n$ depend on a particular subset of equations which we can arbitrarily select from N possibilities. In order to utilize all available N equations the most satisfactory method to determine the coefficients is the method of least squares (see eq. 54a, b). In this method the sum of the squared differences between the analytical ζ_i and the observed Z_i is a minimum:

$$\frac{\partial}{\partial a_j}[\sum (\zeta_i - Z_i)^2] = 0 \qquad (268)$$

The last term in eq. 267, a or b, is ε which stands for a random error (measurement, insufficient terms, etc.). In most texts it is omitted. Let us postulate in agreement with a random variate that $\sum \varepsilon = 0$, and ε has a Gaussian distribution with standard deviation $\sigma_\varepsilon \neq 0$. ε can also serve for an evaluation of the goodness-of-fit but the type of distribution for ε has no effect on the least square solution. However, the assumption that ε has a Gaussian distribution makes the task of establishing confidence limits or significance tests much easier. The value of ε and σ_ε gain importance in the analysis of variance.

Several other postulations for Y_j reduce the complexity of the system. It is customary to postulate that the observations are independent, and that the correct model has been chosen. Another prerequisite is that the data are typical. For predictions the validity of stationarity (homogeneity) in time or space is important. Under ideal conditions the predictors Y_j are known without error.

We can procure a set of least square estimators a_j by various mathematical techniques. Let us establish a matrix as given below. The summation in the terms of the matrix is taken over the total set of data, i.e., from $i = 1, \ldots, N$ (the subscript i is omitted for Z_i and Y_{ji}).

$$\mathbf{M}=\begin{bmatrix} 1 & \sum Z & \sum ZY_1 & \sum ZY_2 & \dots & \sum ZY_n \\ a_1 & N & \sum Y_1 & \sum Y_2 & \dots & \sum Y_n \\ a_2 & \sum Y_1 & \sum Y_1^2 & \sum Y_1 Y_2 & \dots & \sum Y_1 Y_n \\ \vdots & & & & & \vdots \\ a_n & \sum Y_n & \sum Y_1 Y_n & \sum Y_2 Y_n & \dots & \sum Y_n^2 \end{bmatrix} \tag{269a}$$

We call $||\mathbf{M}_{11}||$ the minor determinant*[1] (eliminating the first line and column) and $||\mathbf{M}_{a_j}||$ the cofactor (eliminating the line and column where a_j appears). We obtain the value of a_j by:

$$a_j=(-1)^{j-1}\mathbf{M}_{a_j}/\mathbf{M}_{11} \tag{269b}$$

Another solution is based on the diagonalization of a matrix. We write (omitting again the subscript i for Z_i and Y_{ji}):

$$\begin{bmatrix} Na_0 & + \; a_1 \sum Y_1 & + \; a_2 \sum Y_2 & + \; \dots a_n \sum Y_n \\ a_0 \sum Y_1 & a_1 \sum Y_1^2 & + \; a_2 \sum Y_1 Y_2 & + \dots a_n \sum Y_1 Y_n \\ a_0 \sum Y_2 & a_1 \sum Y_2 Y_1 & + \; a_2 \sum Y_2^2 & + \dots a_n \sum Y_2 Y_n \\ \vdots & & & \\ a_0 \sum Y_n & a_1 \sum Y_n Y_1 & + \; a_2 \sum Y_n Y_2 & + \; \dots a_n \sum Y_n^2 \end{bmatrix} = \begin{bmatrix} \sum Z \\ \sum ZY_1 \\ \sum ZY_2 \\ \\ \sum ZY_n \end{bmatrix} \tag{270a}$$

The matrix provides $n+1$ equations and $n+1$ coefficients. Diagonalization of the matrix permits us to determine every $n+1$ coefficient (see Essenwanger, 1976, p. 373).
Let us now assume that x_{ji} is a variable of an observation with reference to the mean value:

$$x_{ji}=Y_{ji}-\bar{Y}_j \tag{270b}$$

Then:

$$\sum_{i=1}^{N} x_{ji}=0 \tag{270c}$$

Now $a_0=\sum Z/N$ or $a_0=0$ for $z_i=Z_i-\bar{Z}$, i.e., we deduce from eq. 267a by summation over i and division by N:

$$a_0=\bar{Z}-a_1\bar{Y}_1-a_2\bar{Y}_2-\dots a_n\bar{Y}_n \tag{270d}$$

It shows that a_0 is $f(\bar{Z}_1 a_j, \bar{Y}_j)$ unless all $\bar{Y}_j$ and $\bar{Z}$ are zero. They would be substituted: $\bar{Z}=\bar{z}$ and $\bar{Y}_j=\bar{x}_j$. Otherwise a_0 depends on the number of terms. Systems where the coefficients are dependent on the number of terms are called non-orthogonal (see p. 134).
Let us reformulate eq. 267a after the assumptions of eq. 271a, b are substituted:

$$z_i=A_1x_{1i}+A_2x_{2i}+\dots+A_nx_{ni} \tag{267c}$$

$(\bar{z}=0)$

*[1] Although the determinant is denoted by $||\mathbf{M}||$ in various texts, and by $|\dots|$ when matrix elements are specified, for simplification the bars are omitted in cases where confusion does not result.

The coefficient matrix 269a is now reduced to:

$$\begin{bmatrix} 1 & 0 & \sum zx_1 & \sum zx_2 & \ldots & \sum zx_n \\ 0 & N & 0 & 0 & \ldots & 0 \\ A_2 & 0 & \sum x_1^2 & \sum x_1x_2 & \ldots & \sum x_1x_n \\ \vdots & \vdots & \vdots & & & \\ A_n & 0 & \sum x_1x_n & \sum x_2x_n & \ldots & \sum x_n^2 \end{bmatrix} \tag{271a}$$

Other techniques include the well-known Doolittle scheme (see NELSON, 1974), a method first established by Gauss and later modified by Doolittle (see DWYER, 1941). In this process the following matrix system is established:

$$\begin{bmatrix} \sigma_{11}^2 & \mathrm{Cov}_{12} & \mathrm{Cov}_{13} & \ldots & \mathrm{Cov}_{1n} & \mathrm{Cov}_{z_1} \\ . & \sigma_{22}^2 & \mathrm{Cov}_{23} & \ldots & \mathrm{Cov}_{2n} & \mathrm{Cov}_{z_2} \\ . & . & \sigma_{33}^2 & \ldots & \mathrm{Cov}_{3n} & \mathrm{Cov}_{z_3} \\ . & . & . & \ldots & . & . \\ . & . & . & \ldots & \sigma_{nn}^2 & \mathrm{Cov}_{z_n} \\ . & . & . & \ldots & . & \sigma_z^2 \end{bmatrix} \tag{271b}$$

where σ_{jj}^2 is the variance of the variate x_j and the covariance $\mathrm{Cov}_{x_jx_k}$ (see eq. 279a) is abbreviated by Cov_{jk} and Cov_{z_j} is Cov_{zx_j}. It can be readily verified that matrix 271b is obtained from 271a by rearrangement of the columns and rows after division of the elements by N.

Matrix 271b is now converted by a mathematical procedure (diagonalization) into the form:

$$\begin{bmatrix} 1.0 & c_{12} & c_{13} & \ldots & c_{1n} \\ 0 & 1.0 & c_{23} & \ldots & c_{2n} \\ 0 & 0 & 1.0 & \ldots & c_{3n} \\ . & . & . & \ldots & . \\ 0 & 0 & 0 & \ldots & 1.0 \end{bmatrix} = \begin{bmatrix} C_1 \\ C_2 \\ C_3 \\ . \\ C_n \end{bmatrix} \tag{271c}$$

where the c_{ij} are coefficients. Thus every row is an equation with one unknown. E.g.:

$$A_1+c_{12}A_2+c_{13}A_3+\ldots+c_{1n}A_n=C_1 \tag{271d}$$

and last:

$$A_n=C_n \tag{271e}$$

This conversion process is well-known in matrix algebra in the solution of linear equations. Details of it have also been described by the author (ESSENWANGER, 1976, p. 371).

(For an orthogonal scheme, i.e., $\mathrm{Cov}_{jk}=0$ and $c_{ij}=0$ for $j \neq k$ and $j \geq 2$, the coefficient A_j is simply $\mathrm{Cov}_{z_j}/\sigma^2_{jj}$; see also eq. 370b). A best linear unbiased estimator was suggested by SUZUKI et al. (1980b). NELSON (1976) described a least square estimate for a small number of points.

In recent times linear (or multiple) regression can be found more often in the atmospheric science because electronic data processing has aided the solution of the equation for larger n. E.g., OHTAKI (1977) applied regression analysis to predict probabilities of precipitations, DORMAN and BOURKE (1978) provided a quadratic correction term for temperature, RAO et al. (1979) derived a regression equation for precipitable water, and DYER (1977) utilized regression analysis for precipitation forecasting. These are only a few examples of recent applications of regression analysis.

The precėding discussion was centered on a linear relationship between Z, the dependent variate, and Y_j, the independent variates (eq. 267a). The recommended methods for the calculation of least square coefficients hold if some of the variates are replaced by terms of higher orders than their linear values that have been previously mentioned, e.g., $Y_i = \ln X$, etc. The entire problem becomes very complex, however.

An expansion to non-linear regression and the application of a Gauss-Newton iteration was illustrated by SHAKUN (1966). Weighted regression analysis was treated by JAESH (1966).

The calculation of coefficients is no problem with electronic data processing devices. The question in these linear relation schemes is the selection of the best set of variables from a number of choices. Procedures are available for most electronic data processing systems to select a limited number of variates (predictors) from any chosen original number, say 50 or more. The computational task can be reduced, however, if a number of variates (predictors) are selected on a scientific basis rather than a random selection or with the idea "the more the merrier".

It should be reiterated that the derivation of a non-zero association between Z_i and the set of Y_{ji} does not necessarily imply a causal relationship between the variables Y_j and Z.

Residual variance and percentage reduction

One additional measure is introduced. The dependent variable Z has a variance σ_Z^2. If the representation is perfect, this variance is exactly matched by the linear regression system, and $\sigma_\varepsilon^2 = \varepsilon_R^2$ is zero, where:

$$\varepsilon_R^2 = \sum (Z_i - \zeta_i)^2/N \tag{272a}$$

and:

$$\zeta_i = a_0 + a_1 x_{1i} + \ldots, a_m x_{mi}, \qquad m < n \tag{272b}$$

Therefore, ε_R^2 is called the residual variance or residual error, sometimes the left variance. For $\zeta_i = 0$ for all i's ε_R^2 becomes identical with the variance*[1] σ_Z^2. We can therefore define an "accounted" variance. "Explained" variance is sometimes used, but the author is in agreement with GUTTMAN (1977) that this terminology is meaningless because the

*[1] For certain curve fitting procedures this is the maximum which ε_R^2 can assume (ESSENWANGER, 1976).

achieved reduction in the variance does not "explain" anything. Accounted variance is given by:

$$\varepsilon_{\mathrm{AC}}^2 = \sigma_Z^2 - \varepsilon_{\mathrm{R}}^2 \qquad (273a)$$

The relative measure:

$$R_{\mathrm{R}}^2 = \varepsilon_{\mathrm{AC}}^2 / \sigma_Z^2 \qquad (273b)$$

is called the reduction and:

$$R_{\mathrm{PR}}^2 = R_{\mathrm{R}}^2 \cdot 100 \qquad (273c)$$

is the percentage reduction.
Both parameters, R_{PR}^2 and $\varepsilon_{\mathrm{R}}^2$, must be considered in evaluating the suitability of the linearized system (eq. 267a). Although we strive for $\varepsilon_{\mathrm{R}}^2$ to approach zero, a tolerable limit, say $\varepsilon_{\mathrm{R}}^2 \leq \varepsilon_L^2$, may suffice in practice. R_{R}^2 for this limit error ε_L^2 can then be determined by:

$$R_{\mathrm{R}}^2 = 1 - \varepsilon_L^2 / \sigma_Z^2 \qquad (273d)$$

The question "how far to go" has no simple answer but several suggestions for an "objective" criterion have been made (see Anscombe and Tukey, 1963; Anscombe, 1967). Let us go back to eq. 272a which defines $\varepsilon_{\mathrm{R}}^2$. For n terms in eq. 282 we write $\varepsilon_{\mathrm{R}_n}^2$. Tukey (1977) suggested to calculate a test criterion:

$$\varepsilon_{\mathrm{T}_n}^2 = N\varepsilon_{\mathrm{R}_n}^2 / \nu = \sum (Z_i - \zeta_i)^2 / \nu \qquad (274a)$$

The addition of terms is continued until $\varepsilon_{\mathrm{T}_{n+1}}^2 > \varepsilon_{\mathrm{T}_n}^2$, which minimizes $\varepsilon_{\mathrm{T}_n}^2$. The degrees of freedom $\nu = N - n$ (see eq. 267b). Tukey's rule assumes independence of the predictors Y_j. Mallow (1973) modified this criterion to minimize:

$$\varepsilon_{\mathrm{M}_n}^2 = (1 + n/N) N \varepsilon_{\mathrm{R}_n}^2 / \nu \qquad (274b)$$

which behaves like Tukey's rule for small n. Mallow's subset has the larger n (or the smaller ν).
Another method is to minimize:

$$\varepsilon_n^2 = N\varepsilon_{\mathrm{R}_n}^2 / \nu^2 \qquad (274c)$$

Correlations

Linear correlation

The number of variates Y_j was not restricted in eq. 267a. Let us now limit the variates (predictors) to one Y (the subscript will be omitted). This reduces eq. 267b to:

$$Z_i = a_0 + a_1 Y_i \qquad (275a)$$

or for $a_0 = 0$ to:

$$Z_i = a_1 Y_i \qquad (275b)$$

The following coefficient matrix can be established (summation over i from 1, ..., N):

$$\mathbf{M}=\begin{bmatrix} 1 & \sum Z & \sum ZY \\ 0 & N & \sum Y \\ a_1 & \sum Y & \sum Y^2 \end{bmatrix} \text{ or } \begin{bmatrix} 1 & 0 & \sum ZY \\ 0 & N & 0 \\ A_1 & 0 & \sum Y^2 \end{bmatrix} \tag{276}$$

$$a_1=\begin{vmatrix} \sum Z & \sum ZY \\ N & \sum Y \end{vmatrix} \Big/ \begin{vmatrix} N & \sum Y \\ \sum Y & \sum Y^2 \end{vmatrix} \tag{277a}$$

or for $x_i=Y_i-\bar{Y}$ and $z_i=Z_i-\bar{Z}$:

$$A_1=-\mathbf{M}_{A_2}/\mathbf{M}_{11}=-\begin{vmatrix} 0 & \sum ZX \\ N & 0 \end{vmatrix} \Big/ \begin{vmatrix} N & 0 \\ 0 & \sum X^2 \end{vmatrix} \tag{277b}$$

This leaves:

$$A_1=\frac{\sum Z_i x_i}{\sum x^2}=\frac{\sum z_i x_i}{N\cdot\sigma_x^2}=r\sigma_z/\sigma_x=r\sigma_Z/\sigma_Y \tag{277c}$$

$$a_1=[(\sum Z)(\sum Y)-N\sum ZY]/[N\sum Y^2-(\sum Y)^2] \tag{277d}$$

(r is defined in eq. 280a.)

Let us rewrite eq. 275b by introducing a normalized variable and substituting for A_1:

$$z_i=A_1 x_i=\left(\frac{\sum z_i x_i}{N\sigma_x^2}\right) x_i=\frac{r\sigma_z}{\sigma_x}\cdot x_i \tag{278}$$

where $\sum z_i x_i$ is the mixed moment. We define the covariance:

$$\mathrm{Cov}_{zs}=v_{zx}=\sum zx/N \tag{279}$$

(Notice: in some texts the covariance is defined as $\sum zY$, which in our notation is $N\,\mathrm{Cov}_{zY}$.) This leads to the definition of a "coefficient of correlation":

$$r_{zx}=r=\frac{\mathrm{Cov}_{zx}}{\sigma_z\sigma_x}=\frac{\sum zY}{N\cdot\sigma_Z\sigma_Y} \tag{280a}$$

which is called the "linear" correlation coefficient but it is not necessarily dependent on the concept of regression. It is found under various equivalent forms. For the two variables Z and Y we may write in unabridged form:

$$r=\frac{\sum(Z-Z_m)(Y-Y_m)}{\sqrt{\sum(Z-Z_m)^2\sum(Y-Y_m)^2}}=\frac{\sum(Z-Z_m)Y}{\sqrt{\sum(Z-Z_m)^2\sum(Y-Y_m)^2}} \tag{280b}$$

The right part of eq. 280b discloses that only one variable must be given with reference to the mean value. Another form of the correlation coefficient can be found as:

$$r_{ZY}=\frac{(\sum Z_i Y_i)-NZ_m Y_m}{\sqrt{(\sum Z^2-NZ_m^2)(\sum Y^2-NY_m^2)}}=\frac{\mathrm{Cov}_{ZY}-Z_m Y_m}{\sigma_Z\sigma_Y} \tag{280c}$$

where:

$$\mathrm{Cov}_{ZY}=\sum Z_i Y_i/N=\eta_{ZY} \tag{280d}$$

is the non-central mixed moment.

Introducing the correlation coefficient into eq. 278a we obtain:

$$Z_i/\sigma_Z = r \cdot Y_i/\sigma_Y = r x_i/\sigma_x \tag{281a}$$

or:

$$\frac{Z_i - Z_m}{\sigma_Z} = r\frac{Y_i - Y_m}{\sigma_Y} \tag{281b}$$

Consequently:

$$Z_i = r(\sigma_Z/\sigma_Y)Y_i - r(\sigma_Z/\sigma_Y)Y_m + Z_m \tag{281c}$$

This is the linear relationship of eq. 275a with eq. 267a:

$$a_0 = Z_m - r(\sigma_Z/\sigma_Y)Y_m \tag{281d}$$

and:

$$a_1 = r(\sigma_Z/\sigma_Y) = A_1 \tag{281e}$$

Sometimes the following form of the correlation coefficient, expressed by the variance of the variables X_1 and X_2 and their differences, may be very handy:

$$r = r_{12} = \frac{\sigma_{X_1}^2 + \sigma_{X_2}^2 - \sigma_{(X_1 - X_2)}^2}{2\sigma_{X_1}\sigma_{X_2}} \tag{282}$$

The residual variance (error) can be derived from eq. 372a:

$$\varepsilon_R^2 = \sigma_Z^2(1 - r_{12}^2) \tag{283}$$

We can readily verify the limits of the correlation coefficient from this equation. If $r^2 = |1|$, the residual variance is zero and there is a perfect match. Hence:

$$-1 \leq r_{12} \leq 1 \tag{284}$$

As expected, the maximum ε_R^2 is σ_Z^2 for $r_{12} = 0$. This implies that the error variance cannot be larger than the dispersion of the dependent variable.
Sometimes a coefficient of alienation is defined by:

$$c_a = \sqrt{1 - r_{12}^2} \tag{285}$$

Tests for the significance of the correlation coefficient are discussed (eqs. 622a and 641c). Most of today's correlation analysis is performed by electronic data processing and short methods for computations are less important. If electronic data processing is not available reductions and simplifications in the numerical calculations can be made as follows. The process results in little loss of accuracy but saves considerable time and eases the numerical calculation.
The goal is to obtain numerical values which can be easily multiplied and squared. The original series is converted into whole numbers by taking $(Y_{max} - Y_{min})/20 = \Delta Y$, and selected $d \sim \Delta Y$ as the closest whole number. The original series is transformed into:

$$y_i = (Y_i - Y_{min})/d - 10 \tag{286a}$$

and y_i is truncated to whole numbers. Now the data set comprises only numbers ranging from -10 to $+10$. According to eq. 280b one variable is required to be given with reference to the mean. A second transformation with y_m as a whole number from eq. 286a can be performed:

$$\eta_i = y_i - y_m \tag{286b}$$

which leaves a manageable series of η_i. The second variable (e.g., Z) can be transformed in like manner if necessary. Examples for the calculation of the correlation coefficient are given at the end of the section.

We have introduced a first straight (linear) correlation line designated by eqs. 281a, b, c or 275a. However, the problem can be considered from a second point of view and exchange predictor and predictand. This provides a second line:

$$Y_i = b_0 + b_1 Z_i \tag{287a}$$

or:

$$x_i = B_0 + B_1 z_i \tag{287b}$$

with the coefficient:

$$B_1 = \frac{\sum x_i Z_i}{N\sigma_Z^2} = r_{21}\frac{\sigma_x}{\sigma_z} = r_{YZ}\frac{\sigma_Y}{\sigma_Z} \tag{288}$$

and with eq. 281a:

$$\frac{x_i}{\sigma_x} = r_{21}\frac{z_i}{\sigma_z} \tag{289}$$

In our case:

$$r = r_{12} = r_{21} = r_{YZ} = r_{ZY} \tag{290}$$

The difference between eqs. 289 and 281a is the reciprocal use of the correlation coefficient in eq. 289 compared with eq. 281a. The two resulting correlation lines coincide only when $r_{12} = \pm 1$. For $\sigma_Z = \sigma_Y$ and the correlation $r = 1$ the (linear) correlation line shows a 45° angle to either abscissa or ordinate. Otherwise the angle is determined by the ratio of σ_Z/σ_Y (or σ_Y/σ_Z) and for $r = 1$ by A_1 or B_1. For $r = 0$ the two correlation lines run parallel to the abscissa and ordinate.

The reader is cautioned again that correlation does not mean a causal relationship.

Autocorrelation

The correlation of a set of observations with themselves is called autocorrelation. Then $Z_i = X_i$ and $Y_i = X_{i+j}$, $i = 1, \ldots, N$; where $i + j \leq N$. For the autocorrelation the following simplifying approximation can be made for a long series of data:

$$\sigma_Z = \sigma_Y = \sigma_X \tag{291}$$

This leads to the autocorrelation coefficient:

$$r_j = \frac{\mathrm{Cov}_{x_1 x_{1+j}}}{\sigma_{X_i}\sigma_{X_{i+j}}} = \frac{\mathrm{Cov}_{x_1, x_{1+j}}}{\sigma_X^2} = \frac{\sum x_i \cdot x_{i+j}}{N\sigma_X^2} \tag{292a}$$

Because j is called the lag, the autocorrelation is sometimes referred to as the lag correlation. The autocorrelation can be very rapidly computed from the difference form (eq. 282) which can be reformulated:

$$r_j = 1 - \sigma_j^2/(2\sigma_X^2) \tag{292b}$$

where:

$$\sigma_j^2 = \sum (X_i - X_{i+j})^2/N \tag{292c}$$

Since the variance σ_0^2 for the differences of lag 0 is zero, the lag correlation for lag 0 is $r_0 = 1$.

Example 23. The first 300 autocorrelations have been calculated for a special set of 3980 data, the digital recording of the u component of the wind speed in 1-s intervals at Huntsville, Alabama at 2 m height. Table XXXIII provides an excerpt from the computations. The example illustrates that eq. 291 may not be rigidly valid in practical applications to meteorological time series although the differences are small. The largest deviation (at lag 300) shows about a 5% difference between the standard deviations $S_{1,300}$ and $S_{2,300}$ and about 10% between the respective variances. The differences from σ_Z are smaller (see Table XXXIII, last two columns).

Spurious correlation

Another word of caution is added. The reader should not draw hasty conclusions from a high correlation. The correlation does not provide the reason why the variables are correlated. A typical example is the so-called spurious correlation. Assume, we have a variable X_1 and a second variable $X_2 = X_1 + X_3$. The correlation coefficient becomes:

$$r_{X_1X_2} = (\sigma_{X_1}^2 + \sigma_{X_2}\sigma_{X_3} r_{X_1X_3})[\sigma_{X_1}\sqrt{(\sigma_{X_1}^2 + \sigma_{X_3}^2 + 2\sigma_{X_1}\sigma_{X_3} r_{X_1X_3})}]^{-1} \tag{293a}$$

If X_1 and X_3 are not correlated ($r_{X_1X_3} = 0$) then $r_{X_1X_2} = 0.7$ with equal variance $\sigma_{X_1}^2 = \sigma_{X_3}^2$, i.e.:

$$r_{X_1X_2} = \sigma_{X_1}/\sqrt{\sigma_{X_1}^2 + \sigma_{X_3}^2} = 1/\sqrt{2} \sim 0.71 \tag{293b}$$

TABLE XXXIII

AUTOCORRELATION OF THE *u*-COMPONENT OF THE WIND

Lag i	N_i	r_i	$S_{1,i}$	$S_{2,i}$	$S_{1,0} - S_{1,i}$	$(S_{1,0} - S_{1,i})/S_{1,0}$ (%)
0	3980	1.0	0.7676	0.7676	–	–
1	3979	0.967	0.7675	0.7677	0.0001	0.01
2	3978	0.930	0.7673	0.7678	0.0003	0.04
3	3977	0.902	0.7671	0.7679	0.0005	0.06
4	3976	0.874	0.7668	0.7680	0.0008	0.10
5	3975	0.851	0.7665	0.7681	0.0011	0.14
10	3970	0.745	0.766	0.769	0.0016	0.21
50	3930	0.861	0.761	0.772	0.0066	0.86
100	3880	0.208	0.758	0.776	0.0096	1.25
200	3780	0.093	0.751	0.782	0.0166	2.16
300	3680	0.096	0.754	0.789	0.0136	1.77

$S_{1,i}$ = standard deviation for data set $x_1, \ldots, x_{N_i}$ (i.e. σ_x estimator)
$S_{2,i}$ = standard deviation for data set $x_{1+i}, \ldots, x_{3980}$ (i.e. σ_Y estimator)

This "spurious correlation coefficient" is a function of the variance ratio between the two uncorrelated variables X_1 and X_3. Testing for statistical significance at the 95% level renders that $r=0.7$ is significant for $N \geq 9$. In our case the high correlation is achieved by the inclusion of the first variable in the second variable, however.
Sometimes we may not find a simple addition $X_2 = X_1 + X_3$ but rather $X_2 = w_1 X_1 + w_2 X_3$ which is a weighted combination. Then for $r_{X_1X_3}=0$ we find:

$$r_{X_1X_2} = w_1\sigma_{X_1}/\sqrt{(w_1\sigma^2_{X_1} + w_2\sigma^2_{X_3})} \tag{294a}$$

The spurious correlation for $r_{X_1X_3} \neq 0$ is:

$$r_{X_1X_2} = (w_1\sigma^2_{X_1} + w_2\sigma_{X_1}\sigma_{X_3}r_{X_1X_3})[\sigma_{X_1}\sqrt{w_1^2\sigma^2_{X_1} + w_2^2\sigma^2_{X_3} + 2w_1w_2\sigma_{X_1}\sigma_{X_3}r_{X_1X_3}}]^{-1} \tag{294b}$$

Rank correlation, correlation of attributes

In the previous sections we have dealt with random variables X_i and Y_i. Assume that we do not have a continuous variable but want to treat an element which can only be ranked such as the color of clouds. Then we would also rank the second variable and compute the correlation 280a:

$$r_s = 1 - \frac{6\sum \Delta_i^2}{N(N^2-1)} \tag{295a}$$

As customary, N designates the number of pairs and Δ_i denotes the differences between ranks of corresponding X and Y values. The formula is called Spearman's rank correlation. If there are ties in the ranking, we assign the mean rank of the group. (Ordinarily r would then need a small correction which is less than 0.018 and is generally neglected.)
Another correlation is sometimes sought for attributes which can only be given in classes of a contingency table (such as the various forms of precipitation, rain, snow, shower, thunderstorm, etc.). We define for a table $m \times m$:

$$r_a = \sqrt{\frac{\chi^2}{N(m-1)}} \tag{295b}$$

and χ^2 is defined by eq. 645.
Details on χ^2 are presented on p. 281. For a 2×2 contingency table r_a is often called the tetrachoric correlation.
The exact distribution of Spearman's r_a was recently analyzed by Henze (1979). Critical values of the rank correlation coefficient were calculated by Otten (1973).

The correlation coefficient as a measure of collinearity

Katz (1975) pointed out that the beginning student of statistical analysis may encounter difficulties in understanding the concepts of the correlation coefficient. He suggested to consider the general form of lines in the $x-y$ plane:

$$A_x + B_y + C = 0 \tag{296a}$$

Particular values of A, B, C are sought for which the mean of the squares of the orthogonal distances (MSOD) is a minimum. Now:

$$\text{MSOD}=E[(A_x+B_y+C)^2/(A^2+B^2)] \tag{296b}$$

Consequently $C=0$ for MSOD to be a minimum. Katz showed that MSOD is a minimum for:

$$\text{MSOD}=1-|E(xy)| \tag{296c}$$

but the slope information is lost by taking the absolute value. For two more reasons (see Katz):

$$r=E(xy)=\text{Cov }(xy)/\sigma_x\sigma_y \tag{296d}$$

When $r=0$, MSOD$=1$ for all A and B. Consequently, all lines through the origin provide the least square solution which implies a collinearity of zero.

Linear relationship between climatological stations

In climatological data analysis often the problem arises that threshold values (such as percentiles) must be derived for locations where only a short period of record exists or no data are available but neighboring stations in the same region of homogeneous climate may have inadequate records. The reader may conclude that it is simple to include these neighboring stations by establishing a linear relationship. Let us examine this.
We assume that the task is a prediction of the data set ξ_i at Station A by utilizing η_i, the short record at location A, and another auxiliary data set U_i with a long period of record. Assume that for a specified threshold (subscript th) of the cumulative distribution the probabilities are related, i.e.:

$$P(\xi\leq\xi_{\text{th}})=P(\eta\geq\eta_{\text{th}})=P(U\geq U_{\text{th}}) \tag{297}$$

The following two linear relationships are obvious, with scale parameter β and location parameter γ:

$$\xi_i=\beta_1 U_i+\gamma_1 \tag{298a}$$

$$\eta_i=\beta_2 U_i+\gamma_2 \tag{298b}$$

Under customary rules these are linear equations of the form:

$$Z=a_0+a_1 Y \tag{299}$$

and the least square solution requires:

$$a_0=\bar{Z} \tag{300a}$$

$$a_1=r_{YZ}\sigma_Z/\sigma_Y \tag{300b}$$

provided that Y is $y-\bar{y}$ and r is the linear correlation coefficient.
Sneyers (1969) called attention to the fact that in this case the least square solution is not the most suitable method for the estimators a_0 and a_1. Let us assume we predict Z from Y. Then the variance of Z is reduced for $r<1$ because $\sum(Z-\bar{Z})^2/N\geq r^2\sigma_Z^2$. Although this reduction is acceptable in the concept of predicting Z from Y, in our case we must assume

that $r=1$, which implies:

$$a_1 = \sigma_z/\sigma_y \tag{300c}$$

In other words: we seek a solution where Z and Y are exactly matched except for a scaling factor defined by the ratio of the standard deviation.
We establish now a relationship between ξ_i, the predicted value from η_i, the short series, by eliminating the auxiliary set U:

$$\xi_i = (\beta_1/\beta_2)\eta_i + \gamma_1 - (\beta_1/\beta_2)\gamma_2 \tag{298c}$$

or:

$$\xi_i = a_1^*\eta_i + a_0^* \tag{298d}$$

Sneyers recommended:

$$a_1^* = \hat{b}_1/\hat{b}_2 \tag{301a}$$

$$a_0^* = \hat{c}_1 - a_1^*\hat{c}_2 \tag{301b}$$

where $\hat{b}_1$, $\hat{b}_2$, $\hat{c}_1$, $\hat{c}_2$ are unbiased estimators for β_1, β_2, γ_1, γ_2. E.g., $\hat{b}_1 = \hat{s}_\xi/\hat{s}_U$ and $c_1 = \bar{\xi}$ (see unbiased estimators of the standard deviation (see eq. 48a)).
SNEYERS (1969) also disclosed that a second set of estimators is possible if b_2 and γ_2 are known parameters:

$$\hat{a}_1 = \hat{b}_1/b_2 \tag{301c}$$

$$\hat{a}_0 = \hat{\gamma}_1 - \hat{a}_1\gamma_2 \tag{301d}$$

According to his findings, the set of eq. 301a, b should be preferred if $|r_{\xi\eta}| > r_c$. Sneyers recommended in the case of a bivariate Gaussian distribution $r_c = 1/\sqrt{2}$ for a_1 and $0.5 \leq r_c \leq \sqrt{0.5}$ for a_0. If $\hat{b}_1$, $\hat{b}_2$, $\hat{c}_1$ and $\hat{c}_2$ are linear estimates he suggested an approximate $r_c \sim 0.5$ for both a_1 and a_0 but pointed out that r may be unknown. In order to reduce the possibility of making a wrong decision he advised to use the median r which can be obtained from Fisher's z transformation (see eq. 640a).
After the discussion of the above statistical background, Sneyers concluded that in practical use it is more advantageous to base the prediction on U, the auxiliary variate (see eq. 298a). He suggested:

$$\xi_i = \hat{b}_1 U_i + \hat{c}_1 \tag{302a}$$

or:

$$\xi_i = b_1^* U_i + c_1^* \tag{302b}$$

where $\hat{b}_1$ and $\hat{c}_1$ are the ordinary estimators, and with known b_2 and c_2:

$$b_1^* = \hat{b}_1(b_2/\hat{b}_2) \tag{303a}$$

$$c_1^* = \hat{c}_1 + a_1^*(c_2 - \hat{c}_2) \tag{303b}$$

Sneyers listed the error variance of b_1^* and c_1^* (bivariate Gaussian case):

$$\varepsilon_{b_1^*}^2 = 2(1-r^2)\varepsilon_{\hat{b}_1}^2 \tag{303c}$$

$$\varepsilon_{c_1^*}^2 = 2(1-r)\varepsilon_{\hat{c}_1}^2 \qquad (303d)$$

which shows that for $r^2 > 0.5$ the error variance is $\varepsilon_{b_1^*}^2 < \varepsilon_{\hat{b}_1}^2$; and $\varepsilon_{c_1^*}^2 < \varepsilon_{\hat{c}_1}^2$ for $r > 0.5$.
SNEYERS (1969) also addressed the problem of incorporating areal data. This method applies when no records for Station A are available. We can derive r which is needed for a decision on the set of estimators $r_a = r(d,y)$ where d is the distance and y the angle. Usually:

$$r_a = r_0 - k_1 d \qquad (304a)$$

where r_0 and k_1 are constants to be derived by the least square method. Furthermore:

$$b_a = b_0 - k_2 d \qquad (304b)$$

Again, this is an ordinary linear equation. From b_a an area coefficient a_1 can be procured (eqs. 300c and 301a, c). Then:

$$c_i^* = \hat{c}_1 + a_{1i}(c_2 - \hat{c}_2) \qquad (304c)$$

$$c_i = \hat{c}_1 + a_{1i} r_a (c_2 - \hat{c}_2) \qquad (304d)$$

For additional details the reader is referred to SNEYERS (1969).

Multiple correlation

The relationship of two variables was extensively discussed in the preceding section because it forms the basis for the expansion to more variables. We face two problems, however, the determination of the coefficients of the correlation (regression) equation and the definition of a correlation coefficient.
We find the coefficients $a_2, \ldots, a_n$ or $A_2, \ldots, A_n$ by solving the matrix of Y_i or its counterpart of x_j, eqs. 269a or 271a. The process was discussed in eq. 271c.
The definition of a correlation coefficient is aided by establishing a symmetrical correlation matrix as follows:

$$\mathbf{C}_r = \begin{bmatrix} 1 & r_{12} & \cdots & & r_{1p} \\ r_{12} & 1 & \cdots & & r_{2p} \\ \vdots & \vdots & \ddots & & \vdots \\ r_{1,p-1} & & & & r_{p,p-1} \\ r_{1p} & r_{2p} & \cdots & r_{p-1,p} & 1 \end{bmatrix} \qquad (305)$$

This leads to two types of correlation coefficients: a partial and a total correlation coefficient. The partial correlation coefficient represents the relationship between two variables when the effect of the other variables has been removed. The total correlation coefficient stands for the total (linear) relationship between the predictand and the predictors.
The following equations define the (linear) correlation coefficients. The partial correlation coefficient is given by:

$$r_{n_1 n_2, n_3 \ldots n_p} = -\frac{\mathbf{C}_{n_1 n_2}}{(\mathbf{C}_{n_1 n_1}\mathbf{C}_{n_2 n_2})^{1/2}} \qquad (306)$$

The sign of $\mathbf{C}_{n_1 n_2}$ depends on $(-1)^{n_j \cdot n_k}$, thus eq. 306 assumes a positive sign for $\mathbf{C}_{12}$. $\mathbf{C}_{jk}$ is the cofactor (see definition 269a of the (j,k)th element) and $n_1, \ldots, n_p$ represent the subscripts of the variables, where n_1 and $n_2 = n_3, \ldots, n_n$.
The total correlation coefficient is obtained from:

$$R^2_{n_1}(n_2, \ldots, n_p) = 1 - \frac{\mathbf{C}}{\mathbf{C}_{n_1 n_1}} \tag{307}$$

In general, a multivariate Gaussian distribution is assumed. SUZUKI (1966) has studied some modifications of the correlation coefficient for different types of distribution forms, largely the multivariate binomial distribution.

Three variables

A detailed derivation for three variables will be omitted, but some results follow:

$$Z_i = a_0 + a_i Y_{1i} + a_2 Y_{2i} \tag{308a}$$

or:

$$x_{1i} = A_2 x_{2i} + A_3 x_{3i} \tag{308b}$$

with $x_{1i} = Z_i - \bar{Z}$ and $Y_{ji} - \bar{Y}_j = x_{j+1,i}, j = 1,2$.
In the following the letter x is omitted and only the subscript of the variate x is used.

$$A_2 = \frac{\sigma_1}{\sigma_2} \frac{(r_{12} - r_{13} r_{23})}{(1 - r^2_{23})} = \frac{\sigma_1}{\sigma_2} r_{12.3} \sqrt{\frac{1 - r^2_{13}}{1 - r^2_{23}}} \tag{309a}$$

$$A_2 = \frac{\sigma_1}{\sigma_3} \frac{(r_{13} - r_{12} r_{23})}{(1 - r^2_{23})} = \frac{\sigma_1}{\sigma_3} r_{13.2} \sqrt{\frac{1 - r^2_{12}}{1 - r^2_{23}}} \tag{309b}$$

The partial coefficients are obtained by correlating $X_1 - A_{13} X_3$ with $X_2 - A_{23} X_3$, etc. where A_{13}, A_{23} are sometimes called "conditional" coefficients.
Partial correlations are given by:

$$r_{12.3} = \frac{-\mathbf{C}_{12}}{(\mathbf{C}_{11}\mathbf{C}_{22})^{1/2}} = \frac{r_{12} - r_{13} r_{23}}{[(1 - r^2_{13})(1 - r^2_{23})]^{1/2}} \tag{310a}$$

$$r_{23.1} = \frac{-\mathbf{C}_{23}}{(\mathbf{C}_{22}\mathbf{C}_{33})^{1/2}} = \frac{r_{23} - r_{12} r_{13}}{[(1 - r^2_{12})(1 - r^2_{13})]^{1/2}} \tag{310b}$$

$$r_{13.2} = \frac{-\mathbf{C}_{13}}{(\mathbf{C}_{11}\mathbf{C}_{33})^{1/2}} = \frac{r_{13} - r_{12} r_{23}}{[(1 - r^2_{12})(1 - r^2_{23})]^{1/2}} \tag{310c}$$

Total correlation coefficients:

$$R^2_{1.23} = 1 - \frac{\begin{vmatrix} 1 & r_{12} & r_{13} \\ r_{12} & 1 & r_{23} \\ r_{13} & r_{23} & 1 \end{vmatrix}}{(1 - r^2_{23})} = \frac{r_{12}(r_{12} - r_{13} r_{23})}{(1 - r^2_{23})} + \frac{r_{13}(r_{13} - r_{12} r_{23})}{(1 - r^2_{23})} \tag{311a}$$

$$R^2_{1.23} = (r^2_{12} + r^2_{13} - 2 r_{12} r_{13} r_{23})/(1 - r^2_{23}) \tag{311b}$$

or:

$$1-R_{1.23}^2=(1-r_{12}^2)(1-r_{13.2}^2) \tag{311c}$$

The residual variance for the total correlation coefficient is:

$$\varepsilon_R^2=\sigma_1^2(1-R_{1.23}^2) \tag{312a}$$

Introducing eq. 311c associates ε_R^2 with the partial correlation coefficient:

$$\varepsilon_R^2=\sigma_1^2(1-r_{13}^2)(1-r_{12.3}^2) \tag{312b}$$

Defining a partial residual variance:

$$\varepsilon_{R_{1.23}}^2=\sigma_1^2(1-r_{12.3}^2) \tag{312c}$$

provides the relationship:

$$\varepsilon_{R_{1.23}}^2=\varepsilon_R^2/(1-r_{13}^2) \tag{312d}$$

Consequently, the partial residual variance is $\varepsilon_{1.23}^2$ larger than the total variance ε_R^2 for $r_{13}^2 \neq 0$; and both are equal when no correlation between variables X_1 and X_3 exists. This is logical because the relationship is then based on the variables X_1 and X_2 only. The partial residual variance, eliminating the influence of X_3, discloses all that can be gained by the variables.

In turn eq. 312d implies that some reduction of the variance will be achieved with any existing correlation between X_1 and X_3 except if the correlation between X_1 and X_3 is inversely proportional to the correlation between X_2 and X_3.

Four variables

Although expressions for four variables can be readily derived from the general matrix (305), various important applications in meteorology such as the correlation of two wind vectors (with two components each) justify a more detailed discussion.

Again, let us assume the system:

$$x_{1i}=A_2x_{2i}+A_3x_{3i}+A_4x_{4i} \tag{313}$$

which is obtained from eq. 267c as specified and expanded in eq. 308b.

The coefficients can be derived from the matrix:

$$\mathbf{M}=\begin{bmatrix} 1 & 0 & \sum x_1x_2 & \sum x_1x_3 & \sum x_1x_4 \\ 0 & N & 0 & 0 & 0 \\ A_2 & 0 & \sum x_2^2 & \sum x_2x_3 & \sum x_2x_4 \\ A_3 & 0 & \sum x_2x_3 & \sum x_3^2 & \sum x_3x_4 \\ A_4 & 0 & \sum x_2x_4 & \sum x_3x_4 & \sum x_4^2 \end{bmatrix} \tag{314}$$

The coefficients can be computed (see eq. 269b) by:

$$A_j=(-1)^{j-1}\mathbf{M}_{A_j}/\mathbf{M}_{11} \tag{315}$$

Again, partial correlation coefficients are derived from a correlation matrix (305). The reader may observe that all partial coefficients which exist for three variables were presented by eq. 310 but any permutation of three variables (e.g., 1, 2 and 4) can be based on these equations. The total coefficient for any choice of three variables is also applicable. More interesting, however, is the combination of all four variables. The partial correlation coefficient is defined by:

$$r_{12.34} = -\frac{\mathbf{C}_{12}}{(\mathbf{C}_{11}\mathbf{C}_{22})^{1/2}} \tag{316}$$

The following equivalency, which can be expanded for other combinations, may be useful:

$$r_{12.34} = r_{12.43} = r_{21.34} = r_{21.43} \tag{317}$$

Although only one of these partial coefficients needs to be computed, eq. 317 may serve as a check.
The total correlation coefficients can be deduced:

$$R^2_{1.234} = 1 - \frac{\mathbf{C}_4}{\mathbf{C}_{11}} \tag{318a}$$

where $\mathbf{C}_4$ stands for the correlation matrix of four variables (i.e., eq. 305 limited to four variables). The subscripts 2 through 4 are mutually interchangeable, as can be seen from the complete form:

$$R^2_{1.234} = (a - 2b + 2c)/d \tag{318b}$$

$$a = (r^2_{12} + r^2_{13} + r^2_{14}) - (r^2_{12}r^2_{34} + r^2_{23}r^2_{14} + r^2_{24}r^2_{13}) \tag{319a}$$

$$b = (r_{12}r_{13}r_{23} + r_{12}r_{14}r_{24} + r_{13}r_{14}r_{34}) \tag{319b}$$

$$c = (r_{12}r_{14}r_{23}r_{34} + r_{12}r_{13}r_{24}r_{34} + r_{13}r_{14}r_{23}r_{24}) \tag{319c}$$

$$d = 1 - (r^2_{23} + r^2_{24} + r^2_{34}) + 2r_{23}r_{24}r_{34} \tag{319d}$$

Equivalent to eq. 311b we may write:

$$1 - R^2_{1.234} = (1 - r^2_{12})(1 - r^2_{13.2})(1 - r^2_{14.23}) \tag{320}$$

and:

$$A_2 = \frac{\sigma_1}{\sigma_2} r_{12} \frac{(1 - r^2_{34}) - r_{13}r_{23} - r_{14}r_{24} + r_{13}r_{24}r_{34} + r_{14}r_{23}r_{34}}{(1 - r^2_{23} - r^2_{24} - r^2_{34} + 2r_{23}r_{24}r_{34})} \tag{321}$$

The residual variance becomes:

$$\varepsilon^2_R = \sigma^2_1(1 - R^2_{1.234}) \tag{322a}$$

It is readily deduced from eq. 312d that the residual variance for the partial correlation is:

$$\varepsilon^2_{R_m} = \varepsilon^2_R[(1 - r^2_{12})(1 - r^2_{13.2})]^{-1} \tag{322b}$$

where m designates the partial elements involved (e.g., $m = 1.234$). Example 24 illustrates the calculations.

Conditional correlations and partial correlations

FLEISS and TANUR (1971) analyzed the effect between two random variables Z and Y_1 which are correlated because Z and Y_2 and Y_1 and Y_2 are correlated. In such cases, the partial correlation is of value because by definition it vanishes. This example may also elucidate the meaning of partial correlation coefficient.
The partial coefficient (eq. 310a) is:

$$r_{ZY_1 \cdot Y_2} = (r_{ZY_1} - r_{ZY_2} r_{Y_1 Y_2}) / [(1 - r^2_{ZY_2})(1 - r^2_{Y_2 Y_3})] \tag{323a}$$

or in a version of conditional probabilities:

$$\rho_{ZY_1 \cdot Y_2} = \frac{E(ZY_1 | Y_2 - E(Z | Y_2) E(Y_1 | Y_2)}{[E(Z^2 | Y_2) - (E^2(Z | Y_2)]^{1/2} [E(Y_1^2 | Y_2) - E^2(Y_1 | Y_2)]^{1/2}} \tag{323b}$$

Let us assume a first system:

$$Z = aU + bY_2 \tag{324a}$$

$$Y_1 = cV + dY_2 \tag{324b}$$

thus both Z and Y_1 depend on Y_2; a, b, c, d are constants, $ac > 0$. A second system of linear relation could be:

$$Z = aUY_2 + b \tag{325a}$$

$$Y_1 = cVY_2 + d \tag{325b}$$

Although U and V can be independent of Y_2 they may be correlated (i.e., $r_{UV} \neq 0$). Both systems require a correlation between Z and Y_1 because U and V are correlated and are associated with Y_2. Eq. 323a renders for both eqs. 324 and 325 $r_{ZY_1 \cdot Y_2} = r_{UV}$.
Now assume $r_{UV} = 0$. Then eq. 323a will be zero. LAWRENCE (1976) defined a conditional correlation:

$$r_{Z,Y_1|Y_2} = \frac{E_{Z,Y_1|Y_2}([Z - E(Z|Y_2)][Y_1 - E(Z|Y_2)])}{E_{Z|Y_2}([Z - E(Z|Y_2)]^2) E_{Y_1|Y_2}([E_{Y_1} - E(Y_1|Y_2)]^2)} \tag{326}$$

These two correlations eq. 326 and eq. 323b are not necessarily equal in the case of linearity. They are only equal if the conditional variances and covariances of Z and Y_2 are free of Y_2.

The canonical correlation

Definition

The canonical correlation deals with correlations after a linear transformation of coordinates through which certain correlations between variates will be made zero. Let us assume we have two data sets X_{ji}, Y_{ki}, $j = 1, \ldots, n_x$, $k = 1, \ldots, n_y$, where n_x and n_y do not necessarily have to be equal, and $i = 1, \ldots, N$. We assume a linear transformation into ξ_{ji}, η_{ji}. In vector notations:

$$\mathbf{X} \cdot \boldsymbol{h} = \xi \tag{327a}$$

$$\mathbf{Y}\cdot\boldsymbol{k}=\boldsymbol{\eta} \tag{327b}$$

where $\boldsymbol{\xi}$ and $\boldsymbol{\eta}$ are column vectors (N observations), $\boldsymbol{h}$ and $\boldsymbol{k}$ are coefficient vectors of n_x and n_y elements, and the matrices **X**, **Y** with dimension $n_x xN$ or $n_y xN$. In subscript notations:

$$X_{ji}\cdot h_j=\xi_{ji};\quad Y_{ki}\cdot h_j=\eta_{ki} \tag{328}$$

According to canonical theory, a linear transformation exists such that:

(1) $\sum_{i=1}^{N}\xi_{ji}/N=\bar{\xi}_j=0; \sum_{i=1}^{N}\eta_{ji}/N=\bar{\eta}_j=0$ (means are zero)

(2) $\sum_{i=1}^{N}\xi_{ji}^2=1,\ \sum_{i=1}^{N}\eta_{ji}^2=1$ (sum of squares is unity)

(3) $\sum\xi_{ji}\xi_{mi}=0; \sum\eta_{ji}\eta_{mi}=0$ for $j\neq m$ (certain correlations are zero)

(4) $\sum\xi_{ji}\eta_{mi}=0$ for $j\neq m$, and ρ_j for $j=m$ (some intercorrelations vanish)

ξ_{ji}'s and η_{ji}'s are called canonical variates and ρ_j the canonical correlations. In vector notations (T=transpose):

$$\boldsymbol{\xi}^{\mathrm{T}}\boldsymbol{\xi}=\boldsymbol{h}^{\mathrm{T}}\mathbf{X}^{\mathrm{T}}\mathbf{X}\boldsymbol{h}=1 \tag{329a}$$

$$\boldsymbol{\eta}^{\mathrm{T}}\boldsymbol{\eta}=\boldsymbol{k}^{\mathrm{T}}\mathbf{Y}\mathbf{Y}\boldsymbol{k}=1 \tag{329b}$$

$$\rho=\boldsymbol{\xi}^{\mathrm{T}}\boldsymbol{\eta}=\boldsymbol{h}^{\mathrm{T}}\mathbf{X}^{\mathrm{T}}\mathbf{Y}\boldsymbol{k} \tag{329c}$$

$$\mathbf{X}^{\mathrm{T}}\mathbf{Y}\boldsymbol{k}-\lambda_1\mathbf{X}^{\mathrm{T}}\mathbf{X}\boldsymbol{h}=0 \tag{329d}$$

$$\mathbf{Y}^{\mathrm{T}}\mathbf{X}\boldsymbol{h}-\lambda_2\mathbf{Y}^{\mathrm{T}}\mathbf{Y}\boldsymbol{k}=0 \tag{329e}$$

where $\lambda_1=\lambda_2=\rho$. This leads to:

$$[(\mathbf{Y}^{\mathrm{T}}\mathbf{Y})^{-1}\mathbf{Y}^{\mathrm{T}}\mathbf{X}(\mathbf{X}^{\mathrm{T}}\mathbf{X})^{-1}\mathbf{X}^{\mathrm{T}}\mathbf{Y}-\rho^2\mathbf{I}]\boldsymbol{k}=0 \tag{330a}$$

which is of the form:

$$|\mathbf{A}-\lambda\mathbf{I}|\boldsymbol{k}=0 \tag{330b}$$

Furthermore:

$$\boldsymbol{h}=(1/\rho)(\mathbf{X}^{\mathrm{T}}\mathbf{X})^{-1}\mathbf{X}^{\mathrm{T}}\mathbf{Y}\boldsymbol{k} \tag{330c}$$

which implies that the canonical correlations are the eigenvalues of the matrix **A** in eq. 330b. More details can be found in HOOPER (1959) and ANDERSON (1962). Eigenvalues have been discussed in the author's 1976 text.

Canonical correlation of four variates

Assume that we have the wind components of the wind profile measured on the first and second day. The zonal components are X_{1i} and X_{2i}, the meridional components Y_{1i} and Y_{2i}. We would like to correlate the two sets, but also we want to eliminate the effect of the intercorrelation between the two wind components in each set. This is a typical problem of the canonical correlation.

In the case of four variates the calculation of the canonical correlation coefficients has a simple solution. Denote X_1 and X_2 the wind vector components of the first set, X_3 and X_4 the respective components of the second set. First, make $r_{12}=r_{34}=0$, and eliminate the remaining intercorrelations between variable 2–3 and 1–4. This leaves a matrix:

$$\mathbf{D}=\begin{bmatrix} 1 & 0 & \rho_1 & 0 \\ 0 & 1 & 0 & \rho_2 \\ \rho_1 & 0 & 1 & 0 \\ 0 & \rho_2 & 0 & 1 \end{bmatrix}=(1-\rho_1)^2(1-\rho_2)^2 \tag{331}$$

Since r_{14} and r_{23} have been made zero, only the correlation between equivalent variables X_1–X_3 and X_2–X_4 remains.
The following notation is introduced:

$$A_{12}=1-r_{12}^2 \tag{332a}$$

$$A_{34}=1-r_{34}^2 \tag{332b}$$

$$C=(r_{13}r_{24}-r_{14}r_{23})^2 \tag{332c}$$

$$q^2=C/(A_{12}\cdot A_{34}) \tag{332d}$$

and:

$$z=\mathbf{C}_4/(A_{12}\cdot A_{34}) \tag{332e}$$

Here $\mathbf{C}_4$ denotes the correlation matrix for four variables (see also eqs. 318a and 305). The two canonical correlation coefficients can be computed from:

$$\rho_1\cdot\rho_2=q \tag{333a}$$

$$(1-\rho_1^2)(1-\rho_2^2)=z \tag{333b}$$

The solution is:

$$\rho_1=\tfrac{1}{2}[\sqrt{(1+q)^2-z}+\sqrt{(1-q)^2-z}] \tag{334a}$$

$$\rho_2=\tfrac{1}{2}[\sqrt{(1+q)^2-z}-\sqrt{(1-q)^2-z}] \tag{334b}$$

More details can be found in HOTELLING (1936) and HOOPER (1959). JOHNSON and WEHRLY (1977) applied the canonical correlation to angular–linear correlation.
The reader may be interested that the canonical correlation is not identical with the multiple correlation. We derive from eqs. 332e, 333b and 318a:

$$(1-\mathbf{R}_{1.234}^2)\frac{\|\mathbf{C}_{11}\|}{A_{12}A_{34}}=(1-\rho_1^2)(1-\rho_2^2) \tag{335}$$

This illustrates that $\rho_1^2\equiv R_{1.234}^2$ only for:

$$\frac{\|\mathbf{C}_{11}\|}{A_{12}A_{34}}=(1-\rho_2^2) \tag{336}$$

The canonical correlation coefficient also is not identical with the partial correlation coefficient. They will be identical only when:

$$(1-\rho_1^2)(1-\rho_2^2)=(1-r_{13.24}^2)(1-r_{24.13}^2) \quad (337)$$

However, ρ_1^2 and ρ_2^2 refer to the transformed variables and $r_{13.24}^2$ and $r_{24.13}^2$ to the original. Identity requires that no transformation takes place, i.e., $r_{12}=r_{34}=0$, and $\rho_{23}=\rho_{14}=0$ where ρ_{k1} stands for the correlation between the new variables ξ_j,η_j (see Table XXXVII; Example 24).

Vector correlation

Correlations between two vectors

In previous sections the multiple and the canonical correlation have been discussed. They express a relationship between four variables. Another important relationship between four variables is the vector correlation which is often utilized in climatology.

We define a correlation between two vector quantities $\boldsymbol{v}$ and $\boldsymbol{w}$ in analogy to eq. 280a as:

$$r_{\boldsymbol{vw}}=\frac{\frac{1}{N}\sum \boldsymbol{v}_R\boldsymbol{w}_R}{\sigma_{\boldsymbol{v}}\cdot\sigma_{\boldsymbol{w}}} \quad (338)$$

We are dealing with four components if we assume the two vector quantities to be wind vectors (the vertical wind component is generally neglected).

The above definition assumes that $\boldsymbol{v}_R$ and $\boldsymbol{w}_R$ are resultant wind vectors from the mean:

$$\boldsymbol{v}_{R_i}=\boldsymbol{v}_i-\boldsymbol{v}_m \quad (339a)$$

$$\boldsymbol{w}_{R_i}=\boldsymbol{w}_i-\boldsymbol{w}_m \quad (339b)$$

where $\boldsymbol{v}_m$ and $\boldsymbol{w}_m$ are the vector means of the vectors $\boldsymbol{v}$ and $\boldsymbol{w}$. Since $\boldsymbol{v}_R\boldsymbol{w}_R$ is a vector product, there are two choices of products, the scalar and cross product, with α denoting the angle between $\boldsymbol{v}_R$ and $\boldsymbol{w}_R$.

$$r_s=\frac{\frac{1}{N}\sum v_R\cdot w_R\cos\alpha}{\sigma_{\boldsymbol{v}}\sigma_{\boldsymbol{w}}} \quad (340a)$$

$$r_t=\frac{\frac{1}{N}\sum v_R w_R\sin\alpha}{\sigma_{\boldsymbol{v}}\sigma_{\boldsymbol{w}}} \quad (340b)$$

r_s is the scalar and r_t the cross product, also referred to as the stretch and turn correlation, respectively. The total is:

$$R_v^2=r_s^2+r_t^2 \quad (341)$$

If the wind components of $\boldsymbol{v}_R$ are X_1 and X_2, the components of $\boldsymbol{w}_R$ are X_3 and X_4, then we can rewrite the stretch and turn correlations as:

$$r_s=\frac{\frac{1}{N}\sum(X_1X_3+X_2X_4)}{\sigma_{\boldsymbol{v}}\cdot\sigma_{\boldsymbol{w}}} \quad (342a)$$

$$r_t = \frac{\frac{1}{N}\sum (X_2X_3 - X_1X_4)}{\sigma_v \cdot \sigma_w} \tag{342b}$$

The σ_v and σ_w can be computed from:

$$\sigma_v^2 = \sigma_{X_1}^2 + \sigma_{X_2}^2 \tag{343a}$$

$$\sigma_w^2 = \sigma_{X_3}^2 + \sigma_{X_4}^2 \tag{343b}$$

We substitute $r_{13}\sigma_1\sigma_3$ for $1/N\sum X_1X_3$ etc. where the subscript X has been omitted (e.g. $r_{X_1X_3} \equiv r_{13}, \sigma_{X_1} \equiv \sigma_1$ etc.):

$$r_s = \frac{r_{13}\sigma_1\sigma_3 + r_{24}\sigma_2\sigma_4}{[(\sigma_1^2+\sigma_2^2)(\sigma_3^2+\sigma_4^2)]^{1/2}} \tag{344a}$$

$$r_t = \frac{r_{23}\sigma_2\sigma_3 - r_{14}\sigma_1\sigma_4}{[(\sigma_1^2+\sigma_2^2)(\sigma_3^2+\sigma_4^2)]^{1/2}} \tag{344b}$$

Several modified versions of eq. 344a, b exist, but they do not contribute anything essentially new.
The stretch correlation combines the correlation of the parallel, the turn correlation the perpendicular components. We recognize some difference between the previous correlation characteristics and the ones defined now.
The multiple correlation coefficient includes the interrelationships r_{12} and r_{34} which are disregarded for the vector correlation. The canonical correlation resembles the vector correlation in the utilization of selected correlation coefficients, but is based on the transformation of variables, while the vector correlation retains the original variables X_1 through X_4.
All three different types of characteristics show some advantages in their respective applications. Which of the three presented tools will most efficiently provide a desired information depends on the purpose of the investigation.
More details on the vector correlation can be found in STEPHENS (1979).

Measure of dependence

A measure of dependence for the vector correlation can be defined by:

$$D_V^2 = (-1)^n \begin{vmatrix} 0 & y^Tx \\ x^Ty & x^Tx \end{vmatrix} \bigg/ [|y^Ty||x^Tx|] \tag{345}$$

where the vector components have been called x and y.
Another measure is the vector alienation coefficient. If:

$$D_A^2 = \begin{vmatrix} y^Ty & y^Tx \\ x^Ty & x^Tx \end{vmatrix} \bigg/ [|y^Ty||x^Tx|] \tag{346}$$

the vector alienation coefficient is the positive root of D_A^2. In form of the canonical correlation:

$$D_A^2 = \prod_{j=1}^{n} (1-\rho_j^2) \tag{347a}$$

where n denotes the number of variates.

$$D_V^2 = \prod_{j=1}^{n} \rho_j^2 \tag{347b}$$

These last two equations signify that D_A is unity only if all canonical correlations are zero, in which case D_V will be zero. If all canonical correlations are one, D_V will be one and D_A will be zero.

FUJIKOSHI and VEITCH (1979) recently analyzed the number of non-zero population canonical correlations.

Example 24. Given are the two wind profiles, January 1 and 2, 1964 from the surface to 29 km altitude for Chateauroux (Table XXXVI). Table XXXV gives the correlations that can be computed for the variables X_1, X_2, X_3 and X_4 (=zonal, meridional components of the wind profiles on the first and second day, respectively).

The following multiple correlations can be computed for three variables:

$$r_{12.3} = \frac{0.258-(0.955)(0.162)}{[(1-0.955^2)(1-0.162^2)]^{1/2}} = 0.3549;\ r_{12.3}^2 = 0.1259$$

$$r_{23.1} = -0.2967;\ r_{23.1}^2 = 0.0880$$

$$r_{13.2} = 0.9581;\ r_{13.2}^2 = 0.9181$$

$$R_{1.23}^2 = 0.9236$$

Subsequently the regression line given below can be established with the following coefficients:

$$A_2 = \frac{14.54}{9.82} \cdot r_{12.3} \left[\frac{(1-r_{13}^2)}{(1-r_{23}^2)}\right]^{1/2} = (1.48)(0.3549)(0.0903)^{1/2} = 0.1579$$

$$A_3 = \frac{14.54}{20.51} \cdot r_{13.2} \left[\frac{(1-r_{12}^2)}{(1-r_{23}^2)}\right]^{1/2} = (0.71)(0.9581)(0.9586)^{1/2} = 0.6650$$

$$X_1 = 0.158X_2 + 0.665X_3 \quad \text{(regression line)}$$

TABLE XXXIV

STATISTICAL CHARACTERISTICS

X_j	Mean (m s^{-1})	Standard deviation
$j=1$	7.81	14.54
2	−6.98	9.82
3	10.10	20.51
4	0.50	5.08

TABLE XXXV

CORRELATION COEFFICIENTS AND COVARIANCES

i	j	Cov_{ij}	$\sigma_i\sigma_j$	r_{ij}
1	2	36.89	142.81	0.258
1	3	284.93	298.25	0.955
1	4	27.57	73.81	0.373
2	3	32.65	201.43	0.162
2	4	39.60	49.85	0.794
3	4	41.10	104.10	0.395

TABLE XXXVI

WIND PROFILE FOR JANUARY 1 AND 2, 1964 AT CHATEAUROUX (FRANCE)

Altitude (km)	Direct. (°)	Speed (m s^{-1})	Zonal*[1]	Merid.*[2]	Altitude (km)	Direct. (°)	Speed (m s^{-1})	Zonal	Merid.
0	250	2.0	1.88	0.68	0	90	4.0	−4.00	0.00
1	288	2.0	1.90	−0.62	1	106	10.0	−9.61	2.76
2	346	2.0	0.48	−1.94	2	91	4.0	−4.00	0.07
3	285	3.0	2.90	−0.78	3	95	7.0	−6.97	0.61
4	360	7.0	0.00	−7.00	4	90	3.0	−3.00	0.00
5	36	9.0	−5.29	−7.28	5	99	5.0	−4.94	0.78
6	28	20.0	−9.39	−17.66	6	80	7.0	−6.89	−1.22
7	20	22.0	−7.52	−20.67	7	60	8.0	−6.93	−4.00
8	44	23.0	−15.98	−16.54	8	51	9.0	−6.99	−5.66
9	32	25.0	−13.25	−21.20	9	67	10.0	−9.21	−3.91
10	26	25.0	−10.96	−22.47	10	70	9.0	−8.46	−3.08
11	10	29.0	−5.04	−28.56	11	52	15.0	−11.82	−9.23
12	16	17.0	−4.69	−16.34	12	65	16.0	−14.50	−6.76
13	340	7.0	2.39	−6.58	13	54	10.0	−8.09	−5.88
14	282	7.0	6.85	−1.46	14	324	4.0	2.35	−3.24
15	288	9.0	8.56	−2.78	15	282	8.0	7.83	−1.66
16	272	9.0	8.99	−0.31	16	257	9.0	8.77	2.02
17	270	7.0	7.00	0.00	17	256	12.0	11.64	2.90
18	260	10.0	9.85	1.74	18	260	14.0	13.79	2.43
19	260	12.0	11.82	2.08	19	244	16.0	14.38	7.01
20	260	11.0	10.83	1.91	20	240	18.0	15.59	9.00
21	252	13.0	12.36	4.02	21	244	21.0	18.87	9.21
22	260	18.0	17.73	3.13	22	256	24.0	23.29	5.81
23	265	20.0	19.92	1.74	23	260	27.0	26.59	4.69
24	270	21.0	21.00	0.00	24	260	33.0	32.50	5.73
25	270	24.0	24.00	0.00	25	260	35.0	34.47	6.08
26	270	27.0	27.00	0.00	26	260	41.0	40.38	7.12
27	282	32.0	31.30	−6.65	27	266	48.0	47.88	3.35
28	300	43.0	37.24	−21.50	28	270	54.0	54.00	0.00
29	300	49.0	42.44	−24.50	29	280	57.0	56.13	−9.90

*[1]Zonal $= -v \sin \phi$; *[2]meridional $= -v \cos \phi$.

The solution by the Doolittle scheme (see eq. 271c) can be presented as:

$$\begin{vmatrix} 96.43 & 32.65 & 26.89 \\ 32.65 & 420.66 & 284.93 \\ 36.89 & 284.93 & 211.41 \end{vmatrix} \rightarrow \begin{vmatrix} 1.0 & 0.339 & 0.383 \\ 0 & 409.60 & 272.44 \\ 0 & 272.42 & 197.28 \end{vmatrix}$$

The last line can be neglected. The next step leads to:

$$\begin{vmatrix} 1.0 & 0 & 0.157 \\ 0 & 1.0 & 0.665 \end{vmatrix}$$

The coefficients are the same as previously stated except for rounding.

We can interpret the coefficients in this multiple regression scheme as the weights of the variables. In our case the two zonal components are more strongly correlated than the zonal with the meridional components. Consequently, one would expect the larger weight with X_3.

The regression line does not give a perfect prediction at a particular altitude, e.g., for 0 km we find from Tables XXXVI and XXXIV that $X_2 = 0.68-(-6.98) = 7.66$, and $X_3 = -4.0-10.10 = -14.10$. The regression line provides $X_1 = (0.158)(7.66)+(0.665)(-14.10) = -8.17$. From Table XXXVI we extract $X_1 = 1.88-7.81 = -5.93$ or $Y_1 = -8.17+7.81 = -0.35$ versus $Y_1 = 1.88$ m s^{-1}, etc.

The overall prediction leads to a minimum of the squared deviation, however. With profile values ranging from -16 to 42 m s^{-1} one may consider the prediction for 0 km altitude as good. Of course, the prediction should be checked with independent data. It is obvious, however, that a prediction scheme based on two profiles alone may not be very successful but our purpose is an elucidation of the regression analysis rather than a discussion of a prediction problem.
The multiple correlation for four variables renders the following:

$R^2_{1.234}=0.946$ with $\|C_4\|=0.0155$ and $\|C_{11}\|=0.2884$.

The partial coefficients have been calculated as:

$r_{12.34}=0.617$

$r_{13.24}=0.968$

$r_{14.23}=0.541$

$r_{23.14}=0.645$

$r_{24.13}=0.867$

$r_{34.12}=0.617$

We obtain further:

$(1-r^2_{13.24})(1-r^2_{24.13})=(1-0.9368)(1-0.7515)=0.0157=z$

This z is not identical with the z's in the column of Table XXXVII, although the difference is small (see also eq. 337).
We turn to the vector correlation.
The stretch correlation is:

$$r_s=\frac{(0.955)(298.3)+(0.794)(49.9)}{[(307.90)(446.44)]^{1/2}}=0.875$$

and the turn correlation is:

$$r_t=\frac{(0.162)(201.4)-(0.373)(73.8)}{[(307.9)(446.4)]^{1/2}}=0.014$$

This gives a total vector correlation of:

$R^2_v=0.766+0.000=0.766$

Measures of dependence for the first pair:

$D^2_V=\prod \rho^2_j=0.619$

The other pairs render 0.516.
The vector alienation coefficients are:

$D^2_A=\prod (1-\rho^2_j)=0.0199$ and 0.0185,

i.e., they are very small, which implies a strong association.

TABLE XXXVII

CANONICAL CORRELATION

Sequence	ρ^2_1	ρ^2_2	A_{12}	A_{34}	C	q^2	z
$X_1-X_2-X_3-X_4$	0.942	0.657	0.933	0.844	0.488	0.619	0.020
$X_2-X_3-X_4-X_1$	0.960	0.538	0.974	0.860	0.432	0.515	0.019
$X_3-X_4-X_1-X_2$	0.942	0.657	0.844	0.933	0.488	0.619	0.020
$X_4-X_1-X_2-X_3$	0.960	0.538	0.860	0.974	0.432	0.515	0.019

Correlation ratio

Up to now we have assumed a linear relationship between variables. This assumption may not always be true. Low or poor correlation between variables may not always indicate that there is no correspondence between these variables; low correlation may be caused by a nonlinear relationship. To test the assumption of a nonlinear relationship between two variables we can compute the so-called correlation ratio η^2.

The computation is based on the concept of a contingency table but the establishment of a contingency table is not required. It is necessary, however, that both variables can be grouped into classes, and the resulting fields (rows or columns of the contingency table) must contain at least more than one observation in some of them. If only one value per row or column for all rows and columns exist, the computation of the relationship between two variables should be treated by curve fitting procedures (see p. 132ff).

Assume that a contingency table is given with variables X and Y, and $\bar{X}$, $\bar{Y}$ and s_X^2, σ_Y^2 denote the usual statistical characteristics, mean and variance. The total number of observations is N.

The individual observation can be written X_{ijk} and Y_{ijk}, $i=1, 2, \ldots N$, with subscripts j and k designating the individual field into which the observation will be placed. For a constant k we write X_{ij}; and for a constant j, Y_{ik}.

We can now define:

$$\sigma_{\bar{X}_j}^2 = \sum_i n_{ij}(X_{ij} - \bar{X}_j)^2/N_j \qquad (348a)$$

the variance of an individual line j (for constant k) and:

$$\sigma_{\bar{Y}_k}^2 = \sum_i n_{ik}(Y_{ik} - \bar{Y}_k)^2/N_k \qquad (348b)$$

the variance of an individual column k (for constant j).

N_j and N_k designate the total number of observations in line j (constant k) or column k (constant j), respectively. Thus:

$$\sum_i n_{ij} = N_j \qquad (349a)$$

and:

$$\sum_i n_{ik} = N_k \qquad (349b)$$

Furthermore:

$$\bar{X}_j = \sum_i n_{ij} X_{ij}/N_j \qquad (350a)$$

and:

$$\bar{Y}_k = \sum_i n_{ik} Y_{ij}/N_k \qquad (350b)$$

represent the respective mean values of the row or column; and:

$$\sum_j N_j = \sum_k N_k = N \qquad (351)$$

We define further:

$$S^2_{\bar{X}_j} = \sigma^2_X - \sum N_j(\bar{X}_j - \bar{X})^2/N = \sigma^2_X - \sigma^2_{\Delta\bar{x}} = \sum_j N_j\sigma^2_{\bar{X}}/N \quad (352a)$$

and:

$$S^2_{\bar{Y}_j} = \sigma^2_Y - \sum N_k(\bar{Y}_k - \bar{Y})^2/N = \sigma^2_Y - \sigma^2_{\Delta\bar{y}} = \sum N_k\sigma^2_{\bar{Y}_k}/N \quad (352b)$$

where $\sigma^2_{\Delta\bar{x}}$ and $\sigma^2_{\Delta\bar{y}}$ stand for the term as indicated in eq. 352a, b. The correlation ratio can now be written as:

$$\eta^2_{xy} = 1 - s^2_{\bar{X}_j}/\sigma^2_X = \sigma^2_{\Delta\bar{x}}/\sigma^2_X \quad (353a)$$

or:

$$\eta^2_{yx} = 1 - s^2_{\bar{Y}_k}/\sigma^2_y = \sigma^2_{\Delta\bar{y}}/\sigma^2_Y \quad (353b)$$

We conclude from eq. 352a that $\sigma^2_{\Delta\bar{x}} = 0$ when $X_j = \bar{X}$ in all columns. The case with one value per row (or column) leads to $\sigma^2_{\Delta\bar{x}} \equiv \sigma^2_X$ and $\eta^2 = 1$. This trivial case would be meaningless. To avoid this trivial case, a reduced η^2_r is sometimes used (Mills, 1955) such as:

$$\eta^2_r = 1 - (1 - \eta^2)(N-1)/(N-m) \quad (354a)$$

where η^2 is either η^2_{xy} or η^2_{yx}, and m stands for the number of (non-empty) class intervals of the groups, i.e., rows or columns (see later m_y and m_x, Example 25). Eq. 354a requires $N - m > 0$, because the trivial case renders:

$$\eta^2_r = 1 - [0 \cdot \infty] \quad (354b)$$

For $N - m = 1$, we can write:

$$\eta^2_r = 1 - [(1 - \eta^2)(N-1)] \quad (354c)$$

η^2_r may turn out to be considerably smaller than η^2 even for the case that η^2 is close to 1 where $1 - \eta^2$ in eq. 354a is small. Furthermore, η^2_r must stay positive, otherwise η_r has a negative square root. $\eta^2_r \geq 0$ requires:

$$\eta^2 \geq (m-1)/(N-1) \quad (355)$$

The significance of η^2 cannot be measured by standard test statistics. Evaluation whether $\eta \sim 0$ is based on measures of λ and ζ as follows. First, the mean is:

$$\bar{\eta}^2 = (m-1)/(N-1) \quad (356a)$$

and the variance is:

$$\sigma^2_{\bar{\eta}^2} = 2\bar{\eta}^2(1 - \bar{\eta}^2)/(N+1) \quad (356b)$$

Observe that the boundary values $\bar{\eta}^2 = 0$ for $m = 1$, and $\bar{\eta}^2 = 1$ for $m = N$ (only one value per row or column) render $\sigma^2_{\bar{\eta}^2} = 0$ and cannot be used in λ and ζ.
We calculate:

$$\lambda = (\eta^2 - \bar{\eta}^2)/\sigma_{\eta^2} \quad (357)$$

and compare λ with a significance threshold λ_0. $\bar{\eta}^2$ has been computed for a particular m. Therefore, η^2 in eq. 357 must be taken from eq. 353a or b instead of the reduced η^2_r.

If $\lambda_0 > \lambda$, the correlation ratio is insignificant, if $\lambda_0 < \lambda$, the correlation ratio is significantly different from zero. The latter implies a significant nonlinear relationship between the two variables, which can be expressed as:

$$\zeta^2 = \eta^2 - r^2 \tag{358a}$$

Tables of λ_0 have been computed by Woo (1929). Only positive λ values must be tested because a negative λ automatically implies that η is not significantly different from zero. λ_0 can be approximated by the Gaussian distribution if m and N are not too small. Selected values are provided in Table XXXVIII. Values in Table XXXVIII are based on the assumptions that m and N are large. According to Woo's tables λ_0 varies from 3.50 to 2.73 for the 1% level, $N = 1000$ and m between 3 and 20, and between 3.50 and 2.51 for the same level, but for $N = 51$. The respective λ_0 values for the 2% level are 2.94 to 2.33 and 2.94 to 2.21. These ranges for λ_0 deviate for small m from the Gaussian distribution.
Two other measures besides the linearity ζ are common:

$$\vartheta = \eta - r \tag{358b}$$

$$\omega = \ln (\eta / r) \tag{358c}$$

Significance tests can be based on the Gaussian distribution via the respective error variances (see test procedures, eq. 560a, b).

$$\varepsilon_\zeta^2 = [4(\eta^2 - r^2)/N][(1-\eta^2)^2 - (1-r^2)^2 + 1] \tag{359a}$$

$$\varepsilon_\vartheta^2 = [(\eta - r)/\eta r N][r(1-\eta^2)^2 - \eta(1-r^2)^2 + \eta + r] \tag{359b}$$

$$\varepsilon_\omega^2 = [1/N][(1/r^2) - (1/\eta^2)] \tag{359c}$$

Example 25. The example is based on the same zonal and meridional wind components of Table XXXVI. Assume that we are interested in why the linear correlation between the 60 zonal (X) and meridional (Y) components of the wind $r_{XY} = 0.36$ is so low. Is it a result of nonlinearity or poor correlation?
The data of Table XXXVI are presented in form of a contingency table (Table XXXIX), where x_c and y_c designate the central class values for X and Y. We obtain the following results:

$s_X^2 = 315.52$ $s_X = 17.76$

$s_Y^2 = 83.00$ $s_Y = 9.11$

$\mathrm{Cov}_{XY} = 58.20$

$r_{XY} = 0.360$; $r_{XY}^2 = 0.129$

TABLE XXXVIII

SIGNIFICANCE THRESHOLDS λ_0

Significance level α	λ_0
1%	2.326
2%	2.054
5%	1.645
10%	1.282

TABLE XXXIX

CONTINGENCY TABLE OF DATA FROM TABLE XXXVI

y_c (m s^{-1}) \ x_c (m s^{-1})	−14	−10	−6	−2	2	6	10	14	18	22	27	30	34	38	42	46	50	54	58	62	N_j	$\bar{x}_j$
10	0	0	0	0	0	0	0	1	1	0	0	0	0	0	0	0	0	0	0	0	2	16.0
6	0	0	0	0	0	0	0	2	0	1	1	0	2	0	1	0	0	0	0	0	7	26.6
2	0	1	2	3	1	1	5	1	2	1	2	0	0	0	0	1	0	1	0	0	21	12.1
−2	0	2	2	0	4	2	2	0	0	0	0	0	0	0	0	0	0	0	0	0	12	−0.7
−6	1	1	2	0	2	0	0	0	0	0	0	1	0	0	0	0	0	0	0	0	7	−0.3
−10	0	1	0	0	0	0	0	0	0	0	0	0	0	0	0	0	0	0	1	0	2	24.0
−14	0	0	0	0	0	0	0	0	0	0	0	0	0	0	0	0	0	0	0	0	0	–
−18	1	1	1	0	0	0	0	0	0	0	0	0	0	0	0	0	0	0	0	0	3	−10.0
−22	1	1	1	0	0	0	0	0	0	0	0	0	0	1	0	0	0	0	0	0	4	2.0
−26	0	0	0	0	0	0	0	0	0	0	0	0	0	0	1	0	0	0	0	0	1	42.0
−30	0	0	1	0	0	0	0	0	0	0	0	0	0	0	0	0	0	0	0	0	1	−6.0
−34	0	0	0	0	0	0	0	0	0	0	0	0	0	0	0	0	0	0	0	0	0	–
N_k	3	7	9	3	7	3	7	4	3	2	3	1	2	1	2	1	0	1	1	0	60	+9.0
$\bar{y}_K$	−15.3	−8.3	−9.1	2.0	−2.6	−0.7	0.9	6.0	4.7	4.0	3.2	−6.0	+6.0	−22.0	−10.0	+2.0	–	+2.0	−10.0	–	−3.0	

$s^2_{\Delta\bar{x}} = 115.67;\ s^2_{\Delta\bar{y}} = 43.87$

$S^2_{\bar{X}_j} = 315.52 - 115.67 = 199.85$

$S^2_{\bar{Y}_j} = 83.00 - 43.87 = 39.13$

$\eta^2_{xy} = 115.67/315.52 = 0.367;\ \eta^2_{yx} = 43.87/83.00 = 0.529$

$m_x = 18;\ m_y = 10$

$\eta^2_{rx} = 0.253;\ \eta^2_{ry} = 0.338$

$\bar{\eta}^2_x = 0.153;\ \bar{\eta}^2_y = 0.288$

$\sigma^2_{\bar{\eta}^2_x} = 0.00424;\ \sigma^2_{\bar{\eta}^2_y} = 0.00673$

$\lambda_x = 3.29;\ \lambda_y = 2.93$

$\zeta^2_x = 0.367 - 0.129 = 0.238;\ \zeta^2_y = 0.529 - 0.129 = 0.400$

The findings indicate that indeed a nonlinear relationship would be a better assumption, and the correlation ratio is significant at least at the 5% level of significance. The nonlinear trend can be determined from Table XXXIX.
The computations above are based on the central class values x_c and y_c, given in Table XXXIX. This simplification introduces small errors and small discrepancies with Table XXXV. A calculation utilizing a precise class center of the field renders:

$s^2_X = 316.90\ s^2_Y = 74.79\ \mathrm{Cov}_{xy} = 43.25$

$r_{XY} = 0.281,\ r^2 = 0.079$

$\eta^2_{xy} = 0.468\ \eta^2_{yx} = 0.536\ \eta^2_{rx} = 0.359\ \eta^2_{ry} = 0.349$

$\lambda_x = 4.39\ \lambda_y = 3.03$

$\zeta^2_x = 0.468 - 0.079 = 0.389\ \zeta^2_y = 0.536 - 0.079 = 0.457$

Despite the dispersion the conclusions from the outcome with x_c and y_c remain the same.

Polynomial analysis and curve fitting

In the preceding section some problems of curve fitting have been introduced under the concept of linear regression (correlation) and the problem of fitting a frequency distribution to observed data was solved by selecting some suitable estimators. In the regression analysis (conditional means) the discussion centered largely on linear correlation and their mathematical expressions. All variables were given in the form of predictors and predictand.
The subsequent text deals with topics where mathematical functions replace the role of predictors. Such descriptive variables may be freely selected. E.g., Suzuki (1968) fitted polynomials to the secular variation of annual rainfall amounts. Two major tools have been in widespread use: the representation by polynomials and the Fourier analysis. Although the latter can be used as a tool of curve fitting it will be included into spectrum analysis (p. 143) because of its affinity with the spectrum.

Polynomial series

The first step in curve fitting is the decision which model will likely emerge as the proper mathematical description. Although numerous mathematical expressions can be used, a simple form is the polynomial series. Assume that the variates $Y_i, \ldots, Y_n$ of eq. 267a are all related by powers, and the dependent variable is Z, then:

$$Z_i = a_0 + a_1 Y_i + a_2 Y_i^2 + \ldots a_n Y_i^n + \varepsilon \qquad (360)$$

This is called a polynomial series. As in eq. 267a we need one equation per coefficient for every coefficient to be determined. Thus, the maximum of $n+1$ terms of the polynomial series can equal N, where N denotes the number of available observations Z_i. In this case the system will be saturated, and every Z_i can be exactly recomputed (except for rounding errors).

It is obvious that for large N it is not practical to utilize all $n+1$ coefficients, and generally $n+1 \leq N$. In analogy to eq. 267a we have a problem of ambiguity. The solution depends on the selected set of equations. Again, the ambiguity is resolved by calculating the coefficients $a_0 \ldots a_n$ by the principle of least squares. We establish a matrix similar to eq. 269a or a scheme such as eq. 271a and find the coefficients from:

$$a_j = (-1)^j \mathbf{D}_{aj} / \mathbf{D}_{11} \qquad (361)$$

According to the previous nomenclature it is understood that D_{aj} is the determinant where the line and column in which a_j occurs has been eliminated from the full matrix, and $\mathbf{D}_{11}$ is the minor determinant.

Again, the computation of the determinant can be simplified if we introduce:

$$X_i = Y_i - \bar{Y} \qquad (362)$$

and establish a system:

$$Z_i = A_0 + A_1 X_i + A_2 X_i^2 + \ldots A_n X_i^n + \varepsilon \qquad (363)$$

while:

$$A_0 \equiv \bar{Z} \qquad (364a)$$

and:

$$a_0 = \bar{Z} + A_1 \bar{Y} + A_2 \bar{Y}^2 + \ldots A_n \bar{Y}^n \qquad (364b)$$

The matrix for the system of eq. 360 is:

$$\mathbf{D} = \begin{bmatrix} 1 & \sum Z_i & \sum X_i Z_i & \sum X_i^2 Z_i & \ldots & \sum X_i^n Z_i \\ A_0 & N & \sum X_i & \sum X_i^2 & \ldots & \sum X_i^n \\ A_1 & \sum X_i & \sum X_i^2 & \sum X_i^3 & \ldots & \sum X_i^{n+1} \\ . & . & . & . & \ldots & . \\ . & . & . & . & \ldots & . \\ . & . & . & . & \ldots & . \\ A_n & \sum X_i^n & \sum X_i^{n+1} & \sum X_i^{n+2} & \ldots & \sum X_i^{2n} \end{bmatrix} \qquad (365)$$

Observe, however, that $\sum X^n$ is zero only when n is odd.

Assume we have:

$$Z_i = A_0 + A_1 X_1 + A_2 X^2 \qquad (366)$$

A_0 is determined by eq. 364a and:

$$A_j = \mathbf{D}_{A_J}/\mathbf{D}_{11}; j=1,2 \tag{367a}$$

$$\mathbf{D}_{A_1} = \begin{vmatrix} \sum Z_i & \sum X_i Z_i & \sum X_i^2 Z_i \\ N & 0 & \sum X_i^2 \\ \sum X_i^2 & 0 & \sum X_i^4 \end{vmatrix} = -N(\sum X_i Z_i)(\sum X_i^4) + (\sum X_i^2)^2 \cdot \sum X_i Z_i \tag{367b}$$

$$\mathbf{D}_{11} = \begin{vmatrix} N & 0 & \sum X_i^2 \\ 0 & \sum X_i^2 & 0 \\ \sum X_i^2 & 0 & \sum X_i^4 \end{vmatrix} = N(\sum X_i^2)(\sum X_i^4) - (\sum X_i^2)^3 \tag{367c}$$

Hence, the coefficient becomes:

$$A_1 = \frac{-[-N\sum X_i^4 + (\sum X_i^2)^2]\sum X_i Z_i}{[N\sum X_i^4 - (\sum X_i^2)^2]\sum X_i^2} = \frac{\sum X_i Z_i}{\sum X_i^2} \tag{367d}$$

Similarly:

$$A_2 = [(\sum Z_i)(\sum X_i^2) - N\sum X_i Z]/[N\sum X_i^4 - (\sum X_i^2)^2] \tag{367e}$$

$\sum X_i^n$ can be predetermined for any number of points N but in this original form the sums in the matrix D would assume quite high numerical values and thus various systems of reduction have been established. Although an exhaustive treatment cannot be given, some basic principles will follow.

The calculation of coefficients can also be based on solutions by the Doolittle method by converting matrix 365 into the appropriate form (see 271c). Although eq. 360 contains nonlinear terms the mathematical processes by least square require the same matrix operations.

Orthogonal polynomials

One particular modification of the general system (eq. 360) is worth elaboration. We deduce from eqs. 364b and 367d that the coefficients depend on the number of variables. If evaluation of a system shows that the number of terms is insufficient and we want to add one term, the elaborate process of calculating the coefficients must be repeated. This repetition can be eliminated by introducing orthogonal polynomials:

$$Z_i = B_0 + B_1\phi_{1i} + B_2\phi_{2i} + \ldots B_n\phi_{ni} \tag{368}$$

where:

$$\sum_i \phi_{ji}\phi_{ki} = 0 \quad \text{for } j \neq k \tag{369}$$

Obtaining the coefficients is simple:

$$B_0 = \bar{Z}, \tag{370a}$$

$$B_j = \sum_i Z_i\phi_{ji} / \sum_i \phi_{ji}^2 \tag{370b}$$

Sometimes the denominator is abbreviated by denoting $\phi_j^2 = \sum_{i=1}^{N} \Phi_{ji}^2$. Each coefficient B_j can now be computed separately and independently.

Each set of variables Y_j can be converted into a set of orthogonal polynomials ϕ_j. These "empirical" polynomials are called eigenvectors in mathematics. The canonical variates are also a form of orthogonal functions. In turn, these orthogonal polynomial functions must be known for recomputations of Z_i, while in the system of eq. 363 all real numbers usually can be used for recomputation and the observed Z_i are a limited set contained in the sample space.

Details of orthogonalization and empirical orthogonal polynomials were presented in the author's 1976 text. Various standard orthogonal functions exist such as the Tchebycheff (Chebyshev), Legendre, Lagrange and Laguerre polynomials, etc. See BOYD (1978).

Residual variance and orthogonal polynomials

Although any set of polynomial functions can be used or derived, Tchebycheff's orthogonal polynomials found widespread use and tables are readily available (e.g., PEARSON and HARTLEY, 1958; BEYER, 1966).

In the previous section the residual variance ε_R^2 was introduced (eq. 272a). In the non-orthogonal system (eq. 363) the residual variance must be obtained from:

$$\varepsilon_R^2 = \frac{1}{N} \sum (Z_i - \zeta_i)^2 \qquad (371)$$

where ζ_i denotes the analytical values for the observed Z_i. The fraction $c_{\phi j}^2$ is defined as the standardized variance of the j-th term:

$$c_{\phi j}^2 = B_j^2 \sigma_{\phi j}^2 / \sigma_Z^2 \qquad (372a)$$

where σ_Z^2 is the variance of Z, and:

$$\sigma_{\phi j}^2 = \frac{1}{N} \sum_1^N \phi_{ji}^2 \qquad (372b)$$

Consequently the parameter:

$$c_P^2 = c_{\phi j}^2 \cdot 100$$

expresses the percentage contribution of the ϕ_j's term to the variance, and the summation over the complete number of terms yields:

$$\sum c_{\phi j}^2 = (\sum B_j^2 \sigma_{\phi j}^2)/\sigma_Z^2 = 1 \qquad (373a)$$

or:

$$\sum B_j^2 \sigma_{\phi j}^2 = \sigma_Z^2 \qquad (373b)$$

Since $c_{\phi j}^2$ expresses the contribution of an individual term the total contribution by all chosen terms ($c_{R_m}^2 \cdot 100$ = percentage reduction) is determined by:

$$c_{R_n}^2 = \sum_1^n c_{\phi j}^2 \qquad (374a)$$

The "accounted" variance becomes then:

$$\varepsilon_{AC}^2=\sigma_Z^2\sum_1^n c_{\phi j}^2=\sigma_Z^2 c_{R_n}^2 \qquad (374b)$$

The residual variance is:

$$\varepsilon_R^2=\sigma_Z^2-\varepsilon_{AC}^2 \qquad (374c)$$

and the variance of the individual term is:

$$\varepsilon_j^2=c_{\phi j}^2\cdot\sigma_Z^2 \qquad (374d)$$

Correlation and orthogonal polynomials

It is not difficult to relate the system of orthogonal polynomials to the correlation coefficient. We assume two sets of data expressed in terms of orthogonal polynomials:

$$X_{1i}=B_0+B_1\phi_{1i}+B_2\phi_{2i}, \ldots, +B_n\phi_{ni} \qquad (375a)$$

and:

$$X_{2i}=C_0+C_1\phi_{1i}+C_2\phi_{2i}, \ldots, +C_n\phi_{ni} \qquad (375b)$$

The covariance of X_1, X_2 can be expressed by:

$$\mathrm{Cov}_{X_1X_2}=\sum_1^n X_{1j}\sigma_{X_1}X_{2j}\sigma_{X_2} \qquad (375c)$$

and the correlation coefficient becomes:

$$r=\sum_{j=1}^n c_{\phi_{1j}}c_{\phi_{2j}}+\varepsilon_k^2=\left(\sum_{j=1}^n B_jC_j\sigma_{\phi_j}^2\right)/(\sigma_{X_1}\cdot\sigma_{X_2})+\varepsilon_k^2 \qquad (376a)$$

where $c_{\phi 1j}$ and $c_{\phi 2j}$ stand for the square root of the accounted variance of the dependent variate X_1 and X_2 (see eq. 372a):

$$c_{\phi_{1j}}=B_j\sigma_{\phi_j}/\sigma_{X_1} \qquad (376b)$$

and:

$$c_{\phi_{2j}}=C_j\sigma_{\phi_j}/\sigma_{X_2} \qquad (376c)$$

If the sets of data in eq. 375a are only approximated to the degree k, then the correlation coefficient is erroneous by ε_k^2:

$$\varepsilon_k^2=\sum_{k+1}^n c_{\phi_{1j}}\cdot c_{\phi_{2j}} \qquad (376d)$$

Eq. 376a renders a quick approximation but it is not always easy to estimate ε_k^2.

A representation by orthogonal polynomials is sometimes helpful in the analysis of two variables and their interrelationship. This procedure aids in the recognition which terms disclose common features and where divergence occurs.

It should be added that linearity in regard to the correlation coefficient does not necessitate that the sets of data X_{1i} and X_{2i} must be linear functions. Eq. 376a illustrates that every polynomial term furnishes a positive, negative or zero contribution to the

correlation, depending on the sign and value of $c_{\phi_{1j}}$ and $c_{\phi_{2j}}$. If X_1 and X_2 are both exact second order curves, $c_{\phi_{12}}$ and $c_{\phi_{22}}$ will render a large contribution to the linear correlation, while all other terms $c_{\phi_{1j}}$, c_{ϕ_2}, $j \neq 2$ add nothing. The reader will recognize the difference between "linear correlation" and second order polynomial curve.
The association of correlation and polynomials was utilized by the author (ESSENWANGER, 1966) to establish a classification system of acoustic profiles while LUND (1963) applied a general correlation analysis.

Example 26. We want to express the zonal and meridional wind speed as a function of altitude by orthogonal Tchebycheff polynomials. For simplification we select 13 points at 2 km intervals, starting at the surface. The top altitude would then be 24 km. The computation of the coefficients is demonstrated by Tables XL and XLI which should be self-explanatory ($\sigma^2_{v_x}=114.2$, $\sigma^2_{v_y}=75.5$). This leads to the results of Table XLI, e.g. $B_0=(\sum v_{xi})/13=2.81$; $B_1=369.76/182=2.032$ etc.
The mathematical expressions are:

$$v_x=2.81+2.032\ \phi_{1i}+0.456\ \phi_{2i}-0.445\ \phi_{3i}-0.0108\ \phi_{4i}+0.141\ \phi_{5i}$$

$$v_y=-5.87+0.926\ \phi_{1i}+0.403\ \phi_{2i}-0.703\ \phi_{3i}-0.0256\ \phi_{4i}+0.115\ \phi_{5i}$$

The total reduction of the variance is 95.1% and 92.2%, respectively. This provides a residual variance of 5.6 and 5.8 for the zonal and meridional component. The residual variance is elucidated in Table XLIII.

Empirical polynomials and factor analysis

Let us assume that we seek a mathematical description for the wind profile as a function of altitude, i.e., a set of wind speed data $Y_i(h)$ is given where i denotes the individual day and h the altitude. In the past it was often difficult to find the most suitable type of (orthogonal) polynomial for a mathematical representation especially if n_h, the total number of altitude steps, was above a certain limit, say 10. The suitability of a mathematical function can be examined by the derivation of "empirical polynomials", a task which can be readily solved

TABLE XL

WIND SPEED AND TCHEBYCHEFF POLYNOMIAL VALUES FOR 13 POINTS

Altitude (km)	v_x	v_y	ϕ_1	ϕ_2	ϕ_3	ϕ_4	ϕ_5
Sfc	1.88	0.68	−6	22	−11	+99	−22
2	0.48	−1.94	−5	11	0	−66	33
4	0.00	−7.00	−4	2	6	−96	18
6	−9.39	−17.66	−3	−5	8	−54	−11
8	−15.98	−16.54	−2	−10	7	11	−26
10	−10.96	−22.47	−1	−13	4	64	−20
12	−4.69	−16.34	0	−14	0	84	0
14	6.85	−1.46	1	−13	−4	64	20
16	8.99	−0.31	2	−10	−7	11	26
18	9.85	1.74	3	−5	−8	−54	11
20	10.83	1.91	4	2	−6	−96	−18
22	17.73	3.13	5	11	0	−66	−33
24	21.00	0.00	6	22	11	99	22
$\sum \phi_j^2$			182	2002	572	68068	6188

TABLE XLI

COMPUTATION OF COEFFICIENTS

Altitude (km)	$v_x\phi_1$	$v_x\phi_2$	$v_x\phi_3$	$v_x\phi_4$	$v_x\phi_5$	$v_y\phi_1$	$v_y\phi_2$	$v_y\phi_3$	$v_y\phi_4$	$v_y\phi_5$
Sfc	−11.28	41.36	−20.63	186.12	−41.36	−4.08	14.96	−7.48	67.32	−14.96
2	−2.40	5.28	0.00	−31.68	15.84	9.70	−21.34	0.00	128.04	−64.02
4	0.00	0.00	0.00	0.00	0.00	28.00	−14.00	−42.00	672.00	−126.00
6	28.17	46.95	−75.12	507.06	103.29	52.98	88.30	−141.28	953.64	194.26
8	31.96	159.80	−111.86	−175.78	415.48	33.08	165.40	−115.78	−181.94	430.04
10	10.96	142.48	−43.84	−701.44	219.20	22.47	292.11	−89.88	−1438.08	449.40
12	0.00	65.66	0.00	−393.96	0.00	0.00	228.76	0.00	−1372.56	0.00
14	6.85	−89.05	−27.40	438.40	137.00	−1.46	18.98	5.84	−93.44	−29.20
16	17.98	−89.90	−62.93	98.89	233.74	−0.62	3.10	2.17	−3.41	−8.06
18	29.55	−49.25	−78.80	−531.90	108.35	5.22	−8.70	−13.92	−93.96	19.14
20	43.32	21.66	−64.98	−1039.68	−194.94	7.64	3.82	−11.46	−183.36	−34.38
22	88.65	195.03	0.00	−1170.18	−585.09	15.65	34.43	0.00	−206.58	−103.25
24	126.00	462.00	231.00	2079.00	462.00	0.00	0.00	0.00	0.00	0.00
$\sum$	369.76	912.02	−254.56	−735.15	873.51	168.58	805.82	−413.79	−1752.33	712.97

TABLE XLII

CALCULATION OF COEFFICIENTS, STANDARDIZED (ACCOUNTED) VARIANCE, VARIANCE OF TERMS AND PERCENTAGE REDUCTION ($n=j$)

j	Zonal component v_x:					Meridional component v_y:				
	$\sum v_x\phi_j$	B_j	$c^2_{\phi j}$	ε^2_j	$c^2_{Rn}\cdot 100$	$\sum v_y\phi_j$	B_j	$c^2_{\phi j}$	ε^2_j	$c^2_{Rn}\cdot 100$
0	–	2.81	–	–	–	–	−5.87	–	–	–
1	369.76	2.032	0.506	57.8	50.6%	168.58	0.926	0.159	12.0	15.9%
2	912.02	0.456	0.281	32.0	78.7	805.82	0.403	0.330	24.9	48.9
3	−254.56	−0.445	0.076	8.7	86.3	−413.79	−0.703	0.304	23.0	79.3
4	−735.15	−0.0108	0.005	0.6	86.8	−1752.33	−0.0257	0.0406	3.5	83.9
5	873.51	0.141	0.083	9.5	95.1%	712.97	0.115	0.083	6.3	92.2%
				108.6					69.7	

TABLE XLIII

RECOMPUTATION OF v_x AND v_y BY THE ANALYTICAL FUNCTION (FIVE TERMS) (Δ = obs. − analyt.)

Altitude (km)	Zonal component: $Z_i = v_x$ = obs.	ζ_i = analyt.	Δ	Δ^2	Meridional component: $Z_i = v_y$ = obs.	ζ_i = analyt.	Δ	Δ^2
Sfc	1.88	1.38	0.50	0.25	0.68	0.32	0.36	0.13
2	0.48	3.03	−2.55	6.50	−1.94	−0.57	−1.37	1.88
4	0.00	−3.50	3.50	12.25	−7.00	−8.56	1.56	2.43
6	−9.39	−10.10	0.71	0.50	−17.66	−16.32	−1.34	1.80
8	−15.98	−12.72	−3.26	10.63	−16.54	−20.08	3.54	12.53
10	−10.96	−10.44	−0.52	0.27	−22.47	−18.87	−3.60	12.96
12	−4.96	−4.48	−0.21	0.04	−16.34	−13.67	−2.67	7.13
14	6.85	2.82	4.03	16.24	−1.46	−6.65	5.19	26.93
16	8.99	8.98	0.01	0.00	−0.31	−0.28	−0.03	0.00
18	9.85	12.32	−2.47	6.10	1.74	3.32	−1.58	2.50
20	10.83	13.02	−2.19	4.80	1.91	3.38	−1.47	2.16
22	17.73	14.05	3.68	13.54	3.13	1.09	2.04	4.16
24	21.00	22.16	−1.16	1.35	0.00	0.60	−0.60	0.36
$\sum$	36.59	36.52	0.07	72.47	−76.26	−76.29	+0.03	74.97
$\sum/13$	2.81	2.81	0.005	5.57	−5.87	−5.87	0.002	5.77

through electronic data processing. Empirical polynomials are also called "eigenvectors" in mathematics; some authors now use the term "proper" functions (e.g., BUELL, 1978; GLAHN, 1979).

We establish a symmetric covariance matrix from Y:

$$\mathbf{B}_Y = \mathbf{M}_Y^T \mathbf{M}_Y \tag{377a}$$

where the elements are:

$$Y_{j,k}^2 = \sum_{i=1}^{N} Y_i(j) \cdot Y_i(k) \tag{377b}$$

and $j = 1, \ldots, n_h$; $k = 1, \ldots, n_h$. It is advisable that Y is centered such as $Y_i = X_i - \bar{X}$. Through centering some 'ill-conditioning" is eliminated (GOLUB and WILKINSON, 1976; BRADLEY and SRIVASTAVA, 1979). For $j = k$, and a division by N (or $N-1$), $Y_{j,k}^2$ becomes the variance. The calculation of empirical polynomials is a standard mathematical procedure based on a solution of the matrix equation:

$$\boldsymbol{\phi}^{-1} \mathbf{B}_Y \boldsymbol{\phi} = \boldsymbol{\lambda} \tag{378a}$$

or:

$$\mathbf{B}_Y \boldsymbol{\phi} - \boldsymbol{\lambda} \boldsymbol{\phi} = 0 \tag{378b}$$

The columns of $\boldsymbol{\phi}$ are called "eigenvectors" and $\boldsymbol{\lambda}$ is a diagonal matrix of "eigenvalues." The "eigenvectors" can be examined whether they resemble some standard functions. In some cases they do (see ESSENWANGER, 1975). One advantage of the substitution by standard functions is the use of a mathematical expression for the columns of $\boldsymbol{\phi}$ which permits us a replacement of $\boldsymbol{\phi}$ by an appropriate mathematical expression in:

$$Y_i(h) = a_{0i} + a_{1i}\phi_1(h) \ldots + a_{ni}\phi_n(h) \tag{379a}$$

e.g.;

$$Y(h)=a_0+a_1\sin(\alpha_h+\beta_1)+\ldots+a_n\sin(n\alpha_h+\beta_n) \tag{379b}$$

A second advantage of the use of standard functions is a simple comparison of different data sets. E.g., the first term of the empirical polynomials at two different locations may account for the same percentage of the variance at both locations, but the shapes of the eigenvectors may be completely different. Without a comparison of the eigenvectors, the information about the percentage of the accounted variance is of little value. In turn, an examination of the accounted variance for terms of standard functions (e.g., the first term) can reveal similarity or differences because the first term of standard polynomials (functions) would be the same for both locations.
If $\mathbf{B}_Y$ is a symmetric matrix such as from $\mathbf{M}_Y$ in eq. 377a, then the accounted variance of the individual eigenvectors is related by the eigenvalues:

$$\varepsilon^2_{AC}=\lambda^2_k/\sum_1^{n_h}\lambda^2_i \tag{379c}$$

where k denotes the individual eigenvector, $k=1\ \ldots,\ n_h$ the possible number of eigenvalues. Furthermore:

$$\sum_1^{n_h}\lambda^2_i=\sum_i\sum_j b^2_{ij} \tag{379d}$$

where b_{ij} are the elements of $\mathbf{B}_Y$.
The relationship with $\mathbf{M}_Y$ is in this case:

$$\varepsilon^2_{AC}=\lambda_k/\sum_1^{n_h}\lambda_i \tag{379e}$$

with:

$$\sum_1^{n_h}\lambda_i=\sum_i\sum_j Y^2_{ij} \tag{379f}$$

If eigenvalues of a non-symmetric matrix $\mathbf{C}$ are calculated such as:

$$\mathbf{\Phi}^{-1}\mathbf{C}\mathbf{\Phi}=\mathbf{T}_\lambda \tag{379g}$$

when $\mathbf{T}_\lambda$ is a triangular matrix with eigenvalues in its diagonal. The relationships eq. 379c or 379d are not valid.
If Y is given in deviations from the (column) means $\sum Y^2_{ij}$ becomes the addition of the column variances multiplied by n_i.
The author has devoted extended sections in his 1976 text on the problem of deriving eigenvalues, eigenvectors and empirical polynomials and gave numerous examples. The reader is referred to this text for details.
In atmospheric science LORENZ (1956) was one of the first authors to suggest the use of empirical polynomials. Other references from 1960 to 1970 were given in ESSENWANGER (1976). Examples from the atmospheric literature of the last decade are HOLMSTRÖM (1970), RINNE (1971), KIDSON (1975a, b), SMITH and WOOLF (1976), YAMAZAKI and KINAMI (1977), BUELL (1978) and GLAHN (1979) etc.
Suppose that B_Y is a correlation matrix from j elements $Y_{i,j}$ (such as eq. 305). The determination of ϕ and λ is called principal components analysis if the diagonal of matrix

B_Y is unity (i.e., eq. 305), or factor analysis if "communalities" have been substituted into the diagonal. Factor analysis was treated in the author's 1976 text.
YAMAZAKI and KINAMI (1977) performed a principal components analysis of daily rainfall amounts; WILLIAMS (1979) discussed several factor analysis models and outlined a synthetic basis; TEUBER et al. (1979) applied a principal components analysis to solar flares. Grouping of rainfall stations by principal component analysis was attempted by DYER (1975) and later by OGALLO (1980). An application to monsoon rainfall was given by BEDI and BINDRA (1980), and OVERLAND and PREISENDORFER (1982) used principal components analysis for a cyclone climatology. Other applications were discussed by GABRIEL (1983). STORCH (1983) pointed out that the reliability of empirical orthogonal functions is low for small data samples, especially with a large number of degrees of freedom.

Areal orthogonal polynomials

Previous sections have treated the calculation of polynomials for the one-dimensional case. Several orthogonal functions have been utilized to represent maps. BRYSON and KUHN (1956) and ESSENWANGER et al. (1958) have adopted Chebyshev polynomials to two dimensions, KUTZBACH and WAHL (1965) calculated Fourier-Bessel coefficients (for details see ESSENWANGER, 1976).
A different technique was developed by DIXON (1969) and DIXON et al. (1972). In brief, Dixon recommended a scheme for $Z(x,y)$. E.g., for up to the third order the permutations are 1, x, y, x^2, y^2, xy, x^3, x^2y, xy^2, y^3. The correlations and cross-correlations are established first and then an orthogonalization of the matrix is developed by the Gram-Schmidt process:

$$\phi_0 = 1 \tag{380a}$$

$$\phi_1 = x - (\phi_0 x)\phi_0 \tag{380b}$$

$$\phi_2 = y - (\phi_0 y)\phi_0 - (\phi_1 y)\phi_1 \tag{380c}$$

$$\phi_3 = x^2 - (\phi_0 x^2)\phi_0 - (\phi_1 x^2)\phi_1 - (\phi_2 x^2)\phi_2 \tag{380d}$$

In general:

$$\phi_n = p - (\phi_0 p)\phi_0 - (\phi_1 p)\phi_1 - \ldots - (\phi_{n-1} p)\phi_n \tag{380e}$$

An example of the orthogonalization process is given in the author's 1976 text (p. 339).

Special functions

Although estimators for the coefficients of any functional (mathematical) relationship can be developed, it is almost impossible to provide a comprehensive coverage of all functions and give their solutions. One simple procedure, however, is a transformation of functions to a form where estimators have been deduced or are known. Let us assume the following:

$$Y = a + b \ln (X + c) \tag{381a}$$

where c serves as a location parameter to avoid negative numbers in the logarithm. The equation can be transformed by introducing:

$$Z = \ln (X + c) \tag{381b}$$

Y becomes:

$$Y = a + bZ \tag{381c}$$

The calculation of coefficients a and b for eq. 381c is a known problem in polynomial or regression analysis.
Another example is the relationship:

$$Y = a + be^{cX+d} \tag{382a}$$

We substitute:

$$Z = Y - a \tag{382b}$$

and we formulate:

$$Z = be^{cX+d} \tag{382c}$$

Taking logarithm we write:

$$\ln Z = \ln B + cX + d \tag{383a}$$

Now we replace:

$$\ln Z = Z_y \tag{383b}$$

so that:

$$A = \ln b + d \tag{383c}$$

It follows:

$$Z_y = A + cX \tag{383d}$$

Again, the coefficients can be calculated by known procedures. Additional details can be found in BROOKS and CARRUTHERS (1953) or in ESSENWANGER (1976). In the latter text transformation systems have also been listed for the "stabilization" of the variance.
The transformation, especially into the form of general linearized models, becomes important because modern electronic data processing equipments have routine computer packages for the utilization of these models, e.g. GLIM (see STERN, 1983). The reader is cautioned, however, not to apply these "canned" packages indiscriminately and without scrutiny.

Chapter 4

Fourier and Spectrum Analysis

Harmonic or Fourier analysis

One of the earliest tools in the analysis of meteorological and climatological time series was the Fourier analysis, especially at the beginning of this century. It is also called harmonic analysis in mathematics and physics because the sequence of periodic terms (waves) is related by whole numbers. During the middle of this century the elaborate computational work discouraged its employment but today the laborious computations can be easily handled by electronic data processing and its application has grown again. The Fourier analysis is a convenient technique if periodic phenomena are studied, especially for known periodicities such as the annual, semi-annual, or daily cycles of meteorological elements. In case of unknown periods the spectrum or the periodogram analysis may be more suitable (see later). The Fourier series can also be used as a tool of curve fitting equivalent with orthogonal polynomials.

The mathematical expression for the Fourier series can be given as a periodic relationship between two variables X and Y, i.e., $Y(X)$. Most of these representations in atmospheric science involve time series data. Thus, the formulae are developed for Y as a function of t, i.e., $Y(t)$. We write:

$$Y_i = A_0 + A_1 \sin(t_i + \psi_1) + A_2 \sin(2t_i + \psi_j) +, \ldots, A_n \sin(nt_i + \psi_n) \qquad (384a)$$

or in brief:

$$Y_i = A_0 + \sum_{j=1}^{n} A_j \sin(jt_1 + \psi_j) \qquad (384b)$$

where:

$$t_i = \frac{2\pi i}{p} = \frac{i \cdot 360^\circ}{p}, \quad i = 1, \ldots, p \qquad (384c)$$

Another form also is customary:

$$Y_i = A_0 + \sum_{j=1}^{n} (a_j \sin jt_i + b_j \cos jt_i) \qquad (385a)$$

with:

$$a_j = A_j \cos \psi_j \qquad (385b)$$

$$b_j = A_j \sin \psi_j \qquad (385c)$$

We can define that i runs from 0 to $p-1$ which produces only an adjustment of ψ_j. Thus, the definition of i is immaterial. Sometimes eq. 384a is written for $\cos(nt_i+\psi_n)$. Again, this change affects only the value of ψ_j which will differ by 90° from the sine term. Usually p is identical with N, the number of observations, but occasionally the available set of observations consists of N data, of which we know that the largest non-negligible period is p, then:

$$N=kp \tag{386}$$

Primarily two methods have been developed in the case of eq. 386. The total set of data (up to N) is treated as the basic period and the first terms are omitted until the first term with $A_j \neq 0$ is reached, i.e., the term kt_i which corresponds to the kth period in the data set of N. A second solution involves a reduction of the original set of observations Y_i by calculating:

$$\bar{Y}_i=\frac{1}{k}\sum Y_{ik} \tag{387}$$

Then the basic period is p again, and eq. 384a is suitable. This technique can also be applied if one special periodicity (wave) is singled out and the others are of negligible interest. Thus, all problems can be reduced to eq. 384a, and the subsequent discussion is based on that formula only.

The computation of estimators for the coefficients A_j (the amplitudes or half ranges of the sine waves) and estimators for the reference angles ψ_j is performed via an auxiliary pair of estimators a_j and b_j:

$$A_0=\frac{1}{N}\sum_1^N Y_i=\bar{Y} \tag{388a}$$

$$a_j=\frac{2}{p}\sum_1^p Y_i \sin jt_i \tag{388b}$$

$$b_j=\frac{2}{p}\sum_1^p Y_i \cos jt_i \tag{388c}$$

Subsequently we find:

$$A_j^2=(a_j^2+b_j^2)^{1/2} \tag{388d}$$

$$\tan \psi_j=\frac{b_j}{a_j} \tag{388e}$$

It is sometimes confusing to determine into which quadrant the angle ψ_j falls. The scheme below clarifies the association. For eq. 384a and the definitions in eq. 388a, b we find:

	b_j	a_j	b_j	a_j	
2nd	+	−	+	+	1st
3rd	−	−	−	+	4th

At first glance the reader may be puzzled because a_j, multiplied with the sine, is positive in the fourth quadrant, etc. The multiplication, however, has nothing to do with the designation of a_j, which has the property of a cosine term. The reader should notice that the number of terms is limited to $j=N/2$. The last term $j=n$ always renders:

$$a_n=0 \tag{388f}$$

$$b_n=\frac{1}{p}\sum_1^p(-1)^i Y_i \tag{388g}$$

This can be deduced from:

$$\sin\left(\frac{ji2\pi}{p}\right)=\sin\left(\frac{i\pi N}{p}\right)=\sin(ik\pi)=0 \text{ for all } ik.$$

Similarly the cosine sums are $\cos(ik\pi)=\pm 1$.
It can be further observed that the sequence of Fourier terms is an orthogonal system. Hence, we can add any term without recomputing the coefficients of the prior terms.
It is generally assumed that N is an even number. For odd N, $j=(N-1)/2$ and eqs. 388f and g are not necessary. The number of coefficients is always N. For even N, $N/2-1$ coefficients of a_n and $N/2$ coefficient of b_n exist, plus a_0, which adds up to N; for odd N we have $(N-1)/2$ coefficients a_n and b_n plus a_0, which again renders N coefficients. From:

$$\sigma_y^2=\sum_1^p(Y_i^2-A_0)^2/p=\sum_1^n A_j^2/2 \tag{389a}$$

we derive:

$$\sum_1^n A_j^2=2\sigma_y^2 \tag{389b}$$

Thus, for the individual term:

$$C_{A_j}^2=A_j^2/2\sigma_y^2 \tag{389c}$$

$100\cdot C_{A_j}^2$ is the percentage reduction and the total reduction is:

$$R_R^2=\left(\sum_1^m A_j^2\right)\Big/(2\cdot\sigma_y^2)=\sum C_{A_j}^2 \tag{389d}$$

or $100\cdot\sum C_{A_j}^2$ in percentage, where m denotes the number of terms.
The accounted variance (see eq. 273a) is:

$$\varepsilon_{RD}^2=\left(\sum_1^m A_j^2\right)\Big/2 \tag{389e}$$

where $m<n$, and the residual variance can be calculated from:

$$\varepsilon_R^2=\sigma_y^2-\left(\sum_1^m A_j^2\right)\Big/2 \tag{389f}$$

The quantity j in the Fourier analysis is called the number of the harmonic or the wave number. It measures the number of complete cycles in the basic period. Assume that the basic period p is the year = 365 days. The 10th harmonic is then 36.5 days long and we have 10 cycles in one year. The number of cycles is also called the frequency (repetitions within a determined time frame) and should not be mistaken for the frequency density of the distribution as introduced on p. 3. The length of the period of the jth component is:

$$p_j = p/j \tag{390}$$

a similar relationship as eq. 386.

Before the Fourier analysis is performed, sometimes the trend is removed. Suppose we have a linear trend. Recomputation of the data must then add this trend. This expands eq. 384b to:

$$Y_i = A_0 + B(X_t - \bar{X}_t) + \sum_1^n A_j \sin(jt_i + \psi_j) \tag{391}$$

where B is the coefficient for the linear trend, calculated from the regression line $Y_i = A_0 + Bx$ (see eq. 267b) with $x = X_t - \bar{X}$.

The trend variate X_t corresponds with the chosen basic period p; in most cases $t = 1, \ldots, p$ for X_t. It is very rare that more than the linear trend is eliminated, although no rule prohibits removing a trend which includes polynomial terms of higher order before the data become the subject of the Fourier analysis. It should be kept in mind that then $Y = \text{Trend} + \text{Fourier series}$.

It is not important how much has been removed from the data if the goal is a mathematical description of the data. Because polynomials and Fourier series terms are not necessarily orthogonal to each other, (although they can be orthogonal within themselves) the addition of terms in the trend requires a recomputation of the Fourier coefficients.

The elimination of the trend for the power spectrum and periodogram analysis is an analogous procedure.

The minimum number of data N which must be available is specified by eq. 386. For $k = 1$, $N \geq p$. In other words, the data must have the length of at least one period. Sometimes a dominant climatic cycle (or quasiperiodicity) is used in forecasting and reoccurrence is predicted. In this case it is a handicap that amplitude and phase angles can only be deduced after the data have been observed for at least one length of the cycle. E.g., a 100-year cycle could not ordinarily be established from 50 years of data. Modified schemes of the set of eq. 388a–e are too complex to derive for a reduced data length (less than the period p). A procedure suggested by DIEHL (1948) may be helpful. The crucial point is the determination of A_0 or the average of the set of Y_i. Data for at least $p/2$ must be available. From trigonometry:

$$A_1 \sin(t_i + \psi) + A_1 \sin(t_i + \pi + \psi) = 0 \tag{392a}$$

For a dominate cycle:

$$Y_i = A_0 + A_1 \sin(t_i + \psi) \tag{392b}$$

and:

$$Y_{i+p/2} = A_0 + A_1 \sin(t_i + \pi + \psi) \tag{392c}$$

Consequently:

$$Y_i + Y_{i+p/2} = 2A_0 \tag{392d}$$

If p is known it is possible to approximate A_0 by eq. 392d within an acceptable error tolerance. Usually the period length p is unknown except in special cases. To compensate for the deficiency of an unknown p we must vary the length of p, i.e., $A_0(p)$. In principle, we perform a periodogram analysis (see p. 151) where p can be chosen. The wave with the maximum amplitude and best fit for the data of length $p/2$ is adopted as the prediction, and the data are extrapolated to form the complete cycle p. Two special cases are distinguished:

(*a*) Extrapolation from the maximum or minimum of a sine-wave. In this case $Y_{s+r} = Y_{s-r}$, if the symmetric extrapolation starts at point s and continues, $r = 1, \ldots, p/2$.

(*b*) Extrapolation from 0 or 180° (null points). In this case $Y_{s+r} = -Y_{s-r} + 2A_0$. Symmetry extrapolation between these two special cases must be treated accordingly, i.e., the extrapolation must lead to a complete sine-wave.

This "empirical" extrapolation produces a data set Y_i, $i = 1, \ldots, p$, and amplitude and phase angle can be calculated from eqs. 388a–e. The augmentation of data as outlined under points a or b is simpler than a modification of eqs. 388b–e for a period $p/2$. Diehl (1948) illustrated the method by calculating amplitude and phase angle for the annual surface pressure cycle from six months of data. The reader should observe that in this case the length of the cycle was known.

An example for the calculation of the Fourier coefficients has been given in Example 15. Expansion to the Fourier series on spheres can be found in Orszag (1974). The representation of scalar fields by Fourier-Bessel functions was studied by Kutzbach and Wahl (1965) and Kutzbach (1966) (see also Essenwanger, 1976).

Fast Fourier transform (FFT)

We have introduced the Fourier series but even by electronic data processing the calculation of all coefficients and phase angles may be quite elaborate. Cooley and Tukey (1965) have found a procedure to reduce the computer time considerably by an algorithm which is now called the fast Fourier transform (see Hinich and Clay, 1968; Rayment, 1970; Alsop, 1966; or Brigham, 1974). The method is based on the complex Fourier series. We assume a finite record X_0 to X_n, where $X_s = X(s \cdot \Delta x)$ and Δx is the (equidistant) interval between observations. The usual Fourier series can be written as:

$$X(s) = \frac{a_0}{2} + \sum_{k=1}^{\infty} [b_k \cos(2\pi ks/p) + a_k \sin(2\pi ks/p)] \tag{393}$$

which is a restatement of eq. 385a by replacing A_0 by $a_0/2$. The complex Fourier form can be expressed as:

$$X(s) = \sum_{k=-\infty}^{\infty} C_k \exp(-2\pi iks/p) \tag{394a}$$

where $i = \sqrt{-1}$. The subscripts k and s are self-explanatory, p is the basic period of analysis (usually the data length N).

The inverse transformation from eq. 394a follows as:

$$2C_k = \frac{2}{p} \sum_{s=0}^{\infty} X(s) \exp(2\pi iks/p) = (b_k + ia_k) \tag{394b}$$

(If the interval steps $\Delta x \neq 1$ a multiplication by $2\Delta x/p$ instead of $2/p$ is required.)

It is readily deduced that the computed a_k and b_k coefficients are identical with the definitions in eqs. 388b and c. From this identity we can derive the relationship to the periodogram:

$$A_k^2 = a_k^2 + b_k^2 = C_k^2 \tag{395a}$$

and the power spectrum (eqs. 407a, b, c):

$$L_j = A_k^2/(2\sigma_X^2) \tag{395b}$$

Thus, the FFT can be used for periodogram analysis and power spectrum.
We now introduce a simplification which leads to a combination of terms. Since this combination can be more easily derived for the complex Fourier series, we write:

$$C_k = \sum_{s=0}^{N-1} X(s) W^{sk}/N \tag{396a}$$

where:

$$W = \exp(2\pi i/N) \tag{396b}$$

We remember that k represents the cycle sequence where $k=0$ leads to the mean, $\bar{X}$ or A_0. It can be eliminated from the data set. The length of the periodicity is $p=N/k$ with $k=1, 2, \ldots, N/2$. Only $N/2$ useful coefficients are produced as discussed in the Fourier series. The algorithm is following. We break N into factors such as $N=n_1 \cdot n_2$. Then we split:

$$k = k_1 n_1 + k_0 \tag{397a}$$

where $k_0=0, 1, \ldots, (n-1)$ and $k_1=0, 1, \ldots, (n_2-1)$.
Furthermore:

$$s = s_1 \cdot n_2 + s_0 \tag{397b}$$

where $s_0=0, 1, \ldots, (n_2-1)$ and $s_1=0, 1, \ldots, (n_1-1)$.
Now we introduce a new subscript and write:

$$C_{(k_1,k_0)} = \frac{1}{N} \sum_{s_0} \sum_{s_1} X(s_1,s_0)^{W^{ks_1n_2}W^{ks_0}} \tag{397c}$$

where:

$$W^{ks_1n_2} = W^{k_0s_1n_2} \tag{397d}$$

This correspondence is valid because $W^{N+c} = W^c$ for a periodic function.
Subsequently the inner sum over s_1 is defined as:

$$X_1(k_0,s_0) = \sum_{s_1} X(s_1,s_0) W^{k_0s_1n_2} \tag{398a}$$

and finally:

$$C_{(k_1,k_0)} = \sum_{s_0} X_1(k_0,s_0) W^{(k_1n_1+k_0)s_0} \tag{398b}$$

or in rewriting the equations in the original form:

$$C_k = C_{(k_1,k_0)} = \sum_{s_0} X_1(k_0,s_0) W^{ks_0} = \sum_{s_0} X_1(k_0,s_0) W^{(k_1n_1+k_0)s_0} \tag{396c}$$

with:

$$X_1(k_0,s_0)=\sum_{s_1} X(s)W^{k_0s_1n_2}=\sum_{s_1} X(s_1,s_0)W^{k_0s_1n_2} \quad (396d)$$

This two step algorithm (eqs. 396c and d) requires only $N(n_1+n_2)=Q_p$ operations instead of the N^2 in the original Fourier series. We could continue to develop an m-step algorithm. Then $Q_p=N(n_1+n_2+,\ldots,n_m)$, where $N=n_1\cdot n_2,\ldots,n_m$. Now $W^{(k_1n_1+k_0)s_0}$ must be evaluated by Euler's formula:

$$e^{i\varphi}=\cos\varphi+i\sin\varphi \quad (399)$$

Since W is given by eq. 396b we must set:

$$\varphi=(2\pi/N)\cdot sk \quad (400)$$

or for W in eqs. 396c and d, respectively:

$$\varphi_a=(2\pi/N)(k_1n_1+k_0)s_0 \quad (400b)$$

and:

$$\varphi_b=(2\pi/N)(k_0s_1n_2) \quad (400c)$$

It is reiterated that for a_k the real and for b_k the imaginary part must be summed. The conversion to the form of eqs. 396c and d saves computer time without loss of accuracy (see ALSOP, 1966).

Today many electronic data processing systems have "canned" programs for calculating spectra via the FFT. A word of caution is appropriate. Many of these routines require a basic period of $p=2^k$, k being a whole number. This requirement is especially important for meteorological time series whose data length are multiples of the year. For $p=r\cdot365$ we have $k=r\cdot8.5117$ ... which is not an integer, r being a whole number. Thus, the requirement $p=2^k$ leads to a truncation of the data, and $p<365$.

The effects of an imprecise basic period are demonstrated in Table LI. Therefore, a "canned routine" where p can assume any arbitrary (whole) value is preferable over the one with a basis of $p=2^k$ although the computational efforts may be larger than with the other routine.

Example 27. Fast Fourier transform. Let us check the procedure for $N=6$. Under regular conditions we find $N/2$ useful coefficients (eq. 393):

$$C_0=X(0)W^0+X(1)W^0+X(2)W^0+X(3)W^0+X(4)W^0+X(5)W^0$$

$$C_1=X(0)W^0+X(1)W^1+X(2)W^2+X(3)W^3+X(4)W^4+X(5)W^5$$

$$C_2=X(0)W^0+X(1)W^2+X(2)W^4+X(3)W^6+X(4)W^8+X(5)W^{10}$$

$$C_3=X(0)W^0+X(1)W^3+X(2)W^6+X(3)W^9+X(4)W^{12}+X(5)W^{15}$$

Note, C_0 is merely a summation of the $X(s)$ values, and from C_3 we need only the real coefficient a_3 (see eqs. 388f and g).

The fast Fourier transform requires first the factoring of N. Let us assume $N=2.3$, i.e., $n_1=2$ and $n_2=3$. We now write:

$k=2k_1+k_0$ with $k_0=0, 1$ and $k_1=0, 1, 2$

$s=3s_1+s_0$ with $s_0=0, 1, 2$ and $s_1=0, 1$

We must first determine X_1, which depends on k_0 and s_0. We also need k_0k_1 and k. Table XLIV relates the subscripts.
The following basic summation follows from this operation (eq. 396d):

$X_1(0, 0)=X(0)W^0+X(3)W^0$

$X_1(0, 1)=X(1)W^0+X(4)W^0$

$X_1(0, 2)=X(2)W^0+X(5)W^0$

$X_1(1, 0)=X(0)W^0+X(3)W^3$

$X_1(1, 1)=X(1)W^0+X(4)W^3$

$X_1(1, 2)=X(2)W^0+X(5)W^3$

The second summation leads to C_k (eq. 396c):

$C_0=C_{(0,0)}=X_1(0, 0)W^0+X_1(0, 1)W^0+X_1(0, 2)W^0$

$C_1=C_{(0,1)}=X_1(1, 0)W^0+X_1(1, 1)W^2+X_1(1, 2)W^2$

$C_2=C_{(1,0)}=X_1(0, 0)W^0+X_1(0, 1)W^2+X_1(0, 2)W^4$

$C_3=C_{(1,1)}=X_1(1, 0)W^0+X_1(1, 1)W^3+X_1(1, 2)W^6$

Note that $W^{j+N}=W^j$.
We count the operations in the regular Fourier series computation, 4·6 multiplications and 4·5 summations = 44 operations. The fast Fourier transform reduces this number to 6·2 multiplications plus 6·1 addition = 18. The second part comprises 4·3 multiplications and 4·2 additions = 20 operations. The total of 38 operations against 44 does not really amount to a great saving. This is expected, as according to Cooley and Tukey (1965) we have N^2 operations in the Fourier series versus $N(n_1+n_2)$ in the fast Fourier transform which is 36 against 30 (we count the operations for eq. 394a). The savings in operations grow with increasing N.

TABLE XLIV

AUXILIARY TABLE RELATING THE SUBSCRIPTS OF THE FFT

k_0	s_0	s_1	s	$k_0s_1n_2$	k_1	k	$(k_1n_1+k_0)s_0$
0	0	0	0	0	0	0	0
0	1	0	1	0	0	0	0
0	2	0	2	0	0	0	0
1	0	0	0	0	0	1	0
1	1	0	1	0	0	1	1
1	2	0	2	0	0	1	2
0	0	1	3	0	1	2	0
0	1	1	4	0	1	2	2
0	2	1	5	0	1	2	4
1	0	1	3	3	1	3	0
1	1	1	4	3	1	3	3
1	2	1	5	3	1	3	6

Periodogram analysis

The spectrum

We could enter all computed A_j amplitudes of a harmonic (Fourier) analysis into a diagram with A_j as the ordinate and j as the abscissa. This diagram is called a periodogram. It shows the relative size of the harmonic components.
If we enter the value $S^2_{A_j} = A^2_j/2$ in the ordinate, we establish a relationship with the variance of eq. 389a, and $S^2_{A_j}/\sigma^2_y$ expresses the contribution of each harmonic term to the variance. Customarily the diagram (squared) amplitude versus the wave number is called a spectrum, e.g., a spectrum as is used in optics.
An optical spectrum permits an evaluation of the contribution of the various wave lengths (which can also be expressed as frequencies) to the energy of a given light source. A spectrum for meteorological elements is similar to an optical spectrum. In meteorology the expression power spectrum (e.g., LANDSBERG et al., 1959) is used more often than the term energy or variance spectrum (see BROWN and ROBINSON, 1979) except in turbulence analysis.
The power spectrum relates the coefficients to the variance, i.e., the coefficients are expressed as the accounted variance or the percentage reduction. We designate:

$$L_j = L'_j/\sigma^2_y = A^2_j/(2\sigma^2_y) \tag{401}$$

as the "normalized" spectrum. L_j thus permits the direct deduction of the percentage reduction for the individual harmonic component and $\sum L_j$ provides the accounted variance.
A very comprehensive review on spectrum analysis including the state of the art as of 1960 was provided by JENKINS (1961).

Periodogram analysis

From eq. 384c it is evident that the fundamental or basic period p is an essential component in the harmonic analysis. It is customary to assume that this basic period is the total data length N but a shorter length may be taken. The principal postulation is now that all cycles have the length p/k where k is a whole number. This is not necessarily true. To resolve this discrepancy a periodogram can be established which is merely a Fourier analysis with a limitation to the first term of the Fourier series, i.e., we vary p_s, or p/s is defined by p_s rather than by whole numbers of k.
A periodogram analysis with slowly varying p_s requires much computational efforts if N is large. The work can be reduced by performing first a harmonic analysis (FFT) and adding a periodogram for the regions of high amplitudes only. This technique enables us to determine the exact wave length (or frequency) of a periodicity p_s without calculating the entire spectrum of a periodogram.
Although in atmospheric science the basic period may be known (such as the year) or it can be deduced from physical principles, a harmonic analysis does not always suffice because of "quasi-periodicity," i.e., cyclic phenomena may appear and disappear and are not necessarily harmonics of the basic period (see also JENKINSON, 1975b). For this reason the peaks in the periodogram indicate possible periodicities, but must be checked for their

statistical significance. Quasi-periodicities in meteorological time series can be a product of chance (see also ESSENWANGER, 1980).

SCHUSTER (1898) derived an expectancy value ε_F^2 which can be used as a threshold for testing the significance. If $K^2\varepsilon_F^2 < A_j^2$, the amplitude is significantly different from zero*[1], where:

$$\varepsilon_F^2 = 4\sigma_y^2/N \tag{402a}$$

Since most meteorological time series show persistence, ε_F^2 is not sufficient. As shown by STUMPFF (1937) persistence affects the criterion, and the threshold increases to:

$$\varepsilon_p^2 = \varepsilon_F^2\left[1 + 2\sum_{\tau=1}^{n-1} r_\tau\left(\frac{1-\tau}{N}\right)\cos\tau\alpha\right] \tag{402b}$$

where τ denotes the time lag and α the frequency of the tested component, r_τ are idealized (or smoothed) autocorrelations. The term in brackets can go as high as 4–5, which would double ε_F (ESSENWANGER, 1950).

The effect of unequal spacing and aliasing can also affect the values in the periodogram. These topics were treated in ESSENWANGER, 1976.

One brief comment on the determination of non-harmonic wave components from a harmonic analysis may be added. A non-harmonic wave can be approximated from the two adjacent harmonic components by the following procedure:

Let us assume the true periodicity is:

$$p_T = N/(k+\varepsilon) \tag{403a}$$

instead of $p = N/k$ (see eq. 386). In theory:

$$1/\varepsilon = -a_k/a_{k+1} + 1 = -b_k/b_{k+1} + 1 \tag{403b}$$

(Since a_k and a_{k+1} or b_k and b_{k+1} change signs, ε will be positive.)

In practice it is advantageous to calculate:

$$\varepsilon = (|a_{k+1}| + |b_{k+1}|)/(|a_k| + |a_{k+1}| + |b_k| + |b_{k+1}|) \tag{403c}$$

where || denotes the absolute value. Evidently $\varepsilon \leq |1.0|$. Now:

$$A_\kappa = |\pi(\kappa + k_\varepsilon)(\kappa - k_\varepsilon)(\kappa^2 a_k^2 + k_\varepsilon^2 b_k^2)^{-1/2}/[2\kappa k_\varepsilon \sin(\pi k_\varepsilon)]| \tag{403d}$$

with $k_\varepsilon = \kappa + \varepsilon$. We have two κ_i values, viz. $\kappa_1 = k$ and $\kappa_2 = k+1$. Finally:

$$A_T = (A_{\kappa_1} + A_{\kappa_2})/2$$

The phase angle can be found from the expression:

$$\tan[\pi(\kappa+\varepsilon) + \phi_\varepsilon] = (p_T/p)\tan(\kappa\pi + \phi_\kappa) \tag{403e}$$

where ϕ_ε is the correct phase angle, ϕ_κ the harmonic phase angle (sin ϕ_κ and cos ϕ_κ are either b_κ and a_κ or $-b_\kappa$ and $-a_\kappa$.) Again, $\kappa_1 = k$ and $\kappa_2 = k+1$, with ϕ_{ε_1} and ϕ_{ε_2}, respectively. Then $\phi_T \sim (\phi_{\varepsilon_1} + \phi_{\varepsilon_2})/2$ is the true phase angle. The reader is referred to ESSENWANGER (1976) for additional details on non-harmonic components.

*[1] K is selected in accordance with the probability density of the Gaussian distribution (e.g., for a significance at the 95% level $K = 1.96$ etc.; see p. 241).

While Schuster's criterion is based on a Gaussian distribution KENDALL and STUART, 1966, p. 461) assumed that the distribution of the squared amplitudes follows the exponential law. Then the probability of exceeding a certain threshold A_{th}^2 is given by:

$$P(A_{th}^2 \geq 4\sigma_y^2 K/N) = \exp(-K) \tag{404a}$$

but WALKER (1914) found a more appropriate relationship:

$$P(A_{th}^2 \geq 4\sigma_y^2 K/N) = 1-(1-e^{-K})^n \tag{404b}$$

where n represents the number of independent amplitudes and K is an exceedance factor. BLOOMFIELD (1976) associated testing of the maximum amplitude with Fisher's G_n statistic. Let us designate the maximum amplitude among n independent amplitudes by A_{max}^2. Then:

$$P(A_{max}^2 \geq 4\sigma_y^2 K_2/N) = 1-\exp[-\exp(-K_3)] \tag{404c}$$

where:

$$K_2 = K_3 + \ln n \tag{404d}$$

Eq. 404c has been modified by BROOKS and CARRUTHERS (1953). They suggested testing of:

$$A_{max}^2 \geq \sigma_y^2 K_B^2/N \tag{404e}$$

where:

$$K_B^2/4 = \ln n - \ln P \tag{404f}$$

Because $-\ln P \sim K_3$ for $P \leq 0.05$ the criteria of eqs. 404c and e are equivalent (ESSENWANGER, 1980). After the maximum amplitude proved to be significant it is eliminated and the maximum of the remaining amplitudes is tested. This process is repeated until an amplitude is found which is not significant. This iterative testing avoids the pitfall that significant cycles will not be discovered during testing due to the presence of a dominant wave. Attention is called that σ_y^2 in eq. 404e must be reduced for consecutive testing:

$$\sigma_{y_j}^2 = \sigma_{y_{j-1}}^2 - A_j^2/2, \quad j=2, \ldots, n_t \tag{404g}$$

where n_t is the first non-significant amplitude ($\sigma_{y_1}^2 = \sigma_y^2$).
The "modulation" (=variation) of the amplitude for quasi-periodicity will generate side lobes in the harmonic spectrum (see p. 176). The interpretation of peaks and/or significant waves requires a thorough study of the data and a careful examination about the cause of these peaks. Furthermore, statistical significance does not explain the physical causes. It only assesses the probability and tests whether the peak may have been produced by random play.
The number of required terms in the Fourier series can be tested with the χ^2 test (see eq. 645). This method was illustrated in Example 15 (p. 73).
A quasi-periodogram by computation of spectra for variable record length was suggested by SCHICKEDANZ and BOWEN (1977) who recommended this particular method as a most suitable tool for climatological data sets where the periodicity is unknown. Another method, high resolution frequency analysis, was developed by BRIER et al. (1983) and is especially applicable to the prediction of "almost periodic" functions.

Significance test by analysis of variance

A more elaborate but very efficient test in harmonic analysis was developed by HARTLEY (1949). He related the testing of amplitudes to the χ^2 and F test (see eqs. 645 and 630) i.e.:

$$F_{max} = NA_{max}^2/(4R^2) \tag{405a}$$

where N = number of observations, A_{max} = highest amplitude, m = number of terms, with a maximum of $m_{max} = (N-1)/2$, but N must be odd.

$$R^2 = \left[N\sigma_y^2 - (N/2) \sum_1^m A_i^2 \right] \Big/ (N - 2m - 1) \tag{405b}$$

or identically:

$$R^2 = \left[N \sum_{m+1}^{k} (A_j^2/2) \right] \Big/ (N - 2m - 1) \tag{405c}$$

with $k = m_{max}$, $m < k$. Furthermore, σ_y^2 stands for the variance of the observed data Y_t. Another representation of R^2 would be:

$$R^2 = \sum (Y_t - Y_{at})^2 \tag{405d}$$

where Y_{at} designates the analytical function, i.e., the (truncated) Fourier series. It is evident that R^2 becomes undefined for $m = m_{max}$. Consequently, the test cannot be performed when $2m = N - 1$. In this case $Y_t \equiv Y_{at}$ and $R^2 = 0$.

The test is based on the concept that the residual error R^2 is caused by random fluctuations which are superimposed upon the individual observations. This principle has the same statistical background as the analysis of variance (see SNEDECOR and COCHRAN, 1967, etc.). The procedure is illustrated in Table XLV.

Again we have an iterative testing of the amplitudes. First A_{max}^2 is tested, then the second largest component, etc., until one component is encountered which is not significant. Then the testing stops because all the other amplitudes are smaller and consequently cannot be significant.

The probability that $F_{max} \leq F$ is given by:

$$P(F) = \int_0^\infty \phi_\nu(s)[1 - \exp(-s^2F)^m] \, ds \tag{406a}$$

where $\phi_\nu(s)$ is the distribution of a sample standard deviation based on ν degrees of

TABLE XLV

VARIANCE SCHEME FOR TESTING THE SIGNIFICANCE OF THE AMPLITUDE IN HARMONIC ANALYSIS

	Sum squares	Degrees freedom	Mean square	F-ratio
Total variance	$\sum (y_t - \bar{y})^2$	$N-1$	σ^2	–
Fourier term $i = 1, 2 \ldots m$	$NA_i^2/2$	$\nu_A = 2$	$NA_i^2/4$	$(NA_i^2/4)/R^2$
Fourier term $j = m+1 \ldots \frac{N-1}{2}$	$N \sum_{m+1}^{k} A_j^2/2$	$(N-1-2m)$	R^2 (eq. 405b, c, d)	1.0

freedom, $\nu = N - 2m - 1$. FINNEY (1941) found that:

$$P(F) = \sum_{r=0}^{m} (-1)^r C_r (1 + ra)^{-n} \tag{406b}$$

where C_r are coefficients depending on m, $n = \nu/2$ and $a = 2F/\nu$.
HARTLEY (1949) derived a simple approximation for the (upper) probability that $F_{max} \geq F_u$ with $n_1 = 2$ and $n_2 = \nu$ degrees of freedom:

$$P(F_u) = (1 - \alpha_u)^n \tag{406c}$$

where:

$$\alpha_u \sim (1 + 2F_u/\nu)^{-\nu/2} \tag{406d}$$

and n is the number of (non-random) terms from which A_{max} is taken, i.e., for A_{max}, the maximum amplitude, $n = m$, for the second largest amplitude $n = m - 1$, etc. Eq. 406c can be interpreted that $P(F_u)$ is not 99% as is usually assumed for $\alpha_u = 1\%$ rather it is $(0.99)^n$. E.g., $n = 6$, $P(F_u) \sim 94\%$, i.e., $\alpha \sim 6\%$; or for $\alpha_u = 0.5\%$, $n = 12$, $P(F) \sim 94\%$, again $\alpha \sim 6\%$. In fact, we can approximate F_u from ordinary tables of the F-distribution by utilizing the relationship:

$$P(F_u) \sim (1 - \alpha/n) \tag{406e}$$

where α is the chosen significance level. E.g., if $\alpha = 5\%$, $n = 6$, we extract F_u from the tables of the F-distribution for 2, ν degrees of freedom for the corresponding $\alpha_u = \alpha/n = (5/6)\%$.

Example 28. Let us assume that a data sample is available with $N = 49$ observations, i.e., $m_{max} = (49 - 1)/2 = 24$. Consider now a truncation of the Fourier series after the twelfth term, i.e., $m = 12$, or $N - 2m - 1 = 24$. For simplicity we postulate that the 12 terms have an equal amplitude of 2 except for one term whose amplitude*[1] $A_i = 5$. Again, for simplicity let the amplitudes A_{13} through A_{24} be 1. This information provides all the facts for the evaluation of the significance of the maximum amplitude by the F-test because persistence and the phase angle of the Fourier components are immaterial for this purpose (cf. Table XLVI).
We are now ready to test the maximum F-ratio for significance. First we extract the exceedance threshold F_u from tables of the F-distribution for 2, 24 degrees of freedom. Let us suppose that we test at the level $\alpha = 5\%$, $n = m = 12$, hence $\alpha_u = 5/12\%$. For 2, 24 d.f. and $P(F) = 99.5\%$ we find $F_u = 6.66$. From Table XLVI we find $F_{max} = 25$ while eq. 405a leads to $49 \cdot 25/4 \cdot (12.5) = 24.5$. Consequently, $F_{max} > F_u$, the amplitude 5 is significantly different from zero.
We cannot readily check the exact α-level for F_{max}, since most F-tables stop at $P(F) \geq 99.95\%$. For $P(F) = 99.95\%$, $F = 60.6$. From eq. 406b we calculate $\alpha_u \sim 0.0000135$, and eq. 406c leads to $P(F) \sim 99.98\%$.
The next question is whether the amplitude 2 is significant? From Table XLVI we find $F_{max} = 4$, or eq. 405a renders $49 \cdot 4/4 \cdot (12.5) = 3.92$, but $F_{max} > F_u = 6.66$ is required. The amplitude $A_i = 2$ is below the threshold. Let us check the probability $P(F \leq 4)$ by eq. 406b and c. For $F_u = 4$ and $n = 11$ $\sigma_u \sim 0.0422$, $P(F_u) \sim 62\%$. The second method $\alpha = m \cdot \alpha_u$ gives $\alpha \sim 0.46$ or $P(F_u) \sim 54\%$. A review of the F-tables for $F = 4$ with 2, 24 degrees of freedom, shows that $F \sim 4$ leads to $P(F)$ of approximately 96% which corresponds to α_u, but $P(F_u)$ may lie between 54 and 62%.
A comparison with ε_F^2 (see eq. 402a) is added. $\varepsilon_F^2 = 4 \cdot (41.34)/49 = 3.37$. At the 95% level of significance (two-sided) the factor $k = 1.96$, hence $k^2 \varepsilon_F^2 = 12.96$. The amplitude 5 would prove to be significantly different from zero, although the threshold ε_F^2 is almost double the size of $F = 6.66$. This higher threshold has an interesting consequence. If we add persistence to Schuster's test criterion the amplitude of 5 may not be significantly different from zero because persistence can increase ε_F^2 by a factor 4–5, which would mean that $A^2 = 25 < \varepsilon_P^2$. We are now confronted with non-identical

*[1] To indicate that this amplitude of $A = 5$ can occur for any subscript among 1 through 12, let us denote this amplitude by A_i.

TABLE XLVI

VARIANCE TABLE FOR EXAMPLE 28

	Sum of squares	Degr. freed.	Mean square	F-ratio, eq. 405a
Total variance	1984.5	48	41.34	–
	$N \cdot A^2/2$	ν_A	$NA^2/2\nu_A$	
A_1	98	2	49	49/12.5=4
⋮	⋮	⋮	⋮	
A_i	612.5	2	306.25	(306.25)/12.5=25
⋮	⋮	⋮	⋮	
A_{12}	98	2	49	4
A_{13}	24.5	2	12.25	1
⋮	⋮	⋮	⋮	⋮
A_{24}	24.5	2	12.25	1
$N\sum_{13}^{24} A^2/2$	=294	$N-2m-1=24$	$R^2=12.25$	–

The total sum of squares is 11·(98)+612.5+12·(24.5)=1984.5; $\nu=49-1-24=24$.

conclusions from the two considered test methods. However, this discrepancy is not as confusing as it appears at first sight.

The reader must be aware that the individual test methods are developed for a particular statistical background. Therefore the test must be interpreted based on that particular background.

In the analysis of variance the F-test is performed under the assumption that the amplitudes A_{13} through A_{24} are caused by randomness. Schuster's criterion rests on the background of complete randomness with a variance of 41.34. In the F-test the random background is assumed to be 294/48=6.125, which is lower. Thus, the dissimilarity in the postulation about the random contribution sets a different stage for the test hypothesis. Had we assumed that the variance for $A_{13} \rightarrow A_{24}$ is 41.34 (for the individual component) F_{max} would be 306.25/20.67=14.8. The ratio is now smaller and the ratio F_{max}/F_u is approximately the same as $A_{max}^2/(k^2\varepsilon_F^2)$.

The reader is reminded that the F-test requires the independence of components. This postulation is not exactly fulfilled for many atmospheric data because they may include persistence. In most cases it is not known a priori how much persistence contributes and how it will affect ε_F^2. In our test sample no assumption about persistence has been included. Therefore, the question whether the amplitude for $A=5$ has been produced by persistence cannot be answered. If the autocorrelation function in eq. 402b were known Stumpff's criterion ε_P^2 (see eq. 402b) could be employed but an evaluation of the contribution by persistence is not trivial by the F-test.

The selection of components by application of least square methods was outlined by SNEYERS (1976).

Power spectrum analysis

Power spectrum and autocorrelation

The spectrum of the harmonic analysis generally displays a wide scatter of adjacent amplitudes and it is advisable to smooth the spectrum. If we divide a set of data (e.g., time series) into subsets and subject these subsets to a harmonic analysis, we obtain a spectrum for each individual subset. These individual spectra can show considerable differences between amplitudes of the same harmonics. The smooth spectra of the individual subsets, however, may be very similar or coincide, provided the data set is homogeneous (stationary). It is, therefore, desirable to derive a smooth spectrum directly and not via a detour from a harmonic analysis (PANOFSKY and BRIER, 1965).

We can further incorporate into the calculation of the smooth spectrum an "estimation" principle. Under this concept the task requires an estimate for a spectrum of which only a finite set of data (sample) is known, i.e., the given data are interpreted as a sample from a population.

One way was introduced by TUKEY (1949) and has found widespread application (BLACKMAN and TUKEY, 1958). Our discussion centers on the distribution of amplitudes, and the phase angle which provides the time of the maximum, is of secondary importance. This may also prove advantageous because "quasi-periodicity" which is found in atmospheric time series may have different phase angles in different subsets. The difference of the phase angle leads to a diminishing of the amplitude. The phase angle is unimportant in the power spectrum analysis. Thus, detection of these quasi-cycles may succeed in power spectrum analysis whereas they may remain undiscovered in harmonic analysis. If an analytical expression for an individual wave (cycle) is wanted, the harmonic or periodogram analysis can be engaged afterwards or the relative phase angle can be obtained from the cross-spectrum.

On p. 111 the autocorrelation was discussed. The autocorrelation of a sine or cosine wave is a cosine wave. Thus, the individual harmonic components reflected a transformation to a standard reference point, i.e., normalized phase angles for the autocorrelogram. In other words: the phase angles of the components are all aligned, and at lag zero a value of 90° results (maximum amplitude of a cosine wave).

If we deal with the (linear) correlation coefficients, we obtain a normalized spectrum while employing the covariances renders an overall integral of the spectrum equal to the variance.

The power spectrum permits easy spotting of significant and important periodicities which appear as peaks in the spectrum. We calculate the following line powers L from the autocorrelation series, up to lag m. Consequently, the basic or fundamental period is reduced from N to $2m$. The autocorrelation series for a system is symmetrical at lag zero. Thus, only one side of the autocorrelation series needs to be computed although the power spectrum analysis (described below) is performed on a double-sided symmetric autocorrelation function (R).

$$L_0=(R_0+R_m)/2m+\sum_{1}^{m-1} R_\tau/m=\bar{R} \qquad (407a)$$

where τ represents the lag from 0 through m.

$$L_j=R_0/m+(2/m)\cdot\sum_{\tau=1}^{m-1} R_\tau\cos(\tau j\pi/m)+(R_m/m)\cos j\pi \qquad (407b)$$

$0<\tau<m$

$$L_m=(R_0+(-1)^m R_m)/2m+\sum_{1}^{m-1}(-1)^\tau R_\tau/m \qquad (407c)$$

The summation is taken over τ. Further:

$$R_\tau=r_\tau/r_0 \qquad (407d)$$

where r_τ denotes either the correlation coefficients (then $r_0=1$) or the covariances eq. 279 (then $r_0=\sigma_y^2$). Small m decreases the resolution because the amplitudes of the higher harmonics are then of the same magnitude as the random error fluctuation. Further, all

periodicities larger than m are suppressed. The smaller m in comparison with N, the more smoothing is obtained.
The above formula, however, does not provide the best estimate of the smoothed spectrum. The deviations become quite considerable whenever large oscillations of the true spectrum are in a short sequence of the harmonics j. Tukey suggested a smoothing of the spectral estimates.
A widely used smoothing formula (Tukey and Hamming, see BLACKMAN and TUKEY, 1958) is:

$$Ls_0 = 0.54L_0 + 0.46L_1 \tag{408a}$$

$$Ls_j = 0.54L_j + 0.23(L_{j-1} + L_{j+1}), \quad 0 < j < m \tag{408b}$$

$$Ls_m = 0.54L_m + 0.46L_{m-1} \tag{408c}$$

where m denotes the maximum lag.
Another formula (J. v. Hann, see BLACKMAN and TUKEY, 1958) follows the regular scheme:

$$Ls_0 = 0.50L_0 + 0.50L_1 \tag{409a}$$

$$Ls_j = 0.5L_j + 0.25(L_{j-1} + L_{j+1}) \tag{409b}$$

$$Ls_m = 0.5L_m + 0.5L_{m-1} \tag{409c}$$

The smoothed spectra by either formula differ very little. The main differences appear in the so-called "windows". Spectra from empirical observations show undesirable influences of other frequencies, e.g., one main maximum creates a series of (small) side maxima. These effects will be eliminated by the smoothing process, and thus an "estimated" spectrum is created which is a smoothed spectrum. The effect of smoothing on a given combination of pure "waves" (spectral lines) is discussed later in Examples 29 and 30.
In general, the theory reveals the possibility of large sampling fluctuations. Despite this restriction, the power spectrum has proven an important tool of analysis for the understanding of the physical background, evaluation of forecasting techniques, and instrumental response, just to name a few examples of application.
The computation of the covariance involves the multiplication of the two sets of data; the autocorrelation is based on one set (one variate). The line spectrum values L_j based on the correlation coefficients represent the percentage reduction (accounted variance) of the individual term (see eq. 401).
Tests of significance for the power spectrum will be discussed on p. 170. The effects of a short record length and/or a low signal-to-noise ratio will be discussed on p. 160.

The cross-spectrum

Data sets containing periodicities may display correlation or may appear uncorrelated. In the first case it is usually of interest whether the correlation is due to low- or high-frequency correspondence. In turn, the data may appear uncorrelated because low frequencies be negatively correlated and high frequencies positively and the summation may cancel the correlation. These effects resemble the correlations between two data sets which were studied for orthogonal polynomials (see eq. 375c).
Correlations and cross-correlation between sets of data can be investigated by computa-

tion of the cross-spectrum which consists of the co-spectrum and the quadrature spectrum. The co-spectrum Lco_j is obtained by averaging the cross-covariances (or correlation) at lag τ and $-\tau$.

$$Rco_\tau = (R_\tau + R_{-\tau})/2 \tag{410a}$$

These average values are then subjected to a Fourier analysis with the same formulae as the power spectrum (eqs. 407–409). We denote the lines of the spectrum by Lco_j. The same result will occur by multiplication of the autocovariances with the respective cosine terms in eq. 407a–c. The smoothing of the spectra is carried out with eq. 408 or 409.
Peaks in the co-spectrum Lco_j indicate the correlated part. Because a negative correlation is associated with a negative covariance the displayed ordinate in the co-spectrum is negative.
The relationship between lags can be analysed from:

$$Rqu_\tau = (R_{-\tau} - R_\tau)/2 \tag{410b}$$

Any difference appears as an asymmetry of the cross-correlation about lag zero. This leads to the quadrature spectrum in which one set of data delineates a delay from the other set by a quarter period. We first compute the cross-variances by eq. 410b. The quadrature estimate is then:

$$Lqu_j = (2/m) \cdot \sum_{\tau=1}^{m-1} Rqu_\tau \sin(\pi\tau j/m) \tag{411}$$

followed by smoothing with eq. 408 or 409 where m denotes again the number of positive lags (not counting zero).
The quadrature spectrum provides the relative phase of the harmonic components between set one and two. We can write:

$$Lqu_j/Lco_j = \tan(\pi j\tau/m) = \tan(\omega) \tag{412a}$$

$$\tau = m\omega/(j\pi) \tag{412b}$$

If the phase angle ψ (see eq. 384a) for the first data set is known, the phase angle of the second set is then $\psi + \omega$. It should be repeated that in the autocorrelation the reference angles are all aligned at lag zero, i.e., they are 90° or the maximum of a cosine wave is at $j = 0$.
The "coherence" Coh_j is a measure of the correlation between two variables for particular harmonics j or cycles of length $2m/j$.

$$Coh_j = (L^2_{qu_j} + L^2_{co_j})/[(Lx_j)(Ly_j)] \tag{413}$$

where Lx_j and Ly_j stand for the spectrum estimates L_j of the variables X and Y respectively. The Coh_j can vary from 0 to 1, and has affinity with the correlation ratio except that the coherence is a function of the frequency. A significance criterion (limiting form) for the Coh_j would be the expectancy:

$$\varepsilon_{Coh} = [1 - \alpha^{1/(n_f - 1)}]^{1/2} \tag{414}$$

where n_f stands for the degrees of freedom (see later eq. 426b, relationship with χ^2) and α is the probability level of significance.

The coherence Coh_j obtained from empirical data may exceed the boundary limits 0 to 1 because of sampling fluctuation, roundings, truncations, etc. The coherence stays within limits 0 to 1, however, for significant periods (i.e., the peaks of the power spectrum).

Examples and comparison with Fourier analysis

Example 29. This example serves as the basis of a discussion whether a trend should be eliminated before the Fourier or power spectrum analysis is performed. This question cannot be answered unequivocally although theoreticians favor the removal of a trend. The following example elucidates to the reader some of the problems.

Let us assume that the set of data consists of two superimposed sine waves, one with 112 and one with 56 points length (e.g., days or hours, etc.) both with the same amplitude. The Fourier analysis produces the two given periods with $C^2_{A_j}$ of 50% each (see eq. 389c). This result agrees with the expectation. Amplitude and phase angle render the proper value. Some tolerance must be accepted for computational inaccuracy.

We now perform a power spectrum analysis up to lag $m = 56$. This renders the basic period $2\,m = 112$ which is equivalent to the basic period in the Fourier analysis. First we examine the data where the trend has not been removed. If the autocorrelation function is generated from only 112 data points and L_j is calculated by eq. 407a–d, the answer will not match the original data. The autocorrelation function obtained from 112 points is exhibited in Fig. 3 and the first four line powers follow in the second column. Instead of $L_1 = 0.5$ we find $L_1 \sim 0$. The spectrum differs from the result by the Fourier analysis. The contribution by the first sine wave ($p = 112$) is spread over the first four waves, and L_1 and L_2 in the smoothed spectrum are approximately of the same magnitude. The two sine waves of the original data set cannot be clearly recognized.

The data sample is now expanded to 224 and 448 points by repeating Y_1 through Y_{112} for a second, third and fourth cycle. The autocorrelation function is deduced from two cycles, i.e., 224 points, instead of 112. Let us make a second change. We obtain the lag correlation by computing the covariances from sets of 112 data length which differ in their initial value by the lag L, i.e., Y_1 to Y_{112} and $Y_{1+L} + Y_{112+L}$, a data set simulating infinite length. In contrast, the customary procedure of calculating the autocorrelation shows a variable data length: $n = N - L$ for every lag L.

Fig. 3 illustrates the new autocorrelation function, and the power spectrum of this new curve furnishes the correct amplitudes (see columns 3 and 4 in Table XLVII). The smoothed power spectrum spreads the amplitudes again over four waves. Caution should be exercised in interpreting results from the smoothed and unsmoothed power spectrum analysis.

The differences between results from the power spectrum analysis and the given waves of the data set demonstrate that the correct cycle of the data cannot be discovered with the power spectrum unless the data series is long enough compared with the cycle. In other words: the length of the data series must be considerably longer (say at least 4 times as long) than the longest cycle. The proper

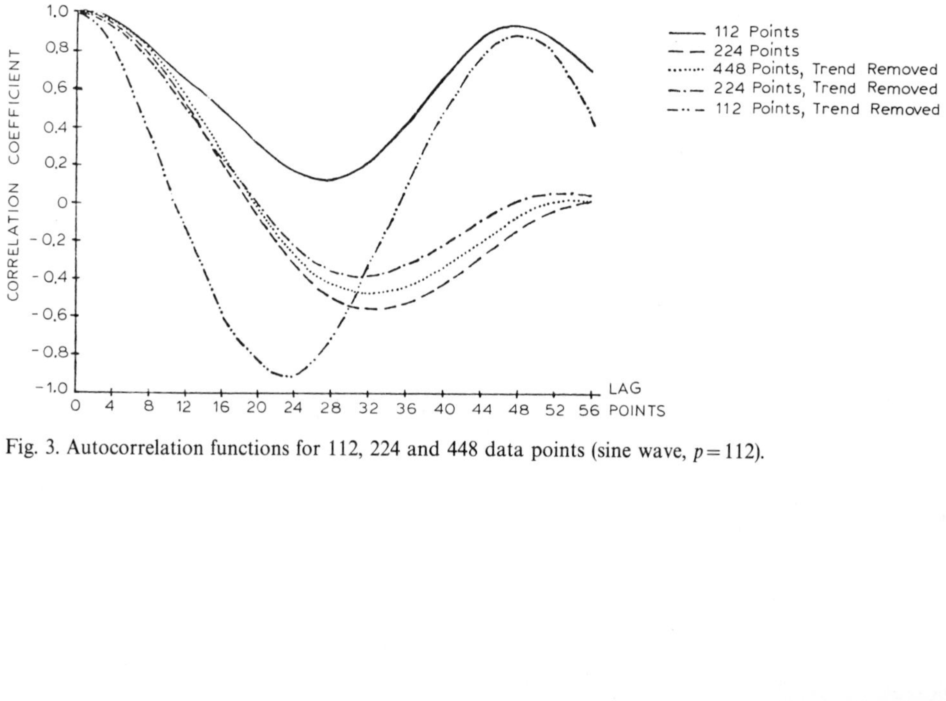

Fig. 3. Autocorrelation functions for 112, 224 and 448 data points (sine wave, $p = 112$).

TABLE XLVII

POWER SPECTRUM ANALYSIS OF 112 AND 56 POINT SINE WAVE, EQUAL AMPLITUDE, MAXIMUM LAG

	Without trend removal				Trend removed					
	112 points		224 points		112 points		224 points		448 points	
	line	smoothed	line	smoothed	line	smoothed	line	smoothed	line	smoothed
112 L_0	0.601	0.307	0.0	0.231	0.100	−0.083	0.099	0.242	0.048	0.243
112 L_1	−0.038	0.206	0.501	0.385	−0.298	0.037	0.410	0.346	0.471	0.374
56 L_2	0.386	0.220	0.499	0.385	0.762	0.436	0.444	0.345	0.471	0.365
37 L_3	0.089	0.117	0.0	0.115	0.406	0.381	0.046	0.124	0.012	0.113

autocorrelation function cannot be obtained from a short data series. Without it the power spectrum cannot be determined with precision.

These severe limitations when records are short have also been pointed out by CURRIE (1981) who has also cautioned about the problem when the signal-to-noise ratio is low.

Let us examine the effect of eliminating a trend before the power spectrum analysis is carried out. A linear trend is assumed. Again, we start with taking a data set of 112 points only ($Y_1, \ldots, Y_{112}$). The set of data with the two sine waves 112 and 56 points with equal amplitude produces a linear correlation coefficient of -0.826 which implies a strong linear trend. This is not unexpected because every sine wave can be approximated by a polynomial function of which the first (linear) term places the largest contribution. In other words, if a cycle close to the basic period $N/2$ exists it is substantially eliminated with the trend.

The result of the Fourier analysis after removing first a trend from 112, 224, and 448 points of the periodically expanded data set is given in Table XLVIII. As displayed in Table XLVIII, the longer the data series the less sensitive is the outcome to trend removal if the trend is caused by a long term cycle. Table XLVIII exhibits the accounted variance of the Fourier components. As illustrated for 448 data points the Fourier analysis leads to the approximately correct amplitude because the data length is 4 times the length of the longest cycle. The absolute value of the amplitude and the phase angle are of secondary importance in this example. Their discussion is omitted here.

Example 29 was chosen to illustrate deficiencies with Fourier and power spectrum analysis. The Fourier analysis appears more suitable than the power spectrum if the data set contains only harmonic components and the basic period (longest wave) is correctly chosen. The power spectrum will show a peak around the wave numbers of a possible cycle. It is more suitable than the Fourier analysis to delineate quasi-periodicities (see ESSENWANGER, 1980).

In our case, the largest cycle ($p = 112$) is close to the period 2 m and is not properly reflected in the power spectrum. This result is caused by the deficiency of establishing a reliable autocorrelation function unless the longest cycle of length p is small enough in comparison with the total length N. The evaluation will be enhanced by calculating several spectra with variable maximum lag m, with and without trend removal. If one suspects cycles whose interrelationship is non-harmonic the Fourier series should be replaced by the periodogram. The plotting of vector diagrams and a distribution of amplitudes for the periodogram analysis may also be helpful (see ESSENWANGER, 1951 and 1976, pp. 226–243).

The trend can be checked for significance by testing the correlation coefficient or the trend coefficient. Although the trend coefficient may prove significant such as in the presented example, the cause and/or its physical background is not provided by a significance test.

Robust estimation of power spectra in order to reduce the influence of outliers was discussed by KLEINER et al. (1979). They suggested a filtering operation (p. 194) or an autoregressive representation with iterative least square solutions.

TABLE XLVIII

ACCOUNTED VARIANCE OF THE FIRST 5 FOURIER COMPONENTS AFTER ELIMINATION OF TREND (FOURIER ANALYSIS) FOR DATA, EXAMPLE 29

Total data points:	448			224		112	True
Trend, correlation coeff.:	−0.206			−0.413		−0.826	
Length of period:	112	224	448*[1]	112*[1]	224*[1]	112*[1]	112
Fourier component (period)							
448	–	–	0.027	–	–	–	0
224	–	0.007	0.007	–	0.125	–	0
112	0.486	0.482	0.466	0.427	0.361	0.014	0.500
56	0.513	0.509	0.492	0.558	0.472	0.466	0.500
37.33	0.0	0.0	0.0	0.004	0.003	0.142	0
28	0.0	0.0	0.0	0.003	0.002	0.086	0
						etc.	

*[1]This column corresponds to the power spectrum analysis of Table XLVII, trend removed.

Example 30. The previous discussion will now be supplemented by an analysis of observed meteorological data. For demonstration purposes 10 years of 3-hourly temperature observations for Yuma, Arizona, January–February (1955–1964) were chosen. To eliminate small fluctuations a 10-year average for every calendar date at the given hour was produced. The data from January 1 to February 25 provide a set of 448 data points. This set, $Y_1, \ldots, Y_{448}$, was condensed by averaging the four periods of 112 points to simplify the Fourier analysis, but the power spectrum was calculated from the set of 448 data points. The results of the power spectrum and Fourier analysis are presented in Table XLIX (up to lag 40). The corresponding autocorrelation function up to lag $m=56$ is exhibited in Fig. 4. For the 112 point data set $\sigma^2=58.08$, while $\sigma^2=66.04$ from the original 448 data points.

As expected, the daily temperature cycle emerges as the major contribution. For $j=14$ and a period of 8 points we recognize the 24-h cycle for 3-hourly observations. The results of the power spectrum and the Fourier analysis are equivalent (compare column L_j with C_{Aj}^2). The Fourier analysis furnishes amplitude and phase angle simultaneously. The power spectrum has the advantage of a much shorter computer time despite the fact that first the autocorrelation coefficients had to be computed but today the FFT is quite time efficient, too.

In addition to the daily cycle a semi-diurnal period ($j=28$, period $=4$ points) with less than 8% of the total variance is apparent. Both periods are statistically significant. The reader may notice that sharp peaks also appear in the smoothed power spectrum but the contribution by the daily cycle is dispersed over the neighboring waves in the smoothed spectrum L_{sj}. This discloses the same features which were discussed in Example 29. The smoothed spectrum places the location of the cycle correctly, but the amount of the contribution must be taken from the unsmoothed spectrum. Therefore, interpretation of the spectrum should be made by considering the regular and smooth line spectrum.

The next two columns (9 and 10) of Table XLIX were computed for the data set after the trend was removed from the set of 112 data points which had been derived by averaging. The results resemble the outcome of the first columns of the table. The linear correlation coefficient of the trend is 0.094, which is negligible for all practical purposes. Columns 9 and 10 are included basically as an exemplification that small changes in the data sets can lead to differences in the results but these differences are not statistically significant.

The last two columns depict the outcome of the power spectrum analysis from the original 448 points, with and without trend removal. The (linear) correlation coefficient of the trend is now 0.275, exceeding the correlation coefficient from the set of 112 points. Inspection of the powers L_j with included trend reveals, however, a contribution of $L_0=0.0016$ for the set of 112 points. The contribution by longer waves is very small while L_0 for the 448 points show 0.0812. After removal of the trend L_0 decreases to 0.0121 which is still larger than 0.0016. Thus in the averaging process (reduction from 448 to 112 points) there is a stronger reduction of the long term trend than the process of removing the linear term alone. The share of the trend is reflected in the differences between the L_{14} and L_{28} spectral values for the data sets 112 and 448 points.

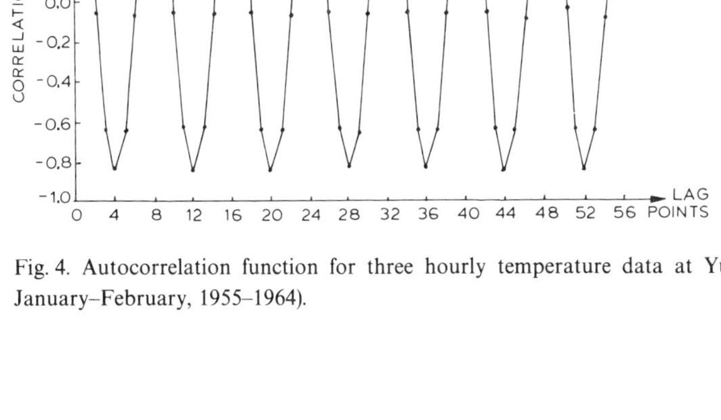

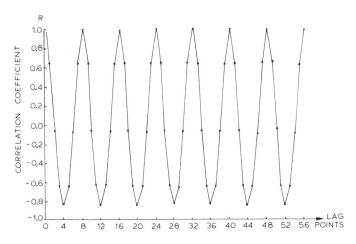

Fig. 4. Autocorrelation function for three hourly temperature data at Yuma, Arizona (ten-year summary, January–February, 1955–1964).

TABLE XLIX

POWER SPECTRA AND FOURIER ANALYSIS FOR THREE-HOURLY TEMPERATURE DATA, YUMA, ARIZONA

j	112 points									448 points	
	Power spectrum			Fourier analysis				Trend removed		without trend	with trend
	period	L_j	Ls_j	a_j	b_j	A_j	$C^2_{A_j}$	L_j	$C^2_{A_j}$ (Fourier)	L_j (power spectrum)	L_j
0	–	0.0016	0.0028	–	–	–	–	−0.0006	–	0.0121	0.0812
1	112.00	0.0041	0.0026	−0.49	0.41	0.64	0.0034	0.0036	0.0024	0.0127	0.0134
2	56.00	0.0001	0.0012	−0.18	−0.35	0.40	0.0013	0.0002	0.0013	0.0029	0.0031
3	37.33	0.0001	0.0002	−0.13	0.09	0.16	0.0002	0.0009	0.0002	0.0013	0.0004
4	28.00	−0.0011	0.0000	0.05	0.12	0.13	0.0001	−0.0007	0.0007	0.0010	0.0006
5	22.40	0.0017	0.0005	−0.01	0.02	0.02	0.0000	0.0017	0.0001	0.0015	0.0012
6	18.67	−0.0007	0.0004	−0.28	0.12	0.30	0.0007	−0.0010	0.0003	0.0009	0.0013
7	16.00	0.0014	0.0004	−0.11	0.15	0.18	0.0002	0.0014	0.0002	0.0007	0.0008
8	14.00	0.0008	0.0004	0.21	0.11	0.24	0.0004	−0.0005	0.0009	0.0009	0.0001
9	12.44	0.0024	0.0006	0.03	−0.04	0.05	0.0000	0.0024	0.0001	0.0009	0.0008
10	11.20	−0.0022	0.0003	−0.12	0.00	0.12	0.0001	−0.0024	0.0000	0.0000	0.0001
11	10.18	0.0040	0.0009	−0.08	0.14	0.16	0.0002	0.0039	0.0002	0.0013	0.0016
12	9.33	−0.0030	0.0007	0.10	−0.24	0.26	0.0005	−0.0030	0.0006	0.0002	0.0000
13	8.62	0.0061	0.2116	0.07	−0.04	0.08	0.0000	0.0063	0.0001	0.0035	0.0025
14	8.00	0.9088	0.4906	−8.80	−5.30	10.27	0.9086	0.9078	0.9065	0.8732	0.8142
15	7.47	−0.0067	0.2061	−0.11	0.00	0.11	0.0001	−0.0065	0.0000	−0.0013	−0.0019
16	7.00	0.0031	−0.0004	−0.05	0.08	0.09	0.0000	0.0031	0.0000	0.0017	0.0014
17	6.59	−0.0026	−0.0002	−0.03	−0.05	0.05	0.0000	−0.0025	0.0000	−0.0003	0.0001
18	6.22	0.0018	0.0001	−0.08	−0.13	0.16	0.0002	0.0016	0.0001	0.0010	0.0011
19	5.89	−0.0013	−0.0001	−0.01	0.04	0.04	0.0000	−0.0013	0.0000	−0.0001	−0.0000
20	5.60	0.0009	0.0001	0.12	0.06	0.13	0.0001	0.0010	0.0002	0.0008	0.0006
21	5.33	−0.0002	0.0002	−0.03	−0.06	0.07	0.0000	−0.0002	0.0000	0.0002	0.0001
22	5.09	0.0006	0.0001	−0.04	−0.08	0.09	0.0000	0.0005	0.0000	0.0003	0.0004
23	4.87	−0.0007	−0.0002	−0.03	0.01	0.03	0.0000	−0.0008	0.0000	−0.0001	−0.0001
24	4.67	0.0004	0.0001	0.03	−0.02	0.04	0.0000	0.0004	0.0000	0.0002	0.0002

25	4.48	0.0002	0.0002	−0.01	0.01	0.01	0.0000	0.0002	0.0000	0.0002	0.0001
26	4.31	−0.0001	0.0004	−0.12	0.08	0.14	0.0001	−0.0001	0.0001	0.0004	0.0004
27	4.15	0.0018	0.0184	−0.05	0.02	0.05	0.0000	0.0019	0.0000	0.0005	0.0004
28	4.00	0.0759	0.0408	2.74	1.18	2.98	0.0763	0.0794	0.0785	0.0755	0.0682
29	3.86	−0.0026	0.0163	0.10	−0.05	0.11	0.0000	−0.0027	0.0001	−0.0006	−0.0006
30	3.73	0.0014	−0.0001	0.04	−0.06	0.07	0.0000	0.0014	0.0000	0.0005	0.0004
31	3.61	−0.0012	−0.0001	−0.02	0.04	0.05	0.0000	−0.0012	0.0000	0.0000	−0.0001
32	3.50	0.0009	0.0001	−0.02	−0.02	0.02	0.0000	0.0009	0.0000	0.0001	0.0001
33	3.39	−0.0012	−0.0003	0.00	−0.06	0.06	0.0000	−0.0012	0.0000	−0.0002	−0.0001
34	3.29	0.0007	−0.0001	−0.08	−0.06	0.11	0.0000	0.0007	0.0000	0.0002	0.0002
35	3.20	−0.0008	−0.0001	−0.02	0.00	0.02	0.0000	−0.0008	0.0000	−0.0001	−0.0000
36	3.11	0.0007	−0.0001	0.04	0.04	0.05	0.0000	0.0007	0.0000	0.0002	0.0002
37	3.03	−0.0011	−0.0003	0.00	−0.00	0.00	0.0000	−0.0011	0.0000	−0.0002	−0.0002
38	2.95	0.0007	−0.0002	−0.01	−0.07	0.07	0.0000	0.0006	0.0000	0.0002	0.0002
39	2.87	−0.0012	−0.0003	−0.04	−0.04	0.06	0.0000	−0.0013	0.0000	−0.0002	−0.0002
40	2.80	0.0008	−0.0005	0.02	−0.01	0.02	0.0000	0.0008	0.0000	0.0002	0.0002
etc.											

The power spectrum analysis for the set of 448 points (Table XLIX) displays another advantage of the power spectrum over the Fourier analysis. L_0 provides a good estimation of the contribution by waves >112 points. This information can only be obtained from the Fourier analysis by expanding the basic period to 448 points and by calculating 224 terms (instead of $m=56$ for the power spectrum). We could omit some harmonics and restrict the calculations to 56 frequencies. The omitted wave numbers can, however, contribute to the variance, and the calculated skeleton of harmonics would not add up to 100%. The power spectrum will total 100% independently of the choice of m.

Examination of the last two columns of Table XLIX (Example 30) shows that the diurnal and semi-diurnal cycle (448 points) are slightly reduced in their contribution to the total variance. This is expected because some energy shifts to shorter (random) cycles. The amplitudes for the 448 point Fourier analysis provide approximately the same numerical values as the power spectrum which have been omitted in Table XLIX.

Fig. 4 contains one autocorrelation curve. The corresponding autocorrelation for the other three configurations of the power spectrum analysis resemble the depicted curve so closely that it would be difficult to distinguish between them.

Example 31. This example demonstrates some results of the cross-spectrum analysis. For simplicity the two sets of data comprise the years 1955 and 1956 for 448 consecutive points of the 3-hourly temperature observations starting with 1 January. Results are given in Table L. The first eight columns list the power spectrum for the individual years, the co-spectrum, and the quadrature spectrum. The first four columns delineate the unsmoothed and the next four columns the smoothed spectral values. The last two columns list the coherence and the phase angle ω between the harmonics of the two sets (smoothed spectra). Only significant cycles have been selected for inclusion into Table L. Maximum lag is again $m=56$.

It is reconfirmed that $j=14$ is the major cycle with a period of 24 h. The smoothed power spectrum was engaged to compute the coherence. Consequently, the coherence stays high in the adjacent classes of significant cycles ($j=14$ and 28). The phase angle indicates very little difference between the two sets for $j=14$ (356° for $j=14$ can be interpreted as $-4°$) and $j=28$. The difference of 98 degrees for $j=1$ is larger but the coherence is smaller and the cycle of 14 days does not show statistical significance (see eq. 426a).

Table L discloses that the coherence lies between 0 and 1.0 for the significant cycles. The coherence remains within the limits if calculated from the smoothed line powers. The coherence calculated from the unsmoothed line powers exceeds the given boundaries, which is an effect of random fluctuations in the non-smoothed power spectrum. These random errors are considerably reduced by smoothing (see central limit theorem). The coherence is therefore meaningless for non-significant cycles.

TABLE L

CROSS SPECTRUM ANALYSIS AND COHERENCE

j	Unsmoothed				Smoothed				Eq. 411, smoothed	
	1955	1956			1955	1956				
	L_j	L_j	Lco	Lqu	L_j	L_j	Lco	Lqu	Coh_j	ω_j
0	0.100	0.072	−0.049	0.000	–	–	–	–	–	degrees
1	0.220	0.111	0.010	0.108	0.153	0.083	−0.010	0.069	0.376	98
2	0.050	0.030	−0.019	−0.044	0.079	0.046	−0.008	0.046	0.589	100
3	0.008	0.019	−0.000	0.013	0.018	0.021	−0.007	0.004	0.163	148
⋮										
13	0.007	0.014	0.006	−0.005	0.118	0.150	0.124	−0.011	0.874	355
14	0.487	0.614	0.526	−0.036	0.266	0.335	0.286	−0.020	0.919	356
15	0.005	0.001	0.001	0.001	0.116	0.143	0.122	−0.007	0.897	357
⋮										
27	0.002	0.000	−0.000	−0.001	0.011	0.012	0.010	−0.000	0.798	359
28	0.040	0.049	0.043	0.000	0.022	0.027	0.023	0.000	0.900	0
29	0.000	0.001	0.001	−0.000	0.010	0.012	0.010	0.000	0.874	1

Example 32. This example is included to illustrate the dependency of the power spectrum on the maximum lag and to delineate some limitations in the separation of waves.
It was demonstrated in Example 29 that the length of the periodicities is not properly reflected in the power spectrum unless the number N of the data set is sufficiently large compared with the longest significant wave length p_L. E.g., if this ratio $N/P_L \leq 3$ the power spectrum analysis is sensitive to trend elimination and choice of maximum lag. Let us first examine the following data set:

$$Y_i = 5 + 5\sin(\pi i/4 + \psi_1) + 4\sin(2\pi i/7 + \psi_2) + 3\sin(\pi i/3 + \psi_3)$$

where:

$\psi_1 = \psi_2 = \psi_3 = 0$ for simplicity.

The data set shows wave lengths of 8, 7, and 6 points. Assume that $Y_1, \ldots, Y_N$ for $N = 504$. This provides $N/p_L = 63$, a ratio well above the limits stated above. The amplitudes lead to variance share of 50, 32 and 18% for $p = 8$, 7, 6, respectively. The average ($A_0 = 5$) is unessential for the following discussion because it only serves as a reference for the three waves. Thus, in this hypothetical set of data the total data length N is apparently large enough. The data reveal that no trend is superimposed. As anticipated, the linear correlation coefficient is close to zero for the data set of $N = 504$. In conclusion, data length and trend are no problems. However, another possible weakness of the power spectrum is delineated.
The three periodicities p_i need a specific basic period in order to be harmonics. An arbitrary maximum lag m does not satisfy this requirement. In fact, all three chosen wave lengths lead only to whole numbers in a system where m is a multiple of 84. Let us arbitrarily choose $m = 31$, 43, 48 and 50. For $m = 48$ two waves have an integer number of the basic period while all other m's lead to fractions. Because the power spectrum (and the Fourier series) is calculated for integer j's of the basic period the cycles are reproduced in the neighborhood of the actual wave number. In turn, in this case the periodogram analysis can pinpoint the correct amplitude and phase angle of the three postulated waves.
The power spectrum has the advantage that the maximum lag m can be considerably reduced below the total data length N. The three waves have a common denominator of 168. Consequently, $m = 84$ would be the smallest optimum maximum length for clear separation. Frequently the correct cycles of observational data are not known a priori. Thus, the "correct" maximum length $2m$ cannot be determined. Some maximum lag numbers m are more suitable than others. Unless the precise length of the cycles is known, however, the optimum m cannot be determined. Thus, the power spectrum is an estimate, and the choice of m is of secondary importance. Values of m smaller than the optimum are possible if the power spectrum is considered as a tool of estimation.
Table LI depicts the dependency of L_j in the power spectrum on the choice of the maximum lag. The spectrum L_j, and the summation $\sum L_j$ are given in the three respective columns up to L_j where $\sum L_j \geq 1.0$. The reader may notice "noise" in the spectra. These random fluctuations may be either an aliasing effect or plain noise (Blackman and Tukey, 1958) or both. In observational data sets this noise may also be generated by instrumental error. The correct wave length of the postulated periods p as fractions of the basic period $2m$ are given at the bottom of the respective columns.
We learn from Table LI that the numerical value of the spectrum L_j depends on the proximity of the true wave period to the given integer wave number j. The peak of L_j appears at the nearest j, and the size of L_j is not easy to predict. Even for the wave numbers $j = 12$ and 16 with maximum lag $m = 48$ for which these cycles are integers the correct L_j of 50 and 18% is not found. These possible limitations in precision should be kept in mind before interpretations of power spectra or the Fourier series are made.

Power spectrum and turbulence spectrum

The Kolmogorov–Obukhov–Corrsin hypothesis requires a one-dimensional velocity spectrum of the wind's u-component of the form:

$$F(\Omega) = \kappa\varepsilon^{2/3}(\Omega)^{-5/3} \qquad (415a)$$

TABLE LI

EFFECT OF MAXIMUM LENGTH IN POWER SPECTRUM ($p=8, 7, 6; j_p=2m/p$)

	$M=31$			$M=43$			$M=48$			$M=50$		
	L_j	Ls_j	$\sum L_j$	L_j	Ls_j	$\sum L_j$	L_j	Ls_j	$\sum L_j$	L_j	Ls_j	$\sum L_j$
0	−0.005	0.002	−0.005	0.019	−0.007	0.019	−0.005	0.002	−0.005	0.020	−0.008	0.020
1	0.011	0.002	0.006	−0.039	−0.007	−0.019	0.011	0.002	0.006	−0.040	−0.008	−0.020
2	−0.012	−0.000	−0.006	0.040	0.003	0.021	−0.011	−0.001	−0.005	0.041	0.003	0.021
3	0.014	0.001	0.008	−0.042	−0.003	−0.021	0.021	0.001	0.006	−0.042	−0.003	−0.021
4	−0.018	−0.001	−0.009	0.044	0.003	0.023	−0.012	−0.001	−0.006	0.044	0.003	0.023
5	0.025	−0.001	0.015	−0.048	−0.003	−0.025	0.013	0.001	0.007	−0.047	−0.003	−0.024
6	−0.043	0.012	−0.028	0.054	0.003	0.029	−0.014	−0.001	0.007	0.051	0.004	0.027
7	0.130	0.178	0.102	−0.063	−0.004	−0.034	0.015	0.009	0.008	−0.057	−0.004	−0.029
8	0.514	0.348	0.616	0.078	0.003	0.044	−0.018	−0.001	−0.009	0.064	0.004	0.035
9	0.177	0.250	0.792	−0.107	0.011	−0.064	0.020	0.001	0.011	−0.077	−0.004	−0.042
10	0.157	0.140	0.949	0.222	0.177	0.158	−0.025	0.002	0.014	0.098	0.003	0.056
11	0.066	0.067	1.015	0.358	0.292	0.516	0.046	0.123	0.032	−0.142	0.035	−0.086
12	−0.019	0.007		0.209	0.222	0.725	0.452	0.278	0.485	0.385	0.227	0.300
13				0.119	0.128	0.843	0.099	0.222	0.584	0.223	0.253	0.522
14				0.068	0.094	0.911	0.280	0.159	0.863	0.193	0.188	0.716
15				0.131	0.071	1.042	−0.065	0.078	0.798	0.140	0.116	0.855
16				−0.067	0.005		0.212	0.096	1.010	−0.017	0.071	0.838
17							−0.017	0.043		0.210	0.092	1.048
										−0.077	0.019	
Cycles (units of j)	$j_p=$ 7.75 8.86 10.83			$j_p=10.75$ 12.3 14.3			$j_p=12$ 13.7 16			$j_p=12.5$ 14.3 16.7		

(see e.g. Busch, in HAUGEN, 1973, p. 53). Taking into account that κ is the Kolmogorov constant and ε, the average dissipation rate, is also independent of Ω we reformulate:

$$\ln F(\Omega) = \text{const} - (5/3) \ln \Omega \tag{415b}$$

which represents a straight line in a double logarithmic coordinate system $x = \ln \Omega$, $y = \ln F(\Omega)$, with slope $-5/3$. Now:

$$\Omega = 2n/\lambda = j/p \tag{415c}$$

where λ is the wave length, $j = 1, 2, \ldots, p/2$ and p is the basic period. Furthermore:

$$F_j(\Omega) = \int_{\Omega_1}^{\Omega_2} A_j^2(\Omega)\, d\Omega = L_j \tag{415d}$$

which was introduced as the power spectrum (see eqs. 407a, b, c and 395b). Thus, turbulence can be evaluated from the slope a_1:

$$\ln L_j = a_0 + a_1 \ln (j/p) \tag{415e}$$

or:

$$\ln L_j = a_0 + a_1 \ln (2n/\lambda) \tag{415f}$$

Example 33. Analysis of the slope from the power spectrum and FFT. Figs. 5 and 6 display diagrams of eqs. 415e, f for the power spectrum and FFT, respectively. The data comprise the one dimensional u-components of the wind which were recorded on 19 August 1974 at Huntsville (Alabama) in one-second time intervals at tower elevations 18 and 30 ft, above ground by Gill uvw anemometers (see STEWART, 1975). The power spectrum and FFT were calculated for a shear interval of 12 ft., $\Delta u = u_{30} - u_{18}$.
In turbulence analysis often the slope is determined by filtering or drawing a line with slope $-5/3$ and comparing it with the slope of the plotted actual observations. For this example the slope lines have been computed by correlation analysis. Consideration must be given that the spectral values of the long waves do not conform with the turbulence slope. (See e.g. BUSCH, 1973.) This fact is confirmed in Fig. 5 or 6. Therefore, the appropriate regression line may be deduced by stepwise truncation of the first data points which corresponds to a high pass filter. The slope value stabilizes after a certain number of truncation steps. The power spectrum has been calculated for $m = 300$, i.e., a basic period of 600 s. The slope line provides the regression line for the spectral values of L_j from $j = 9 \ldots 300$ where the slope had stabilized at $a_1 = -1.63$. The ideal slope value would be $-5/3$ which is within the error tolerance of a_1.
Fig. 6 discloses the diagram for the result from the FFT. In our case, the basic period was selected to be $p = 1024$ (s). At first glance the reader will notice more scatter than in Fig. 5 although the slope appears to be around $-5/3$. The reader will also observe that the amplitudes of the Fourier series at the shortest wave lengths are very small. Thus, small absolute random errors superimposed on the amplitudes lead to large displacements in the scatter diagram. Therefore, a truncation at the lowest end in addition to the long waves is advisable in the case of the FFT. The truncation at both ends corresponds to a band pass filtering process.
The slope in this example has been obtained from the Fourier amplitudes A_j for $j = 9$ through 370 (instead of 1 through 512) and amounted to $a_1 = -1.63$. The excellent numerical agreement with a_1 of the power spectrum appears to be a coincidence although one should expect agreement because the FFT is performed on the same data base as the power spectrum.
We learn from the analysis of the spectrum derived by the FFT that this tool can be utilized for turbulence analysis. The reader must be aware however, that the scatter will be larger than by utilization of the power spectrum analysis. In fact, the error variance ratio $\varepsilon_{FFT}^2/\varepsilon_{POW}^2$ is 5.2 in our case (ε^2 stands for the error variance of the respective regression). The larger error variance of the FFT does not directly affect the slope except that the error for a_1 may be larger than from the power

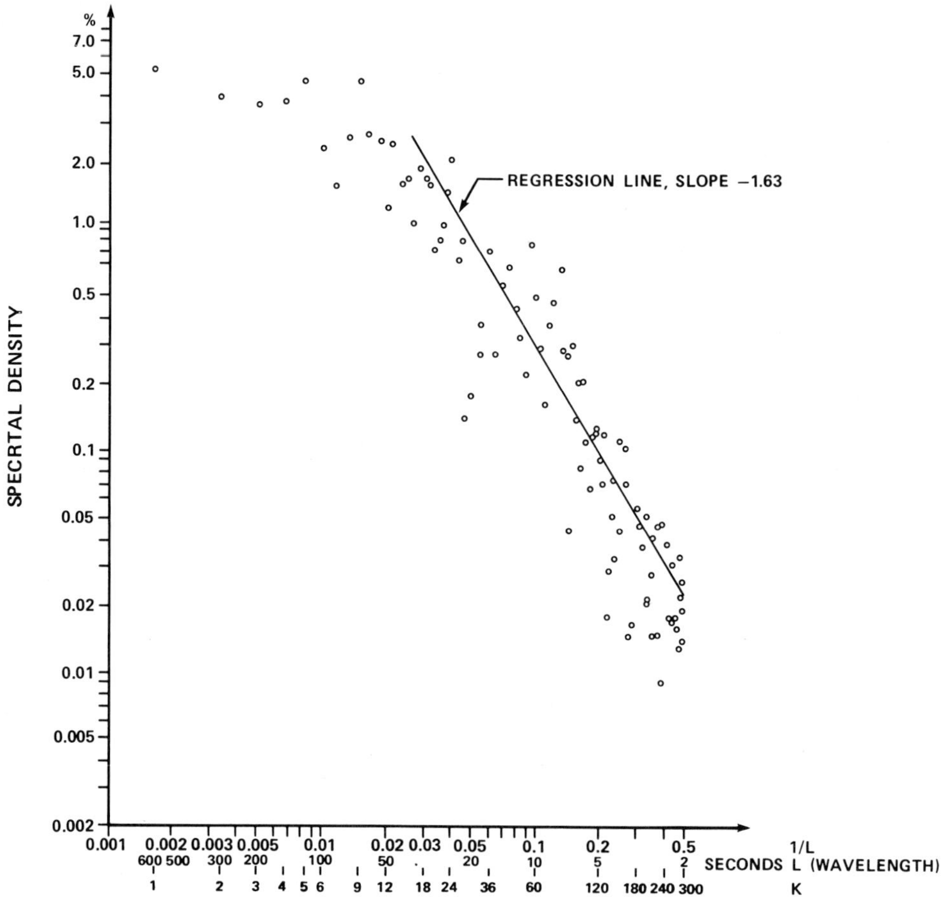

Fig. 5. Power spectrum for $\Delta u = u_{30} - u_{18}$ for wind recordings of one second on 19 August 1974 at Huntsville, Alabama (double logarithmic coordinates). Maximum lag $m = 300$.

spectrum. This larger dispersion of the set of y_i's is also reflected in the correlation coefficient. For the power spectrum we find $r_p = -0.87$ while $r_F = -0.80$.
The slope is independent of the maximum lag or the basic period of the FFT. Fig. 7 depicts the power spectrum analysis with $m = 60$. The calculation of the slope from L_5 through L_{60} leads to $a_1 = -1.67$. The difference between the two numerical values of the slope is well within the customary tolerance. From eq. 624a we find $a_1 = -1.67 \pm 0.09$ within a tolerance limit of 2σ. Fig. 7 reveals that the error variance of the power spectrum for $m = 60$ is smaller than for $m = 300$. This fact is expected because the spectrum for $m = 60$ is smoother than for $m = 300$. The (linear) correlation coefficient is now $r = -0.97$ which confirms the reduced error variance.

Testing of spectra, red noise

Red noise

Statistical significance of the peaks in the power spectrum must be assured because they could be caused by chance. It can be shown that the distribution of the sample spectrum estimates at a given period follows approximately the χ^2 distribution (see eq. 645).
Before testing can take place the basis for the significance test, or the "expectancy" of the power spectrum must be established. Several postulations can be made.

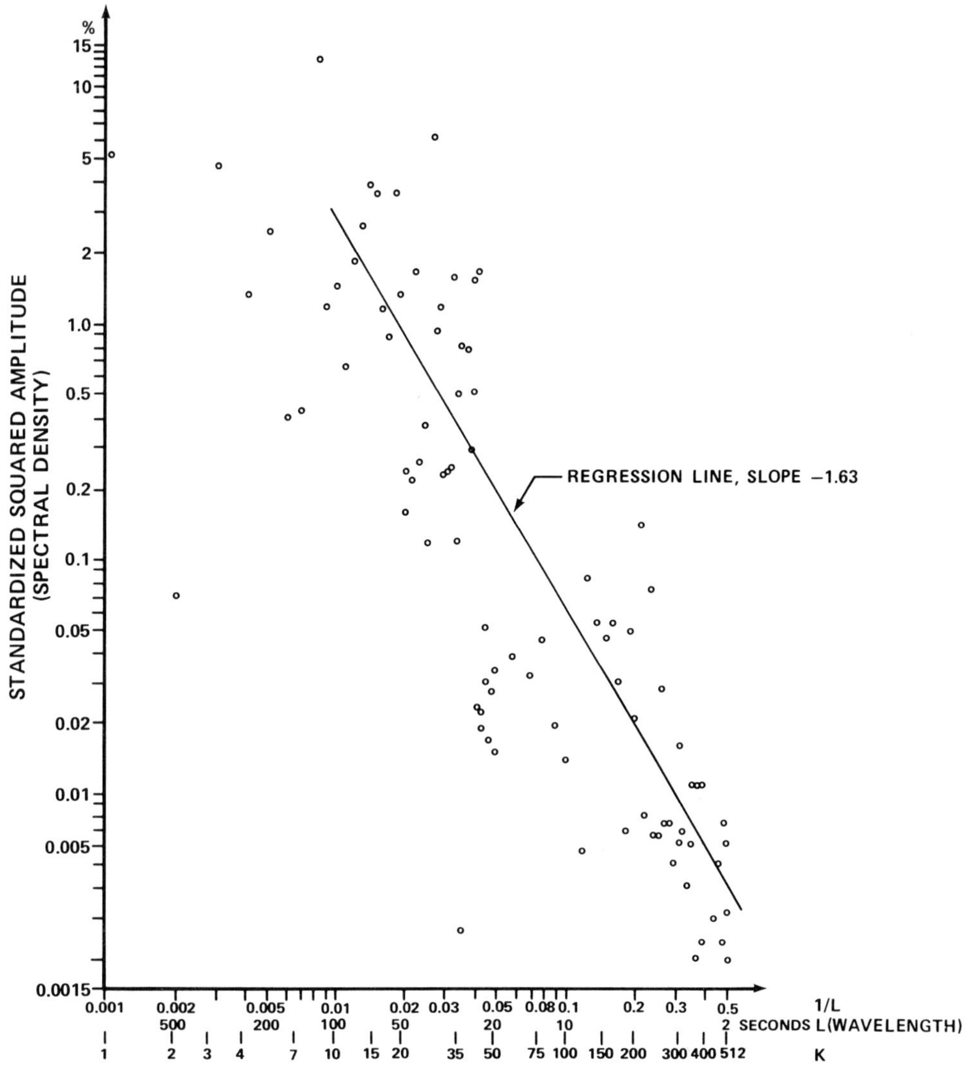

Fig. 6. FFT for $\Delta u = u_{30} - u_{18}$ for wind recordings of one second on 19 August 1974 at Huntsville, Alabama (double logarithmic coordinates). $P_0 = 1024$.

We can assume a "white noise" spectrum (e.g., MADDEN, 1977) which simply implies that every L_j would be the same. Then the expected spectrum is:

$$\bar{L}_j = \left(\sum_{1}^{m} L_j \right) \Big/ m \tag{416a}$$

for all L_j values from L_1 to L_m. In practical applications:

$$R_0 = 1.0 \tag{416b}$$

$$R_j = 0 \text{ for } 0 < j \leq m \tag{416c}$$

The spectrum is then $L_j = 1/m$ except for $L_0 = L_m = 1/2\, m$.

In many cases one would prefer, however, a "red noise" spectrum because it includes persistence. Several forms of red noise may be chosen. We can assume a "Gaussian" form for the autocorrelation function such as:

$$R_t = \exp(-a^2 t^2), \quad 0 \leq t \leq \infty \tag{417a}$$

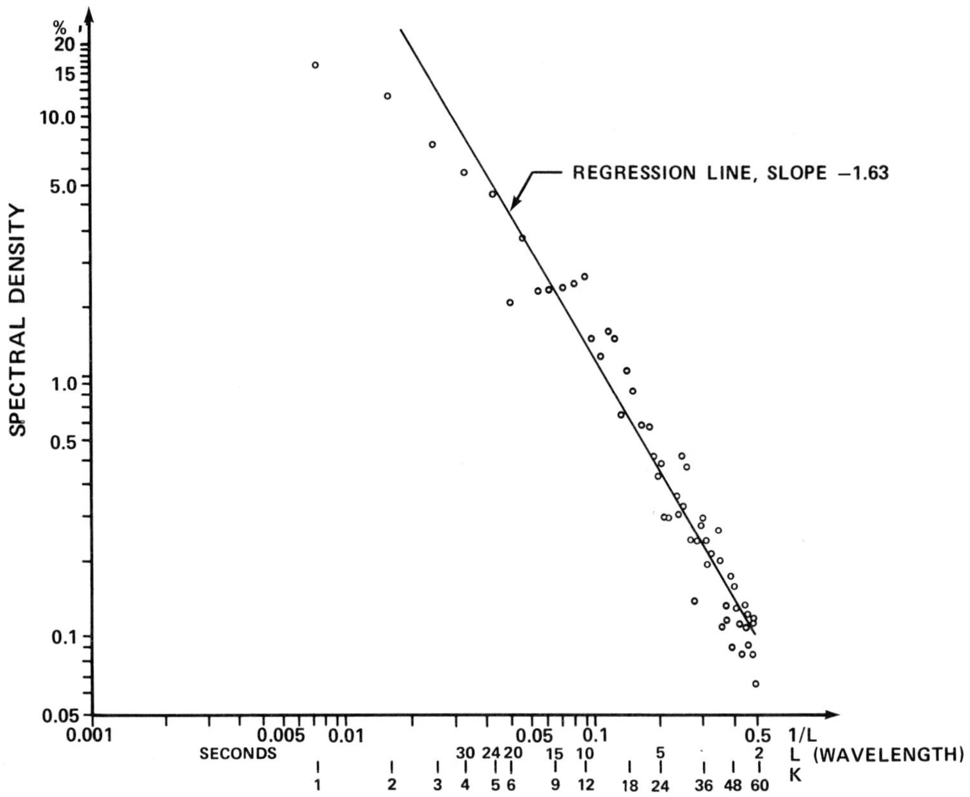

Fig. 7. Power spectrum for $\Delta u = u_{30} - u_{18}$ for wind recordings of one second on 19 August 1974 at Huntsville, Alabama (double logarithmic coordinates). Maximum lag $m = 60$.

With:

$$\sigma_t^2 = \bar{R}^2 m^2 2/\pi \tag{417b}$$

We find:

$$a^2 = \pi/(4\bar{R}^2 m^2) = 1/(2\sigma_t^2) \tag{417c}$$

and:

$$\bar{R} = (\sigma_t/m)\sqrt{\pi/2} \tag{417d}$$

where $\bar{R}$ is the mean value of the R_t. The spectrum for R_t in the form of eq. 417a is:

$$L_j = [\sqrt{\pi}/(am)]\exp[-\pi^2 j^2/(a2m)^2] \quad j = 1, 2, \ldots, m \tag{417e}$$

or:

$$L_j = 2\bar{R}\exp[-\sigma_t^2\pi^2 j^2/(2m^2)] = 2\bar{R}\exp(-\bar{R}^2\pi j^2) \tag{417f}$$

Observe that $L_0 = \bar{R}$ and not $2\bar{R}$ as from eq. 417f ($\Delta x = 0.5$ for the class L_0). Furthermore, a small σ_t^2 leads to a rapid decrease of R_t and to a slow diminishing of L_j, but the decline is reversed for a large σ_t^2. The maximum lag cannot be shorter than σ, usually $m > 3\sigma$. The most common "red noise" spectrum is based on the exponential autocorrelation:

$$R_t = \exp(-bt) \quad \text{for } t \geq 0, b > 0 \tag{418}$$

Because the autocorrelation is symmetric about $t = 0$, in some writings t is replaced by its absolute value $|t|$. R_t goes asymptotically to zero and is zero for $t=\infty$. In practical applications R_t can be truncated after a reasonable finite length, let this be called $t=m$. This length is somewhat arbitrary but can be related to the parameters $\bar{t}$ and σ_t of the exponential distribution. From the author's 1976 text (p. 113) we derive:

$$\sum_0^\infty R_t = 1/b \tag{419a}$$

$$\sum_0^\infty R_t / \sum R_t = \bar{t} = 1/b \tag{419b}$$

$$\sum_0^\infty R_t (t-\bar{t})^2 / \sum R_t = \sigma_t^2 = \bar{t}^2 = 1/b^2 \tag{419c}$$

The spectrum for this distribution is listed in many texts (e.g. TAUBENHEIM, 1969; BÅTH, 1974; HALL, 1975, etc.) as:

$$L_j = (2/b)/[1+\pi^2 j^2/b^2] \tag{420a}$$

or in summation form (i.e., $\sum L_j/N = F(x)$):

$$F(x) = (2/\pi)\text{arc tan}(x\pi/b) \tag{420b}$$

The reader may recognize that for $x=\infty$ the summation $F(\infty)=1.0$, i.e., $F(x)$ assumes the role of a cumulative distribution with $m=\infty$ commensurate with the exponential distribution.

Following the customary nomenclature we can state for a finite length:

$$\sum_1^m R_t/m = \bar{R} \tag{421a}$$

Considering eq. 419a we derive:

$$m\bar{R} = 1/b \tag{421b}$$

For white noise $L_j = 1$. Consequently $\sum_1^m L_j = m$ for white and red noise. L_j is normalized so that it conforms to the power spectrum as introduced by eq. 407, and we define $L'_j = L_j/m$. Then:

$$L'_j = 2\bar{R}/[1+(\pi j\bar{R})^2] \quad j=1, 2, \ldots, m \tag{422a}$$

For finite m the modified form of eq. 420b is given by:

$$F(x) = a_0\text{arc tan}(x\pi\bar{R}) = a_0\text{arc tan}(x\pi/mb) \tag{422b}$$

where:

$$a_0 = 1/\text{arc tan}(\pi/b) \tag{422c}$$

Consequently:

$$L'_0 = 1/(mb) = \bar{R} \tag{422d}$$

The first term L'_0 expressed by eq. 420a renders:

$$L'_0 \sim F(x=0.5) = a_0\text{arc tan}(\pi\bar{R}/2) \sim \bar{R} \tag{422e}$$

In many cases the calculation of L'_h from the difference $F(h)-F(h-1)$ is more appropriate than the utilization of eq. 422a, especially for the first terms. $F(x)$ is a continuous function, but L'_j is taken in discrete steps, and the class interval may be too large to permit a precise value. Notice that $F(x)=0$ for $x \leq 0$.

Before a final recommendation for m is made let us examine the power spectrum for a Markov chain. A first order Markov chain (see ESSENWANGER, 1976, p. 300) can be written as:

$$R_k = \rho^k \tag{423a}$$

Consequently, $\ln R_t = -bt$, and $\ln R_k = k \ln \rho$. If $k=t$, $b=-\ln \rho$, which is a positive number for $0<\rho\leq 1.0$. This links the Markov model with the exponential red noise. The spectrum of a Markov process (see ESSENWANGER, 1976, p. 297, or GILMAN et al., 1963) can be written:

$$L_k = (1-\rho^2)/(1+\rho^2-2\rho \cos k\pi/m) \tag{423b}$$

Again, normalizing requires:

$$L'_j = L_k/m \tag{423c}$$

Therefore, one should expect that the two forms of the spectrum (eqs. 422a and 423b) agree because they are based on the same autocorrelation function. However, for $\rho<0.5$ the actual spectral values are not precisely the same which can be readily demonstrated by examining L_0 in both cases.

From theory $\int_0^\infty R_k = -1/\ln \rho$, and $\int_0^\infty R_t = 1/b = -1/\ln \rho$, which is the same. If the integration is carried out over a sufficient interval 0 to $m-1$, then the integral approximates $-1/\ln 0$ in both cases. From the models we find that $L_{0E} = -1/\ln \rho$ for the exponential but $L_{0M} = (1+\rho)/[2(1-\rho)]$ for the Markov spectrum. If $L_{0E} \equiv L_{0M}$:

$$-\ln \rho = 2(1-\rho)/(1+\rho) \tag{424}$$

The reader may recognize that the right side is the first term in the series approximating the logarithm. Thus, the models diverge when eq. 424 is not sufficient approximation of $\ln \rho$, which is for $\rho<0.5$, and $L_{0M} \neq 1/b$ (see Table LII). The discrepancy has consequences in estimating ρ from the spectrum and for the interpretation of the maximum length m for red noise.

In the exponential series $1/b = \sigma_t$ (see eq. 419c). Because $m_T = -\sigma_t \ln R_T$, a negligible

TABLE LII

VALUE OF $1/b$ FROM THE EXPONENTIAL AND MARKOV MODEL AND m_T (INTEGERS)

	ρ: 0.9	0.8	0.7	0.6	0.5	0.4	0.368	0.3	0.2	0.1
$-1/\ln \rho$	9.49	4.48	2.80	1.96	1.44	1.09	1.00	0.831	0.621	0.434
$(1+\rho)/[2(1-\rho)]$	9.50	4.50	2.83	2.00	1.50	1.17	1.08	0.929	0.750	0.611
m_T for $R_T=0.001$	66	31	20	14	10	8	7	6	5	3
m_T for $R_T=0.01$	44	21	13	9	7	5	5	4	3	2

contribution after $R_T \leq \varepsilon$ leads to:

$$m_T = 6.908\ \sigma_t = -6.908/\ln\rho \quad \text{for } R_T = 0.001 \tag{425a}$$

and:

$$m_T = 4.605\ \sigma_t = -4.605/\ln\rho \quad \text{for } R_T = 0.01 \tag{425b}$$

We take the closest integer $\geq m_T$ from eq. 425a or b. Them m_T represents the minimum length of the autocorrelogram for classes of $\Delta t = 1$. Because for $\Delta t = 1/k_t$, $k_t > 1.0$, $m_{\max} = m_T > k_t$, the length m_t acts as a scaling factor. In practical applications truncation for $R = 0.01$ is sufficient and $m_T = 5\sigma_t$.
We can interpret the spectra for the individual ρ as essentially different in scale only. This implies that we can establish a normalized series $R_x = \rho^{sx}$ where $sx = ct/\sigma_t$, and $\Delta x = c/s\sigma_t$ (for $\Delta t = 1$). Basically the series $R_t = 0.5^t$ comprises twice as many points R_t than the series $R_t = 0.25^t = 0.5^{2t}$ which implies that it is essentially the same autocorrelogram. In calculating the spectrum we replace $\int_0^\infty R_t\,dt$ by $\sum R_z\,\Delta z$ where R_z declines exponentially. The summation by finite steps Δz will not be adequate to equate the numerical value of $\int_0^\infty R_t\,dt$. The power spectrum is based on a finite steps autocorrelation function $R_z\Delta z$. Consequently, $-\ln\rho$ by eq. 424 illustrates the limitations, and eq. 423b should be used. The autocorrelation function transforms:

$$\rho^t = \rho^{b_k k} \tag{425c}$$

so that $k = t/b_k$ and $m = m_T b_k$, which is a simple relationship. No simple scaling can be derived, however, for eq. 422b. More details can be found in the author's 1977 and 1980 articles.

Testing of spectra

The power spectrum can be related to the χ^2 test. The test criterion is:

$$L_j/L_j(E) = \chi^2/n_f \tag{426a}$$

where $L_j(E)$ is the expected value. Any of the functions previously introduced (i.e., eqs. 416a, 417e, 422a, or 423b) may serve as the expected value $L_j(E)$.
The number of degrees of freedom are:

$$n_f = 2N/m - 0.5 \tag{426b}$$

where N is the number of data points of the original data set and m is the number of employed lags. (Some sources take 2/3 instead of 0.5.) The judgment by the χ^2 test usually gives a result that is more on the pessimistic side of the evaluation. Note, that the fraction $L_j/L_j(E)$ can be larger or smaller than one. We must therefore consider χ^2 over 95% for the fraction >1 and under 5% for <1 at the 95% level of significance.
Eq. 426a is also applicable to test Ls_j because Ls_j is the "estimated" spectrum from an empirical set of data but Ls_j may also serve as $L_j(E)$ for testing L_j.

Another possible noise form of the autocorrelation function is seldom used:

$$R_t=(c_2t_2+1)^{-1} \quad 0\leq t_2\leq \infty \tag{427a}$$

with:

$$c=\pi/(2\bar{R}) \tag{427b}$$

Miscellaneous Fourier and power spectrum analyses

Several examples of special cases of spectral analysis have been discussed in the author's 1976 text. Among them is the important case of the power spectrum for a varying amplitude such as $Y=x\cdot A\sin(\alpha_x+\alpha_0)$ where x is not a constant, or two amplitude multiplications. The case of non-harmonic waves is also treated.

Modulation of amplitude

A varying amplitude is an important case in atmospheric science, where quasi-periodicity can mean that a cycle commences, reaches a maximum amplitude, and fades away. Even pure cycles such as the daily wave show variations of the amplitude through the year (ESSENWANGER, 1980).
Assume a daily cycle (subscript d):

$$Y_t=A_j\sin(j_d\alpha_t+\psi_d) \tag{428a}$$

with a varying amplitude:

$$A_j=B_j+D_j\sin(j_s\alpha_t+\psi_s) \tag{428b}$$

where α_t was defined (see t_i in eq. 384c).
The author (ESSENWANGER, 1980) showed that this type of modulation generates:

$$Y_t=B_j\sin(j_d\alpha_t+\psi_d)+D_j\sin(d_d\alpha_t+\psi_d)\sin(j_s\alpha_t+\psi_s) \tag{428c}$$

The first term is a sine wave with periodicity $p=2\pi j_d/N$. The second term resembles $\sin(2\alpha_1)\pm\sin(2\alpha_2)$. Although at the wave length p the amplitude is $A_d^2=B^2/(B^2+D^2/2)$ which is a reduction from B^2, side lobes at $j_d\pm j_s$ with amplitude $D^2/4$ will appear. The total cycle has a (squared) amplitude $B^2+D^2/2$.
Another treatment for varying amplitudes and frequencies in time was outlined by HAYASHI (1977, 1979) who employed progressive and retrogressive wave components. This so-called maximum entropy method leads to finer resolutions for shorter time periods than the customary methods but is based on the complex time series.
The fitting of spectra for unequally spaced data was treated by JONES (1979).

Separation of waves and aliasing effect

STUMPFF (1937) pointed out that two periods of length p_1 and p_2 with wave-length angle α_1 and α_2 such as:

$$\alpha_1=2\pi/p_1 \quad \text{or} \quad p_1=2\pi/\alpha_1 \tag{429a}$$

$$\alpha_2 = 2\pi/p_2 \quad \text{or} \quad p_2 = 2\pi/\alpha_2 \tag{429b}$$

lead to a resulting wave-length variation of:

$$p_\alpha = 2\pi/(\alpha_2 - \alpha_1) = p_1 p_2/(p_1 - p_2) \tag{429c}$$

In order to separate these waves in a spectrum diagram, the total number N of the observations must then be at least $N > p + p_\alpha$, i.e. in the analysis of an interval with length p we must be able to shift the interval at least by p_α. If the two waves p and p_2 are adjacent (neighboring) waves in a harmonic wave pattern, e.g., $p = rp_1$ and $p = (r+1)p_2$, then $p_\alpha = p$ and $N \geq 2p$.

Another effect leading to fictitious periodicity is the "aliasing" effect. Assume a series of data is given at equidistant intervals (e.g., time). Because we need two more points besides the initial observation to determine a sine-wave, the minimum length of a periodicity is $2\Delta x$, where Δx is the distance between two observations (either time or space). Thus the minimum cycle has the length $L_n = 2\Delta x$. The frequency is then:

$$\nu_N = 1/L_N = 1/(2\Delta x) \text{ (cycles per unit)} \tag{430a}$$

This is the so-called Nyquist frequency. In case $\Delta x = 1$, this frequency would be $\nu_N = 1/2$ cycle per unit.

The series of alias frequencies which cannot be distinguished are listed as:

$$\nu,\ 2\nu_N \pm \nu,\ 4\nu_N \pm \nu \text{ etc.} \tag{430b}$$

The first frequency ν must be smaller than ν_N.

More details on estimation of spectra can be found in the author's 1976 text (p. 237ff).

Chapter 5

Smoothing, Filtering, Inter- and Extrapolation

General concepts, filtering

It is well-known that many meteorological data display small-scale fluctuations and irregularities if observed by sensitive instrumentations such as in microclimatology or for turbulence analysis. These small-scale variations show up irrespective of the method of recording, whether digital readings or plottings. A closer inspection of even apparent "smooth" records (such as original data in maps) reveals fluctuations and irregularities. The small-scale oscillations are caused by the influence of random error or turbulent motions. Often they may be undesirable "ballast" for finding solutions to problems in statistical analysis, and their elimination is sought. The smoothing of isolines in synoptic or climatological maps is a generally accepted concept to remove "noise" and enhance the principal features. In accordance with this concept a meteorological data series can be expressed by two basic terms:

$$y(x) = S(x) + \varepsilon(x) \tag{431}$$

where y is the data series as function of time or space, x denotes either the time or space coordinate(s) or both. The letter S symbolizes the smooth part, and ε the small-scale oscillation. This model is frequently used in the time series analysis, in the analysis of variance and in regression or polynomial analysis eq. 267a, b or 360, etc. The smooth part can be a regular function, a periodic fluctuation, etc. In many cases ε stands for a random error. Eq. 431 is the basic formula for smoothing.

The simplest smoothing by eq. 431 is a trivial model: $S(x) \equiv \bar{y}$, the mean (see later eq. 432). Then $\sum \varepsilon(x) = 0$ and the random error is only determinable as a range of a dispersion, such as the variance $\sigma_\varepsilon^2 = \sum \varepsilon^2/N$. Eq. 431 also serves as the basis for a concept of optimum information retrieval (e.g., BENDAT and PIERSOL, 1971; REISIG, 1977).

If we are interested solely in a smoothing process then the set of original observations y_i can be transformed into a set of smoothed data such as:

$$\bar{X}_j = \left(\sum_1^n \omega_i y_i \Big/ \sum_1^n \omega_i \right) \Big/ n \tag{432}$$

where $\bar{X}_j$ denotes the smoothed value and ω_i a weighting function. The selection of n and ω_i is subjective and depends on the problem under consideration. The original variable y_i need not be given in a linear scale (i.e., equal linear spacing) but the effect of unequal or non-linear spacing must be taken into consideration (e.g., modification of the weighting

coefficients, etc.). Otherwise valid conclusions about physical causes in the relationship between x and y may be distorted and may reflect only the effects of unequal spacing.
The process of smoothing suppresses or at least dampens the effect of (non-random or random) oscillations shorter than or equal to the interval length comprising the n points. Thus, the smoothing process resembles an application of filters in electrical engineering, i.e., smoothing and filtering are closely related, and eq. 432 also can be interpreted as the basic principle of filtering. Sometimes the term filtering is applied only for the elimination of (non-random) periodic variations but here we use the wider sense, and no distinction between periodic and non-periodic fluctuations is made unless specified.
The effect of the smoothing process on waves is of primary interest, and can be evaluated by the "frequency response" function $R(f)$:

$$R(f)=\omega_0+2\sum_{1}^{h}\omega_k\cos(k2\pi f\Delta x) \qquad (433a)$$

where f denotes the frequency, Δx the data interval, and ω_0 the so-called "central weight," i.e., the weight ω_k of the observation y_k in eq. 432.
Since the smoothing process $\bar{X}_j$ is applied on y_i which includes a random error (see eq. 431), $\bar{X}_j$ is not necessarily free of a random error. According to the principal error law in statistics (see central limit theorem, ESSENWANGER, 1976, p. 14), $\varepsilon_y^2 > \varepsilon_{\bar{X}_j}^2$. In other words, the smoothed variable has a smaller random error than the original observation. Consequently, features of physical behavior are enhanced by smoothing unless our interest is focused on the parts suppressed by filtering.
The frequency response in eq. 433a is merely the real part of a complex response function:

$$R(f)=\int_{-\infty}^{\infty}\omega(x)\cos(2\pi fx)\,dx+i\int_{-\infty}^{\infty}\omega(x)\sin(2\pi fx)\,dx \qquad (433b)$$

In order to eliminate a "phase shift" by the smoothing process, $\omega(-x)=\omega(x)$ is assumed, and the imaginary (second) term in eq. 433b becomes zero ($i=\sqrt{-1}$). We recognize further that eq. 433b is the inverse Fourier transform of $\omega(x)$.

Smoothing

Moving averages, inter- and extrapolation, weights

We assume equally spaced observations y_i and set $\omega_i=1$ in eq. 432 for all values $i=1, \ldots, n$. Then $\sum\omega_i=n$, and:

$$\bar{X}_j=\sum_{i=j}^{n+j-1} y_i/n, \quad (j=1, \ldots, n_m) \qquad (434a)$$

We can immediately deduce that $\bar{X}_j$ is the mean for $n\equiv N$, the total number of observations. For $n<N$ we can calculate j values of $\bar{X}_j$, with a maximum n_m of:

$$n_m=N+1-n \qquad (434b)$$

The set of $\bar{X}_j$ values are called "overlapping means" because adjacent values to $\bar{X}_j$ (either $\bar{X}_{j-1}$ or $\bar{X}_{j+1}$) have $n-1$ points in common. An odd number of n leads to symmetric smoothing. E.g., overlapping means of 3 data points require:

$$\bar{X}_j=(y_j+y_{j+1}+y_{j+2})/3, \quad (j=1, \ldots, N-2) \tag{434c}$$

Since $n_m<N$ for $n>1$, a reduction in the number of overlapping (or running) means can only be avoided by arbitrarily adding points at the margins unless we have a (closed) periodic time series y_i. Although the choice of an "extrapolation" method is an arbitrary decision, objective methods for the supplementation of values at the margins can be designed. Most commonly the original data are substituted or other special extrapolation rules are designed (see examples and eq. 435).
The frequency response function of the moving average (equally weighted and spaced) can be calculated from:

$$R(f)=\sin(\pi f\Delta y)/(\pi f\Delta y) \tag{434d}$$

with the same symbol notation as for eq. 433a. The frequency f must be measured in cycles per Δy unit. Smoothing by overlapping means is illustrated in Example 36.
Linear inter- or extrapolation can be performed based on:

$$y=\Delta y\cdot(\Delta w/w)+y_b \tag{435}$$

where $\Delta y = y_u - y_l$, the difference between the upper and lower class value (see eq. 13a). For interpolation $y_b=y_l$, for extrapolation $y_b=y_u$ or y_l, depending toward which end the extrapolation is sought. (Extrapolation from $y_b=y_l$ requires a negative Δy.) While Δy denotes the interval $y_{i+1}-y_i$ of the variate (or observation) w stands for the width of spacing (e.g., time or space) of the y, and Δw expresses the fraction of the desired inter- or extrapolation. For interpolation $0<\Delta w<w$; for extrapolation $\Delta w>0$, but $\Delta w>w$ is permissible for extrapolation.
The inter- or extrapolation can also be performed on transformed variables such as $y=\ln z$, $y=1/z$, etc. Other sophisticated inter- or extrapolation schemes exist, e.g., Beyer (1966) and eq. 519, etc. "Optimum interpolation" for automated streamline analysis was treated by Dartt (1972), who based his method on a study by Gandin (1963). A scalar variable (in Dartt's case the zonal wind $u(x)$, where x is a multidimensional argument) is restructured by an estimate $\hat{u}(x)$ from an appropriate weighting function $\omega(x,x_j)$ as follows:

$$\hat{u}(x)=\sum_{j=1}^{n} u(x_j)\omega(x,x_j) \tag{436a}$$

As derived by Dartt, the normal equations providing the minimum error variance are formulated as:

$$C[u(x),u(x_j)]=\sum_{k=1}^{N}\omega(x,x_k)C[u(x_j),u(x_k)] \quad j=1, 2, \ldots, n \tag{436b}$$

where:

$$C[\xi(x),\eta(x_j)]=E[\xi(x)\cdot\eta(x_j)] \tag{436c}$$

In other words C is a multidimensional covariance function (see p. 109) with zero mean, i.e.:

$$E[\xi(x)]=E[\eta(x_j)]=0 \tag{436d}$$

According to Dartt, the wind velocity obtained by optimum interpolation generally is more accurate than estimates by other analytical interpolation functions.
We can deduce from the technique of optimum interpolation that the selection of a proper weighting function is quite important, although this selection in the smoothing process is a subjective decision. The choice depends largely on the goal and the particular problem at hand.
A Gaussian weighting function is in widespread use. We introduce:

$$\omega_\kappa=(\sigma\sqrt{2\pi})^{-1}\exp(-\kappa^2/2\sigma^2) \tag{437a}$$

although the weighting coefficients are more often approximated by the binomial law:

$$\omega_\kappa=n!/[\kappa!(n-\kappa)] \tag{437b}$$

The frequency response function is then:

$$R(f)=\exp(-2\pi^2\sigma^2 f^2) \tag{437c}$$

The weighting procedure can be applied not only to smoothing of observations but also to computing a weighted mean or standard deviation. This is employed especially if there is reason to believe that some observations are more trustworthy than others and the data are unreliable toward the extremes. First, mean and variance from the unweighted set of observations y_i are calculated and the ratio $Y_r=(y_i-\bar{y})/\sigma_y$ is computed. The weights are then adjusted by the corresponding frequency value of the Gaussian distribution. Mean and variance are recalculated with the weights and adopted as the new statistic. This process can be repeated until mean and standard deviation before and after recalculation display little change. The procedure is independent from the type of frequency model of y_i, although it is most effective for distributions following the Gaussian law. This process reduces the effect of "outliers" (see p. 318).
A simplified method is based on the same ratio Y_r, but the weights for extreme deviations are larger than in the Gaussian case. An example is given in Table LIII.
Another condition for the selection of a weighting function could be the requirement that this function corresponds to a specified response function. This postulation can be expressed by:

$$\omega(x)=2\int_{-\infty}^{\infty} R(f)\cos(2\pi fx)\,df \tag{438a}$$

A simple example may illustrate the application. Let us assume that a two-step response function is desired:

$$R(f)=\begin{cases}1 \text{ for } 0\leq f\leq f_{max}\\ 0 \text{ for } \quad f>f_{max}\end{cases} \tag{438b}$$

TABLE LIII

WEIGHTING OF OBSERVATIONS

Y_r	<0.6	0.61 to 1.03	1.04 to 1.35	1.36 to 1.66	1.67 to 2.06	2.07 to 2.47	2.48 to 3.14	3.15 to 4.09	4.10 to 5.45	≥ 5.46
ω_κ	1.0	0.9	0.8	0.7	0.6	0.5	0.4	0.3	0.2	0.1

The substitution of eq. 438b into 438a leads to:

$$\omega(x) = (\pi x)^{-1} \cdot \sin(2\pi x f_{max}) \qquad (438c)$$

A good survey on smoothing and filtering of meteorological time series was presented by HOLLOWAY (1958) and LEE (1981). WIENER (1949) gave various examples on inter-, extrapolation and smoothing. Optimal smoothing of frequency density estimates was treated extensively by WAHBA (1977a, b) who also dealt with smoothing periodograms (WAHBA, 1978). Smoothing and prediction was examined by BROWN (1963).

Example 34. This example serves to demonstrate interpolation (eq. 435). Assume that we need the wind speed at 4.2 km on 1 January 1964 (Table XXXVI) $\Delta X = 9.0 - 7.0 = 2.0$ m s^{-1}; $\Delta w = 4.2 - 4.0 = 0.2$ km and $w = 1$ km. Then:

$$X = 2.0 \cdot (0.2) + 7.0 = 7.4 \text{ m s}^{-1}$$

Let us assume that the wind speed at 4.2 km altitude for the time of 24h GMT is required. In Table XXXVI data are available for 1 and 2 January at 12h GMT. Double interpolation is required, in time and space, performed in two steps.
First the interpolated value at altitude 4.2 for 1 January and 2 January at 12h GMT is computed. Afterwards we interpolate for the time. The sequence of time and altitude interpolation is irrelevant in linear interpolation.
The wind speed at 4.2 km altitude for 1 January has been determined to be 7.4 m s^{-1}. For the second day we find:

$$X = (5.0 - 3.0) \cdot 0.2 + 3.0 = 3.4 \text{ m s}^{-1}$$

Now we interpolate for the time 24h GMT:

$$X = (7.4 - 3.4) \cdot (0.5/1.0) + 3.4 = 5.4 \text{ m s}^{-1}$$

Sometimes the original data are linearly related but a transformation of the original set of data generally is possible which will convert the data so that eq. 435 can be applied. More sophisticated interpolation schemes have been developed by mathematicians. The reader is referred to texts such as WHITTAKER and ROBINSON (1944), ABRAMOVITZ and STEGUN (1964), BEYER (1966), etc.

Exponential smoothing

Smoothing by moving averages based on eq. 434 has been introduced. The calculation of moving averages for n data points usually poses no problem if n is small, e.g., $n < 10$. For large n, however, a long record of data must be kept. This is avoided by exponential smoothing which is based on:

$$\bar{X}_t(y) = a y_t + (1 - a)\bar{X}_{t-1}(y) \qquad (439a)$$

where a is called the smoothing constant and $\bar{X}_{t-1}$ denotes the previous smoothed value. Eq. 439a can be written in expanded form of previous observations:

$$\bar{X}_t(y) = a \sum_{k=0}^{t-1} (1 - a)^k y_{t-k} + (1 - a)^t y_0 \qquad (439b)$$

It can be recognized that the influence of y_i in $\bar{X}_t$ decreases the greater y_i is separated from y_t. The decrease is expressed by the weight $\omega = (1 - a)^k$ which has a geometric decrease or an exponential smoothing effect.
The problem in exponential smoothing is the start because for $y_t = y_1$ no $\bar{X}_0$ is available. A similar case is a start where previous records are missing because $\bar{X}_0$ cannot be calculated

from previous records. In these cases $\bar{X}_0$ must be estimated by substituting a suitable $\hat{X}_0$. This can be a simple average of some recent observations (e.g., no continuous set $y_0, \ldots, y_t$ may exist but previous y values may be known). If all previous values are missing, however, $\hat{X}_0$ must be obtained from a prediction (e.g., from maps, neighboring stations or plain expectations). If confidence can be placed in $\hat{X}_0$ the smoothing constant a can be held small (close to zero); otherwise it is advisable to keep a close to unity in which case the influence of the initial value decreases rapidly.

The pure statistician may frown upon the compromises which must be made for the initial case but by continued application of eq. 439a $\bar{X}_t(y)$ becomes more reliable as y_i increases. Then a will cease to be chosen in an arbitrary way and can be selected, either $a=1/n$, or better, $a=2/(N+1)$. From the latter relationship the equivalency of the smoothing constant to the corresponding moving average can be evaluated. E.g., $a=0.05$ corresponds to $n=39$. More details can be found in special texts such as BROWN (1963) or WHITTAKER and ROBINSON (1944), etc. Exponential smoothing for climatic records (e.g., 30-year means and their expansion by addition of 10 years) was suggested by OGAWARA (1980).

Smoothing by differences

In the preceding sections the smoothing of original values has been discussed. It is also possible to smooth derived differences instead, but some restrictions must be pointed out. We may assume a series of observations and express the set of data by polynomials (see eq. 360):

$$X_i=a_0+a_1\phi_{1i}+a_2\phi_{2i}+a_3\phi_{3i}+, \ldots, a_n\phi_{ni} \tag{440a}$$

where ϕ_{ji} represents polynomial functions. The first differences are:

$$\Delta_1 X_i=X_{i+1}-X_i \tag{440b}$$

and the second differences:

$$\Delta_2 X_i=\Delta_1 X_{i+1}-\Delta_1 X_i \tag{440c}$$

In general:

$$\Delta_j X_i=\Delta_{j-1} X_{i+1}-\Delta_{j-1} X_i \tag{440d}$$

We can continue with this process until constant $\Delta_j X_i$ values are finally obtained (in accordance with eq. 440a). In many cases the third differences $\Delta_3 X_i$ can be considered constant, depending on the significance of higher order terms in eq. 440a.

A judgment can be made whether the differences between $\Delta_j X_i$, $i=1, \ldots, n_j$ are negligible and the $\Delta_j X_i$ show only random errors. We compute the mean difference $\overline{\Delta_j X}=(\sum \Delta_j X_i)/n_j$ as well as, $\overline{\Delta_j X_1}$, $\overline{\Delta_j X_2}$, etc., the means of subsequent subsets. Sometimes two subsets may suffice. If $\overline{\Delta_j X_1} \approx \overline{\Delta_j X_2} \approx \overline{\Delta_j X}$ the computation of differences is stopped. The constant difference would then be $\overline{\Delta_j X}$. (Notice that $\overline{\Delta_j X}=0$, requires $\overline{\Delta_{j-1} X}$ to be constant.)

Let us assume a constant third difference $\overline{\Delta_3 X}$. The second differences $\Delta_2 x_i$ can now be recalculated (eq. 440d), afterwards $\Delta_1 x_i$, and finally the smooth x_i. Clearly, the set of equations (eq. 440d) (replacing the observed X_i by the smoothed x_i), either $\Delta_{j-1} x_{i+1}$ or

$\Delta_{j-1}x_i$ must be known. Thus, for recalculations eq. 440d is defined except for one unknown, e.g., $\Delta_{j-1}x_1$. In our case $\Delta_2 x_1$ is not known. It can be determined by a complex formula (see BROOKS and CARRUTHERS, 1953) but a simple method leads to the same goal. We define that either $\Delta_2 x_1$ or the central value $\Delta_2 x_c$ is zero. This assumption provides a value for the unknown, and it enables computation of all differences from that basic reference. It will provide preliminary differences $\Delta_2 x_i'$, which deviate from the correct $\Delta_2 x_i$ by a constant. This constant can be found from:

$$c_{\Delta_2} = \overline{\Delta_2 X} - \overline{\Delta_2 x'} \tag{441a}$$

or in general form:

$$c_{\Delta_j} = \overline{\Delta_j X} - \overline{\Delta_j x'} \tag{441b}$$

Then:

$$\Delta_j x_i = \Delta_{j-1} x_{i+1}' - \Delta_{j-1} x_i' + c_{\Delta_j} \tag{441c}$$

Consequently, it is unessential which difference $\Delta_j x_i' = 0$ is selected. A central $\Delta_j x_c' = 0$ will often keep the numerical values of the $\Delta_j x_i'$ at a minimum. The difference method is elucidated in Example 35.

One word of caution is appropriate. The numerical values of the differences are very sensitive to any type of errors in the original observations and the average $\overline{\Delta_j X}$ is largely controlled by the difference between the first and last value X_1 and X_N. If the observational data include turbulent fluctuations or large random errors the smoothing by differences may fail. Large random errors in X_1 and X_n or considerable deviations from an (unknown) correct smoothed observation may create a completely distorted set of smoothed x_i data. The derived data by the difference method may provide anything but the expected smoothed curve which can be derived from the general trend of the data (see Example 35). The smoothing technique by differences is therefore most suitable for sets of data where the error of the marginal values X_1 and X_N is negligible or zero such as in table values which are based on mathematical formulae, etc.

Example 35. The smoothing by differences for 23 given data (first column Table LIV) is illustrated. This particular case exemplifies when smoothing by differences is not a suitable method.

The first three differences $\Delta_1 X_i$ through $\Delta_3 X_i$ are displayed in the respective columns of Table LIV with the 10th difference $\Delta_{10} X_i$ next. We learn after inspection of the column $\Delta_{10} X_i$ that the differences $\Delta_{10} X_i$ have increased from the magnitude of $\Delta_3 X_i$. Continuation would not make them smaller.

The means of subsets are provided in lines $\overline{\Delta_j X_1}$ and $\overline{\Delta_j X_2}$ ($n = 11$ for the observed data X_i and $\Delta_1 X_i$; $n = 10$ for $\Delta_2 X_i$ and $\Delta_3 X_i$). The differences of the subsets $\overline{\Delta_j X_1} - \overline{\Delta_j X_2}$ show a minimum at $\Delta_3 X_i$ ($\Delta_4 X_i$ is not included into Table LIV). Consequently, one could postulate that the third differences are constant, i.e., $\overline{\Delta_3 X} = -0.189$.

The recomputed smoothed observations from the third differences are contained in the column next to the last one with heading x_i. The reader will notice immediately that x_i shows considerable departure from the observed data X_i. A three-term polynomial curve fitted to the observed data is provided in the last column y_i which is much closer to X_i.

The mean differences $\overline{\Delta_j X_p}$ for the three-term polynomial curve y_i are given in the respective (last) line of Table LIV. $\overline{\Delta_j X}$ and $\overline{\Delta_j X_p}$ for ($j \geq 1$) differ. In this case $\overline{\Delta_j X}$ is accounted for by the difference between the first and last data point of the previous column, i.e., $\Delta_{j-1} X_1$ and $\Delta_{j-1} X_{n_j}$ (divided by n_j). Because $X_i = y_i + \varepsilon_i$ the dissimilarity between $\overline{\Delta_j X}$ and $\overline{\Delta_j X_p}$ is explained, i.e., $\sum (\Delta_j \varepsilon_{i+1} - \Delta_j \varepsilon_i) \neq 0$.

TABLE LIV

SMOOTHING BY DIFFERENCES

	X_i	$\Delta_1 X_i$	$\Delta_2 X_i$	$\Delta_3 X_i$	$\Delta_{10} X_I$	$\Delta_3 x'_i$	$\Delta_2 x'_i$	$\Delta_1 x'_i$	$\Delta_1 x_i$	x'_i	x_i	y_i
	$j=0$	1	2	3	10	3	2	1	1	0	0	
14,300	9.05		–	–	–		–			−0.409	11.27	6.51
		−0.96						−10.395	−6.577			
	8.09		0.79		–		1.890			−6.986	4.69	8.19
		−0.17		0.96		−0.189		−8.505	−4.687			
14,400	7.92		1.75		–		1.701			−11.673	0	9.64
		1.58		−1.00		−0.189		−6.804	−2.986			
	9.50		0.75		–		1.512			−14.659	−2.98	10.86
		2.33		−4.67		−0.189		−5.292	−1.474			
14,500	11.83		−3.92		–		1.323			−16.133	−4.45	11.87
		−1.59		7.05		−0.189		−3.969	−0.151			
	10.84		3.13		242.2		1.134			−16.284	−4.60	12.68
		1.54		−1.08		−0.189		−2.835	0.983			
14,600	11.78		2.05		67.2		0.945			−15.301	−3.62	13.31
		3.59		−4.95		−0.189		−1.890	1.928			
	15.37		−2.90		−366.1		0.756			−13.373	−1.69	13.76
		0.69		3.38		−0.189		−1.134	2.684			
14,700	16.06		0.48		544.5		0.567			−10.689	0.99	14.05
		1.17		−4.83		−0.189		−0.576	3.242			
	17.23		−4.35		−622.2		0.378			−7.447	4.23	14.20
		−3.18		6.67		−0.189		−0.189	3.629			
14,800	14.05		2.32		661.8		0.189			−3.818	7.86	14.21
		−0.86		−3.13		−0.189		0	3.818			
	13.19		−0.81		−714.2		0			0	11.68	14.10
		−1.67		5.79		−0.189		0	3.818			
14,900	11.52		4.98		759.1		−0.189			3.818	15.50	13.87
		3.31		−8.88		−0.189		−0.189	3.629			
	14.83		−3.90		−708.8		−0.378			7.447	19.13	13.55
		−0.59		5.02		−0.189		−0.576	3.242			

15,000	14.24		1.12		533.7		−0.567			10.689	22.37	13.15
		0.53		−3.13		−0.189		−1.134	2.684			
	14.77		−2.01		−317.6		−0.756			13.373	25.05	12.68
		−1.48		1.03		−0.189		−1.890	1.928			
15,100	13.29		−0.98		162.2		−0.945			15.301	26.98	12.14
		−2.46		0.78		−0.189		−2.835	0.983			
	10.83		−0.20		−90.9		−1.134			16.284	27.96	11.56
		−2.66		2.15		−0.189		−3.969	−0.151			
15,200	8.17		1.95		–		−1.323			16.133	27.81	10.95
		−0.71		0.04		−0.189		−5.292	−1.474			
	7.46		1.99		–		−1.512			14.659	26.34	10.31
		1.28		−1.22		−0.189		−6.804	−2.986			
15,300	8.74		0.77		–		−1.701			11.673	23.35	9.67
		2.05		−3.75		−0.189		−8.505	−4.687			
	10.79		−2.98		–		−1.890			6.986	18.67	9.03
		−0.93		–				−10.395	−6.577			
15,400	9.86		–		–		–			0.409	12.09	8.40
n_j	23	22	21	20	13							23
$\overline{\Delta_j x}$	11.68	0.037	0.001	−0.189	11.60	−0.189	0.00	−3.781	0.037	0	11.68	11.68
$\overline{\Delta_j X_1}$	11.97	0.376	0.010	−0.160								
$\overline{\Delta_j X_2}$	11.32	−0.303	0.074	−0.217								
$\overline{\Delta_j X_p}$	11.68	0.086	−0.110	0.011								

x_i = observed data (m s^{-1}); $\overline{\Delta_j X_p}$ = mean differences for the three terms polynomial curve (last column, y_i), $\overline{\Delta_j X}$ = means of columns, $\overline{\Delta_j X_1}$, $\overline{\Delta_j X_2}$ = means for the subset (see horizontal separation line at 14,850).

This implies that X_i is a set of observed data with an undeterminable random and unknown error that affects the differences $\overline{\Delta_j X_i}$ which cannot be calculated with the necessary accuracy. Under these circumstances the difference method is not suitable to smooth the observations. Had we known x_1, the first, and x_{23}, the last smoothed observation of X_i (e.g., $x_1 = y_1$ or $x_{23} = y_{23}$), a smooth curve could have been constructed from the differences $\Delta_j X_i$ which would resemble y_i and consequently accommodates the correct trend of X_i.
The recomputation of $\Delta_j x_i$ and x_i is illustrated in the respective columns of Table LIV based on $\overline{\Delta_3 X} = \text{constant} = -0.189$. In our particular case $\overline{\Delta_2 X} - \overline{\Delta_2 x'} \sim 0$. Consequently, $\Delta_2 x'_i \equiv \Delta_2 x_i$, and the column $\Delta_2 x_i$ has been omitted. $\overline{\Delta_1 X_1} - \overline{\Delta_1 x'_1} = 0.037 - (-3.781) = 3.818$ and $\bar{X} - \bar{x}' = 11.68$.
The reader may question whether the assumption of $\overline{\Delta_2 X} = 0$ would have been a better choice than $\overline{\Delta_3 X} = -0.189$. It would lead to $\Delta_1 x_i = \text{constant} = \overline{\Delta_1 X} = 0.037$ which provides $x_i = 11.236 + 0.037i$. This is somewhat better than x_i in the next to last column of Table LIV but is not as good an approximation of x_i as y_i is. Therefore, smoothing by differences should only be applied when it can be assumed that the first and last value of a set of data (e.g., X_i and X_N) are free of random influences such as in tables or in mathematical formulations.

Smoothing by functions

Previous discussions on smoothing centered on processes like moving averages, predetermined weighting functions, or differences. Curve-fitting techniques, however, can also be employed. In fact, any representation of data by certain mathematical expressions and truncation before the full possible number of terms (coefficients) is a smoothing process. If the set of data to be smoothed is large (e.g., $N > 100$), the polynomial series display certain weaknesses. Some normalizing or weighting procedures to higher order terms is advisable in order to reduce the disproportionate weight of the margin data (e.g., X_1 and X_N). The random errors included into X_1 and X_N may cause an excessive influence in the calculation of coefficients for higher order terms. Curve-fitting procedures have been extensively treated in Chapters 3 and 4 and in the author's 1976 text.
If orthogonal (empirical) polynomial functions must be calculated, the task is sometimes tedious for $N > 100$ although electronic data processing has generally reduced the time for the calculations. The Fourier analysis is not burdened with restrictions in the number of points, because the equations (eq. 384a) can be adjusted to any data length N but the amplitudes of the Fourier series may only slowly converge towards zero for the higher order terms. The slow convergence can be observed especially for data sets which are not a compound wave pattern, and we may need many terms to reach a predetermined tolerance limit of the residual variance. Representation by polynomials would not improve the situation. In fact, any representation by more than six polynomial terms and $N \geq 40$ becomes problematical even for electronic data processing.
A smoothing technique by the truncated polynomials or Fourier series may be applicable to hardware systems which do not respond to small-scale fluctuations. Truncation is made at that point where small variations are negligible. This technique is sometimes recommended for analytical representation of the wind profile with respect to rocket response and can be considered as a filtering technique (see ESSENWANGER and BILLIONS, 1965). Fourier filtering by setting the Fourier amplitudes zero for wave numbers which are greater than a specified cut-off point was employed by WILLIAMSON (1976) to the shallow water equations.

Example 36. Smoothing by moving averages and a truncated polynomial series is demonstrated in Table LV. The first column contains wind speeds from angle of attack measurements (REISIG, 1956;

TABLE LV

VARIOUS SMOOTHING TECHNIQUES

Altitude (m)	Polynomial smoothing				Moving averages					
	observed	first 23 points		last 23 data	unweighted			weighted		
	m s^{-1}	2 terms	6 terms	2 terms	3	7	11	3	7	11
14,300	9.05	7.49	9.19		–	–	–	–	–	–
14,350	8.09	8.64	7.79		8.35	–	–	8.29	–	–
14,400	7.92	9.68	8.11		8.50	–	–	8.36	–	–
	9.50	10.61	9.28		9.75	9.77	–	9.69	9.64	–
14,500	11.83	11.43	10.74		10.52	10.67	–	10.85	10.54	–
	10.24	12.14	12.14		11.28	11.81	11.92	11.02	11.44	11.60
14,600	11.78	12.74	13.29		12.46	13.14	12.30	12.29	12.71	12.83
	15.37	13.23	14.13		14.40	13.79	12.61	14.64	14.31	14.09
14,700	16.06	13.61	14.65		16.22	13.99	13.24	16.18	15.45	14.95
	17.23	13.88	14.90		15.78	14.17	13.67	16.14	15.48	15.06
14,800	14.05	14.04	14.92		14.82	14.61	13.93	14.63	14.58	14.53
	13.19	14.10	14.78		12.92	14.44	14.21	12.99	13.59	13.90
14,900	11.52	14.04	14.50		13.18	14.26	14.12	12.76	13.32	13.61
	14.83	13.87	14.10		13.53	13.70	13.47	13.85	13.72	13.71
15,000	14.24	13.59	13.56		14.61	13.24	12.69	14.52	14.09	13.78
	14.77	13.21	12.87		14.10	12.52	11.92	14.27	13.78	13.38
15,100	13.29	12.71	12.01		12.96	11.94	11.62	13.04	12.60	12.35
	10.83	12.10	11.00		10.76	11.07	11.32	10.78	10.86	10.95
15,200	8.17	11.39	9.91		8.82	10.58	11.20	8.66	9.30	9.73
	7.46	10.56	8.93		8.12	9.88	10.53	7.96	8.68	9.12
15,300	8.74	9.63	8.36		9.00	9.44	9.74	8.93	9.03	9.16
	10.79	8.58	8.73	10.39	9.80	8.95	9.05	10.04	9.63	9.41
15,400	9.86	7.43	10.81	9.63	10.30	8.58	8.47	10.19	9.73	9.37
	10.26			8.93	9.17	8.54	7.96	9.44	9.03	8.83
15,500	7.40			8.29	7.74	8.27	7.81	7.66	7.89	7.99
	5.57			7.71	6.71	7.48	7.74	6.42	7.00	7.21
15,600	7.16			7.19	6.54	7.01	7.43	6.70	6.60	6.71
	6.89			6.74	6.42	6.50	6.99	6.54	6.41	6.44
15,700	5.21			6.35	6.23	6.20	6.72	5.97	6.25	6.29
	6.58			6.02	6.15	6.26	6.29	6.26	6.19	6.20
15,800	6.66			5.75	6.20	6.21	6.08	6.31	6.14	6.14
	5.35			5.54	6.00	6.02	6.09	5.84	6.06	6.08
15,900	6.00			5.40	6.06	6.00	5.97	6.04	6.05	6.03
	6.82			5.31	6.12	5.88	5.80	6.30	6.01	5.94
16,000	5.54			5.29	5.81	5.76	5.69	5.74	5.79	5.79
	5.07			5.33	5.46	5.71	5.60	5.36	5.58	5.63
16,100	5.76			5.43	5.53	5.43	5.76	5.59	5.50	5.48
	5.76			5.60	5.52	5.26	6.02	5.58	5.36	5.35
16,200	5.03			5.82	4.95	5.66	6.16	4.97	5.15	5.32
	4.06			6.11	4.90	6.12	–	4.69	5.30	–
16,300	5.61			6.46	6.01	6.36	–	5.91	6.11	–
	8.36			6.87	7.40	–	–	7.64	–	–
16,400	8.23			7.34	8.04	–	–	8.09	–	–
16,450	7.53			7.87	–	–	–	–	–	–

ESSENWANGER and BILLIONS, 1965) in 50-m intervals from 14,300 m through 16,450 m altitude at Cape Kennedy observed on August 14, 1959. These data display non-stationary fluctuations. The first four columns demonstrate the Tchebycheff polynomial smoothing for 23 points, two and six terms of the series. The first 23 points have been recomputed by:

$$X_i = 11.68 - 0.0027\Phi_{1i} - 0.0548\Phi_{2i} + 0.0127\Phi_{3i} + 0.0013\Phi_{4i} - 0.00066\Phi_{5i} + 0.00016\Phi_{6i}$$

The percentage reduction per term is: 0.0; 57.7; 2.8; 12.7; 0.0; 2.0%. The last 23 points render the equation:

$$X_i = 6.76 - 0.114\Phi_{1i} + 0.0309\Phi_{2i}$$

with 0.0; 19.3; 49.3% as the respective percentage reduction values.
Moving 3, 7 and 11 point averages, unweighted and weighted, follow in the next six columns of Table LV. The weighting factors are based on the binomial coefficients.
Only some smoothing has been achieved by three point averages, the weighted averages following closely the observed data as illustrated by Fig. 8 (right hand side). The 3 point overlapping weighted averaging data stay closer to the observed data than the curve with six term smoothing by polynomials, although the latter may be preferable because good approximation of the observed data is combined with a smooth enough overall pattern.
More smoothing is accomplished by utilizing only two polynomial terms (Fig. 8). This is approximately equivalent to an 11 point moving average although the latter is not as smooth.

Smoothing by overlapping polynomials (filtering)

In the preceding sections the smoothing by a mathematical system comprising the entire data set was discussed. This technique may be pursued when N is small. Besides the difficulties with huge numerical values arising for large N one additional point may be important. Time series data may be non-stationary or show rapid changes of the frequency (cycle) or the set of data may comprise different regimes (e.g., the structure of the wind profile). Then the set of observed data may consist of incompatible (different) populations. In this instance smoothing in sections of the data set is more suitable. It may also be desirable not to alter some smoothed parts of an original data sequence or to preserve the curvature structure of data such as for the wind profile. Smoothing techniques tend to dampen the amplitude of fluctuations, and create smoothed curves which shift towards the inside of curve reversals like maxima or minima of the original data sequence such as for wind profiles (see Example 36).
A technique developed by the author (1961) and illustrated jointly with Billions (ESSENWANGER and BILLIONS, 1965) may be helpful. Subsequent overlapping data sets are fitted by polynomials, but the number of polynomial terms, i.e., the truncation, is decided on account of the lag correlation (STECKLER, 1960). To assure continuity, the middle portions of the fitted polynomial approximation is used except at the margins (beginning or end) of the profile, where the analytical data at the margins are used in addition to the

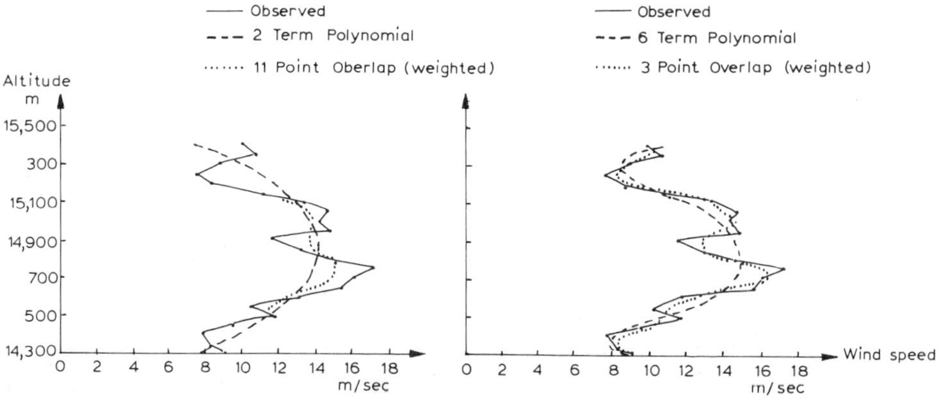

Fig. 8. Comparison of smoothing methods.

middle points (see Fig. 9). This procedure does not decrease the number of data points. It gives no "curvature effect" at the points of profile inflexion and is not an "abrupt" filter. The cut-off point is individually determined for every subset of data varying with the subsets as conditions require. This technique can be considered as a piecewise curve fitting. We return to eq. 431 and assume a polynomial (orthogonal) series:

$$Y_i = a_0 + a_1\Phi_{1i} +, \ldots, a_k\Phi_{ki} \tag{442a}$$

The last terms represent small-scale and/or error fluctuations. In practice, the term Φ_{ki} contributes to Y by changes of the sign from minus to plus for $i = 1, 2, \ldots, n$, while $a_1\Phi_{1i}$ provides a "string" of the same sign. We may postulate that the first terms are characteristics of the "smooth" curve, while the last terms contribute to an error ε. In agreement with this concept the border between S and ε lies somewhere between Φ_{1i} and Φ_{ki}.

The dominance of the error term ε is indicated by either a negative first or second lag correlation. This postulation is illustrated for the 23 points of the orthogonal Tchebycheff series. The calculated lag correlations of the first six terms are exhibited in Table LVI. The sixth order term has a lag correlation sequence "plus–minus" from the first to the second lag and r_1 decreases steadily.

As an objective working tool we adopt the rule that either the correlation coefficient for lag 1 and 2 must change signs from plus to minus after separation of the smooth $= S$ part from the "turbulent" or "noise" $= \varepsilon$-part, or the lag 1 correlation is negative.

The following steps are required:

$$y_{1i} = a_0 + a_1\Phi_{1i} \quad \text{(postulated smooth profile)} \tag{442b}$$

$$Y_{1i} = Y_i - y_{1i} \quad \text{(assumed noise)} \tag{442c}$$

Then the two lag correlations are calculated for y_{i1}. If neither of the above stated criteria are fulfilled we continue:

$$y_{2i} = a_0 + a_1\Phi_{1i} + a_2\Phi_{2i} \quad \text{(new postulated smooth profile)} \tag{442d}$$

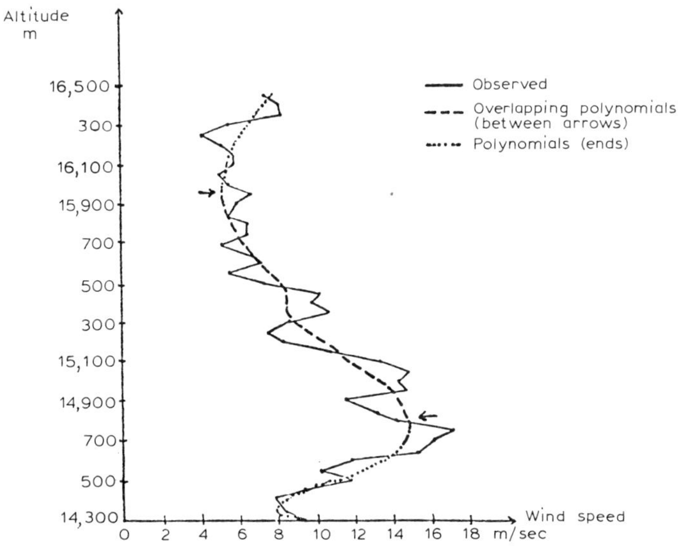

Fig. 9. Smoothing by overlapping polynomials.

TABLE LVI

LAG CORRELATIONS FOR THE FIRST SIX TERMS OF 23 POINT TCHEBYCHEFF ORTHOGONAL POLYNOMIALS

Lag	Order: 1	2	3	4	5	6
1	0.91	0.82	0.73	0.64	0.55	0.46
2	0.81	0.62	0.44	0.27	0.11	−0.04
3	0.71	0.42	0.16	0.07	−0.26	−0.41
4	0.59	0.22	−0.10	−0.35	−0.51	−0.58

$$Y_{2i} = Y_i - y_{2i} \quad \text{(assumed noise)} \tag{442e}$$

or:

$$Y_{2i} = Y_{1i} - a_2\Phi_{2i} \tag{442f}$$

The process is continued until the criteria are fulfilled for:

$$Y_{ji} = Y_i - y_{ji} \tag{442g}$$

Finally by definition the lag correlations will fulfill the correlation rule before six terms of the polynomial series for the set of 23 data points or the smooth profile S is accepted as having six but no more terms. In reality the dominance of the ε may show up for lag correlations calculated from less than six terms. See Example 37.

In Example 37 the center three points of the polynomial curve were adopted as the "smooth" profile, and the next data set was shifted by three points but this choice is an arbitrary decision. Five points could have been accepted and the data set shifted by five points (more details see example).

The sign rule for the first two lag correlations of the remainder Y_{ji} for 23 points may need some alteration if $n \neq 23$. E.g., with 11 points, lags 1 and 2 display opposite signs already after the first two terms have been eliminated (see Table LVII). This must be expected, because the total number of points has now been decreased. If smoothing by two terms (for 11 points) is considered insufficient, the criterion for truncation can be changed, e.g., requiring a negative lag 1 correlation, which occurs for truncation of eq. 442a after five terms.

The described technique has been utilized for the separation of the stationary from the non-stationary component of the wind profile by subtracting the analytically determined

TABLE LVII

LAG CORRELATION FOR THE FIRST THREE TERMS OF 11 POINTS TCHEBYCHEFF ORTHOGONAL POLYNOMIALS

Lag	Order: 1	2	3
1	0.94	0.74	0.46
2	0.74	0.20	−0.19
3	0.40	−0.27	−0.65

smooth profile part from the data (see ESSENWANGER, 1961; ESSENWANGER and BILLIONS, 1965). The remainder is the non-stationary part.

If smoothed values are subtracted from the original observations, only the high frequencies will remain. Thus, the process of smoothing by overlapping polynomials functions like a high-pass filter. If further smoothing is applied to the high-frequency oscillations, the procedure resembles a band-pass filter because intermediate components are being determined. Therefore, the technique is one of the procedures to separate any set of observational data into high, intermediate, and low bands of frequencies. Although the cut-off is somewhat arbitrary it is obtained by an objective procedure. Thus, the smoothing by overlapping polynomials may be interpreted as the application of a variable filter.

Example 37. Smoothing by overlapping polynomials is illustrated in Table LVIII and Fig. 9. The data series comprises wind velocity observations at 50-m intervals, starting at an altitude of 14,300 m (see Table LV). Table LVIII exhibits the first and second lag correlation for the overlapping data sets listed by the altitude of the respective Y_1. We deduce from Table LVIII that the smooth part comprises six terms (eq. 441b) for the first five sets (altitude bases 14,300 through 14,900 m) until the sign sequence + − is reached. Data sets starting at altitude 15,050 m require five terms, the set for altitude 15,200 m needs four terms and the last set (altitude 15,350 m) two terms.

The smooth curve (stationary profile) comprises a varying number of polynomial terms which represent the "smooth" profile for the individual data sets. In this example the number of terms decreases systematically with increasing altitude. A continuous decrease is not a prerequisite, however. The gradual change for a sequence of overlapping subsets manifests continuity but other atmospheric data may not follow a pattern of systematic changes.

The following analytical model emerges as the smooth profile:

$$Y_i(h) = a_0(h) + a_1(h)\Phi_{1i} + \ldots + a_k(h)\Phi_{ki} \tag{442h}$$

where k varies with the data set (see Table LVIII) and $i = 1, \ldots, 23$. The first entry for the smooth profile stretches from $i = 1, \ldots, 13$. Three points, y_{11}, y_{12} and y_{13} are adopted for the smooth profile at every altitude but y_1 through y_{10} and y_{14} through y_{23} are added at the margins in order to keep

TABLE LVIII

LAG CORRELATION AFTER ELIMINATION OF THE RESPECTIVE TERM FOR OVERLAPPING 23 POINT POLYNOMIAL SMOOTHING

Beginning of 23 points meter	Lag	Term: 1	2	3	4	5	6
14,300	1	0.79	0.49	0.44	0.34	0.34	0.25
	2	0.65	0.17	0.13	0.06	0.06	−0.03
14,450	1	0.67	0.55	0.41	0.41	0.38	0.36
	2	0.47	0.31	0.09	0.09	0.12	−0.03
14,600	1	0.40	0.40	0.38	0.40	0.40	0.38
	2	0.12	0.12	0.10	0.10	0.10	−0.03
14,750	1	0.42	0.41	0.39	0.40	0.42	0.36
	2	0.13	0.13	0.11	0.12	0.15	−0.02
14,900	1	0.50	0.35	0.36	0.41	0.39	0.26
	2	0.26	0.08	0.10	0.14	0.13	−0.07
15,050	1	0.53	0.43	0.43	0.41	0.26	–
	2	0.19	0.09	0.10	0.11	−0.07	
15,200	1	0.35	0.33	0.33	0.10	–	–
	2	0.11	0.07	0.07	−0.12		
15,350	1	0.63	0.22	–	–	–	–
	2	0.40	−0.08				

the data length of the smooth profile from $h=14{,}300$ through $h=16{,}450$ m (see Fig. 9). Fig. 10 exhibits a final product from surface to about 28 km (ESSENWANGER and BILLIONS, 1965).

Filters

General filters

Filtering can be based on the same principal equation as previously introduced. Eq. 432 indicates that the variate y_i has been transformed into a smoother variable $\bar{X}_j$. We generalize eq. 432 by writing:

$$\bar{X}_j = \sum \omega y_i \tag{443a}$$

or reversed:

$$\phi(y) \rightarrow \psi(x) \tag{443b}$$

and consider a filtering process a transformation of $\phi(y)$ uniquely into another function $\psi(x)$ where the spectral value of $\phi(y)$ is different from the one at $\psi(x)$. The form of the spectral value of $\phi(y)$ needs specification by a modification function which is called a filter. The derivation of the spectrum for any arbitrary function $\phi(y)$ or $\psi(x)$ follows mathemat-

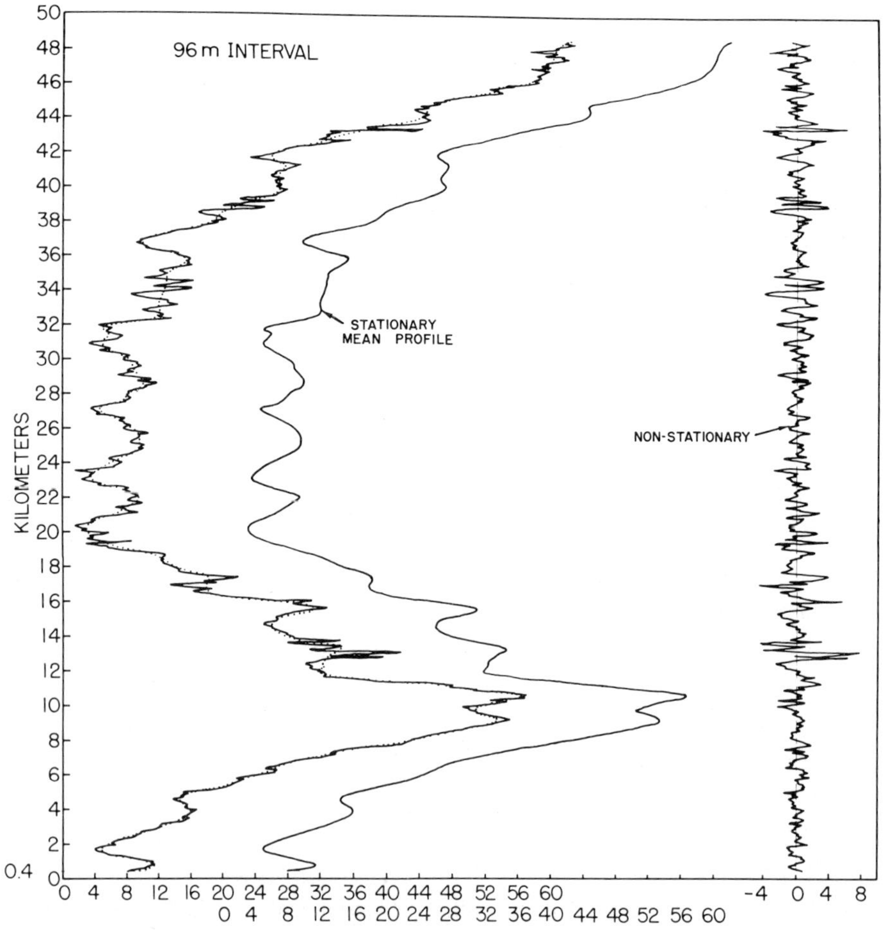

Fig. 10. Separation of the wind profile into stationary and non-stationary parts.

ical procedures which were outlined (eq. 407a, b, c). We postulate that the frequency ν has the bounds $-\infty<\nu<\infty$, $A_\nu=A_{-\nu}$ for the amplitude, and the phase angle $\beta_\nu=\beta_{-\nu}$. Then (with $i=\sqrt{-1}$):

$$\phi(y)=(A_\nu/2)\exp[i(2\pi\nu y-\beta_\nu)] \tag{444a}$$

$$\psi(x)=g(\nu)\phi(y)=g(\nu)(A_\nu/2)\exp[i(2\pi\nu y-\beta_\nu)] \tag{444b}$$

Although the components A_ν and β_ν have the same numerical values in the original and the transformed function, $g(\nu)$ depends on the frequency ν and is the filter characteristic or pass characteristic. It is also called the response characteristic or weighting function (see later eq. 447).

If $g(\nu)$ is real, $\psi(x)$ will disclose only a change in the amplitude of certain frequencies, e.g., $g(\nu)>1$ means fortification, $g(\nu)=1$ no change, $g(\nu)<1$ diminution and $g(\nu)=0$ extinction. If $g(\nu)$ is complex, i.e.:

$$g(\nu)=a_\nu+ib_\nu \tag{445a}$$

with:

$$G_{(\nu)}=(a_\nu^2+b_\nu^2)^{1/2} \tag{445b}$$

and:

$$\tan\alpha_\nu=b_\nu/a_\nu \tag{445c}$$

then $\psi(x)$ will exhibit also a phase change, namely:

$$\psi(x)=G(\nu)(A_\nu/2)\exp[i(2\pi\nu y-\beta_\nu+\alpha_\nu)] \tag{445d}$$

Filters where $g(\nu)$ remains real are called phase preserving because they produce either a zero shift or only a shift of 180° for negative $g(\nu)$.

The power spectrum of $\phi(y)$ is denoted with L_ϕ and the one for $\psi(x)$ with L_ψ. We can write:

$$L\psi(\nu)=T(\nu)L_\phi(\nu) \tag{446a}$$

where:

$$T(\nu)=G^2(\nu) \tag{446b}$$

We distinguish three cases: (*a*) low pass filters, where $g(\nu)$ decreases with increasing ν; (*b*) high pass filters, where $g(\nu)$ increases with increasing ν; (*c*) band pass filters, where $g(\nu)$ has a maximum at a specified frequency ν_{max} and decreases with increasing distance from ν_{max}.

Filters are sometimes desirable, but they often have undesirable effects. A desirable effect may be the elimination of noise by a low pass filter. The "aliasing effect" in Fourier or power spectral analysis can be minimized or eliminated with the aid of a low pass filter. High pass filters are often employed for suppression of slow changes in the observational data such as a trend or long-term fluctuations in time series. Many investigations in atmospheric physics, climatology or meteorology have benefitted by engaging a band pass filter to accentuate certain periodicities (e.g., see CRADDOCK, 1965, 1968).

Digital filtering in geophysics was the topic of a special text by KULHÁNEK (1975). GOLD and RADER (1969) elaborated on digital processing of signals. HERRERO and WILLONER (1966), ZVEREV (1967) and MEYER and VAN ISACKER (1975) dealt with the synthesis of filters.

Low, high, and band pass filters

Transverse filters *(see also p. 203)*

We may design a transverse filter of the form:

$$g(\nu)=\left|\int_{-\infty}^{\infty}\omega_s \exp(i2\pi\nu s)\,\mathrm{d}s\right| \tag{447a}$$

where $-\infty<s<\infty$ and:

$$\left|\int_{-\infty}^{\infty}\omega_s\,\mathrm{d}s\right|<\infty \tag{447b}$$

In eq. 447a ω_s can be interpreted as a weighting function. We can limit ω_s to an interval $s_l<s<s_u$. Within the bounds s_l and s_u the weights are non-zero but they are zero everywhere else, i.e., $g(\nu)$ disappears outside the specified bounds. Often $g(\nu)$ is called the Fourier transform of ω_s.
The reversibility of eq. 447a leads to:

$$\omega_s=\int_{-\infty}^{\infty}g(\nu)\exp(-i2\pi\nu s)\,\mathrm{d}s \tag{448}$$

Only filters symmetric about $s=0$ are phase preserving. This condition is identical with the statement that $g(\nu)$ is a real function.
Transverse filtering can be compounded, i.e.:
either:

$$g(\nu)=g_1(\nu)\pm g_2(\nu) \tag{449a}$$

or:

$$g(\nu)=g_1(\nu)\cdot g_2(\nu),\ \text{etc.} \tag{449b}$$

Eq. 449b implies that $\phi(y)$ is transformed to $\psi_1(x)$ and later to $\psi_2(x)$. In eq. 449a $\phi(y)$ is transformed to $\psi_1(x)$, to $\psi_2(x)$, etc. and finally $\phi(y)$ becomes:

$$\psi(x)=\psi_1(x)+\psi_2(x),\ \text{etc.} \tag{449c}$$

A transformation with a transverse filter may be expressed:

$$\bar{X}_j=\sum_{s=-\infty}^{\infty}\omega_s y_{j+s} \tag{450a}$$

with:

$$\left|\sum_{s=-\infty}^{\infty}\omega_s\right|<\infty \tag{450b}$$

It is evident that eq. 450a resembles eq. 432 with one difference, ω_s is normalized, i.e.: $\sum\omega_s=1.0$.

Low pass filters

The simplest form of a low pass filter is the moving average with a constant weight. The transformation is identical with eq. 432 or 434a. In a slightly modified form:

$$\bar{X}_j=(2n+1)^{-1}\sum_{s=-n}^{n} y_{j+s} \qquad (451a)$$

The weight $\omega_s=(2n+1)^{-1}$ is a constant for all data between $-n<s<n$, and ω_s is 0 for all y_k values where $|k|>|n|$. The summation runs from $-n$ to $+n$ and the averaging interval can be obtained from:

$$\Delta_a=X_n-y_n \qquad (451b)$$

The pass characteristics is:

$$g(\nu)=[\sin(\pi\nu n\Delta y)]/[n\sin(\pi\nu\Delta y)] \qquad (451c)$$

which in the continuous case would amount to:

$$g(\nu)=[\sin(2\pi\nu\Delta y)]/(2\pi\nu\Delta y) \qquad (451d)$$

This corresponds to eq. 434d.
Another frequently employed low pass filter is a weighting based on the Gaussian distribution (see eq. 437a):

$$\omega_s=(\Delta y\sqrt{\pi})^{-1}\exp[-s^2/(\Delta y)^2] \qquad (452a)$$

with:

$$g(\nu)=\exp[-\pi\nu^2(\Delta y)^2] \qquad (452b)$$

In practical applications we define a boundary ν_b, beyond which $\omega_s=0$. It is customary to postulate:

$$\nu_b=0.685/\Delta y \qquad (452c)$$

at which the amplitude $A_{\nu_b}\leq 1\%$.
We can replace the Gaussian weighting by the binomial series:

$$\bar{X}_j=2^{-n}\sum_{s=0}^{n}\binom{n}{s} y_{j+s} \qquad (453a)$$

where $\bar{X}_j$ is usually assigned to the center point of smoothing, e.g., $m=2$, $\bar{X}_j=(y_j+y_{j+1})/2$ and $\bar{X}_j$ is placed at the midpoint position:

$$g(\nu)=\cos^n(\pi\nu/2\nu_N) \qquad (453b)$$

where ν_N describes the Nyquist frequency $\nu_N=1/(2\Delta y)$, i.e., the frequency of the minimum cycle (see eq. 430a). Additional details on the characteristics and behavior of low pass filters in instrumental application can be found in TAUBENHEIM (1969) or BROWN (1963). An application of a low pass filter was given by HOSHIAI et al. (1974) for the quasi-biennial oscillation of the ultra-long waves at the 500 mbar geopotential field.
Low pass filters often have been utilized for smoothing of data (signals) to suppress "noise." The moving average is the simplest example for it (see eq. 451a). The product of smoothing depends primarily on the weighting function ω_s. Polynomials were suggested by CRADDOCK and GRIMMER (1960) or special polynomials such as Tchebycheff or Butterworth by KAISER and REED (1977) while PASSI (1976) recommended "optimized" weights which were derived for and from autoregressive models. LEE (1981) compared

various filter-types and favored the properties of the Bessel filter and DUCHON (1979) described "Lanczos" filtering.

High pass filters

The process is the opposite of a low pass filter and is expressed as:

$$g_H(\nu) = 1 - g_L(\nu) \tag{454a}$$

Consequently, the data series is obtained by:

$$\psi_H(x) = \phi(y) - \psi_L(x) \tag{454b}$$

where the subscript L denotes the low pass and H the high pass component. A process of differentiation can also lead to a high pass filter:

$$X_j = y_j - \omega_{y_{j-1}} \tag{455a}$$

The response characteristic leads to:

$$g(\nu) = 1 - \omega\cos(-2\pi\nu\Delta y) - i\omega\sin(-2\pi\nu\Delta y) \tag{455b}$$

where again $i = \sqrt{-1}$. The absolute part of $g(\nu)$ is:

$$|g(\nu)| = [1 + \omega^2 - 2\omega\cos(2\pi\nu\Delta y)]^{1/2} \tag{455c}$$

According to TAUBENHEIM (1969) analysis of atmospheric turbulence has been performed with setting $\omega = 0.75$. If $\omega = 1$, then:

$$g(\nu) = 2\sin[\pi\nu/(2\nu_N)] \tag{455d}$$

and the phase shift α becomes:

$$\tan\alpha_\nu = \cot[\pi\nu/2\nu_N)] \tag{455e}$$

or after some modifications:

$$\alpha_\nu = (1 - \nu/\nu_N)\pi/2 = (1 - 2\nu\Delta y)\pi/2 \tag{455f}$$

Band pass filters

The third category of filters is the band pass filter, where $g(\nu)$ possesses a maximum at a specified frequency which passes through. Several characteristics describe which type of band pass filters is considered.

(*1*) The half-power bandwidth:

$$B_h = \nu_2 - \nu_1 \tag{456a}$$

with:

$$G^2(\nu_1) = G^2(\nu_2) = G^2(\nu_{max})/2 \tag{456b}$$

(Note, G stands for the absolute value, defined by eq. 445b, and is also called the gain factor.)

The frequency response function $g(\nu)$ is here defined by:

$$g(\nu)=\int_0^{\infty} \nu_s \exp(i2\pi\nu s)\, ds \qquad (456c)$$

whose integration ranges from 0 to ∞ instead of from $-\infty$ to ∞ such as in eq. 447a.
(*2*) The noise bandwidth:

$$B_n=\left[\int_0^{\infty} G^2(\nu)\, d\nu\right]\Big/ G^2(\nu) \qquad (457)$$

is the width of an equivalent rectangular filter with the property that a signal passes through it with the same mean square value as it passes the actual filter when the input is white noise.
(*3*) The equivalent statistical bandwidth:

$$B_e=\left[\int_0^{\infty} G^2(\nu)\, d\nu\right]^2\Big/\left[\int_0^{\infty} G^4(\nu)\, d\nu\right] \qquad (458)$$

is the width of an equivalent rectangular filter through which a signal passes with the same mean square statistical error as through the actual filter, again for white noise input. We can construct a simple band pass filter by subtraction of two low pass filters:

$$g(\nu)=g_{L_1}(\nu)-g_{L_2}(\nu) \qquad (459)$$

where the second pass characteristic must have a stronger smoothing than the first one. Hence, the transformation function:

$$\bar{X}_j=\bar{X}_{j_1}-\bar{X}_{j_2} \qquad (460a)$$

is a band pass filtering of the original function y. In a similar way:

$$\omega_s=\omega_{s_1}-\omega_{s_2} \qquad (460b)$$

Let us consider an example. Assume two binomial filterings:

$$\bar{X}_{j_1}=(x_{j-1}+2x_j+x_{j+1})/4 \qquad (461a)$$

$$\bar{X}_{j_2}=(x_{j-2}+4x_{j-1}+6x_j+4x_{j+1}+x_{j+2})/16 \qquad (461b)$$

then:

$$\bar{X}_j=(-x_{j-2}+2x_j-x_{j+2})/16 \qquad (461c)$$

and the frequency response function becomes:

$$g(\nu)=g(\nu_1)-g(\nu_2) \qquad (462a)$$

or:

$$g(\nu)=\cos^2(\pi\nu/2\nu_N)-\cos^4(\pi\nu/2\nu_N)=(1/4)\sin^2(\pi\nu/\nu_N) \qquad (462b)$$

For binomial filtering with even numbers of n_1 and n_2, where $n_2>n_1$ (see eq. 461) we can generally cast:

$$g(\nu)=\cos^{n_1}(\pi\nu/2\nu_N)-\cos^{n_2}(\pi\nu/2\nu_N) \qquad (463a)$$

The maximum frequency follows from:

$$\nu_{max} = (2\nu_N/\pi) \text{ arc } \cos[(n_1/n_2)^b] \tag{463b}$$

where $b = 1/(n_2 - n_1)$.

The band pass filters eqs. 462b, 463a have the disadvantage that they are broad and are associated with the Nyquist frequency. An alternative is the retention of a cosine wave from $-\pi$ to π, with the length $2\Delta y = 1/\nu_c$, where Δy denotes the distance 0 to π. Thus:

$$\bar{X}_j = \frac{1}{\Delta y} \int_{-\Delta y}^{\Delta y} \cos(\pi s/\Delta y) y_{j+s} \, ds \tag{464a}$$

or in discrete steps:

$$\bar{X}_j = (\Delta y)^{-1} \sum_{s=-\Delta y}^{\Delta y} \cos(\pi s/\Delta y) y_{j+s} \tag{464b}$$

Here y_{j+s} is a function of j and s which may be determined or defined (e.g., j represents the time t). Then:

$$g(\nu) = -2 \frac{\sin(2\pi\nu\Delta y)}{2\pi\nu\Delta y} \cdot \frac{(2\nu\Delta y)^2}{(2\nu\Delta y)^2 - 1} \tag{464c}$$

which can be completely transformed into a frequency form by setting $\nu_c = 1/2\Delta y$:

$$g(\nu) = -2 \frac{\sin(\pi\nu/\nu_c)}{\pi\nu/\nu_c} \cdot \frac{(\nu/\nu_c)^2}{(\nu/\nu_c)^2 - 1} \tag{464d}$$

This response function or filter characteristic is now independent of ν_N. It is real, which means the phases are preserved. While $\nu_{max} = 1.13\nu_c$, the filter function $g(\nu) = 1$ for ν_c; $g(\nu)$ assumes zero for $\nu = 0$ and $N\nu_c$; N is an integer. Eq. 464a can now be modified by a moving average over m periods instead of $2\Delta y$.

The transfer process is:

$$\bar{X}_j = \frac{1}{m\Delta y} \int_{-m\Delta y}^{+m\Delta y} \cos(\pi s/\Delta y) y_{j+s} \, ds \tag{465a}$$

with the filter characteristic:

$$g(\nu) = (-1)^m 2 \frac{\sin(m\pi\nu/\nu_c)}{m\pi\nu/\nu_c} \cdot \frac{(\nu/\nu_c)^2}{[(\nu/\nu_c)^2 - 1]} \tag{465b}$$

In discrete steps we can write ($2\Delta y = n\Delta j$ and $\Delta j = 1$):

$$\bar{X}_j = (1/a_1) \sum_{s=-a_1}^{+a_1} y_{j+s} \cos(2\pi s/n) \tag{465c}$$

with $a_1 = m \cdot n/2$.

Band pass filters can also be employed in forecasting (Brown, 1963 or Czepa, 1967). Bettge and Baumhefner (1980) discussed the application of band filters to examine spatial wave number characteristics of a 500 mbar geopotential field.

Special filters

Filters are as numerous as definitions of their properties. Some special cases which have found application in meteorology are presented in the following:

Martin-Graham filter

The author (1976, chapter 3.6) has described some frequency response function and spectra for white and red noise, and for Gaussian smoothing. These filters may be suitable in many meteorological applications but exhibit some deficiency for turbulence analysis, however. MARTIN (1962) and GRAHAM (1963) have characterized a filter with excellent response flexibility. This filter was chosen by CROOKS et al. (1968) and LESTER (1972) in analysis of clear air turbulence for averaging data.
The Martin-Graham filter is a low pass filter with a cut-off frequency ν_c and a termination frequency ν_t where $\Delta\nu_r = \nu_t - \nu_c$ is called the roll-off interval. The weights for the frequency ν are given by:

$$g(\nu) = g(-\nu) \tag{466a}$$

$$g(\nu) = 1 \text{ for } |\nu| \leq \nu_c \tag{466b}$$

$$g(\nu) = 0 \text{ for } |\nu| \geq \nu_t \tag{466c}$$

Between these boundaries we define:

$$g(\nu) = 0.5\{1 + \cos[\pi(\nu - \nu_c)/\Delta\nu_r]\}; \ \nu_c \leq \nu \leq \nu_t \tag{467a}$$

or:

$$g(\nu) = 0.5\{1 + \cos[\pi(\nu_c + \nu)/\Delta\nu_r]\}; \ -\nu_t \leq \nu \leq \nu_c \tag{467b}$$

This leads to a general formula for the weights (see eq. 448):

$$\omega_s = [\sin(2\pi\nu_c s\Delta y) + \sin(2\pi\nu_t s\Delta y)]/\{2\pi s\Delta y[1 - 4(\Delta\nu_r)^2 s^2(\Delta y)^2]\} \tag{467c}$$

The total number of weights is $\sum \omega_s = 2N + 1$, and $\Delta y = 1/\nu_j$, where j represents the sampling rate, and Δy is the sampling interval.
The central weight is:

$$\omega_c = (\nu_c + \nu_t)\Delta y \tag{467d}$$

eq. 467c discloses a singularity at:

$$4s^2(\Delta\nu_r)^2(\Delta x)^2 = 1 \tag{467e}$$

Hence the weight ω_s for $s = 1/[2(\Delta\nu_r)(\Delta x)]$ must be specially defined, e.g., we may set:

$$\omega_s = [(\nu_c\Delta x)\cos(2\pi s\nu_c\Delta x) + (\nu_t\Delta x)\cos(2\pi s\nu_t\Delta x)]/[1 - 12s^2(\Delta\nu_r)^2(\Delta x)^2] \tag{467f}$$

Because $\sum \omega_s = 2N + 1$ standardization is achieved with division by $2N + 1$. Then $R(\nu = 0) = 1$ (see eq. 433a).
The high pass filter associated with this low pass filter is given by the difference between the low pass filter and the all pass filter, (i.e., central weight $\omega_c = 1$ and all other $\omega_s = 0$, see also eq. 454a). GRAHAM (1963) found that the optimum number of weights N^*_ω is given by:

$$N^*_\omega = 1 + 4\nu_s/\Delta\nu_r \tag{468a}$$

This type of filter satisfies the Reynolds averaging rule and:

$$u'_{(t)} = u(t) - \bar{u}(t) \tag{468b}$$

$$\bar{u}_{(t)} = \int_{-\infty}^{\infty} \omega(\tau) u(t+\tau)\, \mathrm{d}t \qquad (468c)$$

Here u' stands for the deviation from the mean motion, u is the observation (i.e., wind component) and the average is defined above. This scheme was designed by A. A. Isakson (see discussion by J. M. Burgers in OSEEN, 1930).

The transition from continuous to discrete data may cause some problems as pointed out by LESTER (1972). Fig. 11 depicts three conditions of overlaps for the high and low pass filter.

In situation (*a*) (Fig. 11): $u \neq \bar{u} + u'$ and $\sum u' \neq 0$.

Condition (*b*) (Fig. 11) renders: $u = \bar{u} + u'$, but $\sum u' \neq 0$.

In the last case (*c*) (Fig. 11): $\sum u' = 0$, but then $u \neq \bar{u} + u'$.

LESTER's (1972) solution was the utilization of the not overlapping situation (*c*) and to keep the interval $(\nu_3 - \nu_1)$ as small as practical. For Lester's data a cut-off frequency was 0.1 Hz (or about 1 km distance) and $\nu_3 - \nu_1 = 0.03$ Hz (or about 400 m). The approximation of $u \sim \bar{u} + u'$ comes very close to the real $u = \bar{u} + u'$.

LESTER (1972) applied various filter conditions (see Table LIX). For longitudinal gust data he employed a high pass filter. He first used the set $\nu_c = 0.085$ and in a re-analysis either $\nu_c = 0.200$ or $\nu_c = 0.042$. The corresponding distances were 850 and 395 m in the first case or 1000 and 1670 m for the second combination $\nu_c = 0.085$ and $\nu_c = 0.042$.

The response function for the high and low pass filter of $\nu_c = 0.067$ and $\nu_t = 0.100$ Hz is given in Fig. 11.

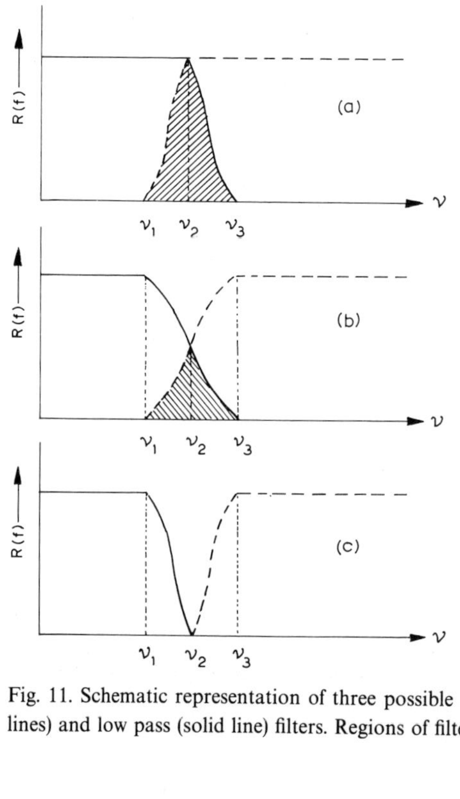

Fig. 11. Schematic representation of three possible arrangements of response functions for high pass (dashed lines) and low pass (solid line) filters. Regions of filter overlap are shaded. (From LESTER, 1972.)

TABLE LIX

CHARACTERISTIC PARAMETERS FOR THE MARTIN-GRAHAM FILTER

Low pass:			High pass:		
ν_c	ν_t	N_w^*	ν_c	ν_t	N_w^*
0.067	0.100 Hz	501	same as low pass		
0.070	0.085	1001	0.085	0.100	1001
0.185	0.200	1001	0.200	0.215	1001
			0.042	0.060	1001

Kertz and Olberg system

(*1*) KERTZ (1966) has suggested a numerical (digital) filter which is a transverse filter, and is phase preserving (OLBERG, 1973). It can be constructed relatively easy with the aid of a shift operator. We assume that a set of observations is given by $y_1, y_2 \ldots y_n$. This set of data can be considered as an n-dimensional vector y_i which can be complex, i.e. $y_j = a_j + ib_j$, with $i = \sqrt{-1}$.
The scalar vector product is then defined by:

$$z = yx = \sum_{j=1}^{n} y_j^* x_j \tag{469}$$

where y_j^* is the complex conjugate (i.e., $y_j = a_j + ib_j$; $y_j^* = a_j - ib_j$). The definition in eq. 469 guarantees that $y^* \cdot y$ stays positive and real.
Suppose there is a closed cycle, i.e., $y_{n+1} = y_1$. A shift operator S^q is now defined so that $y_1, y_2 \ldots y_n$ is shifted by q observations, i.e.:

$$S^q y_j = (y_{q+1}, y_{q+2}, \ldots y_n, y_1, \ldots y_q) \tag{470a}$$

The notation on the right side of eq. 470a is abbreviated by the symbol:

$$S^q y_j = y_{q+j} \tag{470b}$$

(See backward and forward shift operator, Example 38, and ESSENWANGER, 1976, section 3.6.2.) Consequently:

$$S^0 = S^n y = I \text{ (unity operator or identity)} \tag{470c}$$

i.e., the same series of the observations as the original series results. Consequently:

$$S y_n = y_{n+1} = y_1 \tag{471a}$$

Furthermore:

$$S^{-q} y_j = S^{n-q} y_j \tag{471b}$$

e.g.:

$$S^{-1} y_j = S^{n-1} y_j \tag{471c}$$

Based on the definitions of eqs. 470–471 we introduce an adjugate operator S^*:

$$S^* = S^{-1} \tag{472a}$$

and (for a non-cyclic data series, see Example 38):

$$(Sy)x = y(S^*x) \tag{472b}$$

for any arbitrary x, y.

The operation S^q symbolizes a moving of the data series to the left, i.e. moving y_q to become y_1. Then S^{-q} means a shift to the right. Furthermore:

$$I^q = I \tag{472c}$$

$$S^p I^q = S^p \tag{472d}$$

Example 38. The shift operator. Assume that a cyclic series of observations is given, with the cycle repeated after $n = 12$.

$y_j = 5, 2, 0, 4, 1, -2, 7, 2, -1, 3, 0, -6$

$x_j = -7, -2, 1, -4, -1, 3, -6, 0, 3, -1, 2, 7$

Then:

$Sy_j = 2, 0, 4, 1, -2, 7, 2, -1, 3, 0, -6, 5$

$S^{-1}y_j = -6, 5, 2, 0, 4, 1, -2, 7, 2, -1, 3, 0$

$S^{n-1}y_j =$ same as $S^{-1}x_j$, since $S^n = I$

$y_j x_j = -35, -4, 0, -16, -1, -6, -42, 0, -3, -3, 0, -42$

The complex conjugate is not needed since all y_j and x_j are real.

$(Sy)x = -14, 0, 4, -4, 2, 21, -12, 0, 9, 0, -12$

$S^*x = S^{-1}x$: $b, -7, -2, 1, -4, -1, 3, -6, 0, 3, -1, 2$

$yS^*x = b, -14, 0, 4, -4, 2, 21, -12, 0, 9, 0, -12$

$b =$ blanc

For a non-cyclic data series the shift $S^{-q}y$ implies that only $n-q$ pairs x,y are available. Consequently, the first pair in yS^*x starts with $2\cdot(-14)$, and the last pair in Syx is $(-6)\cdot 2$.

Assume that the eigenvalue problem is:

$$SP = \alpha P \tag{473}$$

(Eigenvalues and eigenvectors have been discussed by the author: ESSENWANGER, 1976, section 4.8.) The statement in eq. 470c implies that the eigenvalues can be expressed in Fourier terms:

$$\alpha_\nu = \exp(i2\pi\nu/n) \tag{474a}$$

or:

$$\alpha_\nu = \cos(2\pi\nu/n) - i\,\sin(2\pi\nu/n) \tag{474b}$$

with $\nu = 0, 1, \ldots, n-1$.

The eigenvectors are p_ν. We set $\alpha_\nu^0 = 1$, and write:

$$p_\nu = (1, \alpha_\nu, \alpha_\nu^2, \ldots, \alpha_\nu^{n-1}) \tag{475a}$$

with:

$$\alpha_\nu^q = \exp(iq2\pi\nu/n) \tag{475b}$$

Consequently:

$$y = \sum_{\nu=0}^{n-1} u_\nu p_\nu \tag{476a}$$

or in components:

$$y_t = \sum_{\nu=0}^{n-1} u_\nu \alpha_\nu^t = \sum_{\nu=0}^{n-1} u_\nu \exp(it2\pi\nu/n) \tag{476b}$$

In turn:

$$u_\nu = (1/n) p_\nu y \tag{477a}$$

or:

$$u_\nu = (1/n) \sum_{t=0}^{n-1} y_t \exp(-it2\pi\nu/n) \tag{477b}$$

where $t = j - 1$ (see given observations).

It is evident that eqs. 476a and 477a represent merely a harmonic analysis (or the Fourier series, see eq. 384a) for complex arguments, or the coefficients u_ν are the Fourier coefficients for y_t.

Now we consider the filter operation:

$$\bar{X} = G(\mu) y = \sum_{\mu=0}^{n-1} \omega_\mu S^\mu y = \sum_{\nu=0}^{n-1} d_\nu u_\nu p_\nu \tag{478a}$$

which is formulated in terms of the pass characteristic:

$$d_\nu = \sum_{\mu=0}^{n-1} \omega_\mu \alpha_\mu^\nu \tag{479}$$

where d_ν denotes the change of the amplitudes in the filter operation. In expanded form:

$$\bar{X}_t = G(\mu) y_t = \omega_0 y_t + \omega_1 y_{t+1} + \ldots \omega_{n-1} y_{t+n-1} \tag{478b}$$

This formula can be compared with the calculation of a weighted running average where the weights are calculated from cosine terms. KALLMANN (1940) called this operation a transverse filter (see p. 214) for properties).

KERTZ (1966) showed that the number of "waves" can be limited to $n/2$. The filter operation can be set up as a high-, low-, or band-pass filter. The narrowest band is:

$$d_\nu = \begin{cases} 1 \text{ for } \nu = \xi \text{ and } \nu = n - \xi \\ 0 \text{ elsewhere} \end{cases} \tag{480a}$$

The weighting coefficients can be written as:

$$\omega_\mu \xi = (1/n) \sum_{\nu=0}^{n-1} d_\nu \alpha_\nu^{-\mu} \tag{480b}$$

or with Fourier terms:

$$\omega_\mu \xi = (2/n) \cos(2\pi\mu\xi/n) \quad \text{for } \xi = 1, 2, \ldots, \left(\frac{n}{2} - 1\right) \tag{480c}$$

For $\xi = 0$:

$$\omega_{\mu,0} = 1/n \tag{480d}$$

and for $\xi = n/2$:

$$\omega_{\mu,n/2} = (-1)^{\mu}(1/n) \tag{480e}$$

where μ corresponds with the exponent of the shift operation $2^{\mu}y$.

The derivation of weights will now be illustrated. It is advisable to select an even number for n, let us assume $n=8$. This leads to the shift operation from S^{-3} to S^4, with "waves" W_0 to W_4. In order to simplify the writing, W_0 is multiplied by n for $\xi=0$ or $n/2$ and by $n/2$ for $\xi \neq 0$ or $\neq n/2$.

Table LX provides the weights as calculated from eq. 480b for $n = 8$. The first waves are calculated from:

$$\bar{X}_t = W_{0,t}/8 = S^{-3}y_t + S^{-2}y_t + S^{-1}y_t + Iy_t + S^1y_t + S^2y_t + S^3y_t + S^4y_t \tag{481a}$$

$$\bar{X}_t = W_{1,t}/4 = -aS^{-3}y_t + aS^{-1}y_t + Iy_t + aSy_t - aS^3y_t - S^4y_t \tag{481b}$$

etc.

Eq. 481a can be simplified. From eq. 471b we reduce eq. 481a to only a few shift operations. We find:

$$8W_0 = [(I+S^{-2})(I+S^{-1})](I+S^4) \tag{482a}$$

$$4W_2 = (I-S^{-2})(I+S^4) \tag{482b}$$

$$8W_4 = [(I+S^{-2})(I-S^{-1})](I+S^4) \tag{482c}$$

$$4W_1 = [I+aS^{-1}(I-S^{-2})](I-S^4) \tag{482d}$$

$$4W_3 = [I-aS^{-1}(I-S^{-2})](I-S^4) \tag{482e}$$

The multiplications in eq. 482 are not difficult to carry out and we may check the correctness of the coefficients.

More insight into the functioning of the filter can be obtained from the pass characteristic.

TABLE LX

CALCULATION OF WEIGHTS

	S^{-3}	S^{-2}	S^{-1}	$S^0=I$	S^1	S^2	S^3	S^4
$8\ W_0$	+1	+1	+1	+1	+1	+1	+1	+1
$4\ W_1$	$-a$	0	a	+1	a	0	$-a$	−1
$4\ W_2$	0	−1	0	+1	0	−1	0	+1
$4\ W_3$	a	0	$-a$	+1	$-a$	0	a	−1
$8\ W_4$	−1	+1	−1	+1	−1	+1	−1	+1

$a = \sqrt{1/2} = 0.707$.

We expand eq. 479:

$$d_\nu=(2/n)\left[1+2\cdot\sum_{\mu=1}^{(n/2)-1}(\cos 2\pi\mu\xi/n)\cos(2\pi\mu\nu/n)+(-1)^{\xi}\cos\pi\nu\right] \tag{483a}$$

For $\xi=0$:

$$d_\nu=(1/n)\left[1+2\cdot\sum_{\mu=1}^{(n/2)-1}\cos 2\pi\mu\nu/n+\cos\pi\nu\right] \tag{483b}$$

and for $\xi=n/2$:

$$d_\nu=(1/n)\left[1+2\cdot\sum_{\mu=1}^{(n/2)-1}(-1)^{\mu}\cos 2\pi\mu\nu/n+(-1)^{n/2}\cos\pi\nu\right] \tag{483c}$$

The lowest frequency to pass is W_1, the highest $W_{n/2}$, which is identical with the Nyquist-frequency (see aliasing effect, p. 176).
The following relationships between the filter characteristics exist: ξ, frequency $=\nu$; $\Delta\nu$, frequency difference $=\Delta\xi$; ν_N, Nyquist-frequency $=1/(2\Delta t)$; Δt, distance between observations; T_ν, periodicity $=1/\xi=1/\nu$; L, filter interval $=1/\Delta\nu$; n, points in filter $n(\Delta\nu)\cdot(\Delta t)=1$. Only three filter parameters can be selected independently. Alias frequencies can be suppressed by:

$$My=(1/m)[S^{-(m-1)/2}+\ldots+S^{-1}+I+S+\ldots+S^{(m-1)/2}]y \tag{483d}$$

The operator M is a low pass filter, and:

$$d_M(\nu)=(\sin\pi\nu m\Delta t)/(m\sin\pi\nu\Delta t) \tag{483e}$$

where m is odd.

Example 39. Calculations of waves by Kertz filtering method. The computation of wave is illustrated in Table LXI. The original data series comprises 28 points, of which 24 are given in the first line of Table LXI. The remaining 4 are the last 4 numbers in line 4 (at the shift operator S^4). We can deduce from eq. 482 that only a limited number of shifts are necessary. Consequently, only S^{-1}, S^{-2} and S^4 follow the original data set I in Table LXI. (The line S^4 could be omitted because its sole purpose is the control of the calculations.) Lines 5 and 10 contain $I+S^{-2}$ and $I-S^{-2}$, respectively. The operation $S^{-1}(I+S^{-2})$ represents merely a shift of line 5 with $I+S^{-2}$. Furthermore: $(I+S^{-1})(I+S^{-2})\equiv(I+S^{-2})+S^{-1}(I+S^{-2})$. Hence line 7 is the addition of lines 5 and 6, line 13 the subtraction of line 6 from line 5.
The application of S^4 to $(I+S^{-1})(I+S^{-2})$ is strictly a shift of line 7. The final 4 points have been filled in from calculations not shown in this table, but they can be checked from the last 4 data points in S^4, line 4. Finally, $8W_0$ is obtained by addition of lines 7 and 8. We make use of the identity $8W_0\equiv(I+S^{-1})(I+S^{-2})+S^4(I+S^{-1})(1+S^{-2})$. Analogously, the calculation of $4W_2$ and $8W_4$ follows, and the detailed description is omitted here.
Line 16 displays the operation $aS^{-1}(I-S^{-2})$. In this case $a=\sqrt{1/2}=0.707$. The result has been rounded to whole numbers. Compared with line 5 a shift to the right took place in row 16. It is evident because S^{-1} is in front of $(I-S^{-2})$. The subsequent operations are performed in a similar manner as previously outlined. The lines 19 and 22 provide $4W_2$ and $4W_3$, respectively.

The example illustrates that the calculations of the filter waves are not only suitable for electronic data processing, but can also be carried out relatively easily on a desk calculator. Various control schemes can be designed in order to limit the possibility of arithmetic

TABLE LXI

CALCULATIONS FOR KERTZ FILTER

Line																									
1	I	2	5	3	−1	1	3	1	0	3	4	2	−2	−2	2	−3	−4	0	2	0	−5	−4	2	−3	−5
2	S^{-1}		2	5	3	−1	1	3	1	0	3	4	2	−2	−2	2	−3	−4	0	2	0	−5	−4	2	−3
3	S^{-2}			2	5	3	−1	1	3	1	0	3	4	2	−2	−2	2	−3	−4	0	2	0	−5	−4	2
4	S^{4}	1	3	1	0	3	4	2	−2	−2	2	−3	−4	0	2	0	−5	−4	2	−3	−5	0	3	1	−3
5	$I+S^{-2}$			5	4	4	2	2	3	4	4	5	2	0	0	−5	−2	−3	−2	0	−3	−4	−3	−7	−3
6	$S^{-1}(I+S^{-2})$				5	4	4	2	2	3	4	4	5	2	0	0	−5	−2	−3	−2	0	−3	−4	−3	−7
7	$(I+S^{-1})(I+S^{-2})$				9	8	6	4	5	7	8	9	7	2	0	−5	−7	−5	−5	−2	−3	−7	−7	−10	−10
8	$S^{4}(I+S^{-1})(I+S^{-2})$				5	7	8	9	7	2	0	−5	−7	−5	−5	−2	−3	−7	−7	−10	−10	−6	−5	−1	1
9	$8W_0$				14	15	14	13	12	9	3	4	0	−3	−5	−7	−10	−12	−12	−12	−13	−13	−12	−11	−9
10	$I-S^{-2}$			1	−6	−2	4	0	−3	2	4	−1	−6	−4	4	−1	−6	3	6	0	−7	−4	7	1	−7
11	$S^{4}(I-S^{-2})$			0	−3	2	4	−1	−6	−4	4	−1	−6	3	6	0	−7	−4	7	1	−7	3	8	1	−6
12	$4W_2$			1	−9	0	8	−1	−9	−2	8	−2	−12	−1	10	−1	−13	−1	13	1	−14	−1	15	2	−13
13	$(I-S^{-1})(I+S^{-2})$				−1	0	−2	0	1	1	0	1	−3	−2	0	−5	3	−1	1	2	−3	−1	1	−4	4
14	$S^{4}(I-S^{-1})(I+S^{-2})$				1	1	0	1	−3	−2	0	−5	3	−1	1	2	−3	−1	1	−4	4	0	1	3	−1
15	$8W_4$				0	1	−2	1	−2	−1	0	−4	0	−3	1	−3	0	−2	2	−2	1	−1	2	−1	3
16	$aS^{-1}(I-S^{-2})$				1	−4	−1	3	0	−2	1	3	−1	−4	−3	3	−1	−4	2	4	0	−5	−3	5	1
17	$I+aS^{-1}(I-S^{-2})$				0	−3	2	4	0	1	5	5	−3	−6	−1	0	−5	−4	4	4	−5	−9	−1	2	−4
18	$-S^{4}[I+aS^{-1}(I-S^{-2})]$				0	−1	−5	−5	3	6	1	0	5	4	−4	−4	5	9	1	−2	4	4	−5	−7	2
19	$4W_1$				0	−4	−3	−1	3	7	6	5	2	−2	−5	−4	0	5	5	2	−1	−5	−6	−5	−2
20	$I-aS^{-1}(I-S^{-2})$				−2	5	4	−2	0	5	3	−1	−1	2	5	−6	−3	4	0	−4	−5	1	5	−8	−6
21	$-S^{4}[I-aS^{-1}(I-S^{-2})]$				0	−5	−3	1	1	−2	−5	6	3	−4	0	4	5	−1	−5	8	6	−4	−1	5	4
22	$4W_3$				−2	0	1	−1	1	3	−2	5	2	−2	5	−2	2	3	−5	4	1	−3	4	−3	−2
	Control:																								
23	$2(I-S^{4})$				−2	−4	−2	−2	4	10	4	10	4	−4	0	−6	2	8	0	6	0	−8	−2	−8	−4
24	$4(I+S^{4})$				−4	16	28	12	−8	4	24	−4	−24	−8	16	−12	−36	−16	16	−12	−40	−16	20	−8	−32

errors. In our case the last two lines (23, 24) serve the purpose of checking. One can find:

$$8W_0+2(4W_2)+8W_4=4(I+S^4) \tag{484a}$$

and:

$$4W_1+4W_3=2(I-S^4) \tag{484b}$$

A further control is the recalculation of the data series:

$$y_j=W_{0j}+W_{1j}+W_{2j}+W_{3j}+W_{4j} \tag{484c}$$

In this case the first j starts with y_4. Hence:

$$14/8+0/4-9/4-2/4+0/8=-1 \tag{484d}$$

In general, W_0 represents a long term trend, in this case longer than 24 points (see Fig. 12), and W_1 shows a cycle of 8 points. In the construction of the observed data (3 hourly observations) the amplitude changes for every day. Consequently, the waves W_1-W_4 do not comprise pure harmonic Fourier terms. In fact, these filter functions have the advantage that the waves do not need to be Fourier terms. Therefore, localized shorter cycles or quasi-periodicity can be approximated with fewer terms than with the Fourier analysis.

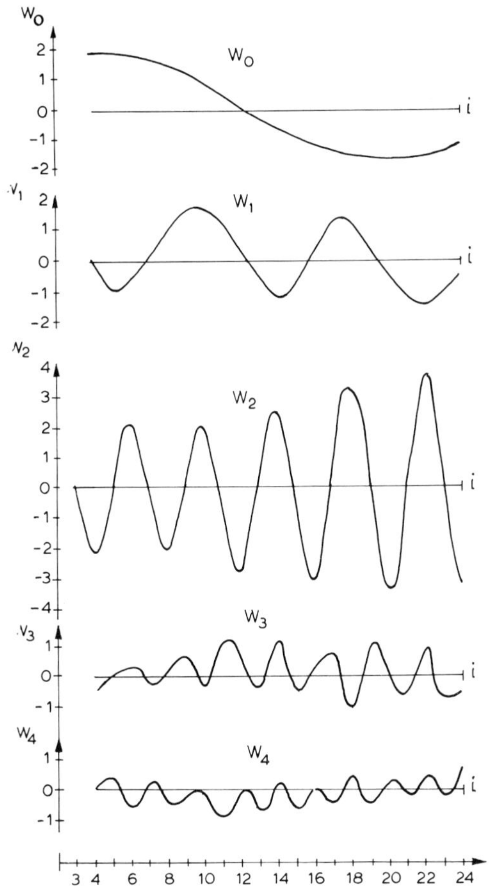

Fig. 12. Wave pattern used in Example 39.

In our example of 24 data points the complete representation of the data by a Fourier series would have needed 12 terms $A_\nu \sin(\nu\alpha_j+\beta_\nu)$. Only four waves are utilized here (plus the long term trend). These four waves are displayed in their relative scale in Fig. 12. In this example a semi-diurnal cycle is most dominant with increasing amplitude. The daily cycle is next. This pattern is typical for atmospheric surface pressure in the tropical region (KERTZ, 1966). However, every meteorological time series is different, and the data sample was chosen mostly for the purpose of demonstrating the filter analysis.
Although fewer terms are needed, the wave functions W_j cannot always be readily expressed in analytical mathematical terms. Sometimes this may be a disadvantage, especially where N is large.
(*2*) A special filter was described by OLBERG (1973) utilizing the suggestion by KERTZ (1966). The concept is based on the operation ψ_τ (see eq. 444b) and eq. 470a.

$$\psi_\tau = \sum_{k=-p}^{p} \omega_{k,\tau} Z^k \tag{485}$$

where Z^k is a shift operator (see eq. 470a). The sign of k determines the shift by k steps, positive to the left and negative to the right (see Example 38). The weights are denoted by $\omega_{k,\tau}$, with $\tau=0, 1, 2 \ldots p$. The filter interval has the width of $2p\Delta x$ (or for time observations $2p\Delta t$).
As defined by Kertz the weights are:

$$\omega_{k,\tau} = [(1-0.5\delta_{|k|,p})/\text{denom}]\cdot\cos(\tau k\pi/p) \tag{486a}$$

with:

$$\text{denom} = (1+\delta_{\tau,0}+\delta_{\tau,p})\cdot p \tag{486b}$$

and δ denotes the Kronecker delta, i.e.:

$$\delta_{h,k} = \begin{cases} 1 \text{ for } h=k \\ 0 \text{ for } h\neq k \end{cases} \tag{486c}$$

The pass characteristic for the weights introduced by eq. 486a can be found after some algebraic operation:

$$g_\tau(\nu) = [(-1)^\tau(\sin\gamma)/(2\ \text{denom})][\cot(\alpha\pi)+\cot(\beta\pi)] \tag{486d}$$

The following abbreviations have been adopted:

$$\gamma=\nu\pi, \quad \alpha=(\nu+\tau)/(2p) \quad \text{and} \quad \beta=(\nu-\tau)/(2p)$$

A time series with $n>2p$ equidistant observations has $n/2$ harmonics with frequency $f=j/(n\Delta x)$ for $j=1, 2 \ldots n/2$ (see Fourier analysis, eq. 384a). The filter is normalized by setting $2p\Delta x=2\pi$. Then $f=\nu/(2\pi)$ or $\nu=2pj/n$. In this case ν does not necessarily lead to integer numbers.
The weighting function of eq. 486a has been adapted to the condition that its imaginary argument (see eq. 445a) is zero. This version implies that no phase shift occurs except for the negative side lobes of $g(\nu)$ where the shift is π (or 180°).
The filter operation as introduced by eq. 485 can be expanded to multiple dimensions. E.g., for the horizontal wind components:

$$\psi_t\cdot\psi_t = \sum_{k=-p}^{p} \omega_{k,\tau} Z^k \sum_{h=-p}^{p} \omega_{h,\tau} Z^h \tag{487a}$$

or:

$$\psi_t^2 = \sum_{k=-p}^{p} \sum_{h=-p}^{p} \omega_{k,\tau}\omega_{h,\tau} Z^{k+h} \tag{487b}$$

This form can be finally transformed to:

$$\psi_t^2 = \sum_{j=-2p}^{2p} \tilde{\omega}_{|j|,\tau} Z^j \tag{487c}$$

where:

$$\tilde{\omega}_{|j|,\tau} = (2\ \text{denom}^2)^{-1}(A_\delta \cos \tau\pi j/p + \sin \tau_1/\sin \tau_2) \tag{487d}$$

and:

$$A_\delta = 2p - |j| - 1 + 0.5\delta_{||j|-p|,p} - 3\delta_{j,0}/2 \tag{487e}$$

$$\tau_1 = (2p - |j| + 1)\tau\pi/p; \quad \tau_2 = \tau\pi/p \tag{487f}$$

OLBERG (1972a) provided a test statistic under the assumption of white noise. This statistic is asymptotically distributed like $N(0.1)$. He found:

$$a_\tau = [s_\tau^2/(s_{\tau N}^2) - 1]/(2\delta_\tau/n)^{1/2} \tag{488a}$$

Consequently, a_τ measures the probability thresholds corresponding to the Gaussian distribution (e.g. $a_\tau = 2$, $F(a_\tau) = 97.7\%$). The test does not include persistence (e.g., red noise, etc.) which OLBERG (1974) treated later.
The letters in the test criterion have the following meaning:

$$\delta_\tau = \sum_{j=-n+1}^{n-1} (1 - |j|/n) R_\tau^2 \tag{488b}$$

For $j \leq 4p$:

$$R_\tau = \sum_{k=|j|-2p}^{2p} \tilde{\omega}_{|k|,\tau} \cdot \tilde{\omega}_{|k-|j||,\tau} / \sum_{k=-2p}^{2p} \tilde{\omega}_{|k|,\tau} \tag{488c}$$

but for $j > 4p$ we can assume $R_\tau = 0$. Consequently, from eq. 488c R_τ is an autocorrelation function of the filtered series normalized to unity. We can state:

$$s_{\tau N}^2 = s_N^2 \sum_{k=-2p}^{p} / \tilde{\omega}_{|k|,\tau}^2 \tag{488d}$$

where σ_N^2 is the variance s^2 of the original data series, and s_τ^2 is the variance of the filtered series.
Generally, the significance threshold for filtered data (band filter) can be formulated (e.g., OLBERG, 1974):

$$A_s^2 = 2\sigma_F^2(1 + a_t\sqrt{2\delta_F/n})/D_F \tag{489a}$$

where:

$$D_F = 1 + \cos[(n+1)2\pi/r + 2\phi][\sin(2\pi n/r)]/[\sin(2\pi/r)] \tag{489b}$$

$$\delta_F(n) = \sum_{j=-n+1}^{n-1} (1 - |j|/n) R_F^2 \tag{489c}$$

A_s^2 denotes the (quadratic) wave height (amplitude) of the wave, σ_F^2 is the variance of the filter, i.c.:

$$\sigma_F^2 = \sigma^2 \sum_{k=-2p}^{2p} (R_M(|k|)W_k) \tag{489d}$$

σ^2 is the variance, and R_M the autocorrelation of the model (e.g., white or red noise). R_F stands for the autocorrelation of the filtered data:

$$R_F(j) = (\sigma/\sigma_F)^2 \sum_{k=-2p}^{2p} W_k R_M(|k-j|) \tag{489e}$$

$$W_k = \sum_{1=|k|-p}^{p} \omega_i \omega_{i-|k|} \tag{489f}$$

Further, n is the number of (equidistant) data per time section, r the number of data per wave length and ϕ the phase angle of the first data point in the time section. The constant a_t corresponds to sigma of a Gaussian distribution at the level of significance α (see eq. 488a and p. 241).

For white noise $\sigma^2 = \sigma_w^2$ (white noise), $\sigma_F^2 = \sigma_w^2$. W_0 and $R_M = R_w$ (e.g., $R_M = 1$ for $k=0$ and 0 for $k \neq 0$), $R_F = W_j/W_0$ for $|j| \leq 2p$ and 0 for $|j| > 2p$.

For red noise (see p. 170) $\sigma^2 = \sigma_R^2$, $R_M(k) = \rho^{|k|}$, and:

$$R_F = (\sigma_R/\sigma_F)^2 \sum_{k=-2p}^{2p} W_k \rho^{|k-j|} \tag{489g}$$

$$\sigma_F^2 = \sigma_R^2 \sum_{k=-2p}^{2p} W_k \rho^{|k|} \tag{489h}$$

Olberg (1974) provided numerical values for the Landsberg filter operation (see Landsberg et al., 1963).

Despite the described significance criteria the testing of statistical significance remains a problem for many of the filter wave patterns (e.g., Fig. 12), especially those which do not correspond to simple mathematical series.

A symmetric linear filter

Shapiro (1971) adapted a simple linear filter for use in a numerical model as substitution for an explicit horizontal diffusion term. At a grid point i in the direction of τ the initial transform can be written:

$$\bar{X}_i^{\tau} = y_i + F_\tau(y_i) \tag{490a}$$

where:

$$F_\tau(y_i) = (y_{i-1} + y_{i+1} - 2y_i) \cdot g/2 \tag{490b}$$

with g standing for a numerical filter element. From the definition of F_τ Shapiro concluded that:

$$F_\tau(y_i) = (\Delta\tau)^2 (g/2) d_{\tau\tau}(y_i) \tag{490c}$$

where the last term is the (centered) finite difference in anology to $\partial^2 y/\partial\tau^2$. It can be derived from:

$$d_\tau(y_i) = (y_{i+0.5} - y_{i-0.5})/\Delta\tau \tag{490d}$$

With $g = 0.5$ the operation eq. 490a eliminates the wave component of length $2\Delta\tau$.
As outlined by Shapiro, the operator of eq. 490a can be expanded to a multi-element filtering operator. The operator is "ideal" because (with $g = 0.5$) it restores the amplitudes damped by eq. 490a to a maximum degree without an increase of any wave component. This generalized operation is written:

$$\bar{X}_i^{n\tau} = y_i + F_{n\tau}(y_i) \tag{491a}$$

where:

$$F_{n\tau}(y_i) = (-1)^{n-1}(\Delta\tau/2)^{2n} d_{2n\tau}(y_i) \tag{491b}$$

and $d_{2n\tau}(y_i)$ is the finite difference analogue of $\partial^{2n}y/\partial\tau^{2n}$ at the grid point i (see eq. 490d). The response function (SHAPIRO, 1970) for the operation of eq. 490a is:

$$R(f) = 1 - \sin^{2n}(k\Delta\tau/2) \tag{491c}$$

where $k = 2\pi/L$ denotes the wave numbers, and L is the wave length (in units of $\Delta\tau$). Consequently $L_k = 2\pi/k$. Thus $L_1 = 2\pi$ provides the basic period.
The operation of eq. 491a leads to strong damping of waves $< 4\Delta\tau$ for $n = 8$ but waves longer than $4\Delta\tau$ are not strongly affected. As shown by SHAPIRO (1971) this ideal operator corresponds to Fickian diffusion motion (see e.g., STERN et al., 1973).
In a later article SHAPIRO (1972) compared the ideal filter with the Fourier truncation. He concludes that for most applications the ideal filter should be preferred.
Another series of low, high and band pass filters was more recently suggested by JULIAN et al. (1977). A three-dimensional filter was developed by SHUMAN (1957) and was analysed by NELSON and WEIBLE (1980). The filter dampens even long waves which may not always be desirable.

Filtering and persistence

As a measurement of persistence BARTELS (1943) introduced the "equivalent number" of repetitions ω_R (see eq. 43a) where normally $1 \le N_I \le n$ and $n \ge \omega_R \ge 1.0$. This equivalent number was then expressed (see eq. 43h) in terms of the autocorrelation function:

$$\omega_R = f(r) \tag{492}$$

As pointed out by OLBERG (1972b) the application of a band pass filter which does not include the basic frequency may lead to a "negative" persistence. Calculation of ω_R via eq. 43h provides $0 \le \omega_R < 1$, which in turn requires $\sigma_g^2 < \sigma^2/n$. In this case the significance threshold is lower than for the regular series of N observations. In order to eliminate this erroneous result, Olberg suggested the use of:

$$N_I = n/\omega_{R*} \tag{493a}$$

where:

$$\omega_{R*} = \sum_{i=n_1}^{n_2} (1-|i|/n)|r_i| \tag{493b}$$

with $n_1 = -n+1$ and $n_2 = n-1$. Now $\omega_R \geq 1.0$ is fulfilled.

Kalman filtering

In the last two decades Kalman filtering has become a well-known technique in engineering applications, although the basic principle requires familiarity with advanced statistical theory. Kalman filtering is based on sampling techniques and may be considered as a multi-dimensional filter. It can be derived from several existing processes. The classical new approach by KALMAN (1960) was developed for a prediction problem using the state-transition method of dynamical systems similar to Markov processes. Its validity includes stationary and non-stationary sequences. Later KALMAN and BUCY (1961) associated the optimal filtering process with the solution of a non-linear differential equation of the Riccati type (e.g., LEVIN, 1959).
In principle, the Kalman filtering process can be described as a combination of two well-known techniques, the "state-transition method" and "linear filtering." As Kalman and Bucy pointed out this duality makes the results directly applicable to the WIENER (1949) problem. It is not the intention to add a complete description of all filtering techniques or methods for analysis of stationary time series in this chapter. The basic principle will be discussed, however. Although filtering has not been utilized too often in atmospheric physics problems it has some potential (e.g., GOVIND, 1974; BETTGE and BAUMHEFNER, 1980).
The subsequent presentation is a buildup from the single to the multidimensional case and should serve to explain the technique for readers unfamiliar with the literature of WIENER (1949), BROWN (1963), BOX and JENKINS (1970), HANNAN (1970), or LEONDES (1970). etc.

One-dimensional model

We assume a quantity x for which two independent estimators exist, say θ_1 and θ_2 (e.g., mean values). The variances of these estimators are $\sigma^2_{\theta_1}$ and $\sigma^2_{\theta_2}$. We require now a combination of these estimators by defining a "best estimate" $\hat{x}$ with minimum variance. If ω is the weight, then:

$$\bar{\theta} = (1-\omega)\theta_1 + \omega\theta_2 \tag{494a}$$

The expected value for $\bar{x}$ can be written in the form:

$$E(\bar{\theta}) = (1-\omega)E(\theta_1) + \omega E(\theta_2) \tag{494b}$$

Hence the variance $\sigma^2_{\theta_b}$ of $\bar{\theta}$ can be obtained as:

$$\sigma^2_{\theta_b} = (1-\omega)^2\sigma^2_{\theta_1} + \omega^2\sigma^2_{\theta_2} \tag{494c}$$

because the correlation between the set of estimators θ_1 and θ_2 is assumed to be zero (independence!).

We must now determine the weight for which $\sigma^2_{\theta_b}$ is a minimum. Hence:

$$\frac{\partial \sigma^2_{\theta_b}}{\partial \omega} = 0 = -2(1-\omega)\sigma^2_{\theta_1} + 2\omega\sigma^2_{\theta_2} \tag{495a}$$

This equation can be solved for ω, namely:

$$\hat{\omega} = \sigma^2_{\theta_1}/(\sigma^2_{\theta_1} + \sigma^2_{\theta_2}) \tag{495b}$$

By substitution into eq. 494a we continue with:

$$\hat{\theta} = (\theta_1\sigma^2_{\theta_2} + \theta_2\sigma^2_{\theta_1})/(\sigma^2_{\theta_1} + \sigma^2_{\theta_2}) \tag{496a}$$

and:

$$\hat{\sigma}^2_{\theta_b} = \sigma^2_{\theta_1}\sigma^2_{\theta_2}/(\sigma^2_{\theta_1} + \sigma^2_{\theta_2}) \tag{496b}$$

Assume θ_2 to be a measurement which is made to improve or update the estimate for θ_1. Now eqs. 496a and b are converted to the modified form:

$$\hat{\theta} = \theta_1 - \hat{\omega}(\theta_1 - \theta_2) \tag{497a}$$

$$\hat{\sigma}^2_{\theta} = \sigma^2_{\theta_1}(1 - \hat{\omega}) \tag{497b}$$

The weight ω is the Kalman filter in this trivial case.

Multidimensional model

Assume now that $\boldsymbol{m}_{\theta_1}$ and $\boldsymbol{m}_{\theta_2}$ are vectors (matrix dimension $n \times 1$) that stand for two independent estimates (no error correlation) of the n-dimensional vector $\boldsymbol{x}$. Eq. 494a is expanded to the weighted mean matrix of $\bar{\boldsymbol{\theta}}$. Thus:

$$\bar{\boldsymbol{\theta}} = \boldsymbol{m}_{\theta_1} - \mathbf{W}(\boldsymbol{m}_{\theta_1} - \boldsymbol{m}_{\theta_2}) \tag{498a}$$

Analogously, $\mathbf{W}$ is an $n \times n$ dimensional matrix of weights. With $\mathbf{I}$ denoting the unity matrix we can reformulate:

$$\bar{\boldsymbol{\theta}} = (\mathbf{I} - \mathbf{W})\boldsymbol{m}_{\theta_1} + \mathbf{W}\boldsymbol{m}_{\theta_2} \tag{498b}$$

The best estimate $\hat{\boldsymbol{\theta}}$ again is found by determining a matrix $\mathbf{W}$ so that the variance matrix of $\bar{\boldsymbol{\theta}}$ is a minimum. The following process specifies and delineates the solution.
Since the two estimates from eqs. 498a or b do not necessarily coincide, an optimum solution must be defined. We assume that:

$$\mathbf{W} = \mathbf{W}_2 \cdot \mathbf{M}_y \tag{498c}$$

where $\mathbf{W}_2$ is another arbitrary weighting matrix and $\mathbf{M}_y$ a rectangular matrix of $m \times n$ dimension operating on $\boldsymbol{x}$ to give an m-dimensional estimate. Then eq. 498c is substituted into eq. 498a to give:

$$\bar{\boldsymbol{\theta}} = \boldsymbol{m}_{\theta_1} - \mathbf{W}_2\mathbf{M}_y(\boldsymbol{m}_{\theta_1} - \boldsymbol{m}_{\theta_2}) \tag{498d}$$

We substitute into eq. 498b and call $\boldsymbol{y}_2$ an estimate of $\boldsymbol{m}_{\theta_2}$. Then:

$$\bar{\boldsymbol{\theta}} = (\mathbf{I} - \mathbf{W}_2\mathbf{M}_y)\boldsymbol{m}_{\theta_1} + \mathbf{W}_2\boldsymbol{y}_2 \tag{498e}$$

where $\boldsymbol{y}_2$ is an estimate of $\boldsymbol{y} = \mathbf{M}_y\boldsymbol{x}$ with variance matrix $\mathbf{V}_{y_2}$.

The variance matrix of $\bar{\boldsymbol{\theta}}$ is denoted with $\mathbf{V}_{\bar{\theta}}$. This matrix is given by:

$$\mathbf{V}_{\bar{\theta}} = E\{[\bar{\boldsymbol{\theta}} - E(\bar{\boldsymbol{\theta}})][\bar{\boldsymbol{\theta}} - E(\bar{\boldsymbol{\theta}})]^T\} \tag{499a}$$

where T denotes the transpose.
After some algebraic operations and the assumption that $\boldsymbol{m}_{\bar{\theta}_1}$ and $\boldsymbol{y}_2$ are uncorrelated, we arrive at:

$$\mathbf{V}_{\bar{\theta}} = (\mathbf{I} - \mathbf{W}_2\mathbf{M}_y)\mathbf{V}_{\theta_1}(\mathbf{I} - \mathbf{W}_2\mathbf{M}_y)^T + \mathbf{W}_2\mathbf{V}_{\theta_2}\mathbf{W}_2^T \tag{499b}$$

where $\mathbf{V}_{\theta_1}$ and $\mathbf{V}_{\theta_2}$ are the variance matrices of the estimates for $\boldsymbol{\theta}_1$ and $\boldsymbol{\theta}_2$.
The problem is now to find a solution for $\mathbf{W}_2$ which minimizes $\mathbf{V}_{\bar{\theta}}$ and at the same time fulfills the particular condition that each diagonal element of $\mathbf{V}_{\bar{\theta}}$ would be a minimum variance. The solution can be formulated as:

$$\mathbf{V}_{\bar{\theta}} = \mathbf{V}_{\theta_1} + (\mathbf{W}_2\mathbf{S} - \mathbf{A})(\mathbf{W}_2\mathbf{S} - \mathbf{A})^T - \mathbf{V}_{\theta_1}\mathbf{M}_y^T(\mathbf{M}_y\mathbf{V}_{\theta_1}\mathbf{M}_y^T + \mathbf{V}_{\theta_2})^{-1}\mathbf{M}_y\mathbf{V}_{\theta_1} \tag{499c}$$

Each diagonal element of $\mathbf{V}_{\bar{\theta}}$ is a minimum variance if $\mathbf{W}_2$ is a solution of:

$$(\mathbf{W}_2\mathbf{S} - \mathbf{A}) = 0 \tag{500a}$$

This can be expressed as:

$$\mathbf{W}_2 = \mathbf{V}_{\theta_1}\mathbf{M}_y^T(\mathbf{M}_y\mathbf{V}_{\theta_1}\mathbf{M}_y^T + \mathbf{V}_{\theta_2})^{-1} \tag{500b}$$

If this expression is substituted into eq. 499c, we derive:

$$\mathbf{V}_{\bar{\theta}} = \mathbf{V}_{\bar{\theta}_1} - \mathbf{W}_2\mathbf{M}_y\mathbf{V}_{\theta_1} \tag{500c}$$

Thus:

$$\hat{\boldsymbol{\theta}} = \boldsymbol{\theta}_1 - \mathbf{W}_2(\mathbf{M}_y\boldsymbol{\theta}_1 - \boldsymbol{y}_2) \tag{500d}$$

The matrices $\mathbf{S}$ and $\mathbf{A}$ are auxiliary matrices given by $\mathbf{S}\mathbf{S}^T = \mathbf{M}_y\mathbf{V}_{\theta_1}\mathbf{M}_y + \mathbf{V}_{\theta_2}$ and $\mathbf{S}\mathbf{A}^T = \mathbf{M}_y\mathbf{V}_{\theta_1}$. Now $\mathbf{W}_2$ corresponds to the Kalman filter (see eq. 517d).

Linear dynamical systems

It can be shown that the behavior of a physical process can be expressed by two major constituents, a (precisely) predictable part and a random noise about a zero mean. These two components have been assumed in earlier discussions without specific emphasis of their existence (see eq. 431). Furthermore, a process in which the behavior of a future state is a mere function of its present state or at a particular time plus the structure of a perturbation term is called a Markov process (see eq. 423a). We assume now that such a process exists and we specify a future behavior as:

$$\boldsymbol{x}_j = \boldsymbol{\phi}_{j-1}\boldsymbol{x}_{j-1} + \boldsymbol{\psi}_{j-1}\boldsymbol{y}_{j-1} \tag{501a}$$

The true state at time t_{j-1} was $\boldsymbol{x}_{j-1}$ where $\boldsymbol{x}_{j-1}$ and $\boldsymbol{x}_j$ have $n \times 1$ dimension, i.e., they are vectors, and n denotes the number of parameters which are necessary to describe the particular state of the system. Hence, $\boldsymbol{x}_{j-1}$ and $\boldsymbol{x}_j$ are often termed the state vectors. This basic formulation has resemblance to the factor pattern (see ESSENWANGER, 1976, section 3.5) but the goals of the solution are different.
$\boldsymbol{\phi}_{j-1}$ is an $n \times n$ matrix, called transition matrix, and in physics represents a process such as

the dynamics or the equation of motion etc. Further, y_{j-1} stands for the random input with $E[y_{j-1}]=0$ and (in simple notation) $E[y_{j-1}^2]=\sigma_{yj-1}^2$. If the dimension or the number of sources of a random input is m, then y_{j-1} is a vector $(m \times 1)$ called the "plant noise" by BARHAM and HUMPHRIES (1970), or "control vector" by SORENSON (1966), and KALMAN and BUCY (1961). Then ψ_{j-1} is an $n \times m$ matrix characterizing the effects of the m noise elements on the n system parameters. It is also termed the constraint which affects the state of the system.

Eq. 501a can be converted to a linear dynamical system governed by:

$$dX/dt = \phi_{(t)}x_{(t)} + \psi(t)y(t) \tag{501b}$$

which is the "input" equation.

In a description of a physical system a corresponding "output" equation must necessarily be added, such as:

$$z(t) = \mathbf{\Omega}(t)x(t) + \mathbf{Y}(t) \tag{501c}$$

where $\mathbf{\Omega}(t)$ designates the constraint of observing the true state of the process from the available output data. In some sources the random noise which is also contained in $\mathbf{Y}(t)$ is added to the system, in others it is omitted.

Another formulation (e.g. SORENSON, 1966) of the dynamical system is:

$$x_j = \phi_{j,j-1}x_{j-1} + \psi_{j,j-1}y_{j-1} + v_{j-1} + w_{j-1} \tag{502a}$$

where the definitions from above have been applied correspondingly. Now v_j is a vector forcing function which is known as a function of time, and w_j represents a random noise vector with known statistical properties, i.e., $E(w_j)=0$ and:

$$E(w_j w_k^T) = v_j \cdot \delta_{j,k} \tag{502b}$$

where $\delta_{j,k}$ is the Kronecker delta (see eq. 486c), v_j is a definite non-negative vector. The transition matrix has the following assumed properties:

$$\phi_{r,r} = \mathbf{I} \tag{503a}$$

$$\phi_{rs}\phi_{st} = \phi_{r,t} \tag{503b}$$

and:

$$\phi_{r,i}^{-1} = \phi_{i,r} \tag{503c}$$

(eigenvector system, see ESSENWANGER, 1976).

Kalman filters

Suppose we have an input system of one term only:

$$\mathbf{x}_j = \phi_{j,j-1}\mathbf{x}_{j-1} \tag{504a}$$

with the measurement equation (output):

$$z_j = \mathbf{\Omega}_j x_j + \mathbf{Y}_j \tag{504b}$$

The vector $\mathbf{Y}_j$ as a random vector must fulfill:

$$E(\mathbf{Y}_j)=0 \tag{504c}$$

$$E(\mathbf{Y}_j\mathbf{Y}_k^T)=\mathbf{V}_{\mathbf{Y}_j}\delta_{j,k} \tag{504d}$$

where $\mathbf{V}_{\mathbf{Y}_j}$ is a non-negative-definite variance matrix: $\delta_{j,k}$ is again the Kronecker delta. A random (white noise) process requires:

$$E(\mathbf{Y}_j\boldsymbol{w}_k^T)=0 \text{ for } j,k>0 \tag{505a}$$

and:

$$E(\mathbf{Y}_j\boldsymbol{x}_0^T)=0 \text{ for all } j \tag{505b}$$

where $\boldsymbol{x}_0$ is an initial state expressed by a random vector with:

$$E(\boldsymbol{x}_0)=0 \tag{506a}$$

$$E(\boldsymbol{x}_0\boldsymbol{x}_0^T)=V_0 \tag{506b}$$

$$E(\boldsymbol{w}_j\boldsymbol{x}_0^T)=0 \text{ for all } j \tag{506c}$$

We define now an unknown matrix $\mathbf{K}_j$ and combine the input and the k_j weighted output:

$$\hat{\boldsymbol{x}}_j=\boldsymbol{\Phi}_{j,j-1}\hat{\boldsymbol{x}}_{j-1}+\mathbf{K}_j(z_j-\boldsymbol{\Omega}_j\boldsymbol{\Phi}_{j,j-1}\hat{\boldsymbol{x}}_{j-1}) \tag{507}$$

$\mathbf{K}_j$ must be minimized. The matrix $\mathbf{K}_j$ is also referred to as weighting or gain matrix. This problem can be transformed to the determination of $\mathbf{W}_2$ in the system of eq. 499b. The optimal gain matrix can be written as:

$$\mathbf{K}_j=\mathbf{P}_j\boldsymbol{\Omega}_j^T(\boldsymbol{\Omega}_j\mathbf{P}_j\boldsymbol{\Omega}_j^T+\mathbf{V}\mathbf{Y}_j)^{-1} \tag{508a}$$

This resembles (see eq. 500b):

$$\mathbf{W}_2=\mathbf{V}_{\theta_1}\mathbf{M}_y^T(\mathbf{M}_y\mathbf{V}_\theta\mathbf{M}_y^T+\mathbf{V}_{\theta_2})^{-1} \tag{508b}$$

where $\mathbf{W}_2$ is the solution which minimizes $\mathbf{V}_{\bar{\theta}}$.
The matrix $\mathbf{P}_j$ is defined as:

$$\mathbf{P}_j=\boldsymbol{\Phi}_{j,j-1}\mathbf{R}_{j-1}\boldsymbol{\Phi}_{j,j-1}^T \tag{509a}$$

with:

$$\mathbf{R}_j=E(\tilde{\boldsymbol{x}}_j\tilde{\boldsymbol{x}}_j^T) \tag{509b}$$

where $\tilde{\boldsymbol{x}}_j$ has been set as:

$$\tilde{\boldsymbol{x}}_j=\hat{\boldsymbol{x}}_j-\boldsymbol{x}_j \tag{509c}$$

i.e. $\mathbf{R}$ is a covariance matrix.
Comparison of individual terms between eqs. 508, a and b discloses that $\mathbf{K}_j$ is identical with $\mathbf{W}_2$ in eq. 508b. Consequently, the following relationship must also be valid:

$$\mathbf{R}_j=\mathbf{P}_j-\mathbf{K}_j\boldsymbol{\Omega}_j\mathbf{P}_j \tag{509d}$$

The matrix $\mathbf{K}_j$ constitutes the Kalman filter for the system of eq. 504, a and b.

If eq. 504a is expanded by including $\boldsymbol{v}_{j-1}$ and $\boldsymbol{w}_{j-1}$, we start with the input:

$$\boldsymbol{x}_j=\boldsymbol{\Phi}_{j,j-1}\boldsymbol{x}_{j-1}+\boldsymbol{v}_{j-1}+(\boldsymbol{w}_{j-1}) \tag{510}$$

Then the Kalman filter equations are as follows (with eq. 504b):

$$\hat{\boldsymbol{x}}_j=\mathbf{M}_{x_j}+\mathbf{K}_j(z_j-\boldsymbol{\Omega}_j\mathbf{M}_{x_j}) \tag{511a}$$

where:

$$\mathbf{M}_{x_j}=\boldsymbol{\Phi}_{j,j-1}\hat{\boldsymbol{x}}_{j-1}+\boldsymbol{v}_{j-1} \tag{511b}$$

We define now:

$$\mathbf{P}_j=\boldsymbol{\Phi}_{j,j-1}\mathbf{R}_{j-1}\boldsymbol{\Phi}^T_{j,j-1}+\mathbf{R}'_{j-1} \tag{512a}$$

and:

$$\boldsymbol{\Phi}_{j,j-1}\mathbf{R}_{j-1}\boldsymbol{\Phi}^T_{j,j-1}+\mathbf{R}'_{j-1}=E\{[\boldsymbol{\Phi}_{j-1}\tilde{\boldsymbol{x}}_{j-1}-\boldsymbol{w}_{j-1}][\boldsymbol{\Phi}_{j,j-1}\tilde{\boldsymbol{x}}_{j-1}-\boldsymbol{w}_{j-1}]^T\} \tag{512b}$$

The equations for the Kalman filter and the reformulation of R_j, i.e. eqs. 508, a and d, remain the same.
The inclusion of the term $\boldsymbol{\Psi}_{j,j-1}\boldsymbol{y}_{j-1}$ and a full solution of the input system of eq. 502a requires an auxiliary quadratic matrix $\mathbf{A}_N$, whose expectancy must be minimized:

$$E(\mathbf{A}_N)=E\left[\sum_{i=1}^{n}(\boldsymbol{x}_i^T\mathbf{Z}_i^x\boldsymbol{x}_i+\boldsymbol{y}_{i-1}^T\mathbf{Z}_{i-1}^y\boldsymbol{y}_{i-1})\right] \tag{513}$$

where $\mathbf{Z}_i^x$ and $\mathbf{Z}_i^y$ are arbitrary, symmetric, positive-definite weighting matrices. The auxiliary matrix $\mathbf{A}_N$ is also called the performance matrix. The process terminates at time t_N. We postulate that $\boldsymbol{v}_{j-1}$ and $\boldsymbol{w}_{j-1}$ are Gaussian (i.e., first and second moments are sufficient).
The stochastic control process that minimizes eq. 513 is then given by:

$$\boldsymbol{y}_j=\mathbf{C}_j\hat{\boldsymbol{x}}_j \tag{514a}$$

The control matrix $\mathbf{C}_j$ is obtained as the solution of the deterministic control problem (see JOSEPH and TOU, 1961) where $\boldsymbol{\Psi}_{j,j-1}\boldsymbol{y}_{j-1}$ is treated as a known function.
As given previously, the estimate of the state is provided by:

$$\hat{\boldsymbol{x}}_j=\mathbf{M}_{x_j}+\mathbf{K}_j[z_j-\boldsymbol{\Omega}_j\mathbf{M}_{x_j}] \tag{514b}$$

but in this case:

$$\mathbf{M}_{x_j}=(\boldsymbol{\Phi}_{j,j-1}+\boldsymbol{\Psi}_{j,j-1}\mathbf{C}_{j-1})\hat{\boldsymbol{x}}_{j-1}+\boldsymbol{v}_{j-1} \tag{514c}$$

With the abbreviation:

$$\boldsymbol{\Lambda}_{j,j-1}=\boldsymbol{\Phi}_{j,j-1}+\boldsymbol{\Psi}_{j,j-1}\mathbf{C}_{j-1}$$

we can write:

$$\hat{\boldsymbol{x}}_j=\boldsymbol{\Lambda}_{j,j-1}\hat{\boldsymbol{x}}_{j-1}+\boldsymbol{v}_{j-1}+\mathbf{K}_j[z_j-\boldsymbol{\Omega}_j(\boldsymbol{\Lambda}_{j,j-1}\hat{\boldsymbol{x}}_{j-1}+\boldsymbol{v}_{j-1})] \tag{515a}$$

Then eqs. 515a, 514a, 508a and 509d provide the filter equations for the models 502a and 504a. The estimate can be brought into the form:

$$\hat{\boldsymbol{x}}_j=\boldsymbol{\Phi}_{j,j-1}\hat{\boldsymbol{x}}_{j-1}+\boldsymbol{v}_{j-1}+\mathbf{K}_j[z_j-\boldsymbol{\Omega}_j(\boldsymbol{\Phi}_{j,j-1}\hat{\boldsymbol{x}}_{j-1}+\boldsymbol{v}_{j-1})]+\mathbf{Q}_j\mathbf{P}_j\boldsymbol{\Psi}_{j,j-1}\boldsymbol{y}_{j-1} \tag{515b}$$

Special applications

Let us assume for forecasting purposes that the error of $\hat{x}_{j-1}$ is given by:

$$\hat{x}_{j-1} = x_{j-1} + \varepsilon_{j-1} \tag{516a}$$

It is known that the mean of y_{j-1} (e.g., noise) is zero. The best forecast is:

$$x'_j = x_j - \Psi_{j-1} y_{j-1} + \Phi_{j-1} \varepsilon_{j-1} \tag{516b}$$

The variance of $\Phi_{j-1}\varepsilon_{j-1}$ is $\Phi_{j-1}\mathbf{V}_{\hat{x}}\Phi^T_{j-1}$, and the variance of $\Psi_{j-1}y_{j-1}$ is $\Psi_{j-1}\mathbf{V}_y\Psi^T_{j-1}$ where $\mathbf{V}_y$ is the variance of y_{j-1}, and $\mathbf{V}_{\hat{x}}$ of $\hat{x}_{j-1}$.
The variance of x'_j can be written as:

$$\mathbf{V}_{x'} = \Phi_{j-1}\mathbf{V}_{\hat{x}}\Phi^T_{j-1} + \Psi_{j-1}\mathbf{V}_Y\Psi^T_{j-1} \tag{517a}$$

Now the best estimate of x_j is:

$$\hat{x}_j = x'_j - \mathbf{K}_j(\Omega_j x'_j - \mathbf{Y}_j) \tag{517b}$$

The Kalman filter is:

$$\mathbf{K}_j = \mathbf{V}_{x'}\Omega^T_j[\Omega_j\mathbf{V}_{x'}\cdot\Omega^T_j + \mathbf{V}_Y] \tag{517c}$$

where $\mathbf{V}_Y$ is the variance of $\mathbf{Y}_j$. The variance of $\hat{x}_j$ is given by:

$$\mathbf{V}_{\hat{x}} = \mathbf{V}_{x'} - \mathbf{K}_j\Omega_j\mathbf{V}_{x'} \tag{517d}$$

The performance of the matrix operation is explained in Chapter 4 of ESSENWANGER, 1976. A self-optimizing filter was introduced by GOVIND (1974) for the intercomparison of meteorological measuring systems. In this case the filter is designed as:

$$\mathbf{F} = c(\Omega\mathbf{R}^{-1}\Omega^T)^{-1}(\Omega\mathbf{R}^{-1}) \tag{518a}$$

where c is the $1 \times (m+1)$ row matrix:

$$c = [1, 0, 0, \dots 0] \tag{518b}$$

and:

$$\mathbf{R} = \mathbf{X}\mathbf{X}^T \tag{518c}$$

is the correlation matrix $(n \times n)$. Note, that in this case no random noise from $\mathbf{Y}(t)$ is added (see eq. 501c). Govind derived the constraint matrix as:

$$\Omega = \left[\begin{array}{cccc|cccc|c|cccc} 1 & 1 & \dots & 1 & 0 & 0 & \dots & 0 & & 0 & 0 & \dots & 0 \\ 0 & 0 & \dots & 0 & 1 & 1 & \dots & 1 & & 0 & 0 & \dots & 0 \\ \cdot & \cdot & & & \cdot & \cdot & \dots & \cdot & & \cdot & \cdot & \dots & \cdot \\ & & & & & & & & \text{etc.} & & & & \\ \cdot & \cdot & & & \cdot & \cdot & \dots & \cdot & & \cdot & \cdot & \dots & \cdot \\ \cdot & \cdot & & & \cdot & \cdot & \dots & \cdot & & \cdot & \cdot & \dots & \cdot \\ 0 & 0 & \dots & 0 & 0 & 0 & \dots & 0 & & 1 & 1 & \dots & 1 \end{array}\right] \tag{518d}$$

which is a $(m+1) \times n(m+1)$ matrix.

A system of dynamic linear models without a constraint was recently developed by GODOLPHIN and STONE (1980), and LEDSHAM and STAELIN (1978) applied a Kalman-Bucy filter to satellite data retrieval.

Spline functions

General interpolation rules

The problem of interpolation can be regarded as a special case of curve fitting. Simple methods of linear interpolation have been presented (eq. 435). Basically, most interpolation schemes can be reduced to the fitting of polynomials of a specified degree, say n, through N points, $n<N$, and then recomputing the curve by closer spacing of the variate than Δx_i (see eq. 440a), the interval $x_i - x_{i+1}$ of the originally given set of points. This task is also associated with simultaneous smoothing of the observational points, and some of the methods described in the previous sections can be employed (see e.g., p. 180).
The classical interpolation formula can be written as:

$$y_i = c_0 + c_1 x_i + c_2 x_i^2 + \dots c_n x_i^n \tag{519}$$

where the order n determines the smoothing, as $n<N$. This scheme was thoroughly discussed as a problem of curve fitting (see ESSENWANGER, 1976, section 3.1) and no further elaboration follows here.
Newton developed a forward interpolation formula (equal distances):

$$Y = Y_0 + \frac{\Delta Y_0}{k}(x-x_0) + \frac{\Delta^2 Y_0}{2k^2}(x-x_0)(x-x_1) + \dots \frac{\Delta^n Y_0}{n!k^n}(x-x_0)(x-x_1)\dots(x-x_{n-1}) \tag{520a}$$

By substituting $z=(x-x_0)/k$:

$$y = y_0 + \Delta y_0 z + \frac{\Delta^2 y_0}{2} z(z-1) + \dots \frac{\Delta^n y_0}{n!} z(z-1)\dots(z-n+1) \tag{520b}$$

where k designates the equidistant difference $x_{i+1} - x_i$. The set of differences $\Delta^n y_0$ must be obtained, and y_0 and x_0 represent the first point pair in the series (x_0, y_0), $(x_1, y_1) \dots (x_n, y_n)$. In eq. 520a the letter x without subscript stands for the value to be interpolated. The accuracy of y is limited by the set of given y_i and x_i values.
Newton's backward interpolation formula is similar:

$$y = y_n + \frac{\Delta y_{n-1}}{k}(x-x_n) + \frac{\Delta^2 y_{n-2}}{2k^2}(x-x_n)(x-x_{n-1}) + \dots + \frac{\Delta^n y_0}{n!k^n}(x-x_n)\dots(x-x_1) \tag{521a}$$

When the substitution $z=(x-x_n)/k$ is made:

$$y = y_n + \Delta y_{n-1} z - \frac{\Delta^2 y_{n-2}}{2} z(z-1) + \dots + \frac{\Delta^n y_0}{n!} z(z+1)\dots(z+n-1) \tag{521b}$$

Another customary application is Stirling's interpolation formula. Again, $z=(x-x_0)/k$ so that:

$$y = y_0 + z(\Delta y_{-1} + \Delta y_0)/2 + (z^2/2)\Delta^2 y_{-1} + \ldots$$

$$+ \frac{z(z^2-1^2)}{3!} \frac{\Delta^3 y_{-2} + \Delta^3 y_{-1}}{2} + \frac{z^2(z^2-1^2)}{4!} \Delta^4 y_{-2}$$

$$+ \ldots$$

$$+ \frac{z(z^2-1^2) \ldots (z^2-[n-1]^2)}{(2n-1)!} \cdot (\Delta^{2n-1} y_{-n} + \Delta^{2n-1} y_{-n+1})/2$$

$$+ \frac{z^2(z^2-1^2) \ldots (z^2-[n-1]^2)}{(2n)!} \Delta^{2n} y_{-n} \tag{522}$$

Every time the order n is increased by one, two new terms are added.
Bessel's interpolation formula is:

$$y = y_0 + z\Delta y_0 + \frac{z(z-1)}{2!} \frac{\Delta^2 y - 1 + \Delta^2 y_0}{2} + \frac{(z-1/2)z(z-1)\Delta^3 y - 1}{3!}$$

$$+ \ldots + \frac{z(z^2-1^2) \ldots (z-[n-1]^2)(z-n)}{(2n)!} \frac{\Delta^{2n}{}_{y-n} + \Delta^{2n} y_{-n+1}}{2}$$

$$+ \frac{(z-1/2)z(z^2-1^2) \ldots (z-n)}{(2n+1)!} \Delta^{2n+1} y_{-n} \tag{523}$$

The interpolation formula from eqs. 520a through 523 assume equal spacing of the x_i and y_i values. This is not the case for the Lagrange interpolation formula, which is:

$$y = \frac{(x-x_1)(x-x_2) \ldots (x-x_n)}{(x_0-x_1)(x_0-x_2) \ldots (x_0-x_n)} y_0 + \frac{(x-x_0)(x-x_2) \ldots (x-x_n)}{(x_1-x_0)(x_1-x_2) \ldots (x_1-x_n)} y_1 +$$

$$\ldots + \frac{(x-x_0)(x-x_1) \ldots (x-x_{n-1})}{(x_n-x_0)(x_n-x_1) \ldots (x_n-x_{n-1})} y_n \tag{524}$$

This formula does not require equal spacing of the data set x_i. Its drawback is the large number of multiplications for higher orders of n. This handicap is avoided by the use of a spline function, where the condition of equal spacing can also be waived.

Spline fitting

It is well-known that a draftsman can connect a given number of points by a smooth curve, fitting the curve by merely utilizing a draftsman's spline. This spline process has a mathematical formulation but electronic data processing is necessary. Spline functions can be used for smoothing and interpolation.
Assume, given is a set of data points, $y_1, y_2, \ldots, y_n$ as a function of locations $x_1, x_2 \ldots x_n$, where x_i is a strictly increasing number with n. Then the procedure requires the determining of a function, say $S(x)$, of degree m, which has knots at the locations $x_1, x_2, \ldots, x_n$ with solutions $S(x_n) = y_n$. This function must meet two mathematical conditions.
(*a*) $S(x)$ is given by some polynomial of degree m or less in each interval (x_i, x_{i+1}) for $i=0, 1, \ldots, n$, where $x_0 = -\infty$ and $x_{n+1} = +\infty$.

(*b*) The derivatives of $S(x)$ up to the order $m-1$ are continuous everywhere.

Thus, the spline function is a piecewise fitting of a given set of data points by polynomials of degree m. The pieces join in "knots," and the first $m-1$ derivatives are continuous. Consequently, the fitted curve is continuous.

The drawing of a smooth line by a draftsman's spline fulfills the two mathematical conditions. This can be readily proven by drawing a curve through given points with the aid of a spline, then reading off the values at small intervals and computing coefficients by polynomial fits.

Various degrees of polynomials can be utilized but most frequently the cubic spline is applied. The discussion below centers on the derivation of a cubic spline. The technique can be expanded to other degrees of polynomials.

We start out with a given second derivative, because the third derivative is a constant for the cubic spline:

$$y''=D_i w_1+D_{i+1}w_2 \tag{525a}$$

where D_i designates the second derivative of the given points, and w_1 and w_2 can be considered as the weights, splitting the interval between x_i and x_{i+1} at the point x_i, namely:

$$w_1=(x_{i+1}-x)/\Delta_i \tag{526a}$$

$$w_2=(x-x_i)/\Delta_i \tag{526b}$$

with $\Delta_i=x_{i+1}-x_i$. Hence:

$$y''=D_i(x_{i+1}-x)/\Delta_i+D_{i+1}(x-x_i)/\Delta_i \tag{525b}$$

We integrate twice and find:

$$y=D_i(x_{i-1}-x)^3/6\Delta_i+D_{i+1}(x-x)^3/6\Delta_i+c_1x+c_2 \tag{527a}$$

where c_1 and c_2 are integration constants. At the points (x_i,y_i) and (x_{i+1},y_{i+1}):

$$y_i=D_i\Delta_i^2/6+c_1x_i+c_2 \tag{527b}$$

and:

$$y_{i+1}=D_{i+1}\Delta_i^2/6+c_1x_{i+1}+c_2 \tag{527c}$$

These two equations provide:

$$c_1=(y_{i+1}-y_i)/\Delta_i-(D_{i+1}-D_i)\Delta_i/6 \tag{528a}$$

$$c_2=(y_ix_{i+1}-y_{i+1}x_i)/\Delta_i-(D_ix_{i+1}-D_{i+1}x_i)\Delta_i/6 \tag{528b}$$

The integration constants c_1 and c_2 can be introduced into eq. 527a and finally:

$$y=D_i(x_{i+1}-x)^3/6\Delta_i+D_{i+1}(x-x_i)^3/6\Delta_i+(x_{i+1}-x)(y_i/\Delta_i-D_i\Delta_i/6)$$
$$+(x-x_i)(y_{i+1}/\Delta_i-D_{i+1}\Delta_i/6) \tag{527d}$$

All quantities in eq. 527d are known except D_i and D_{i+1} at the marginal points (end) of the interval. These unknowns are obtained with the aid of the slope y' such as:

$$y_k'=-D_i(x_i-x)^2/2\Delta_i+D_{i+1}(x-x_i)^2/2\Delta_i+(y_{i+1}-y_i)/\Delta_i-(D_{i+1}-D_i)\Delta_i/6 \tag{529a}$$

This equation can be written for the preceding interval y_{k-1}' and then for the point (x_i,y_i), (see eq. 527b):

$$y_i' = -D_i\Delta_i/2 + (y_{i+1} - y_i)/\Delta_i - (D_{i+1} - D_i)\Delta_i/6 = D_i\Delta_{i-1}/2 + (y_i - y_{i-1})\Delta_{i-1} - (D_i - D_{i-1})\Delta_{i-1}/6 \quad (529b)$$

The unknown D-terms on the left are sorted so that:

$$D_{i-1}(\Delta_{i-1}/6) + D_i(\Delta_{i-1} + \Delta_i)/3 + D_{i+1}\Delta_i/6 = (y_{i+1} - y_i)/\Delta_i - (y_i - y_{i-1})/\Delta_{i-1} \quad (530a)$$

This equation is valid for all points $i=2, 3 \ldots n-1$ except for the outside points $i=1$ and $i=n$. A reasonable assumption must be made, and several choices are available which in turn affect the fit toward the margins. One could postulate that the second derivative at each margin is a linear extrapolation of the value at the two adjacent points. This implies that the third derivative will be continuous at x_2, y_2 and x_{n-1}, y_{n-1}. This postulation has the solution:

$$-D_1/\Delta_1 + D_2(1/\Delta_1 + 1/\Delta_2) - D_3/\Delta_2 = 0 \quad (530b)$$

and:

$$-D_{n-2}/\Delta_{n-2} + D_{n-1}(1/\Delta_{n-2} + 1/\Delta_{n-1}) - D_n/\Delta_{n-1} = 0 \quad (530c)$$

There are n equations with the set of eq. 530,a through c and n unknowns. This set of equations is now sufficient to determine the unknown D values.
Eq. 528a can be simplified by introducing $c_{j,i}$ such as:

$$y = c_{1,i}(x_{i+1} - x)^3 + c_{2,i}(x - x_i)^3 + c_{3,i}(x_{i+1} - x) + c_{4,i}(x - x_i) \quad (531a)$$

The following abbreviations are used:

$$c_{1,i} = D_i/6\Delta_i \quad (531b)$$

$$c_{2,i} = D_{i+1}/6\Delta_i \quad (531c)$$

$$c_{3,i} = y_i/\Delta_i - D\Delta_i/6 \quad (531d)$$

$$c_{4,i} = y_{i+1}/\Delta_i - D_{i+1}\Delta_i/6 \quad (531e)$$

The set of eq. 530,a through c is written in matrix form:

$$\mathbf{A}_\Delta \cdot \boldsymbol{b}_D = \boldsymbol{b}_y \quad (532a)$$

where $\mathbf{A}_\Delta$ is the matrix of the Δ values as seen below, $\boldsymbol{b}_D$ is the vector of the second derivatives and $\boldsymbol{b}_y$ is a function of y:

$$b_1 = 0 \text{ and } b_n = 0 \quad (532b)$$

$$b_i = \Delta y_{i+1} - \Delta y_i \text{ for } i=2, \ldots, n-1 \quad (532c)$$

where:

$$\Delta y_i = (y_i - y_{i-1})/\Delta_{i-1} \text{ for } i=2, \ldots, n \quad (532d)$$

We denote:

$$a_i = \Delta_i/6 \text{ for } i=1, \ldots, n-1 \quad (533)$$

Then the matrix $\mathbf{A}_\Delta$ can be written as:

$$\mathbf{A}_\Delta=\begin{bmatrix} -1/\Delta_1 & (1/\Delta_1+1/\Delta_2)-1/\Delta_2 & 0 & \ldots & & \\ a_1 & 2(a_1+a_2) & a_2 & 0 \ \ldots & & \\ 0 & a_2 & 2(a_2+a_3) & a_3 \ \ldots & & \\ \vdots & \vdots & \vdots & \vdots & & \\ 0 & 0 & 0 & \ldots a_{n-2} & 2(a_{n-2}+a_{n-1}) & a_{n-1} \\ 0 & 0 & 0 & \ldots -1/\Delta_{n-2} & (1/\Delta_{n-2}+1/\Delta_{n-1})-1/\Delta_{n-1} & \end{bmatrix}$$

(534a)

It can be readily verified that:

$$b_2=\Delta y_3-\Delta y_2=(y_3-y_2)/\Delta_2-(y_2-y_1)\Delta_1 \quad (534b)$$

The left side of the matrix is then:

$$a_1D_1+2(a_1+a_2)D_2+a_2D_3=b_2 \quad (534c)$$

which is eq. 531a for $i-2$.

Spline functions of other than a cubic degree can be derived following the given outline for the cubic spline. The choice depends on which order of the derivative is required to be a continuous function.

In order to determine the coefficients in eq. 531a, the following sequence can be utilized. We assume that the pairs x_i, y_i for $i-1$, ... n are given. First:

$$\Delta_i=x_{i+1}-x_i \quad \text{for } i=1, \ldots, n-1 \quad (535a)$$

$$a_i=\Delta_i/6 \quad (535b)$$

$$\Delta y_i=y_i-y_{i-1} \quad \text{for } i=2, \ldots, n \quad (535c)$$

Then:

$$b_i=y_{i+1}-\Delta y_i \quad \text{for } i=2, \ldots, n-1 \quad (536)$$

Finally, the unknown D_n from the system can be obtained:

$$D_n=B_n/p_{n,n} \quad (537a)$$

$$D_k=B_k-p_{k,k+1}D_{k+1} \quad \text{for } k=n-1, \ldots, 2 \quad (537b)$$

$$D_1=p_{1,2}D_2-p_{1,3}D_3 \quad (537c)$$

Thus eq. 531,b through c is applicable.

The definition of the p coefficients renders a first set of p and B data:

$$p_{1,2}=-1-\Delta_1/\Delta_2 \quad (538a)$$

$$p_{1,3}=\Delta_1/\Delta_2 \quad (538b)$$

$$p_{2,2}=2(a_1+a_2)-a_1p_{1,2} \quad (538c)$$

$$p_{2,3}=(a_2-a_1p_{1,3})p_{2,2} \quad (538d)$$

$$B_2 = b_2/p_{2,2} \tag{538e}$$

Then:

$$p_{k,k} = 2(a_{k-1} + a_k) - a_{k-1} \cdot p_{k-1,k} \tag{539a}$$

$$p_{k,k+1} = a_k/p_{k,k} \tag{539b}$$

$$B_k = (b_k - a_{k-1} b_{k-1}) p_{k,k} \tag{539c}$$

eq. 539, a–c for $k = 3, \ldots, n-1$.
Finally:

$$p_{n,n-1} = 1 + \Delta_{n-2}/\Delta_{n-1} + p_{n-2,n-1} \tag{540a}$$

$$p_{n,n} = \Delta_{n-2}/\Delta_{n-1} - p_{n,n-1} \cdot p_{n-1,n} \tag{540b}$$

$$B_n = B_{n-2} - p_{n,n-1} B_{n-1} \tag{540c}$$

Not all $p_{k,k}$ are needed (see matrix $\mathbf{A}_\Delta$). When the cubic spline is applied, only $p_{k,1}$, $p_{k,2}$ and $p_{k,3}$ are needed for $k = 1, \ldots, n-1$. Consequently a computer program can be based on the calculation of $p_{k,1}$ through $p_{k,3}$ only.
The properties of spline functions, which are here of secondary interest, have been thoroughly discussed in the literature (e.g., GREVILLE, 1969). Other interpolation rules and procedures can be taken from PENNINGTON (1970). Applications of spline functions are illustrated in the proceedings of a symposium, edited by SCHOENBERG (1969).
PURNELL (1976) has employed the cubic spline for interpolation between mesh points. Another application of the cubic spline was pointed out by PASSI and PASSI (1975). They adopted the spline function for the detection of outliers in data editing.

Two-dimensional spline fitting

The usage of the one-dimensional spline fitting should not be difficult based on the preceding descriptions. FRITSCH (1971) and later WOLD (1974) have developed methods to expand the spline fitting to two dimensions in order to smooth areal data. Fritsch assumes a given grid system, which needs not to be rectangular. The spline procedure, therefore, can be used to convert data from one given grid network into a different data field such as from non-regular into a rectangular grid system.
The first step is an equalization of the data points by interpolating for a rectangular (or any regular) grid system. Assume that a set of n data points $z_{p_1}, \ldots, z_{p_n}$ is given at arbitrary locations. At the grid point $x = i$ and $y = j$, the variate $z_{i,j}$ would have a certain surface, which may be approximated by a spherical surface. This spherical surface is later smoothed by a spline function as outlined below. Any grid point has the coordinates x_i, y_j. The equation of a sphere can be written as:

$$(x_k - a_1)^2 + (y_k - a_2) + (z_k - a_3)^2 = a_4^2 \tag{541}$$

with 4 constants, which are fully determined by substituting 4 points, $z_{p_1}, \ldots, z_{p_{i+3}}$ into the system.
Suppose that for the calculation of the sphere the 4 points closest to the grid point, for which the variable $z_{i,j}$ is sought, are the best choices to compute the constants a_1 through

a_4. (See later for supplementary points z'_{p_k}.) Once these constants are known, the corresponding x_i, y_j values for z_{ij} can be inserted into eq. 541 and z_{ij} determined:

$$z_{ij} = \pm[a_4^2 - (x_i - a_1)^2 - (y_j - a_2)^2]^{1/2} + a_3 \tag{542a}$$

It should be noted that:

$$a_4^2 \geq [(x_i - a_1) + (y_j - a_2)^2] \tag{542b}$$

The 4 points $z_{p_1}, \ldots, z_{p_{i+3}}$ need not always be different for every new grid point $x_{i+c}y_{j+c}$. Several of the grid points may have the same sphere combination and thus would lie on the same surface. The question is now how to fill in the marginal grid points for which the sphere of the 4 closest points may render unreasonable z'_{p_k} values because the extrapolation is carried out too far. The following methodology can also be applied if the closest 4 points are not considered to be a satisfactory solution.

Assume there is only one close point z'_{p_1} available. We must then generate $z'_{p_2}, z'_{p_3}, z'_{p_4}$. This can be accomplished by placing two points outside the boundaries of the regular grid system and one inside close to the grid point in question (see Fig. 13). These points can be determined by quadratic extrapolation, or other reasonable extrapolation procedures.

Once the original data point system is converted to a regular grid net by a spherical surface, the data z_{ij} can be smoothed by spline functions along the lines x_i = constant and y_j = constant. According to FRITSCH (1971), after several smoothings (three to four) the directional bias is eliminated and the grid point values converge to a "unique surface". It may be advisable to apply some checking procedures to avoid excessive data errors for the interpolated z_{ij} or the supplementary z'_{p_k}. We could require, e.g. that:

$$z_4 - 2\sigma_p \leq z_{ij} \leq z_4 + 2\sigma_p \tag{543a}$$

where z_4 is the mean of the 4 data points and σ_p the standard deviation of the total data. Similarly:

$$z_m - 2\sigma_p \leq z_{p_k} \leq z_m + 2\sigma_p \tag{543b}$$

can be checked where now the z_m is the overall mean. Most of the supplementary points will lie on the outside of the regular grid net and can be discarded after having served their purpose. Therefore, the eqs. 543, a and b do not restrict the system. Furthermore, a

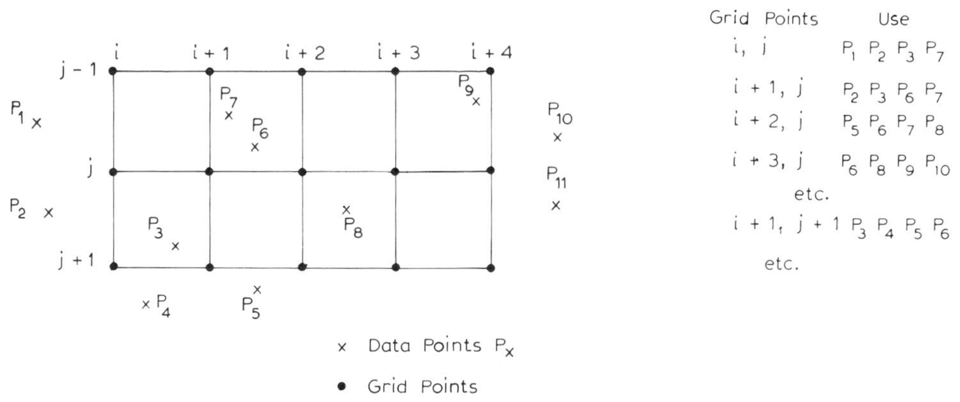

Fig. 13. Example of selecting data points for grid points in two-dimensional smoothing by spline functions.

smoothing by the cubic spline is performed afterward. Thus any z_{ij} can be redetermined by a spline fit, i.e.: every z_{ij} is interpolated from the adjacent points by the cubic spline. Again, comparison between calculated and original z_{ij} value by the procedure of eq. 543, a or b may be helpful, and σ_p is recomputed for the new (smoothed) set of z_{ij}.
Five percent of the data will fall outside the two sigma range (reference mean) if tested by eq. 543b, provided the z_{ij} follow the Gaussian distribution law. Thus, not all data points must fulfill eq. 543b.
The two-dimensional fill-in technique also can be applied to close gaps in contingency tables or other data collection, where a completeness of data is necessary for the analysis. It must be cautioned, however, that in the latter case these filled-in data can bias the results. The maximum amount of tolerable fill-in data depends on various factors. If the fraction is less than five percent the influence of the added data would be negligible. This rule of thumb is valid only for the filling-in of data by procedures which have been outlined in this section.
Where physical processes or synoptic maps are the basis for the elimination of data gaps it can be assumed that the outcome is not distorted or biased and limitations to a certain fraction for the filled-in data are not necessary. WAHBA (1978) addressed the problem of improper priors and spline smoothing and concluded that spline smoothing is a solution to regression problems.
Comparisons between individual methods are provided in Example 40 and by YANG (1974) and SIMMONDS (1975). Simmonds concluded that in his case the cubic spline was superior to a linear interpolation. Yang showed that in his study the cubic spline interpolation was equivalent to GANDIN's optimum interpolation (1963). MAHRER and PIELKE (1978) found spline interpolation useful in numerical mesomodels and MACPHERSON and KELLY (1976) applied spline interpolations for numerical weather forecasting.

Example 40. A spline fit. Table LXII illustrates the fill-in of data by various types of methods. The example utilizes the mean wind direction, given at 2 km altitude steps for January and July at Chateauroux (1956–1964). The mean wind direction was computed as discussed by ESSENWANGER (1964). The missing values at the interim 1-km levels were calculated by various techniques as delineated in the column headings. It is evident that linear interpolation, polynomial fit (Tchebycheff) and spline fit will diverge in certain sections because the goals of the interpolation are different for the individual methods. The different answers, however, reflect the divergence which exists in the postulations.
It can be noticed that in some cases the (cubic) spline fit will be closer to the real observation than the other methods, in other cases it will not. This, too, must be expected because no fill-in technique can accommodate the random fluctuations which are superimposed on the observations in the individual case. We could expect agreement between observed and filled-in data when the missing observations are strictly based on the principal assumptions that furnish the mathematical-statistical background of the three presented procedures in Table LXII. The main purpose for the inclusion of this example into the text is an illustration of differences which arise in the process of interpolation by various methods.

In spline fitting we substitute values into the gaps that lead to a continuous curve and its derivatives based on the degree of order which was selected for the fit. The polynomial fit renders an approximation whose squared deviations (for the given points only!) produce a minimum. Linear interpolation is equivalent to the assumption that the missing data between two given points lie on a straight line.

TABLE LXII

EXAMPLES OF SPLINE FITS

	Given	Spline	Polynomial 6 term	Linear interpol.	Observ.	Given	Spline	Polynomial 6 term	Linear interpol.	Observ.
	January:					July:				
0	117*[1]		114.6*[1]			317		316.3		
1		19.6*[1]	47.7*[1]	45.5*[1]	333		279.6	292.9	292	297
2	334		340.8			267		269.5		
3		322.1	330.8	330	326		269.1	271.6	271.5	277
4	326		320.7			276		273.7		
5		330.4	324.3	329	326		279.6	276.7	278	278
6	332		327.9			280		279.6		
7		330.3	328.6	329	327		279.2	278.8	279	277
8	326		329.3			278		278.0		
9		320.1	325.1	310.5	324		276.8	276.9	277	278
10	315		321.0			276		275.8		
11		312.5	316.1	313.5	313		276.0	277.1	276.5	282
12	312		311.2			277		278.4		
13		312.2	309.4	312.5	309		278.6	280.2	277.5	280
14	313		307.6			278		282.0		
15		314.4	309.4	314	312		273.6	276.9	275	274
16	315		311.2			272		271.9		
17		313.7	313.3	313	311		274.6	251.7	263	266
18	311		315.5			254		231.4		
19		307.9	313.8	308.5	311		190.5	194.0	189	204
20	306		312.1			124		156.6		
21		306.5	306.5	307	309		96.7	118.7	111.5	106
22	308		300.8			99		80.8		
23		308.2	303.8	306.5	308		108.6	93.7	101	102
24	305		306.7			103		106.6		

*[1]Converted by subtracting 360° from the number.

Smoothing and graduation in two dimensions

Smoothing of data in two dimensions has been performed in the past largely by drawing smooth isolines of elements in maps. In essence, in most cases of practical applications the purpose was the drawing of isolines. This principle, although quite subjective, is still in widespread use today and is a valid technique. Many data processing tasks of today require, however, the availability of smoothing methods for electronic data processing. In turn, some objective (mathematical) criteria are difficult to incorporate without the aid of electronic data processing.

The methodology introduced in previous sections can be adapted to computer use (e.g., see eq. 541). In the present section we discuss a two-dimensional smoothing technique which was developed by SCHUMANN (1963).

In the previous sections the smoothing of data was a problem of curve fitting. It was pointed out that any truncation in the number of terms (order) of a mathematical function and a recomputation of a curve by these restricted terms is a smoothing process. Polynomial fits can be expanded to two or more dimensions or computed coefficients can be smoothed, e.g. by recomputing the annual cycle, etc.

SCHUMANN (1963) introduced a different system by expanding the one-dimensional principle to two dimensions. He and others (e.g., WHITTAKER and ROBINSON, 1944) formulated the smoothing process as a compromise between two conditions: (*a*) the smoothed values s_i should display the smallest possible deviation from the original data x_i; and (*b*) the curve through the graduated observations should be as smooth as possible. These two principles which sometimes conflict can be combined in a mathematical formulation for one-dimension:

$$E_1 = k\sum (x_i - s_i)^2 + \sum (s_i - s_{i+1})^2 \rightarrow \text{minimum} \tag{544a}$$

This provision can be expanded to the two-dimensional case:

$$E_2 = k\sum\sum (x_{ij} - s_{ij})^2 + \sum\sum (s_{ij} - s_{i+1,j})^2 + \sum\sum (s_{ij} - s_{i,j+1})^2 \rightarrow \text{minimum} \tag{544b}$$

The expressions above are based on the requirement that the sum of the squared first differences in conjunction with the differences between observed and smoothed data render a minimum.
Expansion of eq. 544a, b to include the third and fourth differences leads to:

$$E_3 = k\sum (x_i - s_i)^2 + \sum (s_i - 3s_{i+1} + 3s_{i+2} - s_{i+3})^2 \rightarrow \text{minimum} \tag{545a}$$

and:

$$E_4 = k\sum\sum (x_{ij} - s_{ij})^2 + \sum\sum (s_{ij} - 3s_{i,j+1} + 3s_{i,s+2} - s_{i,s+3})^2 + \sum\sum (s_{ij} - 3s_{i+1,j} + 3s_{i+2,j} - s_{i+3,j})^2 \rightarrow \text{minimum} \tag{545b}$$

Eqs. 544 a, b and 545 a, b are the fundamental equations. The constant k is an appropriate numerical factor. A solution of these equations can be found by differentiation of E_i and by satisfying the differentiated equation by setting $\partial E_i/\partial p$ to zero. In our notation p designates the respective variable parameters of the systems.

Minimum of E_1

The one-dimensional solution can be found by setting $\partial E_1/\partial s_i = 0$:

$$(k+2)s_i - s_{i-1} - s_{i+1} = kx_i \tag{546a}$$

The calculation of the smooth value follows from:

$$s_i = \sum_{t=-\infty}^{\infty} w_t x_{i+t} \tag{546b}$$

with:

$$w_0 = (1-\alpha)/(1+\alpha) \tag{546c}$$

and:

$$\sum w_t = 1.0 \tag{546d}$$

Furthermore:

$$w_c = w_{-c} = (1-\alpha)\alpha^c/(1+\alpha) \tag{546e}$$

where c is an arbitrary integer which corresponds to t as needed in eq. 546b. Now α can be determined from:

$$\alpha = K - \sqrt{K^2 - 1} \tag{546f}$$

where K is again an integer related with k:

$$K = (k+2)/2 \tag{546g}$$

Minimum of E_2

The two-dimensional case with eq. 544b is based on the solution of the equations:

$$2Kw_{ij} = w_{i-1,j} + w_{i+1,j} + w_{i,j+1} \tag{547a}$$

$$2Kw_{0,0} = 2w_{0,1} + 2w_{1,0} + k \tag{547b}$$

$$w_{i,j} = w_{-i,j} = w_{i,-j} = w_{-1,-j} \tag{547c}$$

$$K = (k+4)/2 \tag{547d}$$

The solution*[1] is:

$$w_{a,b} = (k/\pi) \int_0^{\pi} [(\alpha^a \cos bf)/(1/\alpha - \alpha)]\, df \tag{548a}$$

where:

$$f = \pi t/w \tag{548b}$$

and:

$$df = \pi/n \tag{548c}$$

Now α_t can be obtained from:

$$\alpha_t + 1/\alpha_t = k + 4 - 2\cos f \tag{548d}$$

and t is ranging from 0 to n. (548e)

Again, s_{ij} can again be calculated by:

$$s_{ij} = \sum u \sum v w_{u,v} x_{i+u,j+v} \tag{548f}$$

where:

$$\sum w_{u,v} = 1.0 \tag{548g}$$

and:

$$w_{0,0} = k/2k \sum_{t=0}^{\infty} \{(2t)!/[(2K)^t \cdot (t!)^2]\}^2 \tag{548h}$$

Second condition for E_2

The one-dimensional smoothing based on eq. 547a has the following solution:

$$w_c = w_{-c} = (K/3)[A^c/B + 2C^c/D]\cos(c \cdot \gamma - \psi + \pi/3) \tag{549a}$$

*[1] Here a, b has been substituted for i, j; and α_t provides the values of α for the individual t.

with:

$$A = 1 - 2KB + 2K^2 \tag{549b}$$

$$B = 1 + K^2 \tag{549c}$$

$$C = (2DK \sin\psi - \sqrt{3}\,K^2)^2 + (2DK \cos\psi + 1 - K^2)^2 \tag{549c}$$

$$D^4 = 1 - K^2 + K^4 \tag{549e}$$

$$\tan^2\psi = (2D + B^2)/(2D - B^2) \tag{549f}$$

$$\tan\gamma = (2DK \sin\psi - \sqrt{3}\,K^2)/(2DK \cos\psi + 1 - K^2) \tag{549g}$$

under the conditions:

$$\pi/2 \leq \psi \leq \pi \quad \text{and} \quad 0 \leq \gamma \leq \pi/2 \quad \text{for } K \leq 1 \tag{549h}$$

$$0 \leq \psi \leq \pi/2 \quad \text{and} \quad \pi/2 \leq \gamma \leq \pi \quad \text{for } K \geq 1 \tag{549i}$$

$$64K^2 = k \tag{549j}$$

Third condition for E_2

Eq. 547b requires a solution:

$$w_{a,b} = (Kk/3\pi) \int_0^\pi \{[A^b/B + (2C^c/D)\cos(b\gamma - \psi + \pi/3)]\cos af/F\}\,\mathrm{d}f \tag{550a}$$

with:

$$F = k + 8(1 - \cos f)^3 \tag{550b}$$

The parameters A, B, C, D, γ, ψ have been defined by eq. 549, b–g.
Since eq. 549j is replaced by:

$$64K^6 = k + 8(1 - \cos f)^3 \tag{550c}$$

the parameters A, B, C, D, γ, and ψ are now all functions of f (see eq. 548, b and c). SCHUMANN (1963) tabulated the weighting functions in a special report.

Chapter 6

Tests

In the previous sections various statistical tools have been introduced. They serve largely to characterize, summarize or describe sets of data (observation) samples. However, one fundamental problem of statistical analysis always is the answer to the questions: "how representative are the results," or "how well has a statistical hypothesis been confirmed?" In order to provide some answers to these questions statistical testing has been introduced. This section cannot include every conceivable test method. Excellent textbooks of statistical analyses cover tests in more detail (e.g., MOOD, 1950; COCHRAN and COX, 1957; HALD, 1957; SCHEFFÉ, 1959; BROWNLEE, 1960a; KENDALL and STUART, 1961; FISHER and YATES, 1963; FISZ, 1963; FISHER, 1966, 1970; HOGG and CRAIG, 1967; SNEDECOR and COCHRAN, 1967; etc.) but a few test methods have been selected here. They are restricted to some fundamental tests which are found in widespread use in the atmospheric sciences. Before test methods are presented it is appropriate to discuss some background of testing. It is sometimes difficult to decide which test method is the most suitable one.

In some instances even theoreticians cannot agree which test is the most appropriate method. In other cases the choice depends on the primary goal: what should be achieved by the test. The reader will find, however, that test results which fall into the category "highly significant" or "highly non-significant" seldom change if "more suitable" tests*[1] are applied, i.e., they are robust against changes in the test methods. The outcome which falls into neither of the above categories may switch from significant to non-significant or vice versa. Therefore, results which border the chosen significant threshold should be carefully examined before further statistical inference is applied. The test method must be changed, however, if the statistical background of the particular test disagrees with the background characteristic of the atmospheric data sample. E.g., the data may display persistence while the test method postulates independence of data, etc.

Statistical inference

General concepts

Electronic data processing has enhanced the use of statistical analysis tremendously, and many "canned programs" which contain "packages" of statistical inference are now readily

*[1] The term "highly significant" or "highly non-significant" is not uniquely defined. The author considers a probability of rejecting a true hypothesis, $\alpha \geq 15\%$, as the highly non-significant category, and $\alpha \leq 0.5\%$, as the highly significant boundary (see p. 240).

available. In the beginning this development was hailed by various statisticians and non-statisticians alike. The first group believed that it is a solution to the problem of proper utilization of statistical tests by non-statisticians, and the second group welcomed the opportunity to perform statistical tasks with little worry about the associated technical difficulties. But gradually both groups came to the realization that these "canned packages" are not the answer to every problem, and they may or may not provide the best suitable tool or the correct answer. Despite some progress the confusion in the field of statistical inference remains (e.g., DAUGHERTY, 1980).

It should be stressed that statistical inference should be applied with utter care, and statistical inference is not an answer to all problems in practice. To forget the scientific goal (e.g., the physical process) over mathematical procedure is a mistake which is very easily made. It is essential that the fundamentals of data analysis are taken into consideration before the abstract mechanism of statistical inference is applied. E.g., it is superfluous to apply a statistical test and check whether a (linear) correlation coefficient of $r=0.01$ is significantly different from the assumption that $r=0$ when $r=0.01$ implies a negligible contribution for practical purposes, e.g., in a linear equation. Consequently, in some cases the test effort is justified, in other instances it may mean lost time and costs. Thus, the first question should be: does statistical testing add something to the data analysis?

Statistical inference occasionally can be misused by literal interpretation of poor terminology. Sometimes mathematical statisticians have adopted terms which the non-mathematician can easily misinterpret. E.g., GUTTMAN (1977) quoted as an example the term "regression" which in its present use seldom has any connection with a genetic process for which this method originally was developed. Today it implies the analysis of a "set of conditional means." This more precise description may not lead to an easier understanding of the analysis by the non-mathematician but it may clarify what the mathematician is doing. It is difficult today for any author to avoid all poor choices of expressions which have been adopted by statisticians (mathematicians) in the past and which have been utilized in the statistical literature for so long. The reader is advised, however, to examine the mathematical definitions of terms and processes before attempting a literal interpretation of statistical terminology.

Hypothesis testing

In the early years of data analysis conclusions were drawn by "judgment". Today this subjective approach is frowned upon, some authors even call it "prejudice". Judgment has been widely replaced by an "objective" statistical approach where a hypothesis is selected and tested, and an alternate hypothesis is adopted in the case that the first hypothesis is rejected. Many non-statisticians do not realize that they must decide themselves which postulation should be tested. The statistician provides only the tools, i.e., objective procedures or statistical rules by which different researchers or experimenters would make the same choice or deductions after testing the hypothesis with the same set of observations. Consequently, the statistician is not at fault when the hypothesis is meaningless or has no relationship with physical processes in atmospheric science. An example involving the comparison of several sample means may illustrate how the freedom of choice affects the statistical tool.

First, we postulate that the samples are drawn from the same population. If infinite sampling were available all samples would produce the same mean value, i.e., the population mean. The differences in the observed sample means are considered as being caused by random fluctuations which must be expected in a finite sampling process. This hypothesis can be checked, e.g., by the application of the t-test (see eqs. 614a, b.

A second point of view is the assumption that the samples represent different physical processes. Thus, infinite sampling will not lead to one common population mean. The sample means will be different although equal means are not excluded. The testing of the dispersion of the sample means requires a different statistical approach (e.g., selection by ranking, see BECHHOFER and SOBEL, 1954) rather than the process presented above.

Ordinarily two hypotheses are needed for testing. Most authors call the first hypothesis the "null" hypothesis. GUTTMAN (1977) has pointed out that more precisely it should be called "incumbent" hypothesis. It is customary to accept the hypothesis after the probability for rejecting it is below a selected threshold. More correctly, the probability distribution for the statement expressed by the "null" hypothesis is determined, and a small fraction of this probability distribution is set aside for which the hypothesis is rejected. E.g., we postulate that two sample means are alike. Then the error distribution of the population mean is calculated, and a threshold towards the extreme is selected. If the second sample mean falls into the extreme segment (or segments) the hypothesis is rejected. Consequently, the difference between means must be large before the hypothesis is rejected. Thus, the decision process appears to favor acceptance. In turn, it is never established that the hypothesis is incorrect in the case of rejection. Hypothesis testing establishes only that a postulation (hypothesis) is not very likely to occur under given circumstances, and consequently it should be rejected.

After the null hypothesis is rejected the "alternate" hypothesis replaces it. According to GUTTMAN (1977) the alternate hypothesis should be called "challenging" hypothesis. The null hypothesis also is termed the "original" hypothesis and the "alternate" hypothesis its "replacement." Because of the subjective selection of the null hypothesis EDWARDS (1971) referred to it as "prejudice". These arguments in semantics illustrate that the choice of the null and alternate hypothesis is a subjective choice and hypothesis testing is difficult and complex. The reader is further cautioned that even repeated non-rejection of the null hypothesis is no explicit proof. The acceptance could be caused by a lack of information or too little observational data for a successful challenge of the incumbent hypothesis. The relationship to type I and II error is presented later.

One problem in hypothesis testing found little attention among statisticians but was delineated by GUTTMAN (1977). Assume that the same scientist or another researcher repeats an experiment or expands the analysis by adding a new set of observations. What is the probability that the conclusions about the hypothesis are the same as from the first data collection? Even more profound is the question whether the repetition can be unbiased and/or independent. The practitioner may find it difficult to obtain a clear answer to these questions. By and large, the decision for a repetition is influenced by either dissatisfaction with the first result or the desire to change the outcome of an earlier hypothesis testing.

The difficulty with hypothesis testing and its statistical inference can be exemplified by Brier's study of rainfall anomalies. BRIER (1961a) concluded that a "strong tendency for precipitation anomalies on specific calendar dates" exists. This statement was challenged by Shapiro and MacDonald (1961) who utilized the same data, but Brier (1961b) defended his results successfully. Based on the same data, Hannan (1962) suggested an oscillation of 18 cycles/year as the mechanism for the precipitation anomalies although Brier (1962) was not convinced by this explanation. Later Brier et al. (1963, 1964) expanded the data base. They concluded that the statistical significance was not large enough to support the hypothesis of an anomaly or an oscillation of 18 cycles/year. Various other examples could be added which illustrate later changes in the outcome of hypothesis testing. Examples are not limited to the field of atmospheric science.

Data characteristics

Comparing of data by inspection and drawing of conclusions about the physical processes and background is relatively simple for a few observations. It becomes very difficult if not impossible, however, when a huge collection of data has to be judged. Consequently, simplification is necessary, and representative parameters which reduce the mass of data to a few and manageable characteristics have been sought. They are either simple descriptors such as the maximum, minimum, etc., or they have a unique mathematical definition such as the average (see eq. 24). However, they may not always render an appropriate description of the physical process or behavior.
Before valid statistical inference about any set of data can be made, the statistical descriptors should be examined to see whether they fall into the category of mathematical formalism or are typical properties with physical meaning. E.g., in most cases the average daily temperature of the month at a given geographic location occurs frequently enough on individual days during the month that it forms a suitable representation of the data. In contrast, the average daily cloud cover of the month is seldom observed because the frequency density distribution of cloud cover is "U-shaped" (Essenwanger, 1976, p. 63). The arithmetic mean of the wind direction is another example of a characteristic which may be deficient in its relationship with physical processes (Essenwanger, 1961, 1964). This lack of meaning does not contradict the fact that in statistical analysis the "expected" value is the arithmetic mean (by definition), but the expected value is not always "to be expected".
What has been said for the average can be expanded to other characteristics. Thus, the measure of dispersion such as the standard deviation (or variance) is a meaningful parameter for most bell-shaped frequency (density) distributions but must be interpreted with caution for other types such as the exponential or U-shaped models (see Essenwanger, 1976).
Another misconception can sometimes be found in the interpretation of the correlation coefficient. In most textbooks it is properly explained that a strong correlation does not necessarily mean that a causal relationship exists. However, it is sometimes overlooked to add that x and y can be correlated with z, although x and y may not be correlated.

Orthogonality and independence

It may be the belief of the non-mathematician that orthogonality in data is some magic which is necessary for experimental designs or statistical inference. To the mathematician, however, orthogonality is merely a form of data representation which can always be achieved by proper transformation of the data. In most cases an orthogonal system is preferable because it simplifies distributional theories, but orthogonality has little to do with interrelationship of natural processes. E.g., in the application of multiple correlation techniques the ideal situation is found when the predictors are not interrelated. Although the predictors should be "independent" from one another they must be related with the predictand. Consequently, "independence" of the data is a relative and not an absolute property. Furthermore, independence should not be equalized with "chance". The latter has several meanings such as events with equal probability, or no clear determined law, etc., but independence is not one of them.

Error sources

Before specific test methods are treated, some deficiencies of atmospheric data collections may be briefly summarized. Most of these possible sources of errors are known to an experienced practitioner of data analysis but the peculiarities of the data can easily be overlooked. Consequently, as a precaution some of the error sources will be discussed here even if superfluous material is presented. The importance of the topic has been underlined in articles by BARTELS (1943, 1948), BAUR (1950), VAN DER BIJL (1951), and others.

Sampling effect

All data collections in meteorology are samples. We try to draw conclusions about the behavior of the population from the sample or we search for the physical background. We must guard against statistical inference which is unjustified and has not taken into account the possibility that the parameters derived from sampling are subjected to random variations. We heed against this omission by the establishment of significance criteria and hypothesis testing but we cannot assess the random effect with certainty. Some of the "non-significant" results may reflect in reality true physical causes, and some conclusions drawn from a basis of significance may nevertheless be erroneous because the background of the process is randomness rather than physical law. The risk of an erroneous inference, however, is considerably reduced by utilization of a significance test.

Statistical significance alone may not be sufficient to the practitioner. E.g., a significant linear correlation coefficient $r=0.01$ or even $r=0.1$ may be of little value in practical applications. In turn, a non-significant high linear correlation sometimes can be valuable for descriptive purposes of the available meteorological material. Before general conclusions from this high but non-significant correlation are drawn, however, either the data base should be expanded or theoretical considerations must support the findings. In addition, the possibility that a linear correlation includes only a fraction of the total interrelationship should be taken into consideration.

As explained later in detail, two types of wrong decisions can be made in hypothesis testing. The type I error is the rejection of a hypothesis when it should have been accepted. The type II error is the acceptance of the hypothesis when the alternate hypothesis is true. The type II error is related to the power of a test. Both errors are minimized when statistical principles are obeyed.

Persistence

Meteorological elements are seldom free of persistence, either in time or space (e.g., ESSENWANGER, 1950, 1956a, 1977, 1980; GORDON and WELLS, 1976, etc.). Most observational programs cannot eliminate persistence a priori. In fact, for some purposes (e.g. a prediction) high persistence is very desirable. We should be aware, however, that many of the statistical significance criteria postulate independence of data. Consequently, the significance threshold in hypothesis testing may be exceeded merely on the basis that the assumption of independence of data was incorrect. E.g., persistence can cause peaks in a periodogram. Instead of the assumption of "white noise" the proper basis is "red noise" (see ESSENWANGER, 1980). If it is recognized that persistence is the reason for the exceedance of a statistical significance criterion the reader will probably make the correct data interpretation. Should any conclusion from the results reflect facts, however, which have no relationship to persistence, the findings may be erroneous.

Two avenues exist which can eliminate the influence of persistence and which lead to valid statistical inference. First, the significance criterion can be expanded to include the effect of persistence (e.g., ESSENWANGER, 1950; STUMPFF, 1937). The second possibility is the generation of a reduced series of observations by eliminating data such that the remaining observations are independent. This procedure illustrates that valid conclusions sometimes can be obtained from fewer independent observations without loss of information. The reader is cautioned that in the preparation of the reduced data a selection effect may occur (see p. 239).

The degree of persistence usually can be determined by studying the autocorrelation function (ESSENWANGER, 1950, 1976, 1977). Further details can be found in VAN DER BIJL (1951).

Spurious correlation

The so-called $a_i(a_i+b_i)$ effect appears mostly in correlations, but its influence can be felt in other problems of data analysis such as the parameterization of meteorological phenomena, etc. In parameters from dynamic meteorology or theoretical formulations this particular effect can also appear. E.g., the geostrophic wind includes the density and the pressure gradient. Consequently, it is expected that a close relationship between geostrophic wind and density at either the same altitude or the same pressure level exists.

The correlation coefficient from an $a_i(a_i+b_i)$ effect is called spurious correlation (see eq. 293a). Therefore, the investigator should exercise caution in correlation analysis, e.g., correlating seasonal values with the individual months of these seasons produces spurious correlation. Additional examples can be found in the atmospheric literature.

The effect is analogous when b is negative. E.g., correlating a meteorological element of one month with the difference from the same to the next month will fabricate the $a_i(a_i-b_i)$ effect.

It should be stressed that the choice of the practitioner to analyse two elements which are related to each other through $a(a+b)$ is not a mistake by itself. Wrong deductions are made, however, if the practitioner is not aware of this bond. E.g., the spurious correlation yields a high linear coefficient because of an $a(a+b)$ effect. Consequently, such outcome

should not be a surprise. More desirable in most cases would be the establishment of the relationship between a and b alone.
The findings drawn from an $a(a+b)$ investigation may not be useless, or could be of some value. Usually the drawback is that these studies offer little or no additional information beyond what would be known from a alone. Efforts devoted to investigate apparently unrelated material may reveal more information than studies undertaken with related material.

Selection effect

This error is more frequently found than one may generally assume. Many researchers start an investigation with the hope that the outcome of an investigation proves either a certain hypothesis or a speculation. This implies that in general the researcher knows what is expected. Consequently, the anticipated outcome is rightly called the expectancy in statistical terminology. No objection can be raised if the finding agrees with the expectation. It is wrong, however, when observational data are rejected, or corrected in a manner that the outcome of the investigation is affected. E.g., Kolmogorov's power law for turbulence spectra requires a slope of $-5/3$ (see eq. 415b). One should not be surprised about confirmation of this law in every case if in studies of clear air and other turbulence analysis all non-conforming data are eliminated a priori. This fact should not lead to the interpretation that observational data cannot be corrected, rejected, or omitted. Methods of quality control and assurance are quite legitimate (see p. 314), but rejections of observational data must be based on different grounds than the desired outcome of a research study. E.g., corrections are justified for theoretical reasoning, experimental background, seasonal division, or an instrumental inhomogeneity, etc.
Assume that we are studying the correlation of sunspots with some meteorological elements. It is not permitted to exclude from the set of data the periods of low correlation because these data influence the magnitude of the correlation. However, should the same data in a time span of loose relationship display some instrumental deficiencies (i.e., incorrect calibration, low sensitivity of instruments, or other faulty measurements) it would be legitimate to either correct the data if possible or disregard them. The effect upon the outcome would be the same as an omission a priori, namely, an increase of the correlation. However, the motive in the latter case is not the achievement of an increase of the correlation but the elimination of inhomogeneous or incorrect observations which may be the reason for a low correlation.
The selection effect is even more critical when a periodicity or cycle exists. The tendency of introducing a data bias cannot be overemphasized.
Furthermore, instrumental and observer bias can alter the result of an investigation. E.g., radiosonde observations may often display an instrumental bias because in former times data with strong winds in the troposphere lacked data in the upper atmosphere. These limitations of upper air wind records were pointed out by CHARLES (1959). Further studies were performed by CANFIELD et al. (1966), and STEWART (1971). All these studies disclosed that correlation coefficients, seasonal variations and statistical parameters derived from serially completed observations deviated from those obtained for an incomplete data set. Some differences were significantly large.
Another biasing effect can be created by truncation of data. E.g., GILMAN (1981) limited

data on patent awards to 95 American companies which had more than 44 patents per year. He found an inverse correlation between company size and number of patents. JACKSON et al. (1982) pointed out, however, that the inclusion of all companies with one or more patents shows that no correlation exists. Gilman fell victim to a truncation effect.

Trend

Several causes of errors can be combined into one group called "trend errors". In statistical analysis the term "trend" usually means a more or less steady rise or fall. The term "trend error" as applied here includes any bias which is introduced by a systematic interdependence of data. It is immaterial whether this dependency can be mathematically or only stochastically formulated. What counts is the fact that a trend contrasts to a strictly random behavior.

Although a "trend" may be unimportant or negligible, and many problems of statistical analysis can be solved without consideration of a trend, sometimes a trend can cause biasing of the results or can conceal the correct relationships. A typical example of a trend error is the curvature effect as discussed by BARTELS (1943), or the modification upon a power spectrum if the trend is not eliminated before calculations of the spectrum are performed (see Example 29).

LANDSBERG (1975) pointed out that the trend in atmospheric data may have no predictive value without establishment of the physical causes.

At the beginning of any data analysis, the dependency in atmospheric data sets should be determined by either a mathematical or a stochastic model. Then a judgment should follow concerning the effect of persistence or a trend on the outcome of a subsequent statistical study. Sometimes the "trend error" may not be important, but it should not be forgotten as a possible source of data bias. E.g., if the trend generates a non-stationary time series some of the basic principles in time series analysis may lose their validity (see ESSENWANGER, 1976).

A trend in the form of a curvature (concave or convex) can sometimes be very disturbing in smoothing, filtering, or combining of data (see p. 180).

One of the well known "trend errors" in climatology is caused by disregarding the change of the physical environment in the observation of a long term data series. E.g., the "benchmark" program must consistently be checked for homogeneity. Although many professional and lay observers fulfill their duties painstakingly, the environment can change in a 30-year or longer period which may lead to biasing effects.

It is evident that climatic fluctuations such as the global warming to the decade 1940/50 and the present return to a cooler climate can introduce a trend error in climatological data collections. In fact, any temporal change of the physical conditions or environment affects atmospheric data collection. Some test methods for homogeneity and stability recently were described by SNEYERS (1979a).

Significance and power of the test

Significance and type I error

It was previously mentioned (p. 237) that all atmospheric data collections are samples, and all samples are subjected to sampling errors. Consequently, any outcome of a statistical data analysis must be carefully examined whether the inferred conclusions from the data set are justified. Intuitive conclusions can be correct and logical, and may provide a right answer. They are subjective, however, and it is necessary to establish some objective criteria in support of any deduction from the data or from the parameters of the data.

In practical applications we are interested whether randomness in data sampling has produced a particular outcome or whether the result reflects some physical rule or principle. Thus, we test the findings against the background of a hypothetical model. This procedure is called testing for significance. It requires the selection of a "null" hypothesis H_0 and an "alternate" hypothesis H_1 (see p. 235). The reader should beware of believing that a test of significance is a test for scientific importance. A statistical test can merely reveal the statistical background.

Two types of errors can be made. H_0 can be rejected when it should have been accepted. This mistake has been named "type I error". The definition of type II error will follow on p. 242.

The probability of rejecting a true hypothesis is called the significance level of a test. It is customarily denoted by α, and it is generally kept as small as possible. An empirical equivalent, α_E is calculated from the data. H_0 is rejected for $\alpha_E \geq \alpha$.

No fixed rule for the selection of α can be given, although $\alpha = 5\%$ or 1% is a customary choice. However, the decision on α is left up to the scientist. The only restriction is the rule that α must be determined before the test is being performed.

Choosing α will depend on various factors, and an important one is the risk which the practitioner is willing to accept if the outcome was produced by randomness. There is no guarantee that a type I error will not occur. Because α controls the probability of a type I error, one may think why not set $\alpha = 0$. Then no type I error can arise. This argument does not go very far. Besides the problem of computational difficulties testing would be unnecessary because $\alpha_E \geq 0$. Consequently, H_1 would be accepted in all cases. Undoubtedly $\alpha = 0$ is identical with the postulation that all deviations from expectation are produced by randomness. This extreme view is unreasonable and cannot be supported due to the existence of physical laws. Thus, the determination of α is equivalent to a decision where randomness should stop and physical law is accepted.

It is possible to assure that the risk of making a wrong decision is small. Despite all the precautions, however, type I errors cannot be completely avoided. E.g., Gelhaus et al. (1974) discovered a type I error in an evaluation of a cloud seeding project.

Sometimes the investigator selects several levels of significance or changes α after the completion of the data analysis. This tactic is equivalent to a change of direction in the middle of the stream. One, and only one, level must be selected before a significance test is performed. This should not be construed such that the data cannot be supplemented, converted, or that other legitimate data manipulations cannot take place. The reader must be aware that any change in the data produces a new situation which requires a re-examination of the significance test.

Mostly in engineering problems, the reader may find that the significance level is expressed in multiples or fractions of the standard deviation, e.g., 2 or 3 times the standard deviation. This concept stems from an assumption that random fluctuations produce a Gaussian distribution whose measure of dispersion (standard deviation) has a unique relationship with α. Consequently, a specified multiple of the standard deviation corresponds automatically to a certain value of α (see Essenwanger, 1976, pp. 384–386).

Type II error

A second possibility is the acceptance of H_0 when H_1 is true. This is referred to as "type II error" and is commonly denoted as the probability β. The fraction $1-\beta$ is called the power of the test. Obviously we are interested to keep β as small as possible.

In practice a two-step procedure is widespread. First, the significance level α (tolerance of the type I error) is selected. Afterwards, the fraction $1-\beta$ is maximized. The test which is constructed under this concept can be compared with all other possible tests. In a formulation by NEYMAN and PEARSON (1928, 1933) it was proven that this process leads to the "most powerful" test.

Suppose we have postulated the null hypothesis H_0, $\theta=\theta_0$. An alternate hypothesis is considered H_1, $\theta=\theta_1$. Now the most powerful test is a method which gives maximum assurance that at a given significance level α we would not accept θ_0 when θ_1 is the true parameter. A lemma was provided by NEYMAN and PEARSON (1933). They chose the region A for an unbiased test, which is most powerful in the neighborhood of θ_0, by selecting A so that:

$$\frac{\partial P(A|\theta)}{\partial\theta}=0 \tag{551}$$

and:

$$\frac{\partial^2 P(A|\theta)}{\partial\theta^2}\geq\frac{\partial^2 P(A'|\theta)}{\partial\theta^2} \tag{552}$$

$P(A|\theta)$ is the power of the region A and eqs. 551 and 552 are fulfilled for $\theta=\theta_0$. In many instances, however, we may be more interested in an asymptotically most powerful test as discussed by WALD (1941). Later additional details will be presented in the respective test sections.

Tests of hypothesis can be set up in several ways. For a particular problem the best choice of H_0 will depend on the distribution function of the respective parameter and the alternate hypothesis H_1. A system closely related to the maximum-likelihood method for estimators is the likelihood ratio test.

Assume that a frequency function $f(x_i, \theta_1 \ldots \theta_k)$ depends on k parameters. We test H_0: $\theta_1=\omega$, with an unspecified θ_2, against H_1: $\theta_1\neq\omega$, with θ_2; and ω may represent a special θ_1. In order to maximize $1-\beta$ the likelihood ratio is determined. A threshold λ_0 is selected as a threshold for rejection of H_0 (see also SUZUKI, 1980, p. 14). The ratio of the two likelihood functions is found:

$$\lambda=\frac{L(\hat{\omega})}{L(\hat{\Omega})} \tag{553}$$

where:

$$L(\hat{\omega})=\prod_{i=1}^{N} f_i(x_i, \theta_1 \ldots \theta_k) \text{ for } (\theta_1 \ldots \theta_k)\ \varepsilon\ \omega \tag{553a}$$

and:

$$L(\hat{\Omega})=\prod_{i=1}^{N} f_i(x_i, \theta_1 \ldots \theta_k) \text{ for } (\theta_1 \ldots \theta_k)\ \varepsilon\ \Omega \tag{553b}$$

and $\omega\varepsilon\Omega$. The hypothesis is rejected if $\lambda \leq \lambda_0$. The corresponding significance level is:

$$\alpha = P[\lambda(x_1 \ldots x_n) \leq \lambda_0; H_0] \qquad (554)$$

or:

$$\alpha = \int_0^{\lambda_0} g(\lambda)\, d\lambda \qquad (554a)$$

As previously stated: in testing a simple hypothesis H_0 against a simple hypothesis H_1 the Neyman-Pearson lemma leads to the most powerful test. The relationship of the likelihood ratio λ with χ^2 distribution is discussed (eq. 668).

Confidence limits

In hypothesis testing it is customary to refer to α and β, i.e., the type I and II errors or the significance level and the power of the test, respectively. An additional assurance of the correctness of inference can be gained from the so-called confidence limits which can be attached to the point estimation of parameters. E.g., we have computed the numerical value of a parameter θ_1. Now an interval from θ_L (lower) to θ_U (upper bound) is determined for which the probability can be given that the parameter θ_1 falls within these specified thresholds. The interval is called the confidence interval, and the associated probability the degree of confidence. The confidence interval can be one-sided or two-sided. For a one-sided interval:

$$\theta_L \leq \theta_1 \leq \theta_U \qquad (555)$$

where α applies to either $\theta_1 \leq \theta_L$ or $\theta_1 \geq \theta_U$.
Analogously for a two-sided interval $\alpha/2$ holds for either:

$$\theta_1 \leq \theta_L \text{ or } \theta_U \leq \theta_1 \qquad (555a)$$

or α is proper for:

$$|\theta_B| \leq |\theta_1| \qquad (555b)$$

The probability for the confidence interval is:

$$P(\theta_L \leq \theta_1 \leq \theta_U) = 1 - \alpha \qquad (556a)$$

for a one-sided interval, and for a two-sided interval:

$$P(\theta_1 \leq \theta_L) = P(\theta_1 \geq \theta_U) = \alpha \qquad (556b)$$

which implies:

$$P(\theta_L \leq \theta_1 \leq \theta_U) = 1 - 2\alpha \qquad (556c)$$

Confidence limits can be based on the binomial distribution (see eq. 59). In analogy to the probability statement for the parameter θ_1 (see eq. 556) a lower (P_L) and upper (P_U) bound of the function $F(x)$ is established for a two-sided confidence interval:

$$P(P_L \leq F(x) \leq P_U) = 1 - 2\alpha \qquad (557)$$

where α is the significance level. Because P follows the binomial frequency distribution we can cast:

$$\alpha = \sum_{a=k}^{n} \binom{n}{a} P_{\mathrm{L}}^{a}(1-P_{\mathrm{L}})^{n-a} \tag{558a}$$

or:

$$\alpha = \sum_{a=0}^{k} \binom{n}{a} P_{\mathrm{U}}^{a}(1-P_{\mathrm{U}})^{n-a} \tag{558b}$$

where eq. 558a is used for the lower limit P_{L} and eq. 558b for the upper limit P_{U}. The problem is usually solved by conversion of the binomial function to the incomplete beta function (PEARSON, 1956; ESSENWANGER, 1976, p. 41):

$$F(x,a,b) = \frac{(a+b+1)!}{a!\ b!} \int_{0}^{x} t^{a}(1-t)^{b}\,\mathrm{d}t \tag{559}$$

with the lower limit:

$$\alpha = F(t,\ k-1,\ n-k) \tag{559a}$$

and the upper limit:

$$1-\alpha = 1-F(t,\ k,\ n-k-1) \tag{559b}$$

while t corresponds to P in eq. 558, a or b.
The computation of the confidence interval is independent of the functional form of $F(x)$. The binomial distribution can be approximated by the Gaussian distribution for larger N. This eliminates the need for using tables of the incomplete beta function because normal distribution tables are readily available or computed (e.g., ESSENWANGER, 1976).
For a two-sided test (KENNEY and KEEPING, 1954; BROWNLEE, 1960a) the boundaries can be obtained by a Gaussian approximation where upper (s_{u}) or lower values (s_{l}) are calculated (RAO, 1973):

$$s_{\mathrm{u}} = \frac{n_1 - 0.5 - Np}{[Np(1-p)]^{1/2}} \leq \sigma_{\mathrm{u}(1-\alpha/2)} \tag{560a}$$

$$s_{\mathrm{l}} = \frac{n_1 + 0.5 - Np}{[Np(1-p)]^{1/2}} \geq \sigma_{\mathrm{l}(\alpha/2)} \tag{560b}$$

The following symbols have been utilized: N, the number of trials, p, the probability of the hypothesis (expected value), and n_1, the observed number of favorable events, e.g., the number of heads in the tosses of a coin or the number of positive differences in a set of differences, etc.
Both s_{u} and s_{l} are measured in units of the standard deviation of a Gaussian distribution. Consequently, σ_{u} and σ_{l} must be taken as the fraction of the standard deviation from a Gaussian distribution, which corresponds to $\alpha/2$. We compare s_{u} with σ_{u} as given in eq. 560a. This technique is equivalent to the previous procedure for the significance test except that H_0 is rejected when $s_{\mathrm{u}} \geq \sigma_{\mathrm{u}}$, or correspondingly $s_{\mathrm{l}} \leq \sigma_{\mathrm{l}}$.

A numerical value for the boundary n_b can be computed by transforming eq. 560, a and b into:

$$n_{b_1} = \sigma_u[Np(1-p)]^{1/2} + 0.5 + Np \quad (561a)$$

$$n_{b_2} = \sigma_l[Np(1-p)]^{1/2} - 0.5 + Np \quad (561b)$$

We select σ_u or σ_l according to the predetermined level of significance α and reject the hypothesis when $n_1 > n_{b_1}$ or $n_1 < n_{b_2}$ for the upper or lower boundary, respectively.
The boundaries can also be obtained from:

$$\theta^2(N + \sigma_b^2) - \theta(2n_1 + \sigma_b^2) + Np^2 \leq 0 \quad (561c)$$

The roots of θ provide the boundaries, and σ_b corresponds to σ_u or σ_l. Distribution free tests are treated later (see p. 254).
The estimation procedure of confidence intervals by the Gaussian approximation can be expanded to data whose frequency distributions have been transformed to the Gaussian law (see LAND, 1974). WEISSBERG and BEATTY (1960) have expanded the calculation of tolerance limits when mean and variance may not stem from the same sample (see also NELSON, 1977).
It should be stressed that some restraints are placed on the confidence interval. E.g., we can define the confidence interval for a sample mean, and assume that the true population mean will fall within this interval with a given probability. This rule does not imply that the sample mean for the next sample falls within this interval, even though the sample will be taken from the same population. The prediction of the next sample mean is an entirely different problem of statistical analysis.
GUTTMAN (1977) has pointed out that in many problems of data analysis confidence limits should be determined for simultaneous parameters, a problem not yet solved by statisticians.

Example 41. Computation of confidence limits. Let us assume the sample mean $x_m = 5$, $N = 10$ (identical with the number of trials), $\hat{p} = 0.5$.
In order to apply PEARSON's (1956) tables of the incomplete beta function, which are tabulated for $I(x,p,q)$, we must find the proper conversion of the parameters. In Pearson's notations:

$$y = y_0 x^{p-1}(1-x)^{q-1} \quad (562)$$

We introduce t for x, a for $p-1$ and b for $q-1$ (see eq. 559). Then:

$$p = a + 1 \quad (562a)$$

$$q = b + 1 \quad (562b)$$

since a corresponds to $k-1$, b to $n-k$ for the lower limit, and k, $n-k-1$, for the upper limit, respectively. The following related equations are deduced with $k = N \cdot \hat{p} = x_m$:

Lower limit:

$$p = k = x_m \quad (563a)$$

$$q = N - k + 1 = N - x_m + 1 \quad (563b)$$

Upper limit:

$$p = k + 1 = x_m + 1 \quad (563c)$$

$$q = N - k = N - x_m \quad (563d)$$

Notice, for $q>p$ we must use $p'=q$, $q'=p$, $\alpha'=1-\alpha$ and $I(x',p',q')$. Then we convert $x=1-x'$. We are now ready to carry out the computations of the confidence limits. If a two-sided confidence interval of 95% is desired then $\alpha=0.025$. For the upper limit $p=6$, $q=5$. From the tables $I_x(p,q)=0.975$.

$x=0.81$ for $I_x(p,q)=0.9734$

$x=0.82$ for $I_x(p,q)=0.9787$.

By linear interpolation $x_u=0.813$.
The lower limit of $p=5$, $q=6$ leads to $p'=6$, $q'=5$ and the same table values. Hence:

$x_L=1-0.813=0.187$.

At the preselected 5% level of significance the probability falls into the interval:

$0.187 \leq \hat{p} \leq 0.813$

In numerical counts the bounds are transformed by multiplication with N:

$1.87 \leq x_m \leq 8.13$

HALD's tables (1952) lead to the same thresholds. In Hald's notation x is identical with x_m and $n-x$ with $n-x_m$.
In conclusion: if $x_m=5$ from 10 trials the true sample mean lies between 2 and 8 (including the boundary).
For comparison let us compute the confidence limits by employing eq. 561a and b. We set $\sigma_u \sim 2.0$ and $\sigma_l \sim -2.0$ for the significant level α of 5% as above:

$n_{b_1}=x_m+0.5+2[x_m(1-\hat{p})]^{1/2}=5.5+3.16=8.66$

$n_{b_2}=x_m-0.5-2[x_m(1-\hat{p})]^{1/2}=4.5-3.16=1.34$

$1.34 \leq x_m \leq 8.66$.

We notice that the boundaries do not completely agree with the previous limits. This must be expected because the binomial and Gaussian distributions are not precisely the same for small N. For small N the binomial law is the proper choice such as for $N=10$. From the Gaussian approximation we find even a wider dispersion range, but by rounding to whole numbers the range is the same: $2 \leq x_m \leq 8$.

Example 42. We assume now $N=30$, $x_m=18$, $\hat{p}=0.6$. This provides:

$p=19$, $q=12$, $1-\alpha/2=0.975$

From the tables (see Example 41):

$x=0.77$ for $I_x(p,q)=0.9720$

$x=0.78$ for $I_x(p,q)=0.9800$

By linear interpolation $x_u=0.774$.
The lower limit yields $p=18$, $q=13$, $\alpha/2=0.025$ and $x_l=0.406$. Hence:

$0.406 \leq \hat{p} \leq 0.774$

or:

$N_{b_2}=12.2 \leq x_m \leq 23.2=N_{b_1}$

The approximations in eq. 561a and b lead to boundaries of $n_{b_2}=12.34$. Hence:

$12.3 \leq x_m \leq 23.7$

Notice that the Gaussian approximation is already satisfactory for $N=30$.

Degrees of freedom

In hypothesis testing, the number of degrees of freedom is often required. This number is usually N for a set of independent variables without further limitations, but is determined by the constraints which are placed for the problem at hand. E.g., the derivation of the variance ν_2 requires $\nu_1 = 0$ (see eqs. 25a, 26d). Thus, the number of degrees of freedom for the variance is $N - 1$, because of the added condition. The degrees of freedom will be provided subsequently if necessary.

Standard error

The standard error of a statistical parameter can be interpreted as its confidence interval (see WEITBRECHT, 1979). Therefore, this section is a follow-up on confidence intervals.
It is customary to postulate that random errors produce a frequency distribution which is Gaussian. Consequently, the standard error is equivalent to the standard deviation of a Gaussian distribution whose mean is identical with the particular parameter. Thus, the level of significance and the boundaries of the confidence interval can be approximated from the Gaussian cumulative distribution. Whenever the observed set of data follows a Gaussian distribution, the standard error is true Gaussian. Otherwise, the Gaussian law may be an approximation.
In the following, the standard error is denoted by ε with the parameter for which it stands as a subscript.

Standard error of moments

The standard error*[1] of the mean value $\bar{x}$ is:

$$\varepsilon_{\bar{x}} = \pm\sigma/\sqrt{N} \tag{564a}$$

This formula is also known as the law of error propagation. In sampling without replacement the standard error of the mean must be expanded:

$$\varepsilon_{\bar{x}} = (\sigma/\sqrt{N})\sqrt{(N_p - N)/(N_p - 1)} \tag{564b}$$

where N is the sample size and N_p denotes the population size. A short and elementary proof for this expansion was given by BONDY and ZLOT (1976).
The standard error of any moments (reference mean) is:

$$\varepsilon^2_{\nu_r} = \frac{1}{N}\left[\nu_{2r} - \nu_r^2 + r^2\nu_2\nu_{r-1}^2 - 2r\nu_{r-1}\nu_{r+1}\right] \tag{565}$$

where ν signifies the central moment (see eq. 25). This leads to the standard error of the variance:

$$\varepsilon_{\sigma^2} = \sqrt{(\nu_4 - \nu_2^2)/N} \tag{566a}$$

*[1] The double sign $\pm$ is omitted in all other derivations. By definition the Gaussian distribution is symmetrical about the mean, thus the dispersion is symmetrical about the mean.

By introducing the kurtosis γ_2 (see eq. 27b) into eq. 566a we deduce:

$$\varepsilon_{\sigma^2}=\sigma^2\sqrt{(\gamma_2+2)/N} \tag{566b}$$

For a distribution which is nearly Gaussian $\gamma_2 \approx 0$, and the reduced form is:

$$\varepsilon_{\sigma^2}=\sigma^2\sqrt{2/N} \tag{566c}$$

The standard error for σ is generally computed from $\varepsilon^2_{\sigma^2}/(4\sigma^2)$, which renders:

$$\varepsilon_{\sigma}=(\sigma/2)\sqrt{(\gamma_2+2)/N} \tag{567}$$

See eq. 48h.
The standard error of the third moment is:

$$\varepsilon^2_{v_3}=\frac{1}{N}\left[v_6-v_3^2+9v_2^3-6v_2\cdot v_4\right] \tag{568a}$$

If the data follow a Gaussian distribution eq. 568a can be shortened to:

$$\varepsilon_{v_3}=\sigma^3\sqrt{6/N} \tag{568b}$$

The standard error of the fourth moment (for a distribution which is Gaussian) has the abbreviated form:

$$\varepsilon_{v_4}=\sigma^4\sqrt{96/N} \tag{569}$$

From the standard error of the moments the standard error of the skewness (see eq. 27a) is:

$$\varepsilon_{\gamma_1}=\sqrt{6/N} \tag{570}$$

This expression is independent of sigma. In analogy to γ_1 the kurtosis has the standard error:

$$\varepsilon_{\gamma_2}=\sqrt{24/N}=2\varepsilon_{\gamma_1} \tag{571}$$

Example 43. Assume the following parameters have been derived for a meteorological set of temperature data (see Example 3).

$N=280$

$\mu_1=59.24;\ v_1=0$

$\sigma^2=36.75;\ \sigma=6.06$

$v_3=-0.016;\ \gamma_1=-0.00$

$v_4=3793.688;\ \gamma_2=-0.190$

The given information leads to the following standard errors.
(*1*) Mean value:

$\varepsilon_{\bar{x}}=\pm 6.06/\sqrt{280}=\pm 0.362$

A 95% degree of confidence that the true mean value is within the confidence interval is desired. Consequently, $-2\ \varepsilon_{\bar{x}} \leq \bar{x} \leq 2\ \varepsilon_{\bar{x}}$, or:

$58.8 \leq \bar{x} \leq 59.60$

In the subsequent part of the example, conversion of the standard error to the confidence interval of the parameter will be omitted when self-evident.
(*2*) Variance:

$$\varepsilon_{\sigma^2} = 36.75\sqrt{(-0.190+2.0)/280} = 2.95$$

Under the assumption that the distribution of the data is nearly Gaussian:

$$\varepsilon_{\sigma^2} = 36.75\sqrt{2/280} = 3.11$$

The two numerical values of the standard error differ by about 5%. Because this difference is small one may suspect that the distribution of the data is nearly Gaussian (see discussion below).
(*3*) The standard error for the standard deviation amounts to:

$$\varepsilon_{\sigma} = (6.06/2)\sqrt{(-0.190+2.0)/280} = 2.44$$

(*4*) From eq. 568a the standard error of the third moment is computed:

$$\varepsilon^2_{v_3} = [v_6 - (-0.02)^2 + 9(36.75)^3 - 6(36.75)(3793.69)]/N$$

$$[v_6 - 389810]/N = (708218 - 389810)/N = 318408/280 = 1137.17$$

$$\varepsilon_{v_3} = 33.72$$

For a distribution which is approximately Gaussian we calculate:

$$\varepsilon_{v_3} = (6.06)^3\sqrt{6/280} = 32.58.$$

Again, the difference in this case is small because the sample distribution (see Table I) resembles a Gaussian distribution.
(*5*) For a nearly Gaussian distribution the standard error of the fourth moment is found to be:

$$\varepsilon_{v_4} = (36.75)^2\sqrt{96/280} = 790.8$$

(*6*) Standard error of skewness:

$$\varepsilon_{\gamma_1} = \sqrt{6/280} = 0.146$$

Notice: the confidence bounds are $-0.292 \leq \gamma_1 \leq 0.292$ for the 95% interval.
(*7*) Standard error of kurtosis:

$$\varepsilon_{\gamma_2} = \sqrt{24/280} = 0.293$$

with the confidence bounds (95%): $-0.776 \leq \gamma_2 \leq 0.396$.

Statistical test for a Gaussian distribution

The confidence interval for γ_1 and γ_2 is often utilized to check the hypothesis that the underlying distribution is Gaussian. We test:

$$H_0\colon \gamma_1 = 0;\ H_1\colon \gamma_2 \neq 0$$

and:

$$H_0\colon \gamma_2 = 0;\ H_1\colon \gamma_2 \neq 0.$$

The hypothesis H_0 is accepted whenever 0 falls within the confidence interval.
The test does not prove that the frequency distribution is Gaussian. It is a negative proof, however, i.e., γ_1 and γ_2 must be zero whenever the data have a Gaussian distribution. Consequently, if any of the two postulations of H_0 must be rejected, the data cannot have a Gaussian distribution (subject to the limitations of hypotheses testing, see p. 234 and

240). For a definite proof that the frequency distribution is Gaussian a test of all moments which can be calculated from the data would be required. This task is tedious, and other methods may be more economical.
Goodness-of-fit tests for the comparison of the frequency distributions with the Gaussian frequency are presented later (p. 302). A variety of authors has elaborated on tests for normality. A comprehensive survey comparing eight different tests has been given by Shapiro et al. (1968). Other studies were performed by Sneyers (1974) or by Pearson et al. (1977). Bowman and Shenton (1975) suggested mapping of (standardized) skewness and kurtosis. Gastwirth and Owens (1977) concluded that Cornu's test (see eq. 578b) may be a good indicator for detecting large tails, symmetric departures from the Gaussian distribution and is not necessarily inferior to the evaluation by kurtosis.
Pettitt (1976) studied the use of the Cramer-von Mises statistic (see eq. 706) for testing of normality with censored samples. Atkinson (1973) recommended the use of the likelihood function for testing transformations to the Gaussian distribution. Malkovich and Afifi (1973) have expanded the skewness-kurtosis test and the test statistic by Shapiro and Wilk (1965) for the multivariate Gaussian case.
The quoted literature here provides only a cross-section through the voluminous contributions by statisticians on testing for the validity of a Gaussian distribution in data samples.

Standard error of percentiles

The standard error for the percentile values is sometimes useful:

$$\varepsilon_p - (\sigma/f_p)\sqrt{p \cdot q/N} \qquad (572a)$$

where p stands for the percentile, $q = 1 - p$. The frequency f_p of the percentile class is:

$$f_p = (n_p/N) \cdot (\sigma/w) \qquad (572b)$$

with n_p, the number of observations in the class interval of the percentile, and w, the class width (see eq. 13). This leads to:

$$\varepsilon_p = (w/n_p)\sqrt{pqN} \qquad (572c)$$

The standard error for the median is:

$$\varepsilon_{\text{med}} = (w/n_p)\sqrt{0.25\,N} = (\sigma/f_p)\sqrt{0.25/N} \qquad (572d)$$

For the quartile:

$$\varepsilon_{\text{quart}} = (w/n_p)\sqrt{0.1875\,N} = (\sigma/f_p)\sqrt{0.1875/N} \qquad (572e)$$

The standard error of any *frequency* within a given range $\Delta p = p_2 - p_1$ is:

$$\varepsilon_{\Delta p} = \sqrt{Npq} \qquad (573a)$$

where $p = \Delta p = p_2 - p_1$, i.e., the fraction falling within that range. As usual, $q = 1 - p$. The error $\varepsilon_{\Delta p}$ of eq. 573a provides absolute frequency units $n\Delta_p$. The relative frequency must be obtained from $\varepsilon_{\Delta p}/N$, i.e.:

$$\varepsilon'_{\Delta p} = \sqrt{pq/N} \qquad (573b)$$

Example 44. Standard errors of percentiles. Given is the class width $w = 2°F$, $n_p = 36$, $N = 280$, and the median $x_m = 59.18°F$. The standard error of the median is:

$$\varepsilon_{med} = (2/36)\sqrt{0.25 \cdot 280} = 0.465$$

which leads to a confidence interval:

$$58.25 \leq x_m \leq 60.11.$$

As indicated, the confidence interval implies that the true median of the population is expected to lie between 58.25 and 60.11°F with a degree of 95% confidence.

Standard error of miscellaneous statistical parameters

The standard error of the range R can be found from:

$$\varepsilon_R = \sqrt{\varepsilon_{p_1}^2 + \varepsilon_{p_2}^2 - 2r\,\varepsilon_{p_1} \cdot \varepsilon_{p_2}} \quad (574a)$$

where ε_{p_1} and ε_{p_2} must be computed from eq. 572a, $p_1 < p_2$, and:

$$r = \sqrt{p_1(1-p_2)/(p_2(1-p_1))} \quad (574b)$$

The standard error of the mean deviation from the sample mean is:

$$\varepsilon_d^2 = (\sigma^2 - \delta_{\bar{x}}^2)/N \quad (575a)$$

where $\delta_{\bar{x}}^2$ must be determined. An auxiliary parameter is:

$$d_a = (1/N)\sum_1^N |x_i - a| \quad (576a)$$

which is the mean (absolute) deviation. The expectancy of d_a is δ_a:

$$E(d_a) = \delta_a = E(|x_i - a|) \quad (576b)$$

Under the assumption of a Gaussian distribution with $\bar{x} \equiv a$ we find:

$$\delta_a = \delta_{\bar{x}} = \sigma\sqrt{2/\pi} \quad (577)$$

By substitution into eq. 575a:

$$\varepsilon_d = \sigma\sqrt{(1-2/\pi)/N} \quad (575b)$$

A different formulation of eq. 577 is:

$$2\sigma^2/\delta_{\bar{x}}^2 = \pi \quad (578a)$$

In practice we calculate from the data:

$$a_d = 2s^2/d_a^2 \quad (578b)$$

Then a_d is compared with π. If the distribution is Gaussian, $a_d \approx \pi$. This comparison is called Cornu's theorem or test.

Another common parameter is the probable error which is defined by the probability of 0.5 that the parameter θ falls within the interval $\theta - \varepsilon_{PE} < \theta < \theta + \varepsilon_{PE}$. For these postulations the probable error takes the form:

$$\varepsilon_{PE} = 0.67449\sigma \quad (579)$$

Although the utilization of the probable error has declined in the last decade one continual application is the prediction of the numerical value of the next observation. Under the theorem of the probable error the next observation has a 50% chance to fall within the given bounds. In turn, the probability is 50% that the next observation will lie outside of the interval.

Today the standard error of the correlation coefficient is seldom used in statistical analysis but the formula is simple and independent from the availability of statistical tables or sophisticated distribution forms:

$$\varepsilon_r = (1 - r^2)/\sqrt{N-1} \tag{580}$$

The formula is limited to larger values of N, and for testing the hypothesis H_0: $r = 0$. A more suitable test of the correlation coefficient will be introduced later (eqs. 622a and 641c).

Example 45. Standard error of the range. Given is the frequency distribution of the daily average temperature in February (1955–1964) at Yuma, Arizona, of Table II.

Suppose that we are interested in a range from 10% to 90% of the cumulative distribution. The data are grouped into classes and the exact number of n_R is not readily available. We have a choice of either estimating n_R or finding it by extra- or interpolations. We estimate n_R: 80% of $N = 280$ provides $n_R = 224$.

Now n_R is determined from Table II. We count $N = 215$ from the cumulative distribution for an interval 52.0 through 66.0°. The corresponding frequency is $F(X_5) = 10.3\%$ and $F(X_{12}) = 87.1\%$, respectively. The adjacent lower class provides $f(X_5) = 3.6\%$, and $n_5 = 10$. An interpolation for the interval from 10% to 10.3%, renders $(0.3/3.6) \cdot 10 = 0.8$. The upper adjacent class has $f(X_{13}) = 3.6\%$ or $n_{13} = 10$. Thus, from 87.1 to 90% we obtain $(2.9/3.6) \cdot 10 = 8.1$. In summary:

$$n_R = 215 + 0.8 + 8.1 = 223.9.$$

This number shows an excellent agreement with the previous estimate of 224.

We compute the range for the interval 10% to 90%. Again, we extra-(inter)polate: $66.0 - 52.0 = 14.0$ plus $(0.3/3.6) \cdot 2$ plus $(2.9/3.6) \cdot 2$ (multiplication by 2 because of the class width $w = 2°$).

$$R = 14.0 + 0.17 + 1.61 = 15.78°$$

The standard error for R is now computed as follows:

$$f_p = (10/280)(6.06/2) = 0.1082$$

Since both intervals coincidentally have the same number of observations, $n_i = 10$, only one computation of f_p is necessary. Furthermore: $p_1 = 0.1$ and $p_2 = 0.9$.

$$r^2 = (0.1)(0.1)/(0.9)(0.9) = 1/81$$

from which:

$$r = 1/9$$

$$\varepsilon_{p_1} = (6.06/0.1085)\sqrt{(0.1)(0.9)/280} = 1.001$$

$$\varepsilon_{p_2} = (6.06/0.1085)\sqrt{(0.9)(0.1)/280} = 1.001$$

In this case $\varepsilon_{p_1} = \varepsilon_{p_2}$, which is valid only for ranges with symmetrical bounds about the median. We continue with:

$$\varepsilon_R^2 = (1.001)^2 + (1.001)^2 - 2(1/9)(1.001)(1.001) = (1.001)^2(16/9)$$

and:

$$\varepsilon_R = 1.33$$

With 95% confidence the true range of $R=15.75$ lies between:

$13.12 \leq R \leq 18.44$

We add the standard error of the frequency:

$\varepsilon_{\Delta p} = \sqrt{(280)(0.8)(0.2)} = 6.7$

or the relative frequency:

$\varepsilon'_{\Delta p} = \sqrt{(0.8)(0.2)/280} = 0.024 = 2.4\%$

Consequently, with 95% confidence $n_{\Delta p}$ observations fall within the range R of 15.8 degrees, i.e.:

$211 \leq n_{\Delta p} \leq 237$

or:

$75.2\% \leq f_{\Delta p} \leq 84.8\%$

Example 46. Standard error of the mean deviation. We examine the data sample Table I. First, we need $\delta_{\bar{x}}^2 = 36.75(2/\pi) = 23.40$ (see eq. 577) where $\sigma^2 = 36.75$, and $\delta_{\bar{x}} = 4.84$.
The numerical value of d_a (see eq. 576a) can be obtained by summing the absolute values of $\sum n_i y_{ci}$ (see Table II) where $y_{ci} = i - 9$. Because $\bar{y} = \sum n_i y_{ci}/N = 0.146$ we must adjust for $\bar{y} \neq 0$, i.e., $\sum n_i y_{ci} = 673 + 4.1 = 677.1$ the class width is $w = 2$. Thus from eq. 576a $d_a = (677.1/280) \cdot 2 = 4.84$, i.e., $\delta_{\bar{x}}$ and d_a are close to the second digit, but $d_a^2 = 23.43$. From eq. 575a:

$\varepsilon_d^2 = (36.75 - 23.40)/280 = 0.0477$

or $\varepsilon_d = 0.218$. Utilization of eq. 575b leads to:

$\varepsilon_d = 6.06\sqrt{(1-2/\pi)/280} = 0.218$

which is the same value. The reader must be aware that for a non-Gaussian distribution the two computed values of ε_d from eq. 575, a and b are not identical.
Cornu's test: H_0: $r_d = \pi$; H_1: $r_d \neq \pi$.
We obtain from the data (via eq. 578a: $r_d = 2\sigma^2/d_a^2 = 73.50/23/43 = 3.137$ which is close to π. The closeness to π indicates that the data sample could have a Gaussian distribution.
Finally, the probable error is:

$\varepsilon_{PE} = (0.67449) \cdot (6.06) = 4.09$

Consequently, it should be expected that 50% of the data fall within the range ($\theta = \bar{x}$):

$55.15 < \bar{x} < 63.33$

Examination of the observed data of Table II shows that $n = 137$ data fall within 55.15 to 63.33. This number of n is close to an expected value of 140, i.e., 50% of $N = 280$.

Example 47. Standard error of the correlation coefficient. The standard error for a particular correlation coefficient can be calculated from eq. 580. How large must the coefficient r be to meet the 95% confidence interval test for a specified N? Under an assumption of a Gaussian distribution for ε_r we would set $r \leq 2\,\varepsilon_r$. We substitute ε_r from eq. 580 and finalize after a rearrangement of the terms:

$$r^2 \pm \sqrt{N-1}\,(r/2) - 1 = 0 \qquad (581a)$$

or:

$$r = -0.25\sqrt{N-1} + 0.5\sqrt{(N-1)/4 + 4} \qquad (581b)$$

The negative root can be eliminated because $r \leq |1.0|$. Subsequently some solutions for various values of N are given:

N	10	30	50	100
r	0.5	0.33	0.27	0.19

For $N = 30$ and a basis of the standard error a correlation coefficient $r \geq 0.33$ would be considered different from zero with 95% degree of confidence. The significance of the correlation can be tested by other methods. For comparison the standard errors of a few correlations are presented:

r	0.162	0.258	0.373	0.794	0.955
$1-r^2$	0.9778	0.9334	0.8609	0.3496	0.0880
ε_r	0.182	0.173	0.160	0.065	0.016

Persistence and the standard error

The reader must be aware that the standard error has been derived for "independent" data. Most atmospheric time series are governed by persistence (p. 16).
The degree of persistence and the behavior of the data affect the size of the standard error. By and large, persistence tends to increase the number of observations but the dispersion will remain the same. This situation leads to a smaller error variance than for independent data.
Sometimes the opposite effect can occur. E.g., the decrease of the standard error with increasing time of averaging may be much slower than expected from independent data (LEITH, 1973). Consequently, standard errors derived for the evaluation of climatic changes or long-range forecasting should be carefully examined for modification by persistence (e.g., MADDEN and SADEH, 1975).

Non-parameter tests and homogeneity

General concept

In previous sections it was postulated that data are governed by particular types of distributions and their respective parameters. The conjecture of a certain distribution type may not be true. Therefore, it is desirable to develop some test methods which are applicable to several distribution types or do not require postulation of the distribution type. In addition, these tests do not necessitate the computation of parameters of the distribution. Therefore, they are called "non-parametric" procedures or "distribution free". Only a few topics from the wealth of existing methods (see e.g., WALSH, 1962; CONOVER, 1980) can be included here.
Non-parametric tests are mostly utilized to test the randomness of data. Homogeneity for a population requires that for every data sample the physical processes are the same. E.g., the observations of two or more stations which were taken under the same climatic conditions should only display differences which are caused by random effects. Their "relative" homogeneity can be tested by tests for randomness. Consequently, we postulate in the null hypothesis H_0 that the differences follow a random (Gaussian) distribution. An acceptable level of significance is selected and a confidence interval is computed. If the observed difference falls within this confidence interval, H_0 is accepted, otherwise it is rejected. In the latter case the data may be examined to find the reason for the inhomogeneity.

Sign tests (differences)

We postulate that two sets of data X_i and Y_i are given, $i=1, ..., N$. Relative homogeneity and interchangeability of records X_i and Y_i is assumed. The difference is calculated:

$$z_i = X_i - Y_i \tag{582a}$$

Under random conditions it is expected that the probability for the sign of z_i is:

$$P(z_i > 0) = P(z_i < 0) = 0.5 \tag{583a}$$

In this test procedure it was tacitly assumed that $X_m = Y_m$. If $x_i = X_i - X_m$ and $y_i = Y_i - Y_m$ and $X_m \neq Y_m$, then:

$$z_i = x_i - y_i \tag{582b}$$

Although the two data samples could come from a homogeneous climatic regime, the standard deviations of the two data sets could be different due to orographic effects (e.g., the elevation of the stations is different). Then the difference z_i for eq. 89a should be calculated as:

$$z_i = x_i/\sigma_x - y_i/\sigma_y \tag{582c}$$

One test for eq. 582a is based on the sign of z_i which follows the binomial law. In fact eq. 582a can be expanded for any reference threshold η:

$$P(z_i > \eta) = p_0 \tag{583b}$$

We replace $z_i > \eta$ by $u_i = 1$ and $z_i < \eta$ by $u_i = 0$. Then u_i has a binomial distribution with a probability p_0 and sample size N. For $\eta = 0$, i.e., $p_0 = 1/2$, eq. 583a emerges.
The empirical probability $p = n_u/N$ (where n_u is the number of z_i values with positive or negative sign) is affected by random fluctuations. These variations of the signs can be evaluated by the binomial distribution. The hypothesis that a parameter p has a hypothetical value p_0 is tested by utilizing:

$$P(u) = \{n!/[u!(n-u!)]\} p^u (1-p)^{n-u} \tag{584}$$

The following three cases must be distinguished:

Test 1. Two-tailed, H_0: $p = p_0$; H_1: $p \neq p_0$.
Test 2. Lower tail, H_0: $p \geq p_0$; H_1: $p < p_0$.
Test 3. Upper tail, H_0: $p \leq p_0$; H_1: $p > p_0$.

The probability for these assumptions can be obtained from tables of the binomial distributions (NATIONAL BUREAU OF STANDARDS, 1950; HALD, 1952; OWEN, 1962; BEYER, 1966; etc.)
Under the assumption that z_i follows a Gaussian distribution or is a statistic which can be considered asymptotically as Gaussian, a confidence interval can be used. A test value τ exceeds a certain threshold λ_α of the Gaussian distribution with probability α, or:

$$\tau = \pm\lambda_\alpha \sigma_\xi \pm 0.5 + \bar{\xi} \tag{585a}$$

where $\bar{\xi}$ and σ_ξ are the mean and standard deviation of the test element and 0.5 is an adjustment term for discrete data which is sometimes neglected. The factor λ_α represents the fraction of the standard deviation which corresponds to the significance level α, e.g., $\lambda_\alpha = 1.96$ for $\alpha = 0.05$. The positive sign in eq. 585a is taken for the upper end of the frequency, the negative sign corresponds to the lower tail. We test:

$$P(c_T \geq \lambda_\alpha) = \alpha \qquad (585b)$$

where c_T is the empirical counterpart for τ (see s_u, s_l in eq. 560, a and b).
For the sign test $c_T = n_z$ where n_z is either the number of positive or negative signs. The expected values for mean and variance of $\bar{\xi}$ and σ_ξ are:

$$\bar{\xi} = n/2 \qquad (586a)$$

$$\sigma_\xi^2 = n/4 \qquad (586b)$$

The adjustment term is neglected, and:

$$c_T = (n_z - n/2)/(\sqrt{n}/2) \qquad (585c)$$

where $|n_z - n/2|$ is taken for a two-tailed test.
The sign in eqs. 585a and 585c must be adjusted correspondingly for the upper and lower tail.
A convenient rule was formulated by DUCKWORTH and WYATT (1958). We approximate $\lambda_\alpha \sim 2.0$ for $\alpha = 0.05$, so that:

$$c_T = (2n_z - n)/\sqrt{n} \geq 2 \qquad (585d)$$

One problem with the sign test involves the assignment of $z_i = 0$ into categories u_i. Several avenues are available for a solution. In one method all zeros are counted as plus and the augmented n_z is tested, then the test is repeated by counting the zeros as minus. If the test conclusions from plus and minus are the same, there is no conflict. Otherwise, a different method of counting $z_i = 0$ must be found.
In a second method (BRADLEY, 1969) the cases $z_i = 0$ are omitted which reduces n by the number of zero cases. This method is suitable for a symmetrical distribution of the z_i around zero, i.e., $z_m = 0$.

Example 48. Suppose we are interested whether climatic processes in February 1955 and 1956 at Yuma, Arizona, were similar with respect to temperature, or whether different situations in the individual years lead to inhomogeneity between the two years. A simple sign test of differences of temperatures will suffice as a check. (We could also utilize more sophisticated methods.) Table I contains the daily average temperature in February 1955 and 1956 in the first two columns next to the date. The two columns are denoted by X_i and Y_i, respectively. The first column of Table LXIII displays the sign of the differences $X_i - Y_i$. We observe 16 plus and 12 minus signs. Now postulate H_0: $p = 0.5$ from $N = 28$. Thus the expectation would be 14 positive and negative signs each. The hypothesis is checked by eq. 584. For simplicity, let us use HALD's tables (1952). The boundaries of $p = 0.5$ for $N = 28$ are 0.694 and 0.306, at the 5% level of significance. Consequently, the boundaries are $N \cdot p = 19.4$ positive, and 8.6 negative signs. (The theoretical boundaries are not whole numbers but can be adjusted to 19 and 9, if necessary.) The observed 16 plus and 12 negative signs stay well within the boundaries of random fluctuation. The null hypothesis is accepted, which implies that the Februaries had similar climatic conditions in both years so far as the temperature is concerned. The hypothesis can also be treated by eq. 560, a or b. We find:

$$s_u = \frac{16 - 0.5 - 14}{\sqrt{14(0.5)}} = 0.57$$

TABLE LXIII

AVERAGE DAILY TEMPERATURE IN FEBRUARY AT YUMA, ARIZONA, FOR COMPUTATION OF THE SIGN TEST

Day	Sign of $X_i - Y_i$	x_i $X_i - X_m$	y_i $Y_i - Y_m$	Sign of $x_i - y_i$	$t_1 i$ x_i/s_x	$t_2 i$ y_i/s_y	$x_i - x_{i+1}$
1	+	0.6	−4.0	+			
2	+	−2.7	−10.5	+			3.3
3	+	−7.2	−8.6	+			4.5
4	−	−9.1	−6.2	−	−1.39	−1.16	1.9
5	−	−5.8	−3.2	−	−0.88	−0.60	−3.3
6	−	−5.4	−2.6	−	−0.82	−0.49	−0.4
7	−	−3.0	−2.0	−	−0.45	−0.38	−2.4
8	+	−0.2	−0.3	+			−2.8
9	+	2.5	−0.3	+			−2.7
10	+	1.4	−1.0	+			1.1
11	+	1.3	1.6	−			0.1
12	−	3.3	5.2	−			−2.0
13	+	5.4	5.6	−			−2.1
14	+	8.7	4.3	+			−3.3
15	+	12.9	2.2	+			−4.2
16	+	13.0	−6.1	+			−0.1
17	+	10.6	−9.5	+			2.4
18	+	1.1	−3.8	+			9.5
19	−	−10.2	−0.6	−			11.3
20	−	−9.5	1.2	−			−0.7
21	−	−8.6	5.9	−			−0.9
22	−	−6.2	7.7	−			−2.4
23	−	−3.8	11.6	−			−2.4
24	−	−1.6	3.2	−			−2.2
25	+	5.2	1.1	+			−6.8
26	+	1.9	2.1	−			3.3
27	+	2.8	3.0	−			−0.9
28	−	3.7	5.0	−			−0.9
							(3.1)
	16 plus 12 minus			12 plus 16 minus			

1955 mean 55.0, $s_x = 6.57$, $s_x^2 = 43.13$.
1956 mean 54.3, $s_y = 5.33$, $s_y^2 = 28.42$.

or for the lower boundary:

$$s_l = \frac{16 + 0.5 - 14}{\sqrt{14(0.5)}} = -0.47$$

where s_u and s_l are both in units of the standard deviation. Again, the chosen 5% level of significance would permit s_u and s_l to range from -2.0 through $+2.0$.

One additional point may be of interest. The empirical boundaries of 0.57σ, assuming a Gaussian distribution, comprise 43% of the data (see tables, e.g., CONRAD and POLLAK, 1950; BEYER, 1966; SNEDECOR and COCHRAN, 1967; ESSENWANGER, 1976, etc.). We expect 95% within the $\pm 2.0\sigma$ boundary. Consequently, the calculation of s_u and s_l permits an evaluation of how close the test parameter comes to the boundaries of rejection. In this case, the observed values s_u and s_l are well within boundaries of random fluctuation. By rejecting H_0 a type I error would be committed in 57% ($= 100 - 43\%$) instead of only 5% of the cases.

Although the test discloses a high probability that the two individual Februaries are similar, let us continue testing and ask whether a_0, the difference in the mean temperature, plays a significant role, and a hidden inhomogeneity exists. X_i is transformed to $x_i = X_i - X_m$ and Y_i to $y_i = Y_i - Y_m$ (see next two columns of Table LXIII, headed x_i and y_i). The column following x_i and y_i displays the sign of

the differences for this comparison. We count now 12 plus and 16 minus signs, which again implies a random fluctuation (see prior computations).
The third method, the comparison of the transformed variables $t_{1i} = x_i/s_x$ and $t_{2i} = y_i/s_y$ adds nothing new. Four pairs of x_i/s_x and y_i/s_y have been included in Table LXIII. Because $s_x = 6.56$ and $s_y = 5.33$ are close, inspection of x_i and y_i makes it obvious that few changes in the sign of the difference $t_{1i} - t_{2i}$ can be expected compared with the previous methods. Three values change the sign, however. If we are interested in the sign alone, we need to re-check only values at which $x_i < y_i\sigma_x/\sigma_y$ or $y_i > x_i\sigma_y/\sigma_x$. This can be generalized by writing $|x_i| < |y_i\sigma_x/\sigma_y|$.

Variance test of differences

This criterion has been described by various authors (e.g., Abbe in CONRAD and POLLAK, 1950; BROWNLEE, 1960a, etc). Again, X_i is assume to be the individual observation, and $x_i = X_i - X_m$. Then:

$$T_1 = \sum_{1}^{N} x_i^2 \qquad (586a)$$

$$T_2 = \sum_{1}^{N-1} (x_i - x_{i+1})^2 \qquad (586b)$$

and:

$$\sigma_T^2 = (N-2)/(N^2-1) \qquad (587a)$$

The ratio:

$$r_T = [T_2/(2T_1) - 1]/\sigma_T \qquad (587b)$$

has an approximate Gaussian distribution for $N \geq 10$.

Example 49. We check the homogeneity of February 1955 temperature data at Yuma, Arizona (Table I). The differences $x_i - x_{i+1}$ are provided in the last column of Table LXIII. $T_2 = 404.92$ for the 27 differences, $T_1 = 1164.63$; $\sigma_T = \sqrt{26/(784-1)} = 0.182$; $T_2/(2T_1) = 0.174$; $r_T = (0.174-1)/0.182 = -4.54$. $r_T > |2|$ indicates that the sequence of daily temperatures is not randomly distributed, σ_T is more than twice the significance threshold of $|2.0|$. This outcome is no surprise because of anticipated persistence in meteorological time series, which is confirmed by the variance test of differences.

Wilcoxon rank test of differences

Trivial test procedures were introduced which enable evaluation of the hypothesis that the signs of the differences between sets or within sets of observations are randomly distributed. Confirmation indicates that the two sets of observations come from the same or at least a homogeneous population. The consideration of the sign alone is a simple procedure and it does not include the effects of other factors, i.e. persistence. In the following a series of tests is selected which are based on ranks. Additional procedures are found in HAJEK and SIDAK (1967).
WILCOXON (1945, 1946, 1947) expanded the simple sign test by including the rank of the differences. We first compute $z_i = X_i - Y_i$ for $i = 1, \ldots, N$ where X_i and Y_i denote sets of observations. A rank number is assigned to $|z_i|$ such that the new series of $|z_j|$ follows an ascending sequence, starting with the smallest $|z_j|$ which is rank one. Hence, every $|z_i|$ is

associated with a corresponding rank r_j. For ties we assign a central value, e.g. $(r_j + r_{j+1})/2$, etc.
All positive ranks and all negative ranks are added:

$$R_p = \sum_1^N r_j^+ \tag{588a}$$

$$R_n = \left| \sum_1^N r_j^- \right| \tag{588b}$$

The smaller sum is selected, either R_p for $R_p < R_n$ or R_n for $R_p > R_n$.
Wilcoxon established an expression for the expected (absolute) value of the rank sum R_s, namely:

$$\bar{x}_w = N(N+1)/4 \tag{589a}$$

$$\sigma_w^2 = N(N+1)(2N+1)/24 - c_t/48 = \bar{x}_w(2N+1)/6 - c_t/48 \tag{589b}$$

(Note, eq. 589a, b is written for the sum of R_s and not for the mean $\bar{R}_s$.) For each group of ties the value c_t is subtracted from σ_w^2:

$$c_t = (n_t - 1) \cdot n_t(n_t + 1) \tag{589c}$$

where n_t denotes the number of ties (e.g., one pair of ties counts $n_t = 2$, a triplet counts $n_t = 3$, etc.). If the series has no ties, $n_t = 1$ and $c_t = 0$. The test criterion for $N \geq 20$ is now:

$$\tau_w = (|R_s - \bar{x}_w| - 0.5)/\sigma_w \tag{590}$$

where R_p or R_n is substituted for R_s. The correction factor -0.5 adjusts for continuity and is sometimes omitted. The test statistic τ_w follows an approximately Gaussian distribution (for $N \geq 20$). The probability of exceedance, therefore, can be obtained from the tables of the normal distribution. At the 5% significance level (two-sided test) the expected τ_w is 1.96. For $\tau_w \geq 1.96$ the hypothesis that the data sample is homogeneous or that both sets come from the same sample population is rejected. For $N \leq 20$ WILCOXON (1947) published special tables (e.g., OWEN, 1962; BEYER, 1966; SNEDECOR and COCHRAN, 1967; etc.).
The treatment of zero differences must be clarified. One procedure is the deletion of the pair from the set. Wilcoxon's tables are based on testing R_s, hence:

$$R_\tau \sim \bar{x}_w \pm (\tau_w \sigma_w + 0.5) \tag{591a}$$

and:

$$|R_\tau - \bar{x}_w| = \tau_w \sigma_w + 0.5 \tag{591b}$$

$R_s < R_\tau$ means rejection of the postulated hypothesis (see above) at the significance level corresponding to τ_w. An increase of τ_w requires a decrease of R_τ because the absolute difference must increase, and $|R_\tau| < |\bar{x}_w|$.
A modification of the test is the comparison of two data sets which have been selected from a number of sets. The two data sets are chosen so that they provide the extremes of the test statistics, i.e., the lowest and highest R_τ. Then the Kruskal-Wallis test (see eq. 599b) is appropriate. Table LXIV contains R_τ of the Wilcoxon signed rank test for three selected significance levels α, calculated by TUKEY's (1949b) formula (see also WALSH, 1962, p. 149).

TABLE LXIV

R_τ OF WILCOXON'S SIGNED RANK TEST

N	α_1: 0.05 α_2: 0.1	0.01 0.02	0.005 0.01	N	α_1: 0.05 α_2: 0.1	0.01 0.02	0.005 0.01
6	0.9	–	–	14	21.4	12.7	9.8
7	2.2	–	–	15	25.7	16.0	12.7
8	3.8	0.6	–	16	30.5	19.6	15.9
9	5.7	1.7	0.5	17	35.6	23.6	19.5
10	8.1	3.2	1.7	18	41.2	28.0	23.9
11	10.8	5.1	3.2	19	47.2	32.7	27.7
12	13.9	7.3	5.1	20	53.5	37.8	32.4
13	17.6	9.8	7.3				

α_1 one-sided test; α_2 two-sided test.

CONOVER (1973) investigated again the problem with ties. He deduced that Wilcoxon's suggestion (see above) is more suitable in a number of cases, but a recommendation by PRATT (1959) is more appropriate in other situations. Consequently, other test methods should be added if the number of ties is large.
The robustness of the test was treated by CHOW and HODGES (1975). They concluded that the two-tailed test is more robust against asymmetric distributions than the one-sided tail test. Even results from mildly asymmetric distributions must be treated with caution.

Example 50. Wilcoxon's rank-sign test. Table LXV displays the differences between the first (1955) and second (1956) year of daily average temperatures at Yuma, Arizona in February in the second column (see Table I). The assignment or ranks r_j^+ and r_j^- are disclosed in the third column of Table LXV. We find $R_p = 237.5$ and $R_n = 168.5$. Hence, R_n is selected as R_s, the smaller sum to be tested.
We find one tie $z_i = 2.1$ (rank 18.5) and one triplet, $z_i = 0.5$ (24, 25, 26). We determine $c_t = (2-1)2(2+1) + (3-1)3(3+1) = 30$. Now:

$\bar{x}_w = 28(28+1)/4 = 203$

$\sigma_w^2 = 28(28+1)(56+1)/24 - 30/48 = 1928.5 - 0.625 \sim 1927.88$

$\sigma_w \sim 43.91$

$\tau_w = (168.5 - 203.0 - 0.5)/43.91 = 34.0/43.91 \sim 0.77.$

Because τ_w is less than 1.96 the hypothesis H_0 is accepted, i.e., both data sets stem from one (homogeneous) population. (In our case the correction for ties is an insignificant contribution.)

Wilcoxon's two-sample rank test

The previous test is based on the ranking of differences. A similar procedure can be derived for the ranks of all observations. The two samples are pooled and a rank is assigned to every observation. Sample A with n_1 observations and sample B with n_2 observations will both render a certain rank number. We denote: $N = n_1 + n_2$, $R = \sum r_j$, which is the rank sum for sample A with n_1 observations. For $\bar{R} = R/n_1$:

$$\bar{x}_{RW} = (N+1)/2 + c_k \qquad (592a)$$

TABLE LXV

TESTING BY RANK METHODS

Pair (day)	$\sqrt{z_i}$ $(X_i - Y_i)$	r_j^+	r_j^-	Two sample ranks (Ex. 50, 52)		Mann-Whitney (Ex. 51, 52)		Siegel-Tukey (Ex. 51)	
1	5.3	11		27	56	19	42	37	2
2	8.5	9		36.5	43	25.5	31	35	24
3	2.1	18.5		49	52	36	39	14	8
4	−2.2		17	51	48	38	35	10	16
5	−1.9		20	45	41	33	30	20	26
6	−2.1		18.5	44	39	32	28	22	30
7	−0.3		28	38	36.5	27	25.5	32	35
8	0.8	22		30	31	20	21	39	41
9	3.5	15		17.5	32	13	22	25	42
10	3.1	16		22.5	35	15	24	29	38
11	0.4	27		24	26	16	18	31	35
12	−1.2		21	15	11	11	8	21	15
13	0.5	25		7	10	5	7	9	13
14	5.1	12		5	14	4	10	7	19
15	11.4	6		2	21	2		3	
16	19.8	2		1	47	1		1	
17	20.8	1		4	54.5	3		5	
18	5.6	10		25	42	17		33	
19	−8.9		8	54.5	33	41		4	
20	−10.0		7	53	28	40		6	
21	−13.8		5	50	8.5	37		12	
22	−13.2		4	46	6	34		18	
23	−14.7		3	40	3	29		28	
24	−4.1		14	34	17.5	23		40	
25	4.8	13		8.5	29	6		11	
26	0.5	25		20	22.5	14		27	
27	0.5	25		16	19	12		23	
28	−0.6		23	13	12	9		17	
$\sum$		237.5	168.5	778.5	817.5	562.5	340.5	559	334

$$\sigma_{RW}^2 = (N+1)(N-n_1)/(12\, n_1) \tag{592b}$$

The test criterion is:

$$\tau_{RW} = (\bar{R} - \bar{x}_{RW})/\sigma_{RW} \tag{593a}$$

$$\sigma_{RW} = [2R-(N+1)]/\sqrt{(N+1)(N-n_1)/3\, n_1} \tag{593b}$$

The parameter τ_{RW} is approximately normally distributed. Even for $N=8$ and $n_1=4$ the approximation by the Gaussian distribution is already good. The parameter c_k in eq. 592a is a correction term introduced by KRUSKAL and WALLIS (1952, 1953; see eq. 599b).
When α approximates 0.02 for a one-sided test, i.e. the 98% cumulative values in the Gaussian distribution, the correction factor is $c_k = 1/(2n_1)$. The correction, therefore, should be applied when $\tau_w \sim 2.0$ or greater.
Again, an adjustment is necessary for ties. The new variance under inclusion of this correction is:

$$\sigma_{RW}^2 = \frac{N(N^2-1)-c_t}{12\, N\, n_1} \cdot \frac{N-n_1}{N-1} \tag{593c}$$

The correction c was introduced with eq. 589c. It can be readily checked that for $c_t = 0$ eq. 593c converts to eq. 593b. Since the Gaussian approximation is already sufficient for $N = 8$, no extra tables will be needed in most cases.

Example 51. Wilcoxon's two-sample rank test. The observations for February 1955 and 1956 are pooled and ranked accordingly. Table LXV displays the results. We find $\bar{R} = 778.5/28 = 27.80$. Further, $\bar{x}_{RW} = (56+1)/2 + c_k = 28.5 + c_k$. $\sigma^2_{RW} = (56+1)(56-28)/12.28 = 4.75$. First we check eq. 593b with $c_k = 0$. $\tau_{RW} = (27.8 - 28.5)/2.18 \sim -0.7/2.18 \sim 0.32$. The hypothesis of homogeneity is accepted. Since $\tau_{RW} \ll 2.0$ a correction by c_k is not needed.

Wilcoxon's stratified rank test

Wilcoxon (1946) has expanded the test to include the comparison of stratified samples. An example of a stratification is the distribution of a meteorological variable after a certain weather type has persisted for one or more days (e.g. after the fifth day). We assume k numbers of strata groups, n_k is the number of measurements in each of the samples. Wilcoxon found the following modification for $n_1 \equiv n_2 \equiv \ldots n_k \equiv n$ (sum of mean and variance):

$$\bar{x}_w = kn(2N+1)/2 \tag{594a}$$

$$\sigma^2_w = kn^2(2n+1)/12 \tag{594b}$$

For $n_1 \neq n_2 \ldots \neq n_k$ the mean and variance become:

$$\bar{x}_w = \frac{1}{2}\sum_1^k n_k(2n_k+1) \tag{595a}$$

$$\sigma^2_w = \frac{1}{12}\sum_1^k n_k^2(2n_k+1) \tag{595b}$$

The test criterion τ_w remains the same although the table values for R_s change. R_s is the smallest R_k, the sum of ranks for any sample group. The total number of observations is pooled, $N = \sum n_k$. A rank is assigned to every individual data point ($r_j = 1 \ldots N$). The rank numbers r_j are summed for the individual sets (groups):

$$R_k = \sum_1^n r_{jk} \tag{595c}$$

The smallest R_k is tested. If either $\tau_w > \sigma_\alpha$ or $R_s < R_\tau$, the hypothesis is rejected. The parameter σ_α corresponds to the fraction of the standard deviation for the significance level α (e.g., $\alpha = 5\%$, $\sigma_\alpha = 1.96$ for a two-sided test).

Mann-Whitney test

Although the test is included in Wilcoxon's (1947) article, it is better known in the literature as the Mann-Whitney (1947) test (see Kruskal, 1957). This test is a modification of the previous stratified test, now applied to two sets of data with an unequal number of data points. Again, all observations of both sets of data are combined into one single set. Ranks are assigned to all observations.

The sum of the mean and the variance for the test criterion for $n_1 \leq n_2$ is:

$$\bar{x}_{MW} = n_1(n_1 + n_2 + 1)/2 \tag{596a}$$

$$\sigma^2_{MW} = n_2 \bar{x}_{MW}/6 \tag{596b}$$

The test criterion is (see eq. 590):

$$\tau_{MW} = (|\bar{x}_{MW} - R_s| - 0.5)/\sigma_{MW} \tag{596c}$$

or correspondingly R_τ such as in eq. 591a.

The sum R_s for unequal sample size is formed by the following steps. R_1 is calculated (see eq. 595c) for the sample with the smaller number of observations, say n_1. Then:

$$R_2 = n_1(n_1 + n_2 + 1) - R_1 \tag{597}$$

The smaller value (magnitude), either R_1 or R_2, is then taken as R_s. The hypothesis that both sets come from the same population is rejected when $\tau_{MW} > 1.96$ for the 5% significance level. Tables for R_z with $n_1 \leq 15$ and $n_2 \leq 28$ were given by SNEDECOR and COCHRAN (1967) or in expanded form by OWEN (1962). The hypothesis is rejected when $R_s < R_\tau$. The test indirectly compares the arithmetic mean values of the two data sets. Thus, it is insensitive to differences in the dispersion of the data indicated by a significant difference between the standard deviations. This deficiency may create some problems.

Assume two data sets are given. The first set*[1] comprises wind speed values of 4, 5, 6 m s^{-1}, the second 1, 5, 9 m s^{-1}. Both data sets appear in the ranking procedure with the same rank sum, $R_1 = R_2 = 10.5$. The reader may suspect that the unlikeness in the dispersion of the two sets implies a significant difference between the two sets but the sets lead to the same rank sum.

SIEGEL and TUKEY (1960) suggested a modification of the previous test which eliminates this problem. In the pooled data set the ranks are assigned alternatively from both sides of the extremes. The smallest value receives rank 1, the largest rank 2, the next to smallest rank 3 and the next to largest rank 4, etc. For an odd N the central value is omitted. Extreme observations emerge with low rank numbers, central observations with high rank numbers. The ordinary procedure of the rank test can now be applied. The sum and variance are:

$$\bar{x}_{ST} = n_s(n_1 + n_2 + 1)/2 \tag{598a}$$

$$\sigma^2_{ST} = n_1 n_2 (n_1 + n_2 + 1)/12 \tag{598b}$$

The mean is equivalent with eq. 596a, n_s denotes the number of observations in the sample with the smaller rank number, the variance is identical with 596b.

If the two samples are selected from a series of observational samples and are so chosen because they provide the largest differences, the Kruskal-Wallis test should be applied (see eq. 599b).

GABRIEL and FEDER (1969) have recommended the Mann-Whitney test for the evaluation of rainfall stimulating experiments. Another modification has been suggested by GREEN (1979). The treatment of censored data was described by PRENTICE and MAREK (1979).

*[1] The data set is restricted here to 3 observations for demonstration purpose. One could construct or find data samples with a reasonably large N for which $R_1 = R_2$, and the dispersion is different.

Example 52. Mann-Whitney test and Siegel-Tukey test. Let us test whether the first 14 of February in 1956 at Yuma, Arizona are homogeneous with the month of February 1955 (see Table I). Then $n_1 = 14$, $n_2 = 28$. First, the Mann-Whitney test (eq. 596, a and b) is employed. The ranks for the pooled 42 observations are exhibited in Table LXV. The ranks of the smaller sample are summed, $R_1 = 340.5$. Now eq. 597 is applied which renders $R_2 = 14(14+28+1) - R_1 = 602 - 340.5 = 261.5$. Because $R_2 < R_1$, we take $R_s = R_2$, and:

$$\bar{x}_{MW} = 14(14+28+1)/2 = 301$$

$$\sigma^2_{MW} = 28 \cdot 301/6 = 1404.67 \quad \text{with } \sigma_{MW} = 37.48$$

The test criterion is $\tau_{MW} = (|301 - 261.5| - 0.5)/37.48 \sim 39.0/37.48 \sim 1.04$. The null hypothesis that the first 14 days of 1956 may come from the same (homogeneous) population as February 1955 is accepted. Because the meteorological conditions for Yuma were compatible in 1955 and 1956 the acceptance of the null hypothesis is supported by the meteorological viewpoint.
The modification by Siegel and Tukey follows. Again, the ranking is contained in Table LXV. It is evident that the sample with $n_1 = 14$ has the smaller rank numbers.*[1] Since $n_s = n_1 = 14$, $\bar{x}_{ST} = 301$ and $\sigma_{ST} = 37.48$ remain (see the above calculations):

$$R_2 = 14(14+28+1) - R_1 = 602 - 344 = 258$$

Now:

$$\tau_{ST} = (301 - 258 - 0.5)/37.48 = 42.5/37.48 \sim 1.13$$

The test value is somewhat higher than in the regular ranking, but well below 1.96. No reason is found for rejecting the null hypothesis.

Kruskal-Wallis test

Another resemblance to the one-way analysis of variance is the H-test, introduced by KRUSKAL and WALLIS (1952). The null hypothesis that the k samples which were independently taken come from the same population is tested. The sample size varies from $n_1, n_2, \ldots n_k$. The sample values are pooled as described in the previously introduced methods and are sorted by rank:

$$N = \sum_1^k n_j. \tag{599a}$$

The test is based on:

$$\tau_H = \{12/[N(N+1)]\} \sum R_j^2/n_j \; - 3(N+1) \tag{599b}$$

Again:

$$R_j = \sum_1^N r_{ij} \tag{599c}$$

is the sum of the assigned ranks for the individual sample j.
When the sample size $n_j > 5$, the null hypothesis can be rejected for $\tau_H > \chi^2$ for the significance level α with $k-1$ degrees of freedom (see eq. 645). Special tables were computed by KRUSKAL and WALLIS (1953) for a small size n_j.
The test should be especially chosen when k samples are available and the two sets with the largest differences are compared. Assume the number of samples is k; then $k(k-1)/2$

*[1] Note the difference in the definition of n_s between the Mann-Whitney test and the Siegel-Tukey method.

different pairs of samples can be taken. Since only one pair of these possible combinations is selected, the minimal probability requirement α_m is:

$$\alpha_m = 2\alpha/[k(k-1)] \tag{600}$$

(Assume $\alpha = 5\%$, $k = 5$, then $\alpha_m = 2\%$). Then α_m is the probability level which should have been chosen instead of $\alpha = 5\%$ for the Wilcoxon rank test. With Kruskal-Wallis' more powerful test the entire data sets are incorporated and $\alpha = 5\%$ is restored.
When ties occur, a correction should be applied. The new test criterion is:

$$\tau'_H = \tau_H/\{1 - (\sum c_t)/[N(N^2-1)]\} \tag{599d}$$

where c_t is defined by eq. 589c.

Example 53. Kruskal-Wallis test. We have previously derived the parameter R_j for the two test samples. Consider the sample with equal size, $n_1 = n_2 = 28$. From Table LXV, $R_1 = 778.5$, $R_2 = 817.5$, and $R_1^2/n_1 = 21645$, $R_2^2/n = 23868$.

$$\tau_H = \{[12/56(36+1)] \cdot (21645 + 23868)\} - 3(56+1)$$

$$\sim (12 \cdot 45513)/(56 \cdot 57) - 3.57 \sim 171.1 - 171 \sim 0.1$$

The hypothesis is accepted, both samples come from the same homogeneous regime.
The second example, the Mann-Whitney test, provides $n_1 = 28$ and $n_2 = 14$. We extract from Table LXV that $R_1 = 562.5$, $R_2 = 340.5$. Then $R_1^2/n_1 = 11300$, $R_2^2/n_2 = 8282$. Further:

$$\tau_H = \{[12/42(42+1)]19582\} - 3(42+1)$$

$$= 12 \cdot 19582/42 \cdot 43 - 129 = 130.1 - 129 = 1.1$$

In this example a small difference is obtained from large numerical values. This indicates that τ_H is sensitive to precision errors. In electronic data processing the carrying of a sufficient number of significant digits is advisable for large N.

Run tests, median

A well known criterion in geodesy by Helmert (see CONRAD, 1948, or CONRAD and POLLAK, 1950) is very simple to apply, but is good only as a first estimate. We convert a set of observations X_i into $x_i = X_0 - \bar{X}$ and count the number of sequences, n_s, and the number of changes, n_{ch}. A sequence is a set of observations with the same sign of x_i (either plus or minus), the number of changes is then self-evident. Helmert's criterion states:

$$n_s - n_{ch} = n_H = 0 \tag{601a}$$

with a standard error:

$$\varepsilon_H = \sqrt{N-1} \tag{601b}$$

Then:

$$a_1\varepsilon_H \leq n_H \leq a_2\varepsilon_H \tag{601c}$$

where the factor a_i corresponds to the standard error commensurate with the desired significance level.
A better founded test employs the runs. A run is defined as an unbroken sequence of like elements. E.g., assume a set of data X_i or x_i with n_A elements of type A, n_B elements of type

B, and $n_A + n_B = N$. Elements A and B can be divided by natural boundaries or by an arbitrarily defined threshold x_{th}. In this case the null hypothesis H_0 states that every possible permutation is equally likely. The runs follow the binomial distribution, but if persistence is present they follow the negative binomial law.
However, the criterion can be simplified because the distribution of the length of runs follows the above principle. Therefore, a certain number of runs must develop. Let n_r be the number of runs and n_{ch} the number of changes:

$$n_{ch} = n_r - 1 \tag{602a}$$

We want to find:

$$E(n_r) = E(n_{ch}) + 1 \tag{602b}$$

and the variance:

$$\mathrm{Var}\,(n_r) = \mathrm{Var}\,(n_{ch}) \tag{602c}$$

This leads to:

$$E(n_r) = 1 + \frac{2n_A n_B}{n_A + n_B} \tag{603a}$$

or:

$$E(n_{ch}) = \frac{2n_A n_B}{n_A + n_B} \tag{603b}$$

Further:

$$\mathrm{Var}\,(n_r) = \frac{2n_A n_B(2n_A n_B - n_A - n_B)}{(n_A + n_B)^2(n_A + n_B - 1)} \tag{603c}$$

The statistic:

$$T_r = (n_r - E(n_r))/\sqrt{\mathrm{Var}\,(n_r)} \tag{604a}$$

is approximately normally distributed (for large n_A and n_B). Usually the modified formula by WALLIS (1952) is employed:

$$T_r' = (n_r + 0.5 - E(n_r))/\sqrt{\mathrm{Var}\,(n_r)} \tag{604b}$$

Extension to three types of elements A, B, C with n_A, n_B, n_C leads to the following formula:

$$E(n_r) = \frac{2(n_A n_B + n_A n_C + n_B n_C)}{n_A + n_B + n_C} + 1 \tag{605a}$$

$$n_A + n_B + n_C = N \tag{605b}$$

$$\mathrm{Var}\,(n_r) = [E(n_r) - 1]^2/(N-1) - [E(n_r) - 1]/(N-1) - 6\, n_A n_B n_C/[N\cdot(N-1)] \tag{605c}$$

If the threshold x_{th} is the median, then $n_A = n_B$ and eq. 603a, c can be written as:

$$E(n_r) = 1 + n_A \tag{606a}$$

$$\mathrm{Var}\,(n_r) = n_A(n_A - 1)/(2n_A - 1) \tag{606b}$$

The run test can also be applied to two sets of observations x_i and y_i, which are ranked and combined into one sequence. Runs of x_i or y_i are counted.

Further, MATHISEN's (1943) test for comparison of two samples coming from the same population (null hypothesis) can be adapted as follows. Let n_1 and n_2 be the sample size of the two samples x_i and y_i, respectively. The number n_m of y_i smaller than the median of the set x_i is counted. Let $t_1=(n_1-1)/2$ and $t_2=n_2/2$. Then the mean is:

$$E(n_m)=t_2 \tag{607a}$$

and the variance:

$$\text{Var}\,(n_m)=t_2-t_2^2+\frac{t_2(2t_2-1)(t_1+2)}{(2t_1+3)} \tag{607b}$$

when t_2 is approximately normally distributed. We compute:

$$T=\frac{n_m-E(n_m)}{\sqrt{\text{Var}\,(n_m)}} \tag{607c}$$

and compare T with the expected value for the normal distribution at the significance level α.

Example 54. The temperature data ($x_i = X_i - X_m$ and $y_i = Y_i - Y_m$) of Table LXIII are checked by the sequence test. For February 1955 (i.e., x_i) $n_c=4$, and $n_s=23$. Therefore, $n_s-n_c=19=n_H$. We expect $\varepsilon_H=\sqrt{28-1}=5.20$. At the 5% level of significance the boundaries are $-10.4<n_H<10.4$. The observed $n_H=19$ is outside these limits. February 1956 (i.e., y_i) has $n_c=3$ and $n_s=24$. Hence, $n_H=21$, which is again outside. The null hypothesis of a random data sequence is rejected. Helmert's criterion indicates high persistence.

Let us apply the run test to the sequence x_i-x_{i+1} (last column of Table LXIII). Because $n_{ch}=3$ and $n_r=4$ it is evident that persistence dominates in the X_i and Y_i data. We determine $n_r=8$ and $n_{ch}=7$ with 9 plus and 18 minus signs. Hence, $n_A=9$ and $n_B=18$.

$$E(n_r)=1+(2\cdot 9\cdot 18/27)=13$$

$$E(n_{ch})=2\cdot 9\cdot 18/27=12$$

$$\text{Var}\,(n_r)=[2\cdot 9\cdot 18(2\cdot 9\cdot 18-9-18)]/[(27)^2(26)]=5.08$$

$$T_r=(8-13)/\sqrt{5.08}=-2.22$$

$$T_r'=(8+0.5-13)/\sqrt{5.08}=-2.0$$

Since T_r and T_r' are normally distributed, T_r and T_r' are compared with the 2σ value (i.e., T_r or $T_r'=1.96$). Consequently, the sequence is significantly different from a random sequence if judged by T_r. Wallis' T_r' falls on the boundary. It is difficult in this case to make a decision and further testing is advisable.

Example 55. MATHISEN's (1943) test may be applied to the February 1955 and 1956 data (Table LXIII). The median $X_{med}=55.7$ (or $x_{med}=0.7$). The number n_m of y_i (or Y_i) smaller than the respective median of x_i are counted. We find $n_m=16$ days. The sample size $n_1=n_2=28$. We calculate $t_1=13.5$ and $t_2=14$. Thus the mean $E(n_m)=t_2=14$.

$$\text{Var}\,(n_m)=14-196+[14(28-1)(13.5+2)]/(27+3)=13.3.$$

This leads to $T=(16-14)/\sqrt{13.3}=0.55$. This is not enough to reject the hypothesis that both samples come from the same population. Notice that $R=0.55$ is close to s_u of Example 48, in which the hypothesis of similarity of temperature conditions in both months was checked. Consequently, the data can come from the same population. This does not imply that the sequence within the data shows randomness.

Other non-parametric tests

The most common non-parametric tests have been described in the preceding sections. This section is added to provide some information on additional tests to the interested reader.
A non-parametric two-sample rank test for location and dispersion, introduced by LEPAGE (1971, 1973), is based on the calculation of:

$$R_1 = \sum_{i=1}^{N} i \cdot z_i \tag{608}$$

where $z_i = 1$ for data from set A and $z_i = 0$ for data from set B of the pooled samples.
Another run test with a null hypothesis that the two random samples come from the same (identical) population is the Wald-Wolfowitz test (WALD and WOLFOWITZ, 1940). The number of runs for z_i are judged. For the total number of n runs:

$$\bar{x}_n = [2\, n_1 n_2/(n_1 + n_2)] + 1 \tag{609a}$$

$$\sigma_n^2 = 2\, n_1 n_2 (2\, n_1 n_2 - n_1 - n_2)/[(n_1 + n_2)^2 (n_1 + n_2 - 1)] \tag{609b}$$

$$\tau_n = (n - \bar{x}_n)/\sigma_n \tag{609c}$$

τ_n has an approximate Gaussian distribution for larger n, for smaller n SWED and EISENHART (1943) published tables. Ties affect the outcome. Their influence can be judged by assigning z_i systematically and then unfavorably, i.e., $z_i = 1$ or 0, that the number of runs increases.
Recently NELSON (1979) described a run test by Olmstead which is most suitable to test the length of runs above a certain threshold *after* examination of the data.
In the Wald-Bertram test X_i and Y_i are assigned 0 or 1 according to their exceedance of a threshold X_{th} or Y_{th}. Similar pairs, i.e., 1, 1 or 0, 0 are disregarded, only pairs of 0, 1 or 1, 0 are counted. Wald and Bertram (see BERTRAM, 1960) constructed a diagram to judge rejection of the null hypothesis that the data sets are randomly distributed.
FRIEDMAN's test (1937) is applicable for the comparison of 3 or more random samples. The test is similar to the Kruskal-Wallis test. Suppose that the observation (sample value) is X_{ij} where $i = 1, \ldots, n$ designates the number within the j-th sample, $j = 1, \ldots, k$. (n is the same in every sample.) Let the samples have the same (population) mean and variance. The i-th observations X_{ij} for the samples j through k is ranked by the size of X_{ij} within i (e.g., i is the 5th day of the month in the $k = 10$ years of Februaries). Ties are broken either by taking more decimals into consideration or by averaging the ranks. Thus, every X_{ij} receives a rank r_{ij}. Now we calculate:

$$R = \sum_{j=1}^{k} \left(\sum_{i=1}^{n} r_{ij} \right)^2 \tag{610a}$$

and test τ_F against the χ^2 parameter (see eq. 645).

$$\tau_F = 12R/[nk(k+1) - 3n(k+1)] \tag{610b}$$

The significance level α is selected for χ^2 with $k-1$ degrees of freedom. For $3 \leq k \leq 7$ Friedman has provided special χ^2 values (e.g., LANGLEY, 1970, p. 222) but for $k \geq 8$ the general χ^2 tables can be utilized.

Another test for the comparison of three or more samples is the test criterion Q by COCHRAN (1950). The observations again are "matched" for the i-th observation within each of the j samples ($i=1, ..., n$; $j=1, ..., k$). Within the j-th sample the data x_{ij} are divided into two categories which are given the value $a_{ij}=0$ or 1 (e.g., above or below the mean, median, decile, etc.). $N=n-k$, $n \geq 10$. If $a_{ij}=1$ is the number of successes we form:

$$S_j = \sum_{i=1}^{n} a_{ij} \tag{611a}$$

(Notice, $a_{ij}=0$ does not add to S_j). Now:

$$\bar{S} = \sum_{j=1}^{k} S_j/k \tag{611b}$$

Furthermore:

$$y_i = \sum_{j=1}^{k} a_{ij} \tag{612a}$$

and:

$$\sum_{1}^{n} y_i = k\,\bar{S} = \sum_{i=1}^{n} \sum_{j=1}^{k} a_{ij} \tag{612b}$$

Now:

$$Q = k(k-1) \sum_{j=1}^{k} (S_j - \bar{S})^2 / [k(\sum y_i) - (\sum y_i)^2] \tag{613}$$

The test statistic Q is linked to χ^2 with $k-1$ degrees of freedom (significance level α). BERGER and GOLD (1973) pointed out that Q may have a larger asymptotic significance level than anticipated by Cochran.

Numerous other non-parametric tests exist, e.g. WALSH (1962, 1965), or CONOVER (1980).

Student's *t*-test

A criterion of widespread use in statistical analysis is the t- or "Student" (W. S. Gosset) test. A standardized variate is formed:

$$t = \text{deviate/standard error} \tag{614a}$$

or:

$$t = \text{deviate}/(\sigma/\sqrt{N}) \tag{614b}$$

Although in most problems of data analysis the numerator is relatively simple to determine, the definition of the standard error and the related degrees of freedom is a more intricate problem.

It is known (STUDENT, 1908) that t follows the probability distribution:

$$f(t,n_t) = \frac{\Gamma(1/2 + n_t/2)}{\sqrt{n_t \pi} \cdot \Gamma(n_t/2)} (1 + t^2/n_t)^{-(n_t+1)/2} \tag{615a}$$

where n_t denotes the degrees of freedom f_d. For simple testing $n_t = N-1$, but this

customary assumption is not always correct. Thus, the author has chosen to formulate eq. 615a in notation of n_t rather than the often found version where $n_t = N-1$ is substituted. Thus, eq. 615a is a two-parameter model, t and n_t.
The cumulative distribution does not have a simple explicit form, and requires the solution of:

$$F(x_t) = \int_{-\infty}^{n_t} f(t) \tag{615b}$$

Many texts on statistical analysis include t-tables. For $n_t > 30$ the distribution can be approximated by the Gaussian law.
Student's t-distribution is symmetrical about the mean. Integration from $-\infty$ to $+\infty$ leads to the mean:

$$\bar{x}_t = 0 \tag{616a}$$

and the variance:

$$\sigma_t^2 = n_t/(n_t - 2) \quad (\text{for } n_t > 2) \tag{616b}$$

The t-distribution has a variety of applications in hypothesis testing. Independence in the data sets is required. Examples of typical usage follow in subsequent sections.
Many approximations have been suggested (see JOHNSON and KOTZ, 1970b). DUDEWICZ and DALAL (1972) developed a simple approximation formula for $F(t)$ whose computation for larger n_t requires electronic data processing:

$$F(t) = 0.5 + \theta/\pi \quad \text{for } n_t = 1. \tag{617a}$$

$$F(t) = 0.5 + \pi^{-1}\left\{\theta + \sin\theta\left[\cos\theta + (2/3)\cos^3\theta + \ldots + \frac{2\cdot 4 \ldots (n_t-3)}{1\cdot 3 \ldots (n_t-2)}\cos^{n_t-2}\theta\right]\right\}$$

$$\text{for } n_t > 1 \text{ and odd} \tag{617b}$$

$$F(t) = 0.5 + [(\sin\theta)/2]\left\{1 + 0.5\cos^2\theta + \frac{1\cdot 3}{2\cdot 4}\cos^4\theta + \ldots + \frac{1\cdot 3\cdot 5 \ldots (n_t-3)}{2\cdot 4\cdot 6 \ldots (n_t-2)}\cos^{n_t-2}\theta\right\}$$

$$\text{for even } n_t \tag{617c}$$

with:

$$\tan\theta = t/\sqrt{n_t} \tag{617d}$$

As introduced, n_t denotes the degrees of freedom f_d.

Test of sample means

Assume that the deviate is the difference between the empirical mean x_m and the expected mean μ_1. Frequently the population variance is not known and is replaced by an unbiased estimator:

$$S^2 = \sum (x_i - x_m)^2/(N-1) = \sigma^2 N/(N-1) \tag{618a}$$

Then:

$$t(N-1)=(x_{\mathrm{m}}-\mu_1)/(S/\sqrt{N})=(x_{\mathrm{m}}-\mu_1)/(\sigma/\sqrt{N-1}) \tag{618b}$$

with $N-1$ degrees of freedom $(=n_t)$.
The parameter t can be used to establish a confidence interval for the expected mean so that the degree of confidence is:

$$P[x_{\mathrm{m}}-t\cdot S/\sqrt{N}\leq\mu_1\leq x_{\mathrm{m}}+t\cdot S/\sqrt{N}]=1-\alpha \tag{618c}$$

First, the approximate t-distribution must be determined from the degrees of freedom, then the size of the confidence interval depends on the significance level α, i.e., t in eq. 618c is the inverse x_t from $F(x_t)=\alpha$ or $1-\alpha$ of eq. 615b. Since $f(t)$ is symmetrical only one t value is necessary (see eq. 618c). A reversal is the calculation of the probability that an observed mean x_{m} departs from an expected population mean $\bar{x}=\mu_1$ by a certain amount:

$$P(t_x\leq t_{1-\alpha})=P_\alpha \tag{619a}$$

where:

$$t_x=(x_{\mathrm{m}}-\bar{x})/(S/\sqrt{N}) \tag{619b}$$

Eq. 619a is valid for a one-sided test. For a two-sided test the following formula is substituted:

$$P(|t_x|\leq t_{1-\alpha/2})=P_\alpha \tag{619c}$$

Again eq. 615b is taken and integrated to $x_t=t_x$, and $\alpha=1-F(x_t)$.
A second application of practical interest is the comparison of two sample mean values x_{m} and y_{m} with true variances σ_x^2 and σ_y^2, respectively. We postulate as the null hypothesis that the data sets come from the same population, i.e., H_0: $x_{\mathrm{m}}=y_{\mathrm{m}}$, and H_1: $x_{\mathrm{m}}\neq y_{\mathrm{m}}$. Two cases must be distinguished.
(*a*) $\sigma_x=\sigma_y=S$. Then:

$$t_x=(x_{\mathrm{m}}-y_{\mathrm{m}})/[S\sqrt{1/n_1+1/n_2}] \tag{620a}$$

with $n_t=n_1+n_2-2$ degrees of freedom, and n_1 is the number of observations of x and n_2 the one of y.
(*b*) $\sigma_x\neq\sigma_y$. This case is also called the Behrens-Fisher problem, and requires two estimators, S_x and S_y. Many texts give:

$$t_x=\frac{x_{\mathrm{m}}-y_{\mathrm{m}}}{\sqrt{\dfrac{n_1S_x^2+n_2S_y^2}{n_1+n_2-2}\left(\dfrac{1}{n_1}+\dfrac{1}{n_2}\right)}} \tag{620b}$$

This solution has been criticized. Instead of eq. 620b WELCH (1938, 1947) suggested the modification:

$$t_x=(x_{\mathrm{m}}-y_{\mathrm{m}})/\sqrt{S_x^2/n_1+S_y^2/n_2} \tag{620c}$$

The degrees of freedom f_{d} must be determined from:

$$f_{\mathrm{d}}=(S_x^2/n_1+S_y^2/n_2)^2\cdot\left[\frac{(S_x^2/n_1)^2}{n_1-1}+\frac{(S_y^2/n_2)^2}{n_2-1}\right]^{-1} \tag{621a}$$

An auxiliary parameter is defined as:

$$c_S=(S_x^2/n_1)/(S_x^2/n_1+S_y^2/n_2) \tag{621b}$$

Eq. 621a is rewritten:

$$\frac{1}{f_d}=\frac{c_S^2}{n_1-1}+\frac{(1-c_S)^2}{n_2-1} \tag{621c}$$

This formulation reveals that f_d lies between n_1+n_2-2 and the smaller of the two numbers n_1-1 or n_2-1. This rule can be used as a check for the calculation of f_d. Then t_x is compared with the appropriate t_α (or $t_{1-\alpha}$) with $n_t=f_d$.

SCHEFFÉ (1970) supported the solution by Welch's method (eq. 620c), which he considered as practical and satisfactory. WANG (1971) investigated the effect of Welch's modification on the type I error (i.e., the significance level α). His results indicate that for $f_d=4$ the maximum deviation of α from the selected α is 0.35% for $\alpha=1\%$ (i.e., $\alpha=1.35\%$). The deviation is smaller for $\alpha=5$ and 10%, and the deviation decreases further with increasing f_d. In detail, Wang's study revealed that under certain conditions the confidence interval is larger or smaller than the interval for the true confidence limit of α. Therefore, the error by Welch's method is negligible in most cases except toward the extreme tailends.

Since eq. 621a does not give integers for f_d, Wang recommended either an interpolation of the t-tables or the use of the formula:

$$t_\alpha=[f_d(e^{a^2/g}-1)]^{1/2} \tag{621d}$$

where a is the fractile of σ for the (cumulative) Gaussian distribution corresponding to the level α (e.g. for $\alpha=5\%$ the value of $a=1.645$ for a one-sided test, etc.; see ESSENWANGER, 1976) and g is a function of the degrees of freedom f_d:

$g=0.9990\ f_d-0.480$ for $f\geq 10$
$g=0.9975\ f_d-0.445$ for $f<10$ and $\alpha>0.01$
$g=0.9925\ f_d-0.395$ for $f<10$ and $\alpha\leq 0.01$

This formula is an approximation of the t-distribution and can also be utilized when no t-tables are available.

Basically eqs. 620, a, b and c are most appropriate for testing means from samples whose population is approximately Gaussian. KALBFLEISCH and SPROTT (1973) have derived a modification for the comparison of two sample means whose underlying distribution has a Poisson form:

$$t_x=(x_m-y_m)/\sqrt{x_m/n_2+y_m/n_1} \tag{620d}$$

(Notice the exchange of the divisors, n_1 and n_2.)

Example 56. Let us test two sample means. Given is the zonal mean wind speed $u_{m_1}=7.81$ m s^{-1} and $u_{m_2}=10.10$ m s^{-1} with $S_1=14.54$ and $S_2=20.51$, $n_1=n_2=30$. We postulate H_0: $u_{m_1}=u_{m_2}$; H_1: $u_{m_1}\neq u_{m_2}$. H_0 is rejected for $|t_x|>|t_{1-\alpha/2}|$ for $\alpha=0.05$. We calculate:
deviate $=u_{m_1}-u_{m_2}=-2.29$

The square root expression is:

$$\sqrt{\frac{30(14.54)^2+30(20.51)^2}{58}\left(\frac{1}{30}+\frac{1}{30}\right)}=4.669.$$

Finally:

$t_x = -2.29/4.67 = -0.49$

For $60-2=58$ degrees of freedom $|t_{1-\alpha/2}| \sim 2.0$ for a two-sided test. Consequently, $|t_x| < |t_{1-\alpha/2}|$. It should be noted that t for the two-sided test is listed in most tables (e.g., HALD, 1952) under the column 97.5% or $\alpha = 0.025$.
The modification by Welch provides the square root:

$$\sqrt{(14.54)^2/30 + (20.51)^2/30} = 4.59,$$

with $t_x = -2.29/4.59 = -0.50$ which is the same numerical value for practical applications as the one for t_x calculated above.

$$f_d = \left[\frac{(14.54)^2}{30} + \frac{(20.51)^2}{30}\right]^2 \Bigg/ \left[\left(\frac{14.54}{30}\right)^2 \Big/ 29 + \left(\frac{20.51}{30}\right)^2 \Big/ 29\right] = 52.27$$

$c_S = 0.3345$

The result confirms the rule that f_d lies between 58 and 29. The numerical value of f_d will not always be a whole number (see remarks by WANG (1971), and eq. 621d). We could also round to the nearest whole number, i.e., to the smaller number which reduces α.
In this example both methods lead to accept the hypothesis H_0 at the 5% level of significance. Welch's method renders a slightly higher t_x, but $t_{1-\alpha/2}$ increases, too, with decreasing degrees of freedom (for the same α).
The example illustrates that in many instances the calculation of t by eq. 620b is sufficient. Whenever $|t_x| \ll |t_{1-\alpha/2}|$ the somewhat more sophisticated and elaborate method by Welch is not necessary. When $|t_x| \sim |t_{1-\alpha/2}|$ or S_1 and S_2 are very much different, Welch's method must be employed. Whenever S_1 and S_2 are very much different the degrees of freedom would be close to either $n_1 - 1$ or $n_2 - 1$ whichever is smaller, while eq. 620b requires $n_1 + n_2 - 2$ degrees of freedom. This could change the outcome of hypothesis testing because $t_{1-\alpha/2}$ increases considerably for a small number of observations $n_1 + n_2$.

Test of the correlation coefficient

The linear correlation coefficient was tested on the basis of the standard error in Example 47. Now we test the null hypothesis H_0: $r=0$; H_1: $r \neq 0$ with the t parameter. Student's t and the linear correlation coefficient are related by:

$$t_r = r\left[\frac{N-2}{1-r^2}\right]^{1/2} \tag{622a}$$

This formula applies provided the regression line is linear, the set of dependent variables (y_i) is normally distributed, the mean of the dependent variable (y_m) is the true population mean and the variance of the dependent variable remains the same for all the independent variables (x_i). The approximate degrees of freedom are $n_t = N-2$.
H_0 is accepted for $t_r < t_{1-\alpha}$. Again, α is the selected level of significance. Another test for the correlation coefficient is presented (eq. 641c).
Sometimes it is of interest to compute the correlation coefficient r_α, which would be significantly different from zero at the level α. We reformulate eq. 622a:

$$r_\alpha = t/(t^2 + N - 2)^{1/2} \tag{622b}$$

Example 57. We compute t_r for the correlation coefficients of Example 47 with $n_r = N - 2 = 28$ degrees of freedom.

r	0.162	0.258	0.373	0.794	0.955
$1-r^2$	0.9738	0.9334	0.8609	0.3696	0.0880
t_r	0.87	1.41	2.13	6.91	17.04

From the t-tables (e.g., HALD, 1952) $t_{1-\alpha/2}=2.05$ for $n_t=28$. Consequently, correlation coefficients with $|t_n|\leq 2.05$ imply H_0: $r=0$. The outcome of the t-test does not alter the conclusions given in Example 47.
Utilization of eq. 622b renders:

$r_\alpha = 2.048/(4.19+28)^{1/2} = 0.361$

Correlation coefficients $r>0.361$ would be considered significantly different from zero for $f_d=28$ and $\alpha=0.05$.

Test for regression line coefficients

An expansion to the test of the correlation coefficient is a check for a_1, the coefficient of the linear regression:

$$Y_i = a_0 + a_1(X_i - X_m) \tag{623a}$$

H_0: $a_1=0$ is tested against H_1: $a_1 \neq 0$. The procedure is based on:

$$t_{a_1} = (a_1 - A_1)\frac{r}{a_1}\left[\frac{N-2}{1-r^2}\right]^{1/2} \tag{623b}$$

where A_1 denotes the expected value of a_1. Again, the hypothesis H_0 is rejected for $t_{a_1} < t_{1-\alpha/2}$.
The confidence limits of a_1 may be determined by:

$$a_c = a_1 \pm \frac{a_1}{r} t_{1-\alpha}\left[\frac{1-r^2}{N-2}\right]^{1/2} \tag{624a}$$

which can be simplified by substitution of t_r (see eq. 622a):

$$a_c = a_1 \pm a_1 t_{(1-\alpha)}/t_r \tag{624b}$$

The population coefficient A_1 lies between the boundaries:

$$a_{c_1} < A_1 < a_{c_2} \tag{624c}$$

The coefficient a_0 (ordinarily the mean y_m) of the regression line can be checked by eq. 618b.
BLOCH (1978) investigated the influence of the measurement error ε_i on hypothesis testing of a_1, when $x_i = x_i^* + \varepsilon_i$ where x_i^* is the true value of x_i. He concluded that the standard error of x_i^* would be greater which lowers the value of the t statistic. In order to compensate $t_{1-\alpha/2}$ should be increased by selection of $\alpha^* < \alpha$.

Example 58. Let us establish the confidence intervals of two coefficients a_1 for two data samples ($a_1 = r\,S_y/S_x$, see eq. 300c).

r	0.162	0.955
S_y	9.82	14.54
S_x	20.51	20.21
a_1	0.0776	0.677

In the first case:

$a_c = 0.0776 \pm 0.0776(2.05/0.87) = 0.078 \pm 0.183$

i.e.: $-0.105 < A_1 < 0.261$, and in the second case:

$a_c = 0.677 \pm 0.677(2.05/17.04) = 0.677 \pm 0.081$

i.e.: $0.596 < A_1 < 0.758$.

In the first case the true regression coefficient A_1 of the population could be zero. It implies that the second term could be omitted from eq. 623a, and $Y_i = a_0$. In the second case A_1 is significantly different from zero (at the 5% level of significance). A non-zero linear term is justified.
The reader may notice that the higher the (linear) correlation coefficient the likelier it is that a_1 will be significantly different from zero. This simple rule is not always correct because the ratio S_y/S_x enters into a_1, too.

The non-central *t*-distribution

In certain tests the non-central *t*-distribution is needed. The test statistic is defined by:

$$t_2 = (z + \delta)/\sqrt{w} \tag{625}$$

where z is a Gauss-distributed random variable with $\bar{z} = 0$ and $\sigma_z^2 = 1$, w is a random variable: $w = \chi^2/f_d$, and δ is the non-centrality parameter. The variate χ^2 is defined (eq. 645).
The frequency density distribution of $f(t_2)$ has a lengthy expression (e.g., HOGBEN et al., 1961, or JOHNSON and KOTZ, 1970b) and is seldom needed. The cumulative density also has a lengthy expression. Some approximations are given below.
The non-central *t*-distribution has the following mean:

$$\bar{x}_{t_2} = (n_t/2)^{1/2}\delta \cdot \Gamma(n_t/2 - 1/2)/\Gamma(n_t/2) \tag{626a}$$

and variance:

$$\sigma_{t_2}^2 = [n_t/(n_t - 2)](1 + \delta^2) - \bar{x}_t^2 \tag{626b}$$

The reader can recognize that $\bar{x}_{t_2} = \bar{x}_t$ and $\sigma_{t_2}^2 = \sigma_t^2$ for $\delta = 0$. Again, n_t designates the degrees of freedom, $n_t = f_d$.
The non-central *t*-distribution is well tabulated, e.g., PEARSON and HARTLEY (1958), LOCKS et al. (1963), SCHEUER and SPURGEON (1963), OWEN (1965), BEYER (1966), etc. Earlier tabulations can be found in JOHNSON and WELCH (1940) and others.
From the various types of approximations only HARLEY'S (1957) approach is included here:

$$t_2 = r[n_t(2n_t + 1)(1 - r^2)^{-1}(2n_t + 1 + \delta^2)^{-1}]^{1/2} \tag{627a}$$

where the correlation r is defined by:

$$r_\delta = \delta[2/(2n_t + 1 + \delta^2)]^{1/2} \tag{627b}$$

According to OWEN (1963) an estimation of the percentage points of r_δ via transformation of eq. 627a is a valid application. Other approximations can be found in LAUBSCHER (1960), VAN EEDEN (1961), or JOHNSON and KOTZ (1970b).
The non-central *t*-distribution is exemplified by the calculation of confidence limits for δ.

Previously it was suggested to test H_0: $x_m = y_m$ under the condition $\sigma_x = \sigma_y = S$, etc. We assume now that H_0 was rejected, and H_1: $x_m \neq y_m$ has been adopted. This choice is equivalent to the postulation of a non-zero difference:

$$d = x_m - y_m \tag{628a}$$

or for the population:

$$\delta = \bar{x} - \bar{y} \tag{628b}$$

In this case the non-central t-distribution is the correct test statistic:

$$t_2 = (d - \delta)/(S \cdot \sqrt{1/n_1 + 1/n_2}) \tag{629a}$$

with $n_t = n_1 + n_2 - 2$ degrees of freedom. A reformulation leads to the boundaries:

$$d_c = d \pm t_{2,\alpha} S \sqrt{1/n_1 + 1/n_2} \tag{629b}$$

An example may be omitted because the procedure resembles the previously given cases (see Examples 56 and 58).
The case for $\sigma_1^2 \neq \sigma_2^2$ and the Behrens-Fisher problem (i.e., the true variance ratio is not known) was treated previously. An extensive survey about the non-central t-distribution was given by OWEN (1968).

Fisher's *F*-test

The preceding section treated testing of mean values. The reader became aware that the variances enter the t-test. Mainly, two types of hypotheses testing were required: H_0: $\sigma_x = \sigma_y$ or H_1: $\sigma_x \neq \sigma_y$. Decisions about these postulations are based on testing the variance ratio:

$$F_S = S_1^2/S_2^2 = \sigma_x^2/\sigma_y^2. \tag{630}$$

with $f_{d_1} = N_1 - 1 = n_1$ and $f_{d_2} = N_2 - 1 = n_2$ degrees of freedom.
After Bartlett had introduced this variance ratio, FISHER (1924) gave an exact test for it, which entered into the literature as the F-test.*[1] The probability density distribution of F is:

$$f(F) = [\Gamma_c/(\Gamma_a \Gamma_b)] n_1^a \cdot n_2^b \cdot \Gamma^{(a-1)}/(n_2 + n_1 \cdot F)^c \tag{631}$$

with:

$a = n_1/2$, $b = n_2/2$, and $c = (n_1 + n_2)/2$.

The frequency density can be converted to the incomplete beta function (see ESSENWANGER, 1976, p. 41):

$$f(F) = G(\beta)/B \tag{632a}$$

where:

$$B(a,b) = \Gamma_a \Gamma_b / \Gamma_c \tag{632b}$$

*[1] Sometimes it is called the Snedecor F.

and:

$$G(\beta)=G(y,a,b)=\int_0^y y^a(1-y)^b\,dy, \quad \text{for } 0\leq y\leq 1 \tag{632c}$$

Mean and variance of the F distribution have been deduced as follows:

$$\bar{x}_F=n_2/(n_2-2) \quad \text{for } n_2>2 \tag{633a}$$

$$\sigma_F^2=\frac{2n_2^2(n_1+n_2-2)}{n_1(n_2-2)^2(n_2-4)} \quad \text{for } n_2>4 \tag{633b}$$

The variance ratio is sometimes expressed in terms of the χ^2 distribution (see eq. 645) with n_1 and n_2 degrees of freedom:

$$F=(\chi_1^2/n_1)/(\chi_2^2/n_2) \tag{634}$$

This formulation indicates that F is a ratio distribution but F cannot be obtained directly from the fraction of two χ^2 values. F does not include the variance and depends on the degrees of freedom n_1 and n_2.
For $n_1>2$ the F-distribution shows a single mode at:

$$F_{\text{mode}}=n_2(n_1-2)/[n_1(n_2+2)] \tag{635}$$

In hypothesis testing H_0: $S_1^2/S_2^2=1$ F_S is compared with $F_{1-\alpha}$. Notice:

$$F_\alpha=1/F_{1-\alpha} \tag{636a}$$

and:

$$P(F_S<F_{1-\alpha})=P(F_S>F_\alpha)=P_\alpha \tag{636b}$$

where P_α is the degree of confidence. In analogy, for a two-sided test:

$$P(F<F_{1-\alpha/2})=P(F>F_{\alpha/2})=P_{\alpha/2} \tag{636c}$$

The F-distribution is tabulated in many texts, e.g. HALD (1952), OWEN (1962), BEYER (1966), SNEDECOR and COCHRAN (1967), KURASHIGE (1969), etc. Tables for the power of the F-test have been prepared by TIKU (1967, 1972a, b). Subroutines are available today for most types of electronic data processing equipment (e.g., CROMER, 1975, etc.).

Relationship to χ^2 and t

The F-distribution can be related to the binomial distribution (BRUGGER, 1969b). Direct association with the χ^2 parameter can only be made when one variance is known to be the population variance, i.e., either when $F_S=S_1^2/\sigma^2$ or σ^2/S_2^2. Then we set $n_2=\infty$ for $F_S=S_1^2/\sigma^2$:

$$F_{1-\alpha,n_1,\infty}=\chi^2_{1-\alpha,n_1}/n_1 \tag{637a}$$

or $n_1=\infty$ for $F_S=\sigma^2/S_2^2$:

$$F_{\alpha,\infty,n_2}=n_2/\chi^2_{1-\alpha,n_2} \tag{637b}$$

For $n_t=f_d=1$ we find $(x-\bar{x})^2=\chi^2/1$. Consequently:

$$t_1^2=(x-\bar{x})^2/S^2=\chi_1^2/(\chi^2/n_2)=F_{1,n_2} \tag{638a}$$

This formula relates t and F-distribution with $n_1=1$ and n_2 degrees of freedom f_d. Because of the quadratic form of t in eq. 638a we formulate finally:

$$t_{(1-\alpha/2)}=\sqrt{F_{\alpha,1,n_2}} \tag{638b}$$

e.g., $t^2_{97.5}=F_{95}$, with $n_1=1$ and $n_2=N_2-1$ degrees of freedom. Furthermore:

$$F_{\alpha,1,n_2}=t^2_{1-\alpha/2,n_2} \tag{638c}$$

Although this formula implies that t can be calculated from tables of the F-distribution, in turn, only special F values (for $n_1=1$ and n_2) can be obtained from tables of the t-distribution.

Multiple variances

If several (independent) estimates of the variance have been made, a shortcut method can speed up the decision whether the variances from different populations are alike. The maximum variance ratio can be evaluated from the maximum (S^2_{max}) and minimum variance (S^2_{min}):

$$F_{max}=S^2_{max}/S^2_{min} \tag{639}$$

This ratio can be tested (for 2 to 12 samples) with Table 31 from PEARSON and HARTLEY (1958). It is assumed that all samples have approximately the same degrees of freedom. If H_0: $F_{max}=1$ is accepted, then all variances come from one population or from populations with the same variance and the test task is completed. Otherwise, either the largest or smallest variance S^2 may be eliminated, whichever value leads to the largest change in the new F_{max}. This process is continued until F_{max} is non-significant. The eliminated variances then come from populations with different variances, but not all eliminated variances may be individually different. (See more details in texts on the analysis of variance such as SCHEFFÉ, 1959, COCHRAN and COX, 1957, SNEDECOR and COCHRAN, 1967, etc.).

It may be objected that this technique eliminates the extreme variances first, and the separation is somewhat arbitrary. In turn, we must consider that in any test procedure one variance, e.g., the one in the middle (S^2_{mid}), could be classified into either the population with the S^2_{max} or the S^2_{min}, provided $F=S^2_{max}/S^2_{mid}$ or $F=S^2_{min}/S^2_{mid}$ is not significantly different from unity. Consequently, a decision to establish two or more different groups always depends on the sequence of the individual steps, and an overlap is usually unavoidable unless F_{max} shows that all variances are alike.

Example 59. In Example 58 it was silently assumed that the variances are different. Now we test whether $S_1=14.54$ and $S_2=20.21$ are different, H_0: $S_1=S_2$, H_1: $S_1\neq S_2$, and $\alpha=0.05$. $F_S=408.44/211.41=1.93$ with $n_1=n_2=29$ degrees of freedom. Because this combination is not found in HALD's tables (1952), two F values must be extracted. $F_{95}=1.84$ for $n_1=30$, $n_2=30$, and F_{95} for $n_1=n_2=28$ is 1.88. A linear interpolation may suffice: $F_{95}=1.86$ for $n_1=n_2=29$. Because $F_S>F_\alpha$, i.e., $1.93>F_{95}$, we conclude that the two standard deviations are significantly different. Furthermore, the ratio $(20.51/9.82)^2$ is larger than the previous ratio. Thus, the two other variances from Example 58 are different, too. The multiple variances modification is left up to the reader. In most cases, the variance test should precede the t-test.

Analysis of variance

The F-test has been introduced as a test for comparing variances but only the basic concept of variance testing was included. The problems of testing the homogeneity of variances, significance of differences, and relationship to importance of factors such as in experimental design are part of a special field: the analysis of variance. Even a short treatment of the topic cannot do justice to the extended statistical literature. (The author plans the preparation of a special text on the subject.) Analysis of variance can be found in texts such as LEHMAN (1959), SCHEFFÉ (1959), BROWNLEE (1960a), DAVIES (1961), ANDERSON (1962), SNEDECOR and COCHRAN (1967), etc., and special topics in BARTLETT (1937a), DUNCAN (1958), HILL and DAVIS (1968), HARSAAE (1969), MATHAI and RATHIE (1971), GOSH (1972), SHUKLA (1972), NELSON (1975), or OSTLE and MENSING (1975). This is only an incomplete listing of the existing methods and discussions of variance testing, but it refers to some of the more important texts for testing homogeneity of the variance and methods of the analysis of variance.

Fisher's z-transformation

The computation of the F-distribution (eq. 631) is not a simple task. Therefore, FISHER (1951) introduced the transformation:

$$z=\frac{1}{2}\ln F \tag{640a}$$

whose probability density distribution is:

$$f(z)=\left[2(n_1)^{n_1/2}(n_2)^{n_2/2}/\mathrm{B}\left(\frac{n_1}{2},\frac{n_2}{2}\right)\right]\cdot\left[\mathrm{e}^{n_1 z}/(n_1\,\mathrm{e}^{2z}+n_2)^{(n_1+n_2)/2}\right] \tag{640b}$$

Again, n_1 and n_2 denote the degrees of freedom, $n_1=N_2-1$, and $n_2=N_2-1$, and B is defined by eq. 632b, while $f(z)$ is a transformation of eq. 631.

Testing of the linear correlation coefficient

The z-distribution has an important application in the testing of the correlation coefficient. We calculate:

$$z_r=\frac{1}{2}\ln[(1+r)/(1-r)]. \tag{641a}$$

Fisher proved that z_r has a nearly Gaussian distribution with a mean:

$$\bar{z}_\rho\cong\frac{1}{2}\ln[(1+\rho)/(1-\rho)]+\rho/[2(N-1)] \tag{641b}$$

and a standard error:

$$\varepsilon_z\cong 1/\sqrt{N-3} \tag{641c}$$

This approximation is excellent provided ρ is not too close to ± 1 (see KRAEMER, 1973). N stands for the number of pairs in the correlation, ρ is the population of correlation coefficients. KRAEMER (1973) omitted the second term from eq. 641b but recommended either eq. 641c or an expanded form:

$$\varepsilon_z^2 = 1/(N-1) + 2/[(N-1)(N+1)] + 23/[3(N-1)(N+1)(N+3)] + \ldots \qquad (641d)$$

According to Kraemer this procedure leads to a more accurate solution for ε_z than the calculations by eq. 641b even under the inclusion of the second term.
We postulate that H_0: $r=\rho$, H_1: $r \neq \rho$. Under these postulations $\bar{z}_\rho$ follows closely a Gaussian distribution for $\rho=0$, with a standard deviation equivalent to ε_z. If $|r| \geq a_\alpha \varepsilon_z$ where a_α corresponds to the preselected Gaussian value at the significance level α, then H_0 is accepted. Otherwise, ρ proves to be significantly different from zero.
Eq. 641a can also be used to combine correlation coefficients:

$$z_r = (w_1 z_{r_1} + w_2 z_{r_2})/(w_1 + w_2) \qquad (642a)$$

where w_1 and w_2 are weights proportional to $1/\varepsilon_z^2 = N_i - 3$. Then:

$$r = (e^{2z_r} - 1)/(e^{2z_r} + 1) \qquad (642b)$$

Furthermore, eq. 641a can be employed for the comparison of two correlation coefficients. We compute z_{r_1} and z_{r_2} and the difference $\Delta z_r = z_{r_1} = z_{r_2}$. According to HALD (1952):

$$\Delta z_r \leq a_\alpha \varepsilon_{\Delta z} \qquad (643a)$$

is tested with:

$$\varepsilon_{\Delta z} = [1/(n_1 - 3) + 1/(n_2 - 3)]^{-0.5} \qquad (643b)$$

where n_1 and n_2 denote the number of pairs for r_1 and r_2, respectively. For $n_1 = n_2 = N$ this formula reduces to:

$$\varepsilon_{\Delta z} = \sqrt{2}\,(N-3)^{-0.5} = 1.4142\,\varepsilon_z \qquad (643c)$$

which is the standard error of the regular z. For a_α see explanation after eq. 641c. Again, $\varepsilon_{\Delta z}$ follows the Gaussian law. Then H_0: $r_1 = r_2 = \rho$ is rejected for $|\Delta z_r| > 1.96\,\varepsilon_{\Delta z}$ at the 5% level of significance, and H_1: $r_1 \neq r_2$ is adopted. It is evident that eq. 641c holds rigidly only for $n_1 = n_2$, but it can be utilized for a quick check. From eq. 643c:

$$|\Delta z| \leq 1.41\, a_\alpha \varepsilon_z$$

More than two correlation coefficients are best examined by the χ^2-test (see p. 281). We postulate H_0: $r_1 = r_2 = \ldots r_k$. Then:

$$\chi_k^2 = \sum_{i=1}^{k} (z_i - \bar{z})^2 (n_i - 3) \qquad (644a)$$

with k degrees of freedom. An estimator for $\bar{z}$ can be found from:

$$\bar{z} = \left[\sum_{i=1}^{k} (n_i - 3) z_i\right] \Big/ \left[\sum_{i=1}^{k} (n_i - 3)\right] \qquad (644b)$$

This reduces the degrees of freedom f_d from k to $k-1$. The estimator $\bar{z}$ (eq. 644b) is an estimate of the population correlation coefficient ρ.
IMAN (1977) prepared graphs for the testing of equality of two correlation coefficients.

Example 60. Let us return to the correlation coefficients of Example 50. With $N=30$ we compute $\varepsilon_z=0.192$ and $a_\alpha\varepsilon_z=2\varepsilon_z=0.384$ ($a_\alpha\sim 2.0$ for $\alpha=0.05$).

r	0.162	0.258	0.373	0.794	0.955
z_r	0.164	0.264	0.392	1.082	1.886
$\bar{z}_r$	0.167	0.269	0.399	1.096	1.904

We compare $\bar{z}_r \geq 0.384$ and conclude that three correlations emerge as significantly different from zero (H_0 is rejected at the 5% level of significance).
Let us check some differences between correlation coefficients. Between 0.955 and 0.794 $\Delta z_r=0.804$. We check against $2\varepsilon_{\Delta z}=1.41\ (2\varepsilon_z)=0.541$. Because $\Delta z_r > 2\varepsilon_{\Delta c}$ the two correlation coefficients could be considered as significantly different at the 5% level of significance ($\alpha=0.05$).

Chi-square distribution and test

General

One widespread test statistic is the χ^2-parameter although the discussion continues concerning its proper use, its suitability in particular problems, proper grouping, and the determination of the correct degrees of freedom. According to GUTTMAN (1977) the χ^2-test is rather weak because in many cases no particular alternative hypothesis is given.
The test was originally developed by PEARSON (1900) and was later expanded to "approximate" or "transformed" chi-squares such as the F-test, etc. Assume a quantity:

$$\chi_k^2=\sum_{i=1}^{n}(n_{\mathrm{ob},i}-n_{\mathrm{e},i})^2/n_{\mathrm{e},i} \tag{645}$$

where $n_{\mathrm{ob},i}$ stands for the observed and $n_{\mathrm{e},i}$ the expected frequency in a class unit (or group). The summation takes place over all n classes and $k=f_\mathrm{d}$ stands for the degrees of freedom. Generally $f_\mathrm{d}=k=n-1$, but as has been learned from the t-test, f_d must be examined for every particular problem. The theoretical basis of the χ^2 shows the following probability density:

$$f(\chi^2)=[(1/2)^c\Gamma(c)](\chi^2)^{c-1}\,\mathrm{e}^{-\chi^2/2},\quad \chi^2>0 \tag{646a}$$

$$F(\chi^2)=\int_0^x f(\chi^2)\,\mathrm{d}x \tag{646b}$$

The square notation (i.e., χ^2) was chosen because the numerator is a quadratic number, and no negative values exist because $n_{\mathrm{e},i}>0$. The mean is identical with the degrees of freedom, i.e., $f_\mathrm{d}=2c$. The moments of the distribution are:

$$\bar{x}=2c=k=f_\mathrm{d} \tag{647a}$$

$$\sigma^2=4c=2\bar{x}=2k \tag{647b}$$

$$\nu_3=16c=8\bar{x}=4k \tag{647c}$$

$$\nu_4=48c(2+c)=6k(4+k) \tag{647d}$$

The distribution can be converted into the incomplete gamma function (see eq. 91).

$$f(x)=[1/\beta^\alpha\Gamma(\alpha)][x^{\alpha-1}\exp(-x/\beta)] \tag{648a}$$

$$\alpha=c\quad \text{(see eq. 92)} \tag{648b}$$

$$\beta=2\quad \text{(see eq. 92)} \tag{648c}$$

Consequently, the incomplete gamma function has a χ^2 distribution with 2α degrees of freedom (notice, α and β are shape and scale parameters).
PEARSON (1900) derived mean and variance as:

$$E(\chi^2) = n - 1 = f_d \tag{649a}$$

and:

$$\text{Var}(\chi^2) = 2(n-1) + (n^2 - 2n + 1)/N + \sum_1^n (E_i)^{-1} \tag{649b}$$

where E_i is the expected frequency in the i-th class and n the number of classes. Usually the second and third term in eq. 649b is neglected and the customary solution of eq. 647b is:

$$\text{Var}(\chi^2) = 2(n-1) = 2k \tag{649c}$$

The χ^2 test is performed by assuming a hypothesis H_0, which is rejected when $\chi_k^2 > \chi_\alpha^2$ for the specified level of significance α and f_d. We can procure χ_α^2 from either tables or the cumulative distribution eq. 646b.
It is evident that $\chi_k^2 = \infty$ if any $n_{e,i} = 0$. In fact, $n_{e,i}$ should not be very small, in many tests $n_{e,i} \geq 5$ is specified. Some classes must be pooled to fulfill this condition (see Example 61). In many cases, this adjustment is necessary for the margin classes of all unbounded frequency distributions. The pooling of classes reduces the original number of n classes and the degrees of freedom.
COCHRAN (1952, 1954) pointed out that the condition $n_{e,i} \geq 5$ can be relaxed. Provided the degrees of freedom ≥ 6, one or two expected frequencies can be allowed to fall as low as $n_{e,i} = 1$. This may introduce a small error, e.g., the true significance level for $\alpha_{tr} = 0.05$ may lie between $0.04 < \alpha_{tr} < 0.06$, but the relaxation enhances the power of the test (PAHL, 1969). Recently TATE and HYER (1973) and MALONEY (1978) have reiterated, however, that relaxation of the restriction $n_{e,i} \geq 5$ must be carefully examined before results from the test are interpreted.
Usually the true parameters of a frequency distribution model are not known, and estimators for these true parameters are substituted. Because these estimators are calculated from the data sample, the χ^2-test (e.g., for testing the goodness-of-fit) is affected in two ways. If the estimators are most efficient, the χ^2 is valid but with reduced degrees of freedom, $f_d = k - 1 - n_p$, where n_p denotes the number of estimated parameters from the sample. Furthermore, it cannot always be taken for granted that the limiting distribution of eq. 645 is the χ^2 distribution (see later eq. 668).
One more property of the χ^2 distribution may be of interest. This property is shared with the incomplete gamma function. We can add the χ^2-values such as:

$$\chi_k^2 = \chi_{1,k_1}^2 + \chi_{2,k_2}^2 + \ldots + \chi_{m,k_m}^2 \tag{650a}$$

where the χ_{i,k_i}^2 are stochastically independent, and χ_k^2 has:

$$k = k_1 + k_2 + \ldots k_m \tag{650b}$$

degrees of freedom. The individual distributions (see eq. 647) can be combined to form a single distribution with mean:

$$\bar{X} = \sum \bar{x}_i = 2 \sum c_i = 2C \tag{651a}$$

For the gamma distribution (see eqs. 648a and 92) the combination renders:

$$\bar{\alpha}=\sum \alpha_i \tag{651b}$$

where $2\bar{\alpha}$ is the mean of the combined (compound) distribution.
Application of the χ^2-test for small samples poses some problems. In most cases between 20 to 25 observations are required for every degree of freedom. This rule may be especially helpful for testing contingency tables (see p. 296).
An asymptotic χ^2 for the comparison of two correlation matrices was discussed by JENNRICH (1970).

Tables and approximations

Tables for the χ^2 distribution are numerous and readily available in most cases (e.g., HALD, 1952; PEARSON and HARTLEY, 1958; OWEN, 1962; BEYER, 1966; SNEDECOR and COCHRAN, 1967; etc.). In electronic data processing these tables are of little value. Therefore, methods of calculations (eq. 646b) and approximations have been sought.
Mean and variance as derived by Pearson (see eq. 649a, b) may be utilized for $k \geq 30$ as one of the Gaussian approximations. Three other principle transformations to the Gaussian law have been recommended.
The variate of a Gaussian distribution corresponding to the significance level α is denoted by u_α. Then:

$$\chi_\alpha^2 \simeq k+u_\alpha\sqrt{2k} \tag{652a}$$

More sophisticated and closer approximations are:

$$\chi_\alpha^2 \simeq k-\frac{1}{2}+u_\alpha\sqrt{2k-1}+\frac{u_\alpha^2}{2} \simeq \frac{1}{2}(\sqrt{2k-1}+u_\alpha)^2 \tag{652b}$$

or:

$$\chi_\alpha^2 \simeq k[1-2/(9k)+u_\alpha\sqrt{2/(9k)}]^3 \tag{652c}$$

They are helpful when no direct χ^2 tables are available (see Table LXVI).
LAWAL and UPTON (1980) suggested a log normal approximation. This approximation is valid under the postulation that the frequencies $n_1 \ldots n_m$ in the m class units follow a multinomial distribution and the smallest expectation is $m_5/\sqrt{d_f^3}$, where m_5 is the number of classes with less than $n_i=5$, and d_f denotes the degrees of freedom.

TABLE LXVI

VALIDITY OF THE APPROXIMATIONS (EQ. 652) FOR $k=40$

$1-\alpha$	χ_α^2	u_α	Eq. 652a	Eq. 652b	Eq. 652c
0.5	39.34	0	40	39.50	39.33
0.95	55.76	1.65	54.71	55.47	55.72
0.99	63.69	2.33	60.83	62.91	63.72

Thus:

$$P(\chi^2 > z) \approx P(Z > z) \qquad (652d)$$

where Z has a log normal distribution with parameters $\bar{Z}$ and σ_Z^2.

$$\bar{Z} = 2\ln(m-1) - \psi/2 \qquad (652e)$$

$$\sigma_Z^2 = \psi - \bar{Z} \qquad (652f)$$

$$\psi = \ln[m^2 - 1 + (P_s - m^2 - 2m + 2)/N] \qquad (652g)$$

with $P_s = \sum 1/p_i$, where $p_i = n_i/N$.

Example 61. In Table LXVII the observed frequency distribution $n_{ob,i}$ of Table II is compared with an expected frequency $n_{e,i}$ (Gaussian distribution). We postulate H_0: $n_{ob,i} = n_{e,i}$. The margins have been adjusted to fulfill the condition $n_{e,i} \geq 5$ by combining the first and last two classes. By relaxing $n_e \geq 5$ we could leave the classes as given in Table II. This modification is omitted here.
Table LXVII displays the results of the χ^2-test. The degrees of freedom are: $k = 15 - 1 - 2 = 12$. Because mean and variance for fitting the observed data to the Gaussian distribution have been obtained from the data sample the degrees of freedom f_d are reduced by $n_p = 2$, thus $k = 12$. A χ_k^2 of 10.2 would be exceeded in 60% of the time for $k = 12$, or $\chi_k^2 \gg \chi_\alpha^2$ for $\alpha = 0.05$. Consequently, the analytical frequency $n_{e,i}$ represents $n_{ob,i}$ very well, which implies that the population distribution is very likely the Gaussian law. A modification of the χ^2-test is given later (Example 62).

Expansion of the chi-square application

The χ^2-variate was introduced by eq. 645 where n_{ob} and n_e stand for the number of observations or the frequency of data. This limitation can be waived. E.g.:

$$s^2 = \sum (X_i - X_m)^2/(N-1) \qquad (653a)$$

is the well known variance from empirical data. If the population mean ξ is known:

$$\sigma^2 = \sum (X_i - \xi)^2/N \qquad (653b)$$

The individual variates $X_1 - \xi$, $X_2 - \xi$ ..., etc. are stochastically independent and Gaussian distributed if the underlying population distribution is Gaussian. We define:

$$u_i = (X_i - \xi)/\sigma_u = (X_i - \xi)/\sigma_x \qquad (654a)$$

or for empirical data:

$$u_i = (X_i - X_m)/s_u \qquad (654b)$$

We deduce from eq. 653b:

$$\sigma^2 = (\sigma_u^2/N) \sum u_i^2 \qquad (655a)$$

with $\bar{u} = 0$ and σ_u^2. Now:

$$\chi_{k_1}^2 = \sum u_i^2 \qquad (655b)$$

and:

$$\sigma^2 = \sigma_u^2 \chi_{k_1}^2/N \qquad (655c)$$

TABLE LXVII

COMPUTATION OF χ^2 FOR DATA OF TABLE II

i	$n_{ob,i}$	$n_{e,i}$	$n_{ob,i}-n_{e,i}$	$(n_{ob,i}-n_{e,i})$	$(n_{ob,i}-n_{e,i})/n_{e,i}$
1	7	3.98	3.02	9.1204	2.292
2	3	4.79	−1.79	3.2041	0.669
3	9	8.79	0.21	0.0441	0.005
4	10	14.53	−4.53	20.5209	1.412
5	22	21.53	0.47	0.2209	0.010
6	30	28.62	1.38	1.9044	0.665
7	37	34.19	2.81	7.8961	0.231
8	36	36.65	−0.65	0.4225	0.012
9	35	35.28	−0.28	0.0784	0.002
10	33	30.47	2.53	6.4009	0.021
11	22	23.63	−1.63	2.6569	0.112
12	10	16.46	−6.46	41.7316	2.535
13	12	10.28	1.72	2.9584	0.288
14	9	5.77	3.23	10.4329	1.808
15	5	4.99	0.01	0.0001	0.000
	280	279.98			$\sum=10.062$

$\chi^2=10.062$
$k=15-1-2=12$
$F(\chi^2)\sim 40\%$

Similarly:

$$s^2=s_u^2\chi_{k_2}^2/(N-1) \tag{655d}$$

Consequently, the distribution of σ^2 and s^2 can both be derived from the χ^2 distribution. Notice that $k_1 \neq k_2$. The appropriate degrees of freedom: $f_d=N$ for $\chi_{k_1}^2$ and $N-1$ for $\chi_{k_2}^2$.

Modified chi-square test with equal and optimum classes

MANN and WALD (1942) investigated the number of classes and their width for testing observed frequencies against a continuous distribution. They conclude (see GUMBEL, 1943, and DAHIYA and GURLAND, 1972) that class intervals of equal probability should be chosen. This would modify the χ^2-test to:

$$\chi_k^2=\sum_{i=1}^{n}(n_{ob,i}-n_e)^2/n_e \tag{656a}$$

or:

$$\chi_k^2=\sum_{i=1}^{n}n_{ob}^2/n_e-N \tag{656b}$$

with the same notation as in eq. 645. This type of grouping has three advantages.
First, the denominator n_e is constant. Thus, only $(n_{ob,i}-n_e)^2$ must be calculated and the sum can be divided by a constant (e.g., $n_e=N/n$, where n is the number of quantiles). The degrees of freedom remain the same as before, either $f_d=k=n-1$ or $k=n-1-n_p$, depending on whether the parameters are estimators from the same data sample or not. Second, it is not necessary to calculate the analytical frequency density $f(x)$ because n_e is

simply a fraction of N. However, the class boundaries of the quantiles must be determined from $F(x)$ which may sometimes be easier than the computation of $f(x)$. Finally, eq. 656b shows that a simple squaring of n_{ob} is required instead of a computation of differences $n_{ob}-n_e$ for a variable n_e.

MANN and WALD (1942) developed a formula for the optimum number of classes, for which the power of the test for a null hypothesis of H_0 is 0.5 or more. According to them the number of classes is:

$$n_M = 4[2(N-1)^2/C^2]^{1/5} \tag{657a}$$

The constant C must be obtained from the Gaussian distribution in agreement with the selected significance level α, such as:

$$\alpha = (2\pi)^{-1/2} \int_C^{\infty} \exp(-t/2)\, dt \tag{657b}$$

For $\alpha = 0.05$, $C = 1.645$; for $\alpha = 0.01$, $C = 2.327$.

HAMDAN (1963) has demonstrated, however, that for $n_M/2$ classes the power of the test is already 0.5, and that for more than 20 classes no significant increase of the power is achieved. His findings specify that an optimum partition of classes is reached for 0.4σ with the pooling of the margin classes. Consequently, $n_M/2$ classes are sufficient (see eq. 657a), and the upper limit is 20.

A different approach was outlined by BOFINGER (1973). Because the division of the data into classes is based on quantiles we may write:

$$\chi_Q^2 = N \sum_{i=1}^{k+1} \{[F(x_{n_i}) - F(x_{n_{i-1}})] - p_i\}^2 / p_i \tag{658a}$$

where x_{n_i} denotes the order statistics, with the specification that:

$$n_i = N \cdot \xi_i + 1 \tag{658b}$$

and the selection of ξ:

$$0 < \xi_1 < \xi_2 \ldots < \xi_k < 1.0 \tag{658c}$$

The expected frequency density is then:

$$p_i = \xi_i - \xi_{i-1} \tag{658d}$$

According to Bofinger χ_Q^2 is asymptotically equivalent to χ^2.

Example 62. Again, Table II serves as the data sample. Formula 657a would require $n_M = 36$ classes at the significance level $\alpha = 0.05$. With Hamdon's reduction only 18 equal classes remain. This necessitates a probability of $p_i = 1/18$ for every class, or an $F(x)$ in steps of 1/18. The progression and factors c for $x_m + cS$ are given in Table LXVIII. It should be noted that Dahiya's tables for c go to 15 equal classes only. For $c > 15$ we find c from the Gaussian law for $\bar{x} = 0$ and $\sigma = 1$. The Gaussian distribution is symmetrical, and only one side of c needs computation. $S = 6.06$ and $x_m = 59.22$ have been derived previously (see Example 3).

The computation of the χ^2 test is given in Table LXIX (left side). The $\chi_k^2 = 15.58$ corresponds to $F(\chi_\alpha^2)$ of about 59%. The outcome for equal classes supports the result of Example 61 although $F(\chi_k^2)$ does not correspond to the same $F(\chi_\alpha^2)$ as previously.

The optimum class division (right side of Table LXIX) provides $\chi_k^2 = 7.69$. We have $k = 12 - 1 - 2 = 9$ degrees of freedom. This would correspond to $F(\chi_\alpha^2) \sim 40\%$ which is identical with the result from Table LXVII.

TABLE LXVIII

CLASS DIVISION INTO 18 EQUAL CLASSES AND CALCULATION OF CLASS BOUNDARIES

$F(x)$	c	cS	x_m-cS	x_m+cS
0.0556	1.587	9.62	49.60	68.84
0.1111	1.220	7.39	51.83	66.61
0.1667	0.967	5.86	53.36	65.08
0.2222	0.765	4.58	54.64	63.80
0.2778	0.590	3.58	55.64	62.80
0.3333	0.431	2.61	56.61	61.83
0.3889	0.282	1.71	57.51	60.93
0.4444	0.140	0.85	58.37	60.07
0.5000	0.000	0.00	59.22	–

In Examples 61 and 62 none of the χ_k^2-values exceeds χ_α^2 at the significant level $\alpha=0.05$. Consequently, the class divisions are more or less academic. This is not generally so. Whenever χ^2 is close to the significance threshold, χ_α^2, the grouping into classes may play a major role whether H_0 is rejected or accepted. In this case, division into equal or optimal classes becomes important. Consequently, class division should always be taken into consideration when χ_k^2 is close to χ_α^2 for a selected significance level α.

Other modifications of the chi-square test

Instead of the plain χ^2 NASS (1959) suggested utilization of:

$$\chi_m^2=C_g\cdot\chi^2=m\chi^2/E(\chi^2) \qquad (659a)$$

or:

$$\chi_m^2=[2E(\chi^2)/\mathrm{Var}\,(\chi^2)]\cdot\chi^2 \qquad (659b)$$

where χ_m^2 is tested as a χ^2 variate with m degrees of freedom and:

$$m=2E^2(\chi^2)/\mathrm{Var}\,(\chi^2) \qquad (659c)$$

If n_p parameters of the expected curve are estimated, however, m becomes m_p such as:

$$m_p=m(n-n_p-1)/(n-1) \qquad (659d)$$

This test provides a more suitable goodness-of-fit criterion than the χ^2-test alone. According to Nass, the utilization of χ_m^2 is better than the likelihood ratio (see eq. 668) or the χ^2-test.

Non-central chi-square, non-central *F*

In eq. 654a u_i and χ_k^2 were defined by eqs. 664a and 665b with reference about the mean ξ, now $\xi=0$. Thus:

$$U_i=x_i/\sigma \qquad (660a)$$

TABLE LXIX

CALCULATION OF THE χ^2 TEST, n_e EQUAL IN CLASSES (LEFT) AND OPTIMUM CLASSES (RIGHT)

Class limits (°C)	n_{ob}	$n_{ob}-n_e$	$(n_{ob}-n_e)^2$	Class interval (°C)	n_{ob}	n_e $N=1.00$	n_e $N=280$	$n_{ob}-n_e$	$(n_{ob}-n_e)^2$	$(n_{ob}-n_e)^2/n_e$
≤49.6	18	2.44	5.95							
49.7–51.8	10	−5.56	30.91							
51.9–53.4	15	−0.56	0.31	≤44.7	1	0.0082	2.3 }	+2.6	6.76	1.06
53.5–54.6	21	5.44	29.59	44.8–47.1	8	0.0146	4.1 }			
54.7–55.6	14	−1.56	2.43	47.2–49.5	8	0.0320	9.0	−1.0	1.00	0.11
55.7–56.6	21	5.44	29.59	49.6–52.0	15	0.0603	16.9	−1.9	3.61	0.21
56.7–57.5	17	1.44	2.07	52.1–54.4	30	0.0968	27.1	+2.9	8.41	0.31
57.6–58.4	10	−5.56	30.91	54.5–56.8	39	0.1327	37.1	+1.9	3.61	0.97
58.5–59.2	9	−6.56	43.03	56.9–59.2	34	0.1554	43.5	−9.5	90.25	2.07
59.3–60.1	22	6.44	41.47	59.3–61.7	53	etc.	43.5	+9.5	90.25	2.07
60.2–61.0	15	−0.56	0.31	61.8–64.1	35		37.1	−2.1	4.41	0.12
61.1–61.9	17	1.44	2.07	64.2–66.5	25		27.1	−2.1	4.41	0.16
62.0–62.8	18	2.44	5.95	66.6–68.9	15		16.9	−1.9	3.61	0.21
62.9–63.8	15	−0.56	0.31	69.0–71.4	9		9.0	0	0	0
63.9–65.1	12	−3.56	12.67	71.5–73.8	7 }		4.1 }	1.6	2.56	0.40
65.2–66.6	14	−1.56	2.43	≥73.9	1 }		2.3 }			
66.7–68.8	15	−0.56	0.31							
≥68.9	17	1.44	2.07							7.69

$n_e = 280/18 = 15.56$

$\sum (n_{ob} - n_e)^2 = 242.38$

$\chi^2 = 242.38/15.56 = 15.58$

$k = 18 - 1 - 2 = 15$

$F(\chi^2) \sim 59\%$

$\sum (n_{ob} - n_e)^2 = 218.88$

$\chi^2 = 7.69$

$k = 12 - 1 - 2 = 9$

$F(\chi_k^2) \sim 40\%$

and:

$$\chi^2_{\text{nc},k} = \sum U_i^2 = \sum (x_i/\sigma)^2 \tag{660b}$$

This is the non-central χ^2 distribution because the variate U is defined in a reference system whose origin is zero. Similarly we define:

$$N \cdot S_n^2 = \sum x_i^2 \tag{661a}$$

which differs from the variance σ^2, as S_n^2 is now an estimator for the non-central moment μ_2. As customary:

$$\mu_2 = \sum x_i^2/N \tag{661b}$$

and:

$$\sigma^2 = \mu_2 - \bar{x}^2 \tag{661c}$$

A ratio of two S_n^2 from two data sets which are both estimators for the non-central second moment μ_2 is defined:

$$F_{\text{nc}} = S_{n_1}/S_{n_2} \tag{662}$$

This ratio F_{nc} is called the non-central F distribution.
We return now to the non-central χ^2. The non-central χ^2 distribution is needed in problems of discriminant analysis, the power of tests in the analysis of variance, and in other specific tests. The non-central χ^2 distribution is formulated as:

$$\chi^2_{\text{nc}} = \sum (u_i - d_i)^2 \tag{663a}$$

where u_i represents a set of independent standardized normal variables (see eq. 654a) and d_i denotes a set of constants. The parameter:

$$\delta = \sum_i^{\nu} d_i^2 \tag{663b}$$

is called the non-centrality parameter, $f_{\text{d}} = \nu$ stands for the degrees of freedom. In the following, the notation $\chi_\nu^2(\delta_i)$ or short χ_ν^2 denotes the non-central χ^2 distribution in contrast to χ_k^2 which symbolizes the central χ^2 distribution.
The cumulative distribution can be written:

$$F(\chi_\nu^2 < x_{\text{th}}) = [\exp(-\delta/2)] \sum_{i=0}^{\infty} [(\delta/2)^i/i!] \cdot F(\chi_{k_i}^2 \leq x_{\text{th}}) \tag{664a}$$

which is a "weighted" sum of the central χ^2 probabilities with $k_i = \nu + 2i$. The density function is:

$$f_{\chi_\nu}(x) = \frac{\exp[-(x+\delta)/2]}{2^{\nu/2}} \sum_{i=0}^{\infty} (x)^{\frac{1}{2}\nu + i - 1}\, \delta^i/[2^{2i}(i!) \cdot \Gamma(\nu/2 + i)] \tag{664b}$$

The moments can be expressed in terms of ν and δ:

$$\bar{x} = \nu + \delta \tag{665a}$$

$$\sigma^2 = 2(\nu + 2\delta) \tag{665b}$$

$$\nu_3 = 8(\nu + 3\delta) \tag{665c}$$

$$k_4 = 48(\nu + 4\delta) \tag{665d}$$

where k_4 is the cumulant (see eq. 37). For $\delta = 0$ these moments convert into the known moments of the central χ^2 distribution with $\nu \equiv k$.
Eqs. 664, a and b are not trivial, and several approximations have been suggested.

Approximation by chi-square

PATNAIK (1949) recommended:

$$\chi_\nu^2 \sim c\chi_k^2 \tag{666a}$$

where $c = (\nu + 2\delta)/(\nu + \delta)$ and $k = (\nu + \delta)^2/(\nu + 2\delta)$.
PEARSON (1959) deduced:

$$\chi_\nu^2 \sim c\chi_k^2 + b \tag{666b}$$

with $b = -\delta^2/(\nu + 3\delta)$, $c = (\nu + 3\delta)/(\nu + 2\delta)$, $k = (\nu + 2\delta)^3/(\nu + 3\delta)^2$. When the threshold $F(x_{th}) \leq 0.9$ (see eq. 664a) Patnaik's approximation is better, but for $F(x_{th}) > 0.9$ Pearson's formula gives closer values. Because more problems of interest require $F[(\chi^2, \nu, \delta) > 0.9]$, Pearson's scheme may be appropriate more often. When k is a fraction the standard tables of the central χ_k must be either interpolated or an additional error by rounding must be taken into account. A linear interpolation is usually sufficient (see Example 63). In order to evaluate the magnitude of the error more than one threshold can be computed. Assume $\chi^2_{\nu,95\%}$ is needed. We could add the approximate value of 90 and 98%. When the empirical $\chi^2_{nc} > \chi^2_{\nu,98\%}$ or $\chi^2_{nc} < \chi^2_{\nu,90\%}$, H_0 is rejected or accepted, respectively, at $\alpha = 0.05$ level of significance. Should $\chi^2_{\nu,90\%} < \chi^2_{nc} < \chi^2_{\nu,98\%}$ a precise 95% value must be determined before a decision is made (e.g., tables by JOHNSON and PEARSON, 1969, or others).

Gaussian approximation

A Gaussian approximation is adequate when $\chi^2_{\nu,\delta}$ or δ are not too small. We obtain:

$$u_\alpha = [\chi_\nu^2 - \delta - \nu + 1]/\sqrt{2(\chi_\nu^2 + \delta)} \tag{667a}$$

and compare u_α with a_α which is the fraction of the standard deviation for the level α of the Gaussian distribution. This approximation is due to JOHNSON (1959). PATNAIK (1949) gives the following formula (see x_{th} in eq. 664a):

$$u_\alpha = \sqrt{2x_{th}(\nu + \delta)/(\nu + 2\delta)} - \sqrt{2(\nu + \delta)^2/(\nu + 2\delta) - 1} \tag{667b}$$

The two approximations are of equivalent accuracy.

Moments fit

HAYNAM et al. (1962) prepared tables of the cumulative non-central χ^2 distribution. JENSEN and SOLOMON (1972) took a different approach of a normal distribution approximation. They normalized a definite quadratic form and matched the first three moments. Their formula:

$$u = \theta_1[(\chi_\nu^2/\theta_1)^h - 1 - \theta_2 h(h-1)/\theta_1^2)]/(2\theta_2 h^2)^{1/2} \tag{667c}$$

competes well with eq. 667a, b. The notations have the following meaning:

$$\theta_1 = \nu + \delta = \bar{x} \tag{667d}$$

$$\theta_2 = \nu + 2\delta \tag{667e}$$

$$h = 1 - 2(\nu+\delta)(\nu+3\delta)/[3(\nu+2\delta)^2] \tag{667f}$$

or:

$$h = 1/3 + (2/3)[\nu/\delta) + 2]^{-2} \tag{667g}$$

The central χ^2 requires $h = 1/3$ (for $\delta = 0$ eq. 667f should be taken). In turn:

$$\chi_\nu^2 = \theta_1[(uh\sqrt{2\theta_2})/\theta_1 + 1 + \theta_2 h(h-1)/\theta_1^2]^{1/h} \tag{667h}$$

Example 63. Given is $\nu = 8$, $\delta = 4$. From tables by JOHNSON and PEARSON (1969) we extract $\chi_\nu = 2.082$ for 5% and 7.745 for 95%. Forming the square yields $\chi_\nu^2(5\%) = 4.33$ and $\chi_\nu^2(95\%) = 22.52$.
For eq. 666a (PATNAIK, 1949):

$c = 4/3$, $k = 9$, $\chi_k^2(5\%) = 3.33$, $\chi_k^2(95\%) = 16.9$
$\chi_\nu^2(5\%) = 4.44$, $\chi_\nu^2(95\%) = 22.47$

These values are close to the correct χ_ν^2.
Pearson's approximation provides:

$c = 1.25$, $k = 10.24$, $\chi_k^2(5\%) = 4.10$, $\chi_k^2(95\%) = 18.65$
$\chi_\nu^2(5\%) = 4.32$, $\chi_\nu^2(95\%) = 22.51$

The difference from Patnaik's formula is only in the second decimal. Had we not interpolated, then $k = 10$ and:

$\chi_k^2(5\%) = 3.94$, $\chi_k^2(95\%) = 18.30$
$\chi_\nu^2(5\%) = 4.12$, $\chi_\nu^2(95\%) = 22.08$

Now the differences are somewhat larger.
The approximation by eq. 667a renders:

$$u_5 = (4.32 - 4 - 8 + 1)/\sqrt{2(4.33+4)} = -1.63$$

$$u_{95} = (22.52 - 4 - 8 + 1)/\sqrt{2(22.52+4)} = 1.58$$

The expected value a_α of u_α for 5% and 95% would be -1.65 and 1.65, respectively. (It should be noted that the integration is carried out from $-\infty$ to x_{th}, with $x_{\text{th}} = 4.33$ or 22.52.) The approximation by eq. 667b:

$$u_5 = \sqrt{2(4.33)(8+4)/(8+8)} - \sqrt{2(8+4)^2/(8+8) - 1}$$
$$= \sqrt{6.5} - \sqrt{17} = 2.55 - 4.14 = -1.59$$

$$u_{95} = \sqrt{33.78} - \sqrt{17} = 5.81 - 4.14 = 1.67.$$

The approximation of the correct value |1.65| in the two methods based on the Gaussian distribution is nearly equivalent.
The formula by Jensen and Solomon leads to a better result:

$\theta_1 = 12$, $\theta_2 = 16$, $h = 0.375$

and from eq. 667c:

$u_5 = -1.650$

$u_{95} = +1.653$

In turn, with a value $u_\alpha = |1.645|$ we calculate for 5% and 95% the cumulative $F(\chi^2)$:

$\chi_v^2 = 4.34$

$\chi_v^2 = 22.45$

These approximations are very close to the correct value.

Likelihood ratio tests, G-test

Likelihood ratio

Under certain conditions the likelihood ratio λ introduced by eq. 553 has an approximate χ^2 distribution for $N \to \infty$. Transformation of λ into χ^2 is achieved by the relationship:

$$\chi_\lambda^2 = -2 \ln \lambda \tag{668}$$

with $k-r$ degrees of freedom, where k is the dimension of Ω and r of ω, respectively, $k > r$. ANDERSON (1971) examined the application of the χ^2 approximation to the log-likelihood ratio in a special case where the composite hypothesis $\hat{\text{H}}_0$: $\hat{\sigma}^2 = \sigma_0^2$ versus H_1: $\hat{\sigma}^2 \neq \sigma_0^2$ is tested. This problem may arise in the analysis of variance when a sequence of observations X_{ij} is given ($i = 1, \ldots, n$: $j = 1, \ldots, m$) with:

$$E(X_{ij}) = \bar{x}_i = m^{-1} \sum_{j=1}^{m} X_{ij} \tag{669a}$$

and:

$$\text{Var}\,(X_{ij}) = \sigma^2 \tag{669b}$$

for all i and j.
If the hypothesis is true the maximum-likelihood estimates are:

$$\hat{\bar{x}}_i = m^{-1} \sum_{j=1}^{m} X_{ij} \tag{670a}$$

and:

$$\hat{\sigma}^2 = \sigma_0^2 \tag{670b}$$

Without the assumption of eq. 670b the estimate of $\hat{\bar{x}}$ is the same but:

$$\hat{\sigma}^2 = s^2 = N^{-1} \sum_{i=1}^{n} \sum_{j=1}^{m} (X_{ij} - \bar{x}_i)^2 \tag{670c}$$

where $N = n \cdot m$.
Because the likelihood ratio statistic for the problem is:

$$\lambda = (s^2/\sigma_0^2)^{N/2} \exp[(1 - s^2/\sigma_0^2)N/2] \tag{671c}$$

its transformed version is:

$$2 \ln \lambda = -N \ln (s^2/\sigma_0^2) - N(1 - s^2/\sigma_0^2) \tag{671b}$$

The usual substitution $2 \ln \lambda \sim \chi_\lambda^2$ does not hold because s^2/σ_0^2 is distributed as χ^2/N with $f_d = n(m-1)$ and:

$$E[-2 \ln \lambda] \sim N[\ln m/(m-1) - 1/m] \tag{671c}$$

In order to obtain a limiting χ^2 distribution, replace:

$$s^2 = s_1^2 = [n(m-1)]^{-1} \sum_i \sum_j (x_{ij} - \bar{x}_i)^2 \quad (672a)$$

and m by $m-1$. This distribution modifies the ratio:

$$-2 \ln \lambda_1 = n(m-1)[-\ln (s_1^2/\sigma_0^2) - (1 - s_1^2/\sigma_0^2)] \quad (672b)$$

The statistic:

$$u = [n(m-1)/2](s_1^2/\sigma_0^2 - 1) \quad (672c)$$

is asymptotically Gaussian distributed with $\bar{x}_u = 0$ and $\sigma_u^2 = 1$. Hence $-2 \ln \lambda_1$ can be approximated by χ^2 with $f_d = 1$. According to Anderson this should be called a conditional likelihood ratio test.

Although it is commonly assumed that the use of the likelihood ratio has advantages, HILL (1975) gave an example of abnormal behavior of the likelihood function in a specific case referring to point estimation of a true parameter, however.

SCHICKEDANZ and KRAUSE (1970) have illustrated the application of the general likelihood ratio for testing two scale parameters of the gamma distribution. They tested the parameter β. H_0: $\beta_1 = \beta_2$, provided the shape parameters α_1 and α_2 of the two frequency distributions are alike (see eq. 91).

According to Schickedanz and Krause, the likelihood ratio test is more powerful than the t-test for application to log-normal means. We can write:

$$\begin{aligned} \ln \lambda = {} & N[\ln \Gamma(\alpha_3) - \ln \Gamma(\alpha_4) - \alpha_4 \ln \hat{\beta}] \\ & + \alpha_3(n_1 \ln \hat{\beta}_1 + n_2 \ln \hat{\beta}_2) + (n_1 \bar{x}_{L_1} + n_2 x_{L_2})(\alpha_4 - \alpha_3) \\ & + n_1 \bar{x}_1(\hat{\beta}_1^{-1} - \hat{\beta}^{-1}) + n_2 \bar{x}_2(\hat{\beta}_2^{-1} - \hat{\beta}^{-1}) \end{aligned} \quad (673a)$$

The following symbols were substituted:

$$\bar{x}_k = \sum_1^{n_k} x_{ki} \quad \text{(arithmetic mean)} \quad (673b)$$

$$\bar{x}_{L_k} = \sum_1^{n_k} \ln x_{ki} \quad \text{(logarithmic mean)} \quad (673c)$$

$$\hat{\beta}_k = \bar{x}_k/\alpha_3 \quad (k = 1, 2) \quad (673d)$$

$$\alpha_k = [1 + (1 + 4A_k/3)^{1/2}]/(4A_k) \quad k = 1, 4 \quad (673e)$$

$$A_k = \ln \bar{x}_k - \bar{x}_{L_k}; \quad k = 1, 2 \quad (673f)$$

$$A_3 = (n_1 \ln \bar{x}_1 + n_2 \ln \bar{x}_2 - n_1 x_{L_1} - n_2 x_{L_2})/N \quad (673g)$$

$$A_4 = \ln \bar{z} - (n_1 \bar{x}_{L_1} + n_2 \bar{x}_{L_2})/N \quad (673h)$$

$$\bar{Z} = (n_1 \bar{x}_1 + n_2 \bar{x}_2)/N \quad (673i)$$

$$\beta = \bar{Z}/\alpha_4 \quad (673j)$$

Log-likelihood ratio

A modification of the orignal χ^2-test concept is the log-likelihood ratio. It was later designated by statisticians as the G-test. For the ordinary χ^2-test $(n_{ob} - n_e)^2/n_e$ was defined as the basic comparisons of observed and expected frequency. Now the logarithm are compared weighted by n_{ob}:

$$G=2\sum n_{ob}(\ln n_{ob}-\ln n_e) \tag{674}$$

G is called the log-likelihood ratio.

WOOLF (1956) considers it an alternative to the χ^2 test. WILKS (1935) has pointed out that G is equally valid but easier to compute than χ^2 especially when the expected numbers n_e are not too small. The reader may notice that G requires the multiplication of a difference, while the calculation of the χ_k^2 necessitates the square of a number and a division. This simplification of the arithmetic procedure has lost importance today because easy access to electronic data processing has reduced the computational work. The likelihood ratio has gained in utilization in recent times for other reasons.

COCHRAN (1936) and FISHER (1950) supported the G-test for its better performance when the expected number n_e is small. Earlier FISHER (1922) and NEYMAN and PEARSON (1928, 1933) have concluded that the G-test has a better theoretical foundation than the χ^2 test. Furthermore, Fisher pointed out the corollary to the maximum-likelihood principle. We can define:*[1]

$$L(\Omega)=\sum n_{ob}\ln n_e \tag{675a}$$

$$L(\omega)=\sum n_{ob}\ln n_o \tag{675b}$$

The likelihood ratio is $L(\omega)/L(\Omega)=\lambda$ as given in eq. 553. Consequently:

$$\lambda=G/2 \tag{676a}$$

or:

$$G/2\sim\chi_k^2 \tag{676b}$$

This approximation of G by χ^2 follows from:

$$G=\sum\left[(n_{ob}-n_e)^2/n_e-(n_{ob}-n_e)^3/(3n_e^2)+(n_{ob}-n_e)^4/(6n_e^3)\ldots\right] \tag{676c}$$

where the first term on the right side can be recognized as the ordinary χ^2 variate. According to Fisher the χ^2 approximation loses its validity when $n_{ob}-n_e$ is large compared to n_e because χ^2 fails to measure the departure from expectation for the sample. If the additional terms in eq. 676c cannot be neglected then $G\neq\chi^2$. In that case G is the proper criterion which should be utilized.

Power and sample size for approximate chi-square tests

The G-test is a typical example of an "approximate" χ^2 distribution. In the statistical literature many test statistics are classified into this group. GUENTHER (1977) has stressed that the power of the test or the necessary sample size in these approximations should be examined.

Selection for the power of the test and sample size are based on the non-central χ^2

---

*[1] $L(\Omega)$ is the maximum-likelihood function for the entire parameter space, $L(\omega)$ is the subspace ω with respect to the parameters.

distribution (see eq. 664b) but not in all cases solutions are easy to find. Guenther gave three cases where the non-centrality parameters δ has a specific form if H_0 is rejected. Let p_i be multinomial probabilities.

H_0: $p_i = p_0$ for $i = 1, \ldots k$. H_1: not all p_i are given by p_0.

The approximate χ^2 statistic $\chi_k^2 > \chi_\alpha^2$ is:

$$\chi_k^2 = \sum_{i=1}^{n_p} (x_i - Np_i)/(Np_i) \tag{677a}$$

where x_i is a multinomial random variable whose parameters are N and p_i, $i = 1, \ldots n_p$, with $n_p - 1 = k$. The power $\beta' = 1 - \beta$ is

$$\beta' = P(\chi_k^2 > \chi_\alpha^2). \tag{677b}$$

The non-centrality parameter is needed:

$$\delta = N \sum_{i=1}^{n_p} (p_{i,1} - p_0)^2 / p_0 \tag{677c}$$

where $p_{i,1}$, $i = 1, \ldots n_p$ are p's for an alternate H_1.

Example 64. It is well known that p_0 for a six-sided die is 1/6. Let us assume that one side is biased and $p_6 = 1/3$. Then p_1 through p_5 are 2/15 each. How many observations are necessary to prove the bias?

$\delta/N = 5\cdot(2/15 - 1/6)^2/(1/6) + (1/3 - 1/6)^2/(1/6) = 1/5$

For $\alpha = 0.05$, $\beta = 0.10$ or $\beta' = 0.90$ and $f_d = 5$ we find $\delta = 16.469$. Consequently: $\delta/N = 1/5$ or $N = 5\delta = 5\cdot 16.469 = 80.234$, i.e., 81 throws will determine whether the die is biased.

Test of independence

(Given x_{ij}, $i = 1, \ldots n_i$ and $j = 1, \ldots n_j$ with parameters N, p_{ij}, and $\sum_i \sum_j p_{ij} = 1.0$).

H_0: $p_{ij} = p_{i.} \cdot p_{.j}$ for $i = 1, \ldots, n_i$; $j = 1, \ldots, n_j$.

H_1: not all $p_{.j}$ follow the relationship under H_0.

$\left(\text{Nomenclature: } a_{i.} = \sum_{j=1}^{n_j} a_{ij} \text{ and } a_{.j} = \sum_{i=1}^{n_i} a_{ij}.\right)$

The approximation by χ^2 is:

$$\chi_k^2 = \sum_j \sum_i (x_{ij} - y_{i.} \cdot y_{.j}/N)^2 / y_{i.} y_{.j}/N) \tag{678a}$$

The non-centrality parameter is:

$$\delta = \sum_j \sum_i c_{ij}^2/(p_{i.} p_{.j}) - \sum_i c^2/p_{i.} - \sum_j c_{.j}^2/p_{.j} \tag{678b}$$

where:

$$p_{ij} = p_{i.} p_{.j} + (c_{ij}/\sqrt{N}); \quad \sum_i \sum_j c_{ij} = 0 \tag{678c}$$

and:

$$y_{i.} = \sum_j x_{ij}, \quad y_{.j} = \sum_i x_{ij} \tag{678d}$$

In many cases $p_{i.}$ and $p_{.j}$ are unknown, and estimates (or guesses) must be substituted.

Test of homogeneity

Given are the same data as in the preceding section.

H_0: $p_{ij} = p_{2j} = \ldots\ p_{n_i n_j} = p_{j.}$

H_1: not all p_{ij}'s satisfy H_0.

Again, p_{ij} is defined by eq. 678c, and χ_k^2 by eq. 678b.

$$\delta = \sum_j (1/p_j)\left[\sum_i^{n_i} c_{ij}^2 m_i/N - \left(\sum_i^{n_i} c_{ij} m_i/N\right)\right] \tag{679a}$$

with:

$$y_{i.} = m_i,\ N = \sum_i m_i \tag{679b}$$

Contingency tables

The contingency table was introduced and an example was given in Table XXXIX. Thc contingency table represents the simultaneous occurrence of events (frequencies) by two or more categories of a population or subjects (see Table LXX).
The individual categories are A_i and B_j in Table LXX, the frequencies n_{ij}, where i stands for the rows and j for the columns. Let R_i and S_j be the marginal distribution in the row and column, respectively. Then:

$$R_i = \sum_{j=1}^{n} n_{ij} \tag{680a}$$

$$S_j = \sum_{i=1}^{m} n_{ij} \tag{680b}$$

TABLE LXX

CONTINGENCY TABLE

	B_1	B_2	...	B_n	
A_1	n_{11}	.	.	n_{1n}	R_1
A_2	n_{21}	.	.	n_{2n}	.
.	.				.
.	.				.
.	.				.
A_m	n_{n1}	.	.	n_{mn}	R_m
	S_1	.	.	S_n	N

and:

$$N=\sum_{i=1}^{m} R_i=\sum_{j=1}^{n} S_j \tag{680c}$$

Several postulations can be tested. The most frequent assumption is that the field frequency n_{ij} can be deduced from the marginal distributions R_i and S_j. This postulation H_0 of dependence (or independence as H_1) can be checked by computing:

$$\chi_k^2=N\left(\sum_{i=1}^{n}\sum_{j=1}^{m}\frac{n_{ij}^2}{R_iS_j}-1\right) \tag{681}$$

with $k=(n-1)(m-1)$ degrees of freedom. If $\chi_k^2<\chi_T^2$ (see eq. 645) the deviations $n_{ij}-R_iS_j/N$ are caused by randomness.

KU and KULLBACK (1974) suggested the use of log linear models for the testing of contingency tables and KULLBACK (1974) elaborated on the information gained from contingency tables.

PEARSON (1904) defined a coefficient of mean square contingency:

$$C=[\chi_k^2/(\chi_k^2+N)]^{1/2} \tag{682a}$$

If:

$$N_s=\sum_{i=1}^{n}\sum_{j=1}^{m} n_{ij}^2/(R_iS_j) \tag{682b}$$

then:

$$C=[(N_s-1)/N_s]^{1/2} \tag{682c}$$

where C tends toward 1 as the number of rows and columns increase. For a 2×2 contingency table C cannot exceed $1/\sqrt{2}=0.707$, for 4×4 the maximum C is 0.866.

The 2 × 2 contingency table

If $n=m=2$ the contingency table has a 2×2 field:

	B_1	B_2	
A_1	a	b	R_1
A_2	c	d	R_2
	S_1	S_2	N

Eq. 681 would lead to:

$$\chi_k^2=N(ad-bc)^2/[(a+b)(a+c)(b+d)(c+d)] \tag{683a}$$

or:

$$\chi_k^2=N(ad-bc)^2/[R_1R_2S_1S_2] \tag{683b}$$

Some discussion has taken place in the literature as to the proper test. According to YATES (1934), the approximation to χ^2 is improved by replacing the smallest cell, say d, by $d\pm\frac{1}{2}$, the sign depending whether $ad \lesseqgtr bc$. The correction is made for "continuity" and should be applied unless the cell frequencies are ≥ 5.

PEARSON (1947) clarified the ambiguity. There are three problems involved.

(*a*) The marginal totals are fixed (and known) and *a*, *b*, *c*, *d* are tested for a significant deviation.

R. A. Fisher's "exact" test provides:

$$P(\chi^2)=(R_1!R_2!S_1!S_2!)/(a!b!c!d!N!) \qquad (684)$$

This requires a large amount of computation. According to Pearson we can use a normal approximation:

$$\delta=R_2S_2/N \qquad (685a)$$

$$\sigma_d^2=R_1R_2S_1S_2/[N^2(N-1)] \qquad (685b)$$

$$t=(|d-\delta|-0.5)/\sigma_d \qquad (685c)$$

The probability $P(t)$ is the probability for $P(\chi^2)$. If $P(t)$ exceeds the selected significance level α, the deviations in the cells from R_iS_j are not attributed to randomness.

(*b*) In the second case the null hypothesis $P_1=P_2=P$, is tested, where $P_1=E(a/S_1)$, $P_2=E(b/S_2)$, and $P=E(R_1/N)$. This can be called a comparative trial. Then the probability is:

$$P_s=P(\chi^2)\cdot P(R_1) \qquad (686a)$$

where:

$$P(R_1)=[N!/(R_1!R_2!)]\cdot p^{R_1}(1-p)^{R_2} \qquad (686b)$$

Because $P(\chi^2)$ or $P(R_1)\leq 1.0$, P_s is smaller than either $P(\chi^2)$ or $P(R_1)$. In this case the marginal values are not fixed. After PEARSON (1947) the quantity u may be treated as normal variate:

$$u=(a-\bar{a})/\sigma_a \qquad (687a)$$

$$\bar{a}=R_1S_1/N \qquad (687b)$$

$$\sigma_a^2=R_1R_2S_1S_2/[N^2(N-1)] \qquad (687c)$$

Comparison with eq. 685, a–c renders $\sigma_a^2\equiv\sigma_d^2$, $a\neq\delta$ in theory, but for one contingency table of observed data $a-\bar{a}=d-\bar{d}$ and $a-\bar{a}=-(b-\bar{b})$ etc., which is not difficult to prove. Hence, $P(t)$ and $P(u)$ are only different due to the term -0.5, added in eq. 685c. Consequently, the additional replacement suggested by Yates is not necessary in this second case of comparative trial.

(*c*) The last case is known as double dichotomy. The parent population has a probability $P_1=E(A_1)$, independent of $P_2=E(B_1)$. Then the probabilities of A_1B_1, A_1B_2, A_2B_1 and A_2B_2 corresponding to *a*, *b*, *c* and *d* are determined by:

$$P_a=P(A_1B_1)=P_1P_2 \qquad (688a)$$

$$P_b=P(A_1B_2)=P_1(1-P_2) \qquad (688b)$$

$$P_c=P(A_2B_1)(1-P_1)P_2 \qquad (688c)$$

$$P_d = P(A_2B_2) = (1-P_1)(1-P_2) \tag{688d}$$

The probability P_s of the given sample is:

$$P_s = \frac{N!}{a!b!c!d!} P_a^a P_b^b P_c^c P_d^d \tag{689a}$$

or:

$$P_s = \frac{N!}{a!b!c!d!} P_1^{R_1}(1-P_1)^{R_2} P_2^{S_1}(1-P_2)^{S_2} \tag{689b}$$

Introduction of eqs. 684 and 686b allows the derivation of:

$$P_s = P(\chi^2)P(R_1)P(S_1) \tag{689c}$$

This is a three-dimensional problem, because row and column totals may vary. In this case the regular $P(\chi^2)$ test eq. 683b is suitable unless some marginal totals are small. Both $P(R)$ and $P(S)$ are smaller than one. Hence $P_s \leq P(\chi^2)$. Notice, $P(R)$ and $P(S)$ depend on $E(A_1)$ and $E(B_1)$. Further, this is a multiplication of three probabilities, all ≤ 1.0, P_s is smaller than the lowest probability of either $P(\chi^2)$, $P(R_1)$ or $P(S_1)$.

The discussion of the tetrachoric correlation coefficient for 2×2 contingency tables is omitted because basically the two variables must be Gaussian distributed, and then the correlation coefficient can be obtained in the usual manner. The author does not recommend the utilization of the tetrachoric correlation because of difficulties in testing its significance.

One more problem may be stressed. WRIGHT (1971) pointed out an erroneous use of the chi-square test. In an earlier article DAVIS (1967) tested the existence of a biennial oscillation with the aid of a 2×2 contingency table, investigating a positive temperature change in odd years versus a negative change in even years. Davis concluded that independence of the cells proves significance and supports the existence of a biennial oscillation. Indeed the result disclosed an apparent independence in the fields of the 2×2 contingency, checked by the chi-square test. The significance level was given as $\alpha \sim 0.01$. Wright justly objected that the chi-square test was not properly applied in this case. Independence of the variate which is being tested must be assumed. Although the original variable, the summer temperature of an odd or even year, may discern independence in the sequence, the probability for the sequence of positive and negative signs (as tested by Davis) is not 0.5 even in a random series.

Given is the sequence x_1, x_2 and x_3. A change of sign occurs between $\Delta x_1 = x_1 - x_2$ and $\Delta x_2 = x_2 - x_3$ when $x_2 < x_1$ and $x_2 < x_3$ or $x_2 > x_1$ and $x_2 > x_3$. The position $x_1 < x_2 < x_3$ or $x_1 > x_2 > x_3$ does not lead to a change which implies that the probabilities of ranking in sequence must be calculated, either x_2, x_1, x_3; x_1, x_2, x_3; or x_1, x_3, x_2. It is immaterial which relative position x_1 or x_3 has. The probability for this ranking in a random series is 1/3. Wright concluded correctly that the actual threshold χ_k^2 for the test should have been reduced. By a Monte Carlo method he derived $\chi_{k_2}^2 = 0.6\ \chi_k^2$. This reduction compensates for the loss of independence in the sequence. The reduction decreases the significance, and $\alpha \sim 0.03$. If the null hypothesis is rejected at $\alpha = 0.05$, Davis' conclusion of the existence of a biennial oscillation would still stand. (The existence of a biennial oscillation in certain global regions has meanwhile been accepted by most meteorologists.)

The reader is reminded that the χ^2 is not only a function of the degrees of freedom but indirectly also of N. We test $\Delta_{ij}=A_{ij}-B_{ij}$ where $A_{ij}=n_{ij}/N$ is the observed and B_{ij} the expected cell value. The same Δ_{ij} leads to $\chi_k^2>\chi_t^2$ with increasing N_2 if $\chi_k^2<\chi_t^2$ for N_1 where $N_1 \ll N_2$ provided Δ_{ij} is the same. Thus, the general law of error requires that Δ_{ij} decreases with increasing N.

Example 65. In a research problem of acoustic propagation it was found that returning acoustic rays produced focusing when the gradient of the sound profile μ_i in a layer i was larger than at the surface, μ_0. The question arose whether this was also true for small differences between μ_i and μ_0. A contingency table was tested for sound speed data of New Orleans (La.).
Inspection of Table LXXI reveals 31.6% for the small μ_i against 28.6% for the others. (Notice: the percentage should even be smaller than 31.6%.) Was this difference significant or is it caused by randomness? The general χ^2-test provides the following solution to eq. 683b.

$$\chi_k^2=N[(176)(7136)-(2866)(380)]^2/[(3042)(7516)(556)(10002)]=2.31$$

With $k=(2-1)(2-1)=1$ we find that $\chi_t^2=2.71$ will be exceeded in 10% of the time. Consequently, at the 5% significance level the hypothesis of randomness is accepted. This implies that the cells can be deduced from the marginal distribution, R_1 and R_2, $P(\chi_k^2)\sim 0.15$.
Fisher's exact test leads to the same result in this case. The probability for the given sample, $P(S_1)$ can be computed if $P(R_1)$ and $P(S_2)$ are known.

Example 66. We test now the hypothesis that focusing is more likely when the extreme value (maximum) of the sound speed (V_e) appears above 1 km altitude than when V_e is below 1 km. The null hypothesis requires a significant difference of the cells for acceptance. The contingency table of Table LXXII is established. It displays 26.2% focusing for $V_e \leq 1$ km and 29.5% for $V_0>1$ km. Again, this is only a difference of 3%, nearly the same as in Example 65. Computation of χ^2 results in the following, however:

$$\chi_k^2=10558[(556)(5946)-(1570)(2486)]^2/[(3042)(7516)(2126)(8432)]=9.18$$

This χ_k^2 is exceeded only 0.4% of the time. Therefore, the difference between the cells is significant, even at $\alpha=1\%$.
We now test by Pearson's first concept. First:

$$\delta=(7516)(8432)/10558=6002.5$$

TABLE LXXI

ACOUSTIC FOCUSING AND SOUND SPEED PROFILE GRADIENT

	$\mu_0 \leq \mu_i \leq 0.002$	$\mu_i>\mu_0+0.002$	
No focusing	176 (=31.6%)	2,866 (=28.6%)	3,042 (=28.8%)
Focusing	380 (=68.4%)	7,136 (=71.4%)	7,615 (=71.2%)
	556	10,002	10,558

TABLE LXXII

ACOUSTIC FOCUSING AND EXTREME VALUE (MAXIMUM) OF THE SOUND SPEED, V_e

	$V_e \leq 1.0$ km	$V_e>1.0$ km	
No focusing	556 (=26.2%)	2,486 (=29.5%)	3,042
Focusing	1,570 (=73.8%)	5,946 (=70.5%)	7,516
	2,126	8,432	10,558

$\sigma_d^2 = (3042)(7516)(2126)(8432)/[(10558)^2(10557)] = 367.65$*[1]

From σ_d^2 we obtain $\sigma_d = 19.17$. Hence:

$t = (|5946 - 6002.5| - 0.5)/19.17 = 2.92$

where t corresponds to the ratio of a standard deviation of a normal distribution. For $t = 2.92$ we extract from tables $P(t) = 0.18\%$. This would be valid for a one-sided test. For a two-sided test $P(t)$ must be doubled, namely $P(t) = 0.36\%$. Again, the cells show more than random fluctuations and cannot be produced from the margins in good agreement with the previous result.
Testing of Pearson's described second case requires $P_1 = P_2 = P$ (with $P = 28.8\%$). The following calculations must be added:

$\sigma_a = \sigma_d = 19.17$

$\bar{a} = (3042)(2126)/10558 = 612.5$

$u = (556 - 612.5)/19.17 = 2.92$

This is the same result as above (see remark after eq. 687c).
The third case would not apply. The true probability for the marginal distribution is very seldom given. Assume, however, that the no-focusing-cases with probability of 28.8% are known, and that 20.1% of the extreme sound speed occurs at an altitude lower than 1 km. We would find $(P_{(\chi^2)} = 0.36\%)$

$P_s = (0.0036)(0.288)(0.201) = 0.0002$

The chances that this particular sample is produced from random sampling are 0.0002. P_s is less than the smallest probability in P_s which in this case is $P(\chi^2)$ with 0.0036. Notice that P_s for the second case is (0.0036)(0.288), which is higher. Thus, judgment of the sample probability depends strongly on the postulations of hypothesis testing.

Significance check for Poisson sampling in contingency tables

The independence of the fields of a contingency table with dimensions $r \times s$ can also be checked by a simple procedure developed by HABERMAN (1973). If the table comprises a single multinomial sample with total data N, then the probabilities $p_{ij} = n_{ij}/N$ have the expected value:

$$p_{ij} = P_i P_j \quad \begin{cases} 1 \leq i \leq r \\ 1 \leq j \leq s \end{cases} \tag{690a}$$

where n_{ij} is the individual field frequency, and:

$$P_i = \sum_j p_{ij} \tag{690b}$$

$$P_j = \sum_i p_{ij} \tag{690c}$$

are the marginal probabilities.
HABERMAN (1973) demonstrated that in this case the residuals d_{ij} can be checked by ranking them in order of increasing d_{ij} and plotting them into a normal distribution paper with the cumulative frequency as abscissa and d_{ij} as ordinate. If the multinomial (or Poisson) sampling postulation is correct, d_{ij} will form a straight line, i.e. the d_{ij} are

*[1] We can reduce the elaborate computations by utilizing δ, compute $R_1 S_1/N$ and then (6002.5)(612.5)/10557.

normally distributed where:

$$d_{ij}=m_{ij}/\sqrt{\hat{v}_{ij}} \tag{691a}$$

$$m_{ij}=(n_{ij}-N_iN_j/N)/\sqrt{N_i\cdot N_j/N} \tag{691b}$$

N_i and N_j are the marginal counts:

$$N_i=\sum_j n_{ij} \tag{692a}$$

$$N_j=\sum_i n_{ij} \tag{692b}$$

$$N=\sum\sum n_{ij} \tag{692c}$$

Now $\hat{v}_{ij}$ is the maximum-likelihood estimator of an asymptotic variance:

$$\hat{v}_{ij}=(1-N_i/N)(1-N_j/N)\quad \begin{cases}1\leq i\leq r\\ 1\leq j\leq s\end{cases} \tag{693}$$

Let us apply the testing to the data of Table LXXII. The respective values are:

	n_{ij}		N_i	m_{ij}		$\hat{v}_{ij}$		d_{ij}	
	556	2486	3042	−2.29	1.15	0.754	0.379	−3.04	3.04
	1570	5946	7516	1.45	−0.73	0.480	0.241	3.02	−3.03
N_j	2126	8432	10558						

A plot on (Gaussian) distribution paper is omitted because d_{ij} clusters around $+3$ and -3. This implies deviations of 3 sigma which are expected with less than $F(x)=0.013$, but the c.d.f. of d_{ij} shows $F(-3.04)=0.25$, $F(-3.03)=0.50$, etc. The individual cells cannot be generated from the marginal distributions but display significant individuality. The result agrees with the previous findings (Example 66).

For simplicity, the example was given for the 2×2 contingency in Table LXXII, but in general the procedure is not very suitable for the small number of cells. Some information is provided, however. We may deduce from the d_{ij} how far the normalized deviations depart from the Gaussian law.

Goodness-of-fit tests

General

Any mathematical concept which characterizes a set of data, e.g., regression analysis, contingency tables, polynomials, frequency models, curve fittings, etc. can be tested against a statistical background. The statistical literature on these procedures is so voluminous that only a limited number, mainly dealing with frequency distributions, can be included into this section.

The postulations or null hypotheses that test the agreement between analytical model and observed data are manifold. E.g., we could require that an analytical frequency model shows correspondence in the set of moments. If estimators from moments are utilized, only moments of higher order than the number of parameters in the frequency model are suitable such as in the Gaussian distribution where the parameters skewness and kurtosis are usually tested. Often the test result is an exclusion rather than a confirmation. E.g., the hypothesis that a frequency distribution is Gaussian is rejected on account of differences for the third and fourth (or higher) moments. The conclusion that deviations are not significant, however, does not automatically mean that the distribution is Gaussian. Only if all the moments are tested and agree can it be inferred that the Gaussian law is valid. The process of testing all the moments is tedious, and more effective methods have been sought. Usually they are based on testing the conformity of the cumulative frequency $F(x)$ or the frequency density $f(x)$.

Kolmogorov-Smirnov test

On p. 281 a method of testing the correspondence of two frequency density distributions by the χ^2-test was presented. This test is often applied; e.g., BATTYE (1980) tested the occurrence of singularities. The reader must have noticed that the utilization of the χ^2-test is not without difficulties. Some statisticians avoid the χ^2-test for any comparison of frequency distributions because it is based on the comparison of the frequency density $f(x)$. Consequently, various procedures have been developed for testing the resemblance of the cumulative distribution $F(x)$.

The first of these tests is the Kolmogorov-Smirnov test (KOLMOGOROV, 1933; SMIRNOV, 1948), which was described by WATSON (1961, 1962) and PEARSON (1963). It is based on the determination of the maximum deviation from a cumulative frequency distribution and is especially useful when the χ^2-test fails because the small number N of observation does restrict division of data into classes. We calculate:

$$D_{\mathrm{M}} = \max |F(x) - F_N(x)| \quad \text{(discrete case)} \tag{694a}$$

or:

$$D_{\mathrm{M}} = \sup\,[F(x) - F_N(x)] \quad \text{(continuous case)}^{*1} \tag{694b}$$

where $F(x)$ is an expected cumulative frequency and $F_N(x)$ the observed cumulative frequency. The following definition of the observed frequency is valid:

$F_N(x) = 0$ for $x \leq x_0$; $F_N(x) = 1.0$ for $x \geq x_N$

otherwise:

$$F_N(x_k) = \frac{k}{N} \tag{695}$$

for the interval $x_{k-1} < x < x_k$, where k is the rank of the observation, $k = 1, \ldots, N$.

Since D_{M} does not depend on the form of $F(x)$, the test is a non-parametric (distribution free) test (see p. 254). Confidence bands around $F(x)$ can be constructed based on D_{M}. We test: H_0: $F(x) = F_N(x)$ versus H_1: $F(x) \neq F_N(x)$, i.e., $F(x)$ is the expected frequency distribution of the data sample. H_0 is rejected if $D_{\mathrm{M}} > D_\alpha$ which is the expected threshold of D_{M} at the significance level α. The test can be utilized as a two-sided or one-sided test. It is self-evident that by grouping of the data into discrete classes the supremum of D_{M} cannot be precisely determined, only the "apparent" maximum can be found. Conse-

*1 Sup = supremum, i.e., the absolute largest difference (for a continuum).

quently, the evaluation of the postulation H_0 is somewhat on the conservative side. Although in most texts the opinion is shared that the Kolmogorov-Smirnov test is more suitable than the χ^2-test for $N<50$, SLAKTER (1965) came to an opposite conclusion.

Two-sided test

It is well-known that the limiting form of the test (e.g., DURBIN, 1975) is based on:

$$P(D_M\sqrt{N}\leq z)=1-2\sum_{k=1}^{\infty}(-1)^{k-1}\exp(-2k^2z^2) \tag{696a}$$

or:

$$P(D_M\sqrt{N}>z)=2\sum_{k=1}^{\infty}(-1)^{k-1}\exp(-2K^2z^2) \tag{696b}$$

KOROLYUK (1960) brought eq. 696b into the form:

$$F(z)\sim\sum_{k=0}^{\infty}K_k(z)/N^{k/2} \tag{696c}$$

where $K_k(z)$ is defined by lengthy expressions (e.g., see PELZ and GOOD, 1976). The summation by eq. 696c is tedious, and table values for D_α disagree depending on the method of approximations (e.g., SMIRNOV, 1948; MASSEY, 1951; BIRNBAUM, 1952; CHANG, 1956; STEPHENS, 1970; or DURBIN, 1975).

Setting $z^2=D_\alpha^2N$ in eq. 696c a simple formula is deduced (MASSEY, 1951) where terms for $z>1$ are neglected.

$$P(D_M>D_\alpha)=2\exp(-2ND_\alpha^2)=\alpha \tag{697a}$$

This approximation is good for $N>35$ where:

$$D_\alpha^2=[\sim\ln(\alpha/2)]/(2N) \tag{697b}$$

In Massey's tables:

$$D_\alpha=K(\alpha)/\sqrt{N} \tag{698a}$$

for $N>35$, where:

$$K^2(\alpha)=[-0.5\ln(\alpha/2)] \tag{698b}$$

The factor $K(\alpha)$ is listed in Table LXXIII.

TABLE LXXIII

$K(\alpha)$ FOR KOLMOGOROV-SMIRNOV TEST; APPROXIMATIONS BY EQ. 689a, $N\geq 30$

α:	0.20	0.15	0.10	0.05	0.01
$\alpha/2$:	0.10	0.075	0.05	0.025	0.005
$K(\alpha)$:	1.07	1.14	1.22	1.36	1.63
$K_L(\alpha)$:	0.736	0.768	0.805	0.886	1.031

BIRNBAUM and TINGEY (1951) recommended an approximation for $5 \leq N \leq 35$ by:

$$D_\alpha = \{[-\ln(\alpha/2)]/(2N)\}^{1/2} - 1/(6N) = K(\alpha)/\sqrt{N} - 1/(6N) \qquad (698c)$$

The second term goes to zero for $N \to \infty$, and is negligible for $N \geq 35$.
LILLIEFORS (1969) pointed out that the original table values by Massey are too high if the observed distribution is compared with a Gaussian normal distribution where mean and variance have been estimated (see also IMAN, 1982). The new $K_L(\alpha)$ values by Lilliefors are given in the last line of Table LXXIII and should replace $K(\alpha)$ in eq. 698a. They are valid for $N \geq 30$.
Other approximations for small z are:

$$P[D_M\sqrt{N} \leq z] = \sqrt{2\pi}\, z^{-1} \sum_{k=1}^{\infty} \exp[-(2k-1)^2\pi^2]/(8z^2) \qquad (699a)$$

and with the neglection of all except the first term:

$$P[D_M\sqrt{N} \leq z] \cong \sqrt{2\pi}\, z^{-1} \exp[-(\pi/z)^2/8] \qquad (699b)$$

Example 67. Let us check several frequency distribution models which have been selected to describe the frequency distribution of extreme wind speeds at 22 km altitude at Montgomery (Al.) during the winter months January–March 1957–1964 (see Table LXXIV). Column one, x_i, presents the observed wind speed. The empirical cumulative distribution appears in the second column, i.e., $F_N(x)$. The subsequent three columns disclose the c.f.d. for Gumbel's frequency model (F_G), Fisher-Tippett II with maximum-likelihood fit (F_L) and Fisher-Tippett II moments fit (F_M).
The last three columns display the calculated Δ values, where $\Delta = F_a - F_N(x)$, and F_a is the respective analytical (expected) distribution of $F(x)$ in eq. 694a, b. The maximum deviations D_M are listed in the last line of the respective columns. For $N = 24$ from Massey's tables gives $D = 0.275$ as the threshold at the 5% level of significance. A deviation $0.275 = 27.5\%$ will be exceeded in 5% of the time. The threshold from eq. 697b is 0.278, and by eq. 698c we find 0.270, which does not show a wide dispersion of D_α by the individual formulae. Consequently, the obviously large deviations of almost

TABLE LXXIV

KOLMOGOROV-SMIRNOV TEST FOR MONTHLY EXTREME WINDSPEEDS AT MONTGOMERY (JANUARY–MARCH 1957–1964 AT 22 KM ALTITUDE)

x_i (m s^{-1})	Observed $F_N(x)$ (%)	F_G (%)	F_L (%)	F_M (%)	Δ_G (%)	Δ_L (%)	Δ_M (%)
14.0	12.5	9.61	7.02	7.13	−2.89	−5.48	−5.37
17.0	25.0	21.46	24.01	12.26	−0.04	−0.43	−12.74
19.0	37.5	31.25	36.91	27.22	−6.25	−0.59	−10.28
20.0	50.0	36.37	42.94	35.35	−13.63	−7.06	−14.65
24.0	62.5	56.12	62.45	62.58	−6.38	−0.05	0.08
31.0	75.0	80.51	81.30	85.80	5.51	6.30	10.80
37.0	87.5	91.16	88.93	93.17	3.66	1.43	5.67
40.0	91.67	94.03	91.27	95.10	2.33	−0.40	3.43
42.0	95.83	95.46	92.49	96.01	−0.37	−3.34	0.18
43.0	100.0	96.04	93.01	96.40	−3.96	−6.99	−3.60
D_M					−13.63	−7.06	−14.65

Note: F_G = Gumbel's frequency distribution; F_L = Fisher-Tippett II, maximum-likelihood estimators; F_M = Fisher-Tippett II, moments estimators. For further explanation see text.

15% from the chosen analytical distribution cannot be interpreted as a significant difference for the small sample of $N=24$.
We could consider the reduced thresholds as recommended by Lilliefors because the frequency models have two estimators, although $K_L(\alpha)$ is applicable particularly for a Gaussian distribution. This modification reduces D_α to 18.1% but it stays higher than $D_M \sim 15\%$, and the conclusions remain the same in this case.
One word of caution is in order. The threshold D_α decreases with increasing N. Therefore, one may infer that the significance threshold D_α could be exceeded by an increasing sample size. In turn, D_M may decrease, too, and we cannot readily infer that a larger sample would provide a significant difference at the specified level α.

One-sided test

The Kolmogorov-Smirnov test can be found as a one-sided test:

$$D_M^+ = \max |F(x) - F_N(x)| \tag{700a}$$

$$D_M^- = \max |F_N(x) - F(x)|. \tag{700b}$$

Table LXXIII can be adapted, namely: $P(D^+ \geq D_\alpha) = (1-p)/2$ and $P(D \geq D_\alpha) = (1-p)$ where p is the probability. Because $\alpha = P(\ldots)$, $p = 1-2\alpha$ for D^+ and $p = 1-\alpha$ for D. This relationship implies that $K(\alpha) = 1.22$ for a one-sided and $K(\alpha) = 1.36$ for a two-sided test.
Several modifications exist. Generally it is assumed that $F_N(x_k) = k/N$ (see eq. 695). The following substitution is made:

$$E[F_N(x_i)] = i/(N+1) = G_N(x) \tag{701a}$$

where $i = 1, 2, \ldots, N$, and $x_i \leq x < x_{i+1}$.
DURBIN and KNOTT (1972) have pointed out that another version may even be more appropriate:

$$E[F_N(x_i)] = (i+0.5)/(N+1) = H_N(x) \tag{701b}$$

GREEN and HEGAZY (1976) substituted G_N and H_N for F_N in eq. 700a, b so that:

$$D_{G_1} = \max |i/N - F(x_i)| \tag{702a}$$

$$D_{G_2} = \max |(i-1)/N - F(x_i)| \tag{702b}$$

The maximum is a single value and is easily affected by errors other than random fluctuations. Thus, a summation was suggested by Green and Hegazy by testing:

$$D_2 = \sum |F_N(x) - F(x)| \tag{703a}$$

$$D_{22} = \sum |F_N(x) - H_N(x)| \tag{703b}$$

but tables for testing D_2 or D_{22} are not readily available.
A more powerful test than eq. 694a, b was recommended by FINKELSTEIN and SCHAFER (1971). They select:

$$\delta_i = \max [\Delta_{2i}, \Delta_{1i}] \tag{704a}$$

which is the maximum of the two Δ values, defined by:

$$\Delta_{ji} = |(i-j+1)/N - F(x_i)|, \quad j = 1, 2 \tag{704b}$$

The test statistic is then:

$$D_F = \sum_1^N \delta_i \tag{704c}$$

This test statistic D_F can be modified as specified by LILLIEFORS (1969); the substitution is denoted here with an asterisk:

$$D_F^* = \sum_1^N \delta_i^* \tag{704d}$$

Critical values of D_F and D_F^* for selected N are given in Table LXXV. An expanded table can be found in FINKELSTEIN and SCHAFER (1971).
A special formula for the comparison of continuous symmetric distributions was introduced by SCHUSTER (1973).

Comparison of two empirical distributions

SMIRNOV (1948) expanded the Kolmogorov test for comparison of two empirical distributions. The only modification is the replacement of $\alpha/2$ by α in eqs. 697, 698, and $N = N_1 \cdot N_2/(N_1 + N_2)$, where N_1 and N_2 denote the number of observations in the two samples.
An approximation for a one-sided test in this case was given by GAIL and GREEN (1976). A critical threshold can be found from:

$$D_\alpha^+ = [N_1 N_2 (N_1 + N_2)(-\ln \alpha)/2]^{1/2} \tag{705}$$

which is a somewhat smaller value than the precise threshold which is included in their article for 3 levels of significance, $\alpha = 0.10$, 0.05 and 0.01 and for N_1 and N_2 from 3 to 30.

Other goodness-of-fit tests based on the cumulative distribution

Cramer-von Mises

In eq. 702a, b a single value is selected. CRAMER (1928) suggested another test statistic, which was later modified by SMIRNOV (1936, 1937):

TABLE LXXV

CRITICAL VALUES FOR D_F AND D_F^*
(After FINKELSTEIN and SCHAFER, 1971)

	n	$\alpha = 0.10$	0.05	0.01
D_F	5	1.59	1.76	2.09
	10	2.06	2.30	2.83
	25	3.00	3.41	4.20
D_F^*	5	1.23	1.32	1.50
	10	1.55	1.70	1.98
	25	2.18	2.42	2.88

$$W_N^2 = N \int_{-\infty}^{\infty} [F_N(x) - F(x)]^2 \, df(x) \tag{706}$$

Basically, W_N^2 is the summation of squared differences. This test is also distribution free, and requires no grouping (such as for the χ^2-test). W_N^2 is consistent for $W(t) > 0$.
The moments of W_N^2 (PEARSON and STEPHENS, 1962) are:

$$\mu_1 = 1/6 \tag{707a}$$

$$\sigma^2 = (4N-3)/180N \tag{707b}$$

$$\nu_3 = (32N^2 - 61\text{N} + 30)/3780N^2 \tag{707c}$$

$$\nu_4 = (496N^3 - 1532N^2 - 1671N - 630)/75600N^3 \tag{707d}$$

Calculation of skewness and kurtosis (or β_1 and β_2) discloses that the distribution is non-Gaussian.
The test statistic (e.g., GREEN and HEGAZY, 1976) is equivalent to:

$$W_{N_2}^2 = 1/(12N) + \sum [F(x_i) - (2i-1)/(2N)]^2/N \tag{708}$$

The first term often is ignored because it is negligible even for small N, say $N \leq 10$. (Notice: $i = 1, \ldots N$, and $F_N = i/N$.) The test $W_{N_2}^2$ (without the first term) is also called the Cramer-von Mises test.
By substituting G_N and H_N (see eq. 701a, b) instead of $F_N = 1/N$ Green and Hegazy cast:

$$W_{G_1} = \sum [F(x_i) - 1/(N+1)]^2 \tag{709a}$$

and:

$$W_{G_2} = \sum [F(x_i) - (2i-1)/(2n+2)]^2 \tag{709b}$$

An approximation of W^2 in lieu of tables is provided on p. 309.

Anderson-Darling

Another modification of D_M was suggested by ANDERSON and DARLING (1952). They introduced a simple weighting function $W(t)$ such as:*[1]

$$D_A = \sup |F_N(x) - F(x)| \cdot W(x) \tag{710}$$

This expression can also be found in the form $D_A \cdot \sqrt{N}$. The multiplication can be incorporated into tables for D_A.
Several weighting functions $W(x)$ have been suggested. In one case:

$$W(x) = (ax+b)^{-1} \tag{711a}$$

or:

$$\begin{cases} W(x) = 1 & \text{for } a_1 < x < a_2 \\ W(x) = 0 & \text{otherwise} \end{cases} \tag{711b}$$

*[1] See footnote on p. 311.

Other recommendations are:

$$W(x)=1/x \tag{711c}$$

or:

$$W(x)=1/(1-x) \tag{711d}$$

A second form of the Anderson-Darling criteria is:

$$D_{A_1}=N\int_0^1 [F_N(x)-F(x)]^2/\{F(x)[1-F(x)]\}\,\mathrm{d}F \tag{712a}$$

This formulation resembles eq. 706. By substituting $F_N=i/N$ we can write:

$$D_{A_1}=-\sum(2i-1)\{\ln F(x_i)+\ln[1-F(x_{N-i+1})]\}/N-N \tag{712b}$$

DARLING (1957) justified the modifications.
Interesting modifications were derived by GREEN and HEGAZY (1976). One change is a replacement of N by $N+1$ and $(2i-1)$ by i in eq. 712b.
Substitution of G_N or H_N (see eq. 701a, b for F_N in eq. 712a leads to elaborate expressions (see Green and Hegazy):

$$D_{A_G}=-N_A\sum_1^N\{(2i-1)\ln F(x_i)+(2i+1)\ln[1-F(x_{N-i+1})]\}$$
$$-N_A\{(2N+1)\ln F(x_N)-\ln[1-F(x_N)]\}-N \tag{713a}$$

and:

$$D_{A_H}=-2N_A\sum_1^N i\{\ln F(x_i)+\ln[1-F(x_{N-i+1})]\}-N$$
$$-N_A\{\ln F(x_1)+\ln[1-F(x_N)]\}/4+N_B\{\ln F(x_n)+\ln[1-F(x_1)]\} \tag{713b}$$

where:

$$N_A=N/(1+N)^2 \tag{713c}$$

$$N_B=N+0.75 \tag{713d}$$

According to Green and Hegazy, the modified forms of eqs. 702a, b, 709a, b and 713a, b improve the power of the tests.

Johnson's distribution

JOHNSON's (1949) S_B distribution (see ESSENWANGER, 1976, p. 318) can be used with the transformation:

$$z=3.38625+1.075\ln[(x-0.00909)/(2.72299-x)] \tag{714a}$$

and:

$$x=W_\infty^2,\ \text{i.e. eq. } 706 \tag{714b}$$

For $N=5$:

$$z=2.65+\ln[(x-0.01833)/(1.61005-x)] \tag{715a}$$

and $N=10$:

$$z=2.87+\ln[(x-0.183)/(1.9335-x)] \tag{715b}$$

The approximation renders satisfactory results for the computation of the significance levels when no tables of W^2 are available (MARSHALL, 1958).

Watson's statistic

WATSON (1961, 1962) suggested a simple statistic which requires very little tabulation. The test statistic is based on the computation of:

$$U_N^2=N\int_{-\infty}^{\infty}\{F_N(u)-F(u)-\int_{-\infty}^{\infty}[F_N(v)-F(v)]\,dF(v)\}^2\,dF(u) \tag{716}$$

and was originally sought to be a goodness-of-fit test on a circle, where u and v are the variables of the (two-dimensional rectangular) coordinate system. PEARSON (1963) has expanded the interpretation to the testing for randomness of points on a line. While U_N^2 has a maximum when all data on a circle are concentrated at one point, the statistic has also a maximum when all data are concentrated at either one or both ends.

Consider the deviations of an analytical distribution from a sample distribution in a diagram with an ordinate $v=F(x)$ from 0 to 1 and an abscissa $u=F_N(x)$ from 0 to 1. With this arrangement the U_N^2 statistic can be plotted. The ideal case (i.e., an agreement) is delineated as a straight line with an angle corresponding to the scale between u and v (e.g., if the ratio $\sigma_u/\sigma_v=1$, the angle is 45°).

The moments of U_N^2 are:

$$\mu_1=1/12 \tag{717a}$$

$$\sigma^2=(N-1)/(360\cdot N) \tag{717b}$$

$$\nu_3=(2N^2-5N+3)/(7560N^2) \tag{717c}$$

$$\nu_4=(19N^3-70N^2+87N-36)/(302400N^3) \tag{717d}$$

We assume points on a circle with observations $x, \ldots x_N$ of increasing order and a definition of $v_i=F_i(x_i)$. Then:

$$U_N^2=\sum_{i=1}^{N}\left(v_i-\frac{2i-1}{2N}\right)^2-N(\bar{v}-0.5)^2+1/(12N) \tag{718a}$$

Further:

$$N\bar{v}=\sum v_i=\sum F_i(x_i) \tag{718b}$$

The distribution also was described by STEPHENS (1963, 1964). In its original version WATSON (1961) recommended to calculate:

$$U_N^2=\sum_{i=1}^{N}\left(v_i-\frac{2i-1}{2N}-\bar{v}+0.5\right)^2+1/(12N) \tag{719a}$$

where again $v_i=F_i(x_i)$ and:

$$N(\bar{v}-0.5)=\sum_{i=1}^{N}[v_i-(2i-1)/(2N)] \tag{719b}$$

An equivalent form is:

$$U_N^2 = \sum_{i=1}^{N} v_i^2 - 2 \sum_{i=1}^{N} \frac{2i-1}{N} v_i + \frac{N}{3} + N(\bar{v}-0.5)^2 \tag{720}$$

Kuiper's test statistic

A further test statistic was proposed by KUIPER (1960), which again is an adapted Kolmogorov statistic. By definition*[1]:

$$V_N = \sup\,[F_N(x) - F(x)] - \inf\,[F_N(x) - F(x)] \tag{721}$$

Both sup (maximum) and inf (minimum) are taken over the range $-\infty < x < \infty$.
The distribution is independent of $F(x)$ and also can be used to test the randomness of points distributed on a circle, hence V_N is related to U_N^2. Tables of the distribution for the upper and lower tail have been constructed by STEPHENS (1963, 1964).

Interrelationships

The goodness-of-fit can be illustrated in a graph with abscissa u and ordinate v. E.g., under postulation of eq. 701a, b a function (u_i,v_i), $u=F(i)$ and $v=i/N$ can be plotted. Another function, $F(u_i,v_i) = u_i - v_i$, will render a straight line parallel to the ordinate. We plot:

$$F(x_i) = F(i) - i/N \tag{722}$$

in a system with $x_i = i$ as ordinate, $F(x_i)$ as abscissa (from 0 to 1.0). In the ideal case the line $F(x_i)$ is a vertical line with abscissa $F(x_i)=0$.
The relationship between the test statistics of eqs. 706 and 716 was studied by PEARSON (1963). First:

$$R_N^2 = N(\bar{d})^2 \tag{723a}$$

is defined, where:

$$\bar{d} = 0.5 - \bar{v} \quad \text{and} \quad \bar{v} = [\textstyle\sum F_i(x_i)]/N \quad \text{for} \quad d_i = (2_i - 1)/(2N) - v_i \tag{723b}$$

Then:

$$W_N^2 = U_N^2 + R_N^2 \tag{724a}$$

and:

$$\sigma_{W^2}^2 = \sigma_{U^2}^2 + \sigma_{R^2}^2 + 2\,\mathrm{Cov}\,(U^2, R^2) \tag{724b}$$

The following correlation coefficients exist between the three parameters:

$$r(W^2, U^2) = [2(N-1)/(4N-3)]^{1/2} \tag{725a}$$

$$r(W^2, R^2) = (3N-2)\sqrt{2}/[(4N-3)(5N-3)]^{1/2} \tag{725b}$$

$$r(U^2, R^2) = [(N-1)/(5N-3)]^{1/2} \tag{725c}$$

*[1] For a continuous variate the maximum is replaced by the supremum and the minimum by the infimum.

Goodness-of-fit can also be checked by sequential tests with a variable number of observations N, although these procedures are seldom applied.
The test statistics described on pp. 302–312 are considered to be distribution-free. In recent years the opinion among statisticians has grown that independence from the distribution form may be limited to cases where the parameters of the distribution have not been estimated.

Order statistics

In most of the test statistics the tailends enter with little weight. HEGAZY and GREEN (1975) introduced one of the most powerful tests which give a heavier weighting to the tails. We define first:

$$T = \int_0^1 \frac{[y - F_k(\xi_i)]^2}{y(1-y)} \alpha y \qquad (726)$$

Substitution of $y_i = F(x_i)$ leads to eq. 712a, i.e., the Anderson-Darling test. This equation can be modified to give heavier weighting of the tails by introducing $y_i = x_i$ instead of $F(x_i)$. Correspondingly, ξ_i replaces $F(\xi_i)$. Hegazy and Green distinguished two types of distributions: uniform and Gaussian.

Uniform distribution

The two suggested test criteria for a uniform distribution $U(0,1)$ with mean zero and variance 1 are:

$$T_{HG_1} = \sum |x_i - \xi_i| / N_H \qquad (727a)$$

and:

$$T_{HG_2} = \sum (x_i - \xi_i)^2 / N_H \qquad (727b)$$

where x_i is the empirical, ξ_i its expected value, and N_H is explained below.
When the uniform distribution has unknown parameters $U(a,b)$ then the null hypothesis is said to be composite, while for $U(0,1)$ the null hypothesis is simple. $U(a,b)$ is transformed to $U(0,1)$ by setting:

$$y_i = (x_i - x_1)/(x_N - x_1) \qquad (728)$$

where $i = 1, 2, \ldots N$ which leads to (0,1), the transformation renders $y_1 = 0$ and $y_N = 1$. According to Hegazy and Green, y_1 has a distribution as an order statistic from a random sample of size $N-2$ taken from $U(0,1)$. Therefore, in the simple case $N_H = N$, otherwise $N_H = N - 2$.
For a uniform distribution the expectancy of ξ_i can be written:

$$\xi_i = i/(N_H + 1) \qquad (729)$$

It is known that order statistics have in general skewed distributions (except for the median). Hence Hegazy and Green based their test statistic on the mode instead of the mean. The mode ζ_i is given in this case for the i-th order statistic:

$$\zeta_i = (i-1)/(N-1) \tag{730}$$

The mode is substituted into eq. 727a, b:

$$T'_{HG_1} = \sum |x_i - (i-1)/(N_H - 1)|/N_H \tag{731a}$$

$$T'_{HG_2} = \sum [x_i - (i-1)/(N_H - 1)]^2/N_H \tag{731b}$$

The critical values of the test can be approximated (HEGAZY and GREEN, 1975) for a uniform distribution by:

$$C_T(\alpha) = a + b/\sqrt{N} + c/N \tag{732}$$

The constants are given in Table LXXVI.

Test criteria for Gaussian distribution

HEGAZY and GREEN (1975) recommend as a first step a normalization of the variate. The variance σ^2 is obtained from the unbiased estimator $s_y^2 = \sum (x_i - \bar{x})^2/(N-1)$. Then the normalization $Y_i = (y_i - \bar{y})/s_y$ takes place. The expected value is:

$$\xi_i = \text{Inv. } \phi(t_i) \tag{733}$$

where ϕ is the Gaussian distribution, $t_i = i/(N+1)$ and Inv. means the inverse. Possible test criteria were suggested by Hegazy and Green:

$$T_{GH_3} = \sum |y_i - \xi_i|/N \tag{734a}$$

$$T_{GH_4} = \sum (y_i - \xi_i)^2/N \tag{734b}$$

$$T_{GH_5} = \sum |y_i - \xi_i|/s_{2,i} \tag{734c}$$

$$T_{GH_6} = \sum (y_i - \xi_i)^2/s_{2,i}^2 \tag{734d}$$

where:

$$s_{2,i}^2 = i(N-i+1)/[(N+1)^2(N+2)f^2(\xi_i)] \tag{734e}$$

TABLE LXXVI

COEFFICIENTS IN EQ. 732 FOR UNIFORM DISTRIBUTION (HEGAZY and GREEN, 1975)

	α	a	b	c
T_{HG_1}	0.01	−0.0070	0.8373	−0.2500
	0.05	0.0003	0.5876	−0.0425
T_{HG_2}	0.01	−0.0148	0.1701	0.2745
	0.05	−0.0068	0.0783	0.2419
T'_{HG_1}	0.01	−0.0050	0.7949	−0.0782
	0.05	0.0064	0.5066	0.2364
T'_{HG_2}	0.01	0.0047	−0.0607	0.9330
	0.05	0.0124	−0.1395	0.8212

and:

$$f(\xi) = (2\pi)^{-1/2}\, e^{-\xi^2/2} \qquad (734f)$$

Hegazy and Green have promoted another set of 4 test statistics where ξ_i is replaced by the expected value of a Gaussian order statistic (e.g., BEYER, 1966, p. 259), and s_2^2 by s_{OR}^2, the variance of a normal-order statistic (e.g., BEYER, 1966, pp. 261–265). Incidentally, s_2 is an approximation of s_{OR}. Because the process of T_{GH_5} and T_{GH_6} are comparable to T_{GH_2} and T_{GH_4}, Hegazy and Green recommend limitation to eq. 734, a and b. According to their findings, the replacement of ξ_i by an order statistic does not help much to increase the power.

The formula for the calculation of critical values (eq. 732) is slightly revised for a Gaussian distribution. Two approximations are possible (see Table LXXVII).

Model I:

$$C_T(\alpha) = a + b/N + c/N^2 \qquad (735a)$$

and Model II:

$$C_T(\alpha) = a + b \ln N + c(\ln N)^2 \qquad (735b)$$

Quality control and assurance of observations

This topic is given little attention in most texts on statistical analysis. It deserves discussion in climatology, however.

All raw data from sample surveys and experiments contain errors. This fact is generally accepted. Even in the most carefully prepared projects instrumental or other errors cannot be avoided (e.g., see WILLIAMS, 1978.) The errors may be random or systematic and may be caused by instrumental deficiencies, inaccuracies, unqualified observers, etc., or may be introduced during data preparation or transmission.

Systematic errors can be eliminated if known. E.g., corrections for an erroneous calibration of the baseline can be made. Random errors usually cannot be eliminated. However, some test procedures must be applied in statistical analysis to assure good quality of the data. These test procedures depend on the kind of data samples. E.g., all values of comprehensive matrix tables probably cannot be checked, or maps produced by electronic data processing may be difficult to correct afterwards. Thus, a certain "editing" process of data is very desirable before statistical analysis can follow up. It is evident that

TABLE LXXVII

COEFFICIENTS IN MODEL I (i.e. EQ. 735a) AND MODEL II (i.e. EQ. 735b) FOR GAUSSIAN DISTRIBUTION
(HEGAZY and GREEN, 1975)

	α	a	b	c	Model
T_{GH_3}	0.01	0.7105	−0.1751	0.0108	II
	0.05	0.6027	−0.1481	0.0090	II
T_{GH_4}	0.01	0.0178	2.8736	−8.2894	I
	0.05	0.0126	1.9227	−5.0067	I

one cannot make good data out of bad records, and no editing program can eliminate the small random error. The "big" mistake, i.e., the outliers, such as a 10- or 15-degree error in temperature, needs correction, however. (See ANDREWS and PREGIBON, 1978.)
Industrial quality control has to deal with similar problems (e.g., BURR, 1976). The manufacturer wants to avoid defects. Therefore, similar methods can be adopted for quality control and assurance of atmospheric data. Detailed methods have been described by FILIPPOV (1968), ESSENWANGER (1970), BRYANT (1979), or RICKETTS (1980). Some summary results will be included here, which are particularly suitable for electronic data processing especially radiosonde data and synoptic surface observations; but they can be expanded to include other observational programs.

Individual data checking procedures

Any automatic screening procedure must be suited to discover consistent as well as large inconsistent errors. Simple logic for electronic data processing is another requirement. In atmospheric science large extreme values may not be outliers but can legitimately occur, e.g., hurricanes may lead to excessively low pressure values and wind extremes, and these values may have a biasing influence upon data analysis, although the observations are not erroneous.

Trivial error checks

A first category includes easily recognized errors which permit automatic correction in many cases. Three major error types comprise: faulty coding, incomplete entries, and exceedance of established limits. The last group contains errors outside physical boundaries or established tolerance limits. For example, the dew-point temperature cannot be larger than the air temperature, the wind direction cannot exceed 16 compass points or 360° or the relative humidity 100%, etc.

Error checking by adjacent data

Inconsistencies may be checked against adjacent data in a horizontal field (maps), vertical field (such as cross-sections) or by time relationships. Some procedures have been introduced in topics of homogeneity (p. 14) or on pp. 254–269. Checking procedures also depend on established or derived physical or empirical laws. The goal of checking often is the flagging of suspicious values by electronic data processing. Flagged data are printed and may be corrected by qualified professionals or are flagged and routed to the specified correction procedure of the program in electronic data processing. Some of the test methods are as follows.
(*1*) *Horizontal checks.* This type of check is applicable mostly in the production of maps by electronic data processing. Individual data are checked for homogeneity against neighboring stations. The gradient-wind relationship or similar laws can be employed. Other test procedures have been discussed (p. 247 or p. 254). It is convenient to work with mathematical expressions for which electronic data processing is very simple. Error checks in table form can be established too.

(2) *Vertical relationships.* One of the most useful and widespread checking procedures is a check for vertical consistency such as the dry adiabatic lapse rate for thermodynamic quantities. Automatic correction of errors is possible on a limited scale because often it is not known whether the pressure or temperature observation is wrong, or whether the data are out of sequence, etc. The last data point in a radiosonde ascent must be checked separately because errors cannot be discovered alone by the lapse rate test for this point. As described by ESSENWANGER (1970) a temperature increase of 15°C per 100 mbar between two points such as between the next-to-the-last and the last point may be acceptable; a higher value is flagged. An analytical expression was derived by ESSENWANGER (1967) for the wind profile:

$$\Delta V_{\mathrm{T}} = a_0(\Delta h)^{-2/3} \tag{736}$$

where ΔV_{T} is the critical vector wind shear value above which flagging occurs, Δh is the altitude difference in meters. Although $a_0 \sim 2.5$ has been empirically found by the author as a convenient threshold another constant may be suitable for the particular program of interest. Unfortunately, large deviations of the wind direction will not be flagged by this criterion because they can be associated with low wind speeds. If this is the case, they may be unimportant for practical purposes.

(3) *Time series checks.* It is immaterial whether the time relationship is periodic or aperiodic. Both can be employed but the form of time relationship must be established prior to any testing. Analytical methods such as the Fourier series, eq. 384a, or persistence (p. 16) and autocorrelation, eq. 292a, etc. have been described. Random relationships are useful only to the extent as to establish applicable tolerance limits from the range of the frequency distribution. Application of time series analysis to network data gathering systems with data collection and analysis by computers was presented by MCLOWERY (1973).

Frequency distribution checks

The methods outlined previously will catch the major portions of "suspicious" observations, but some mistakes may be overlooked. Suppose that the surface observation of a radiosonde is missing and all values are shifted one level. The vertical consistency check will not discover this mistake. Assume, that the total ascent is too warm or too cold because of a calibration error. These mistakes, if not tested against neighboring stations, can be checked against the frequency distribution of the element in question.

In statistical analysis sometimes it is suggested to eliminate large errors (outliers) by censoring or truncation of the data sample. In a limited number of cases this technique may be applicable, in climatology (meteorology) extreme values displaying large deviations from the mean can be of special interest. They may be real because of extreme weather conditions. Whether an extreme low pressure value at a Florida station is due to the occurrence of a hurricane or an obvious mistake can probably be decided with much more reliability by a qualified meteorologist than by an elaborate and complex program involving electronic data processing. Even if real, the extreme value may have a disproportionate weight in a short time series of records and adjustment depends on the analysis goal.

The critical problem is the establishment of a test threshold above or below which flagging must occur. Some procedures are presented now.
Some meteorological elements such as the thermodynamic quantities follow the Gaussian distribution law and thresholds can be established by:

$$x_T = \bar{x} \pm k\sigma \qquad (737)$$

with appropriate estimators for $\bar{x}$ and σ and selection of k by the desired level of acceptance. For other elements the cumulative frequency distribution is computed and a certain limit of exceedance is empirically determined. Establishing frequency distributions is costly even by electronic data processing compared with the computation of moments. The Weibull distribution (with moments estimators) can serve as a reasonable tool to keep costs low and provide good approximations to a cumulative distribution (see eq. 111c). Simply:

$$x_T = \theta (\ln P)^{1/\beta} + \gamma \qquad (738a)$$

where:

$$P = 1/[1 - F(x)] \qquad (738b)$$

In this case where exact testing is not a primary goal the approximated test threshold x_T derived from the moments estimators of the Weibull distribution is sufficient. Even the Weibull distribution can be utilized to test a Gaussian distribution. This eliminates different frequency models and different programs for electronic data processing in testing atmospheric elements. Depending on the goal, the shape parameter δ of the Weibull distribution for the Gaussian distribution can be assumed between 3.55 to 3.60 (see ESSENWANGER, 1970). This postulation eliminates the step of calculating β, which is the longest phase in the derivation of moments estimators. The computation of the third moment can also be skipped. If a one-sided criterion is desired, $\delta = 2.96$ for the lower and $\delta = 5.54$ for the upper boundary. More details can be found in ESSENWANGER (1970). For wind speed and vector wind shear data the skewness (eq. 27a) may be approximated by:

$$\gamma_1 = 1.4047E - 0.0646\sigma + 0.0987 \qquad (739a)$$

$$\gamma_1 = 3.1223E - 0.3680\sigma - 0.4515 \qquad (739b)$$

where eq. 739a expresses the wind speed relationship and eq. 739b the vector wind shear relationship for upper air data from surface through 30 km (ESSENWANGER, 1968).

$$E = \nu_3/\sigma^3 = \bar{x}(1 + 3d + 2d^2)/\sigma^3 \qquad (739c)$$

with:

$$d + 1 = \sigma^2/\bar{x} \qquad (739d)$$

Some meteorological elements can be reduced to a Gaussian distribution by a proper transformation. For visibility data a logarithmic transformation may be suitable, for precipitation a $\log x$ or $[\sqrt{x} + \sqrt{x+1}]/2$ transformation may be quite sufficient, although the cube root is often used. More details on transformation are found in ESSENWANGER (1976).

Gross errors and outliers

Any quantity can be read, measured, recorded or transcribed incorrectly, and random errors in measurement cannot be avoided. As long as these random errors stay within reasonable bounds, they seldom bias or distort the results. It is difficult to state a simple rule when an observation should be rejected although subjectively some thresholds can be adopted which serve as boundaries for gross errors. Outside of these values the observation is considered at least to be suspicious, and correction may be necessary.
This threshold is defined as x_T. At the upper boundary $x_T < X_i$. The individual observation is flagged if the inequality holds. Then a correlation is applied or the observation is rejected or omitted. The threshold can be based on the error variance (see eq. 737) where k was introduced as a constant to be determined by the guiding principles of the error analysis based on the Weibull distribution.
ANSCOMBE and TUKEY (1963) provided another mathematical formulation for the calculation of k for any percentage value P of the cumulative distribution function above 95%:

$$k = C[(4df - C^2 - 2)/(4df)]/\sqrt{df/N} \tag{740a}$$

$$C = 1.40 + 0.85C_G \tag{740b}$$

where C_G is the corresponding deviation from the mean of a Gaussian distribution with variance $\sigma_G^2 = 1$ for the percentage P, and df stands for the degrees of freedom.
This mathematical formulation, eq. 740a, of a rejection criterion by Anscombe and Tukey should be used with prudence. ANSCOMBE (1960) cautioned not to regard criteria for the rejection of outliers as significance tests. Rejection rules should fall into the category of insuring good quality of data (GREEN, 1976).
It is reiterated that in atmospheric science outliers are not always wrong observations (ESSENWANGER, 1970), but they can be data which carry an excessive weight in a short data series, and may require corrective action in order to balance their influence.
GRUBBS (1950, 1969) developed a criterion for a judgment whether outliers are "statistical" outliers. For a single outlier: $T_G = (X_{max} - \bar{x})/s$ (741a)

where X_{max} is the maximum, $\bar{x}$ the mean and s the standard deviation. In GRUBBS' (1969) article tables are given for T_G in two cases: where s is calculated from all data or from an independent data set.
A modification was proposed by TIETJEN and MOORE (1972) by testing for k suspected outliers (one-sided criterion):

$$T_{T_1} = \sum_{i=1}^{N-k} (X_i - \bar{x}_k)^2 / \sum_{i=1}^{N} (X_i - \bar{x})^2 \tag{741b}$$

where $\bar{x}$ is the customary mean and $\bar{x}_k$ the mean from $N-k$ observations, eliminating k outliers:

$$\bar{x}_k = \sum_{i=1}^{N-k} X_i/(N-k) \tag{741c}$$

The following two-sided criterion is recommended by the authors:

$$T_{T_2} = \sum (z_j - \bar{z}_k)^2 / \sum (z_i - \bar{z})^2 \tag{742a}$$

where $z_j = |X_i - \bar{x}|$, ordered by absolute magnitude, i.e., $z_j < z_{j+1} < \ldots z_{j+N}$.

$$\bar{z}_k = \sum_{j=1}^{N-k} z_j/(N-k) \tag{742b}$$

Critical values are given by Tietjen and Moore for $\alpha = 0.01$, 0.025, 0.05 and 0.10. An extract is furnished in Tables LXXVIII and LXXIX. The reader is referred to the literature for the detailed tables.

McMillan and David (1971) developed a sequential procedure of testing the maximum residuals. First a check for possible rejection is made:

$$X_{\max} - \bar{x} > c_G \tag{743}$$

where $X_{\max}$ is the maximum residual, and c_G a constant depending on N and α (Grubbs, 1950). If $X_{\max}$ is rejected as an outlier, the procedure is repeated for the sum of the two largest observations. This process was further described by McMillan (1971).

Neyman (1979a) has introduced a new concept into the problem of checking for outliers: outlier-prone and outlier-resistant families of distributions. The Gaussian and the Cauchy distributions are outlier-resistant, but distributions with drawn out tailends such as the log-normal or gamma distribution are outlier-prone. Neyman has especially elaborated

TABLE LXXVIII

CRITICAL VALUES FOR T_{T_1}
(After Tietjen and Moore, 1972)

N	$\alpha=0.01$					$\alpha=0.05$				
	$k=1$	2	3	5	7	$k=1$	2	3	5	7
5	0.044	0.004				0.127	0.018			
10	0.283	0.142	0.070	0.012		0.415	0.230	0.129	0.034	
15	0.440	0.294	0.194	0.090	0.037	0.556	0.382	0.276	0.140	0.066
20	0.539	0.387	0.300	0.175	0.104	0.638	0.480	0.377	0.238	0.150
25	0.607	0.468	0.377	0.246	0.168	0.692	0.550	0.450	0.312	0.222
30	0.650	0.526	0.434	0.312	0.229	0.730	0.599	0.506	0.376	0.283
40	0.722	0.608	0.522	0.408	0.324	0.784	0.672	0.588	0.468	0.378
50	0.768	0.668	0.592	0.483	0.400	0.820	0.722	0.646	0.535	0.450

TABLE LXXIX

CRITICAL VALUES FOR T_{T_2}
(After Tietjen and Moore, 1972)

N	$\alpha=0.01$					$\alpha=0.05$				
	$k=1$	2	3	5	7	$k=1$	2	3	5	7
5	0.029					0.081				
10	0.235	0.101	0.018			0.352	0.172	0.083	0.014	
15	0.404	0.238	0.146	0.054	0.018	0.503	0.317	0.206	0.084	0.030
20	0.499	0.339	0.236	0.121	0.058	0.594	0.416	0.302	0.163	0.085
25	0.571	0.418	0.320	0.188	0.110	0.654	0.493	0.381	0.236	0.146
30	0.624	0.482	0.386	0.250	0.166	0.698	0.549	0.443	0.298	0.203
40	0.704	0.574	0.480	0.347	0.258	0.758	0.629	0.534	0.395	0.297
50	0.748	0.636	0.550	0.424	0.334	0.797	0.684	0.599	0.468	0.373

on the consequences for testing of responses to cloud seeding. A scheme for CLIMAT Data was described by RICKETTS (1980) and archiving of machinable data was presented by SHEARMAN (1980).

General quality control

It is reiterated that no quality assurance program can transform bad records into perfect data. The "editing" of data contributes to elimination of the large errors (outliers), reduces data bias, and provides a general data survey. Correction methods cannot be directed towards an expected analysis result. It is sometimes tempting to omit or correct all observations which contradict an assumed hypothesis. Correction methods must be independent of the subsequent analysis. Thus editing methods must be carefully designed, commensurate with physical laws and meteorological content of the data. Any correction method should be based upon known or derived principles of the error source. Data which have been modified may later prove correct in the light of expanded knowledge.
Establishment of thresholds works for unbounded distributions only. It would be absurd, for instance, to flag all calms in wind distributions or all records of dry periods for precipitation data. Elements with U-shaped distributions can also not be checked by judging the frequency in flagging extremes but negative precipitations or wind speed data, or cloud cover outside the range of 0 to 10 tenth, can be flagged. In principle, methods to assure a good quality of the data must be tailored to the particular data sets and the specific goals of the analysis.

Neyman's $C(\alpha)$ test

One class of tests was developed by NEYMAN (1959, 1979b) who called them $C(\alpha)$ tests. This class may apply where the population is non-Gaussian or other statistical procedures are not suitable for the particular testing problems. NEYMAN (1979b) especially pointed out that non-parametric tests are not always optimal while the $C(\alpha)$ class is optimal (although local and asymptotic). The optimal test criterion is:

$$T_C=(1/\sqrt{N})\sum_{i=1}^{N}\psi(X_i,\hat{\theta})/\sigma_\psi \tag{744a}$$

where $X_i(\xi,\theta)$ are independent random variables with probability density $p(x|\xi,\theta)$, $\hat{\theta}$ is the estimator of (an unknown) nuisance parameter, σ_ψ^2 the variance of ψ. The assumption H_0: $\xi=0$ is rejected, and H_1: $\xi\neq 0$ is adopted for $|T_C|>|t_{\alpha/2}|$, H_1: $\xi>0$ for $T_C>t_\alpha$, or H_1: $\xi<0$ for $T_C<-t_\alpha$, where t_α is optimized from the asymptotic power function:

$$\beta(\xi)\sim(1/\sqrt{2\pi})\int_{S(\alpha)}\exp-(u-\xi\sqrt{N}\rho\sigma_\psi)^2/2 \tag{744b}$$

for $N\to\infty$ and $\xi\to 0$. The optimal $C(\alpha)$ results for $\rho=\pm 1$ (i.e., ρ is the correlation coefficient) and specification of $S(\alpha)$ (either upper or lower boundary: $-\infty$ to $\nu(\alpha)$ or $\nu(\alpha)$ to ∞). Furthermore:

$$\psi=\phi_\xi-\sum_{j=1}^{k}b_j\phi_j \tag{744c}$$

and:

$$\phi_\xi = \partial(\log p)/\partial\xi \text{ for } \xi = 0 \tag{744d}$$

$$\phi_j = \partial(\log p)/\partial\theta_j \text{ for } \xi = 0; j = 1, 2, \ldots k \tag{744e}$$

where k is the number of parameters θ. The coefficients b_j must be found from the variance–covariance matrix ϕ_ξ and ϕ_j and are partial regression coefficients of ϕ_ξ and ϕ_j. The finding of ψ is sometimes elaborate, but NEYMAN and SCOTT (1965) outlined a procedure for which the computational efforts are reduced.

NEYMAN (1979b) gave an example for two variables X and Y having a Poisson distribution:

$$T_C = \left(\sum_{i=1} (X_i - \bar{X})(Y_i - \bar{Y}) \right) \Big/ N(\bar{X}\bar{Y})^{1/2} \tag{745a}$$

and suggested some applications to test weather modification experiments. In accordance with eq. 744c, d, e:

$$\phi_\xi = XY/\theta_1\theta_2 - 1 \quad \phi_1 = X/\theta_1 - 1 \quad \phi_2 = Y/\theta_2 - 1 \tag{745b}$$

Concluding remarks

A variety of basic test procedures has been treated in the preceding sections but many other tests exist. These are partly tests for specific problems and partly they have been developed from a different approach to the statistical background. The author included some of the more fundamental tests tailored to problems in atmospheric science. A more comprehensive description and an expansion to a variety of other tests must be reserved for a special text.

For the analysis of variance (see p. 279) the reader was already referred to the statistical literature. Another special field is the testing by sequential analysis which is based on the principle that the set of observations is not fixed. After the first sample has been analyzed the sampling can continue. In this case, the investigator has three choices: accept H_0, reject H_0 and accept H_1, or continue sampling. The decision is based on the likelihood ratio λ and a specified interval of α for which sampling continues. A classical text was established by WALD (1947). Modifications such as methods by KIEFER and WEISS (1957), ANDERSON (1960), WEISS (1962), FREEMAN and WEISS (1964) require electronic data processing. Other methods were developed by BECHHOFER et al. (1968) and WETHERILL (1975). For the evaluation of hail suppression, THOM (1958c) gave an example for data which follow the negative binomial and the Poisson distributions. Sequential tests with the χ^2 and F distribution were outlined by SIEGMUND (1980). Many more tests exist which could be of interest to the reader, but the inclusion of the voluminous literature is not possible here.

Chapter 7

Characteristics of Meteorological Elements

In many statistical applications it is assumed that the frequency distributions of the data samples follow the Gaussian law or at least are unimodal with a central hump. Samples usually are taken from a homogeneous population. These prerequisites are not always justified for atmospheric elements although the frequency distribution for pressure and temperature come closest to these postulations but even then the uniqueness of the population must be questioned (see e.g., CEHAK, 1967).
A comprehensive treatment of statistical characteristics of atmospheric elements is not possible here. Some special features deserve attention, however. Thus, the wind vector, clouds, and precipitation, as the most common elements besides pressure and temperature are examined in the subsequent sections.

The wind vector

The wind is a three-dimensional vector, but commonly only its horizontal components are used. The horizontal vector can be represented either by wind speed V and direction ϕ or by the zonal (V_z) and meridional (V_m) components. The relationship is:

$$V^2 = V_z^2 + V_m^2 \tag{746}$$

$$V_z = V \cos \alpha = -V \sin \phi \tag{746a}$$

$$V_m = V \sin \alpha = -V \cos \phi \tag{746b}$$

where α is the mathematical angle, measured counterclockwise starting with east. The sign convention used above makes the west and south wind component positive (the angle ϕ represents the direction where the wind blows from) in contrast to the definition by BROOKS et al. (1950). Here $-\cot \alpha = \tan \phi$.
HESSELBERG and BJORKDAL (1929) suggested that the wind components may follow the Gaussian normal distribution. Then the wind vector follows a bivariate Gaussian distribution which was thoroughly discussed in the author's earlier text (ESSENWANGER, 1976). Various other statistical texts treat the bivariate distribution, and information can also be found in BROOKS and CARRUTHERS (1953). A few facts may be worthwhile to recall. The vector mean, also called the resultant wind vector, may be calculated by:

$$V_R^2 = (\bar{V}_z)^2 + (\bar{V}_m)^2 = [(\sum V_z)/N]^2 + [(\sum V_m)/N]^2 \tag{747}$$

The variances*[1] become:

$$\sigma^2_{V_z}=(\sum V^2_z)/N-(\bar{V}_z)^2 \tag{748a}$$

$$\sigma^2_{V_m}=(\sum V^2_m)/N-(\bar{V}_m)^2 \tag{748b}$$

The variance of the scalar speed V_s is:

$$\sigma^2_{V_s}=(\sum V^2)/N-(\bar{V})^2 \tag{749a}$$

or:

$$\sigma^2_{V_s}=\sigma^2_{V_z}+\sigma^2_{V_m}+V^2_R-(\bar{V})^2 \tag{749b}$$

The relation between zonal and meridional component can be expressed by the linear correlation coefficient:

$$r_{zm}=[\sum(V_z-\bar{V}_z)(V_m-\bar{V}_m)]/(\sigma_{V_z}\sigma_{V_m}) \tag{750}$$

The correlation coefficient usually is non-zero. FLOHN (1964) has attempted to interpret the correlation between wind components in terms of the air transport. From a statistical point of view the correlation is caused by the non-alignment of the zonal and meridional components with the axis of a bivariate Gaussian distribution. A simple coordinate transformation can remove the correlation. We set:

$$V_x=(V_z-\bar{V}_z)\cos\beta+(V_m-\bar{V}_m)\sin\beta \tag{751a}$$

$$V_y=(V_m-\bar{V}_m)\cos\beta-(V_z-\bar{V}_z)\sin\beta \tag{751b}$$

Then:

$$\sigma^2_a=(\sigma^2_{V_z}\cos^2\beta-\sigma^2_{V_m}\sin^2\beta)/(\cos^2\beta-\sin^2\beta) \tag{752a}$$

where σ^2_a is the variance along the major axis of a probability ellipse and β represents the angle between the zonal wind direction (west–east) and the major axis of this ellipse. Consequently:

$$\sigma^2_b=\sigma^2_{V_z}+\sigma^2_{V_m}-\sigma^2_a \tag{752b}$$

is the variance of the minor axis, or an equivalent expression to eq. 752a can be derived (ESSENWANGER, 1976, p. 88). Furthermore:

$$\tan 2\beta=2r_{zm}\sigma_{V_z}\sigma_{V_m}/(\sigma^2_{V_z}-\sigma^2_{V_m}) \tag{752c}$$

For additional details see ESSENWANGER, 1976, pp. 83–112.
A standard vector deviation for the wind is defined by:

$$\sigma^2_{\mathbf{V}}=\sigma^2_a+\sigma^2_b=\sigma^2_{V_z}+\sigma^2_{V_m} \tag{753}$$

The interpretation of the standard vector deviation cannot readily be made without a full understanding of the theory of the bivariate Gaussian distribution. The variance of the scalar speed can be rewritten as:

$$\sigma^2_{VS}=\sigma^2_{\mathbf{V}}+V^2_R-(\bar{V})^2 \tag{754a}$$

---

*[1] Dividing by N gives a biased estimator; for an unbiased estimator, divide by $N-1$ (see eq. 48a).

or:

$$\sigma_{VS}^2+(\bar{V})^2=\sigma_V^2+V_R^2 \qquad (754b)$$

Consequently, the standard vector deviation can be computed when variance and mean of the scalar speeds and the resultant wind vector are known. In turn, the variance of the scalar speeds can be computed from the variances of the components, their mean and the mean scalar speed.

Assume that the wind vector can be split into the resultant wind vector V_R and a component deviation (V_d) from the center point of the bivariate ellipse (coordinates $\bar{V}_z$; $\bar{V}_m$) we can write (see Fig. 14):

$$V_d^2=V_R^2+V^2-2V_RV\cos\theta \qquad (755a)$$

where θ denotes the angle between the resultant wind vector V_R and the wind vector V. Summing the components of eq. 755a yields:

$$(\sum V_d^2)/N=V_R^2+(\sum V^2)/N-2V_R(\sum V\cos\theta)/N \qquad (755b)$$

The term on the left hand side is the vector deviation σ_V^2. The second term on the right hand side is $\sigma_{VS}^2+(\bar{V})^2$. The last member on the right hand side sums all wind vectors and becomes V_R. Substitution of these terms leads to eq. 754, a or b.

The constancy of the wind q has been previously discussed (see eq. 42, a–d). In present notations:

$$q=V_R^2/\bar{V}^2 \qquad (756)$$

Representation of wind data was always problematic. Sir Napier Shaw invented the ingenious device of the "wind star". This is a composite wind rose, which shows the annual variation of the wind speed frequency for a restricted number of classes of the wind speed (usually three) for classes of the wind direction (usually sixteen). More details can be found in the text by CONRAD and POLLAK (1950).

The wind speed

BROOKS and CARRUTHERS (1953) suggested plotting the wind speed in units of the Beaufort scale as a cumulative distribution. This plot permits determination of the exceedance of any wind speed threshold by a graphical method.

ESSENWANGER (1968) recommended representation of the wind speed, especially for upper air data, by a Weibull distribution (see MITSUTA and HAYASHI, 1979, and SUZUKI, 1980). The agreement between empirical and analytical cumulative distribution provides good results in the 90 to 99% range of the c.d.f., i.e., the part which represents low wind speeds

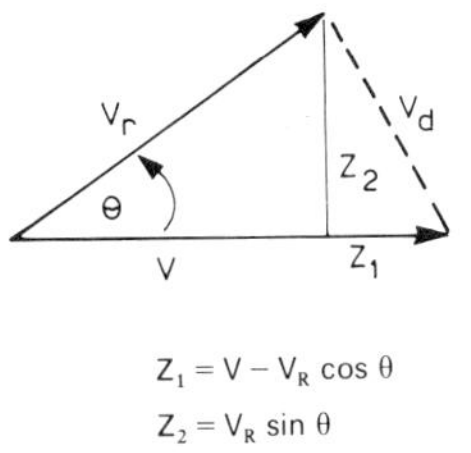

Fig. 14. Vector diagram for eq. 755a.

may not be as good. This disagreement may not be critical for aerospace or wind energy problems, because the low wind speed is usually of secondary interest or is disregarded (STEWART and ESSENWANGER, 1978, or SUZUKI, 1980).

The moments estimator for the Weibull distribution requires the computation of the third moment. In most tabulations, mean and variance alone are available. The author (ESSENWANGER, 1968) developed an approximation of the third moment by a regression relationship. It requires the third moment of the negative binomial distribution which can be derived from mean and variance. The regression line was deduced from four representative global stations and tested on an independent station from the polar region because in the regression analysis the deviations from the straight line were largest in that region. The calculated thresholds of the wind speed between 90 and 99% of the c.d.f. were of the same magnitude as the instrumental errors.

First, $C_1 = M_3/S^3$ where M_3 is the third moment of the negative binomial (see eq. 70a); then $\gamma_V = M_{3V}/S^3$ is calculated, with:

$$\gamma_V = 1.4047C_1 - 0.0646S + 0.0987 \tag{757}$$

where M_{3V} is the third moment sought.

Another engineering problem is the determination of critical stresses in structures at the surface. THOM (1954) outlined a procedure by employing the Fisher-Tippett II distribution (see eq. 207a). Before wind data can be utilized they must be standardized to a defined reference level. Usually the power law is taken:

$$V_{h_1} = V_{h_2}(h_1/h_2)^{1/C} \tag{758a}$$

or in logarithmic form:

$$\ln V_{h_1} = \ln V_{h_2} + (\ln h_1 - \ln h_2)/C \tag{758b}$$

HUSS (1946) recommended a level of 30 ft. (=9.14 m) and a constant $C=7$. The question of standardizing the wind speed in the boundary layer has found wide discussion and a more sophisticated model may be desired. In the lowest 15–20 m these models display no drastic difference other than that induced by terrain conditions.

For example, the variation of the wind speed with height in the boundary layer can be expressed from the generally accepted formula:

$$V_h = V^* k^{-1}\left[\ln\left(\frac{h-h_0}{h_0}\right) + \phi(h)\right] \tag{759}$$

where V_h is the wind speed at height h, V^* the friction velocity, k the Kármán constant, and h_0 the surface roughness, $\phi(h)$ is the integral diabatic influence function as defined by LETTAU (1962). In using V_h for the measured altitude and for the recommended standard level V_{h_s}, the reduction can then be found by the ratio V_{h_s}/V_h. It is evident that eq. 759 is not trivial. Constants could be introduced as recommended by STEARNS (1970) from the KEYPS model.

The problem of wind gustiness was treated by CEHAK (1963) and KLUG (1964). While Cehak suggested a power spectrum analysis of the wind speed and developed formulae from which the velocity of the most frequent gust and the mean interval between gusts can be estimated, Klug supplemented the theory by basing his scheme on a spectral form developed by WIPPERMAN (1961). The description of the complete theory exceeds the intended limit for this section and the interested reader may read the literature cited.

Duration of runs

The wind as an energy source has gained importance in recent time. Therefore, the duration of runs where the (surface) speed exceeds a certain threshold is of special interest. This distribution function was discussed by several authors.
HURST et al. (1977) and COROTIS et al. (1978) have worked with a power-law distribution. SIGL et al. (1979) have suggested a composite distribution of duration time t:

$$F(t) = 1 - (t/t_0)^{1-b}, \quad t_0 \leq t \leq t_1 \tag{760a}$$

$$F(t) = 1 - A e^{-Bt}, \quad t_1 \leq t \leq \infty \tag{760b}$$

EDWARDS (1980) has developed a corresponding model which avoids the somewhat artificial split but which has the same limiting form:

$$F(t) = 1 - (t/t_0)^{1-b} \exp[-B(t - t_0)] \tag{760c}$$

where t_0 is the shortest data resolution time (e.g., Edwards sets $t_0 = 50$ s for observations from New Zealand). The expected mean time $E(t)$ is then (simplified):

$$E(t) = t_0[(Bt_0)^{b-2}\Gamma(2 - b)] \tag{760d}$$

The calculation of estimators was previously discussed (see eq. 266a, b).

The wind direction

The statistical analysis of wind speed data and wind components was discussed in the preceding section. The wind direction is an angular variate. Therefore, standard methods which have been developed for a non-periodic variate will lead to difficulties. Trivial methods have been tried, e.g. the establishment of contingency tables with wind direction classes as one entry and other meteorological elements as the second parameter. Frequency distributions by classes of wind direction (histograms) can be readily obtained. Most other methods will encounter problems.
It is elementary to calculate the moments (e.g., mean, variance) of a non-periodic variate or to deduce its cumulative distribution (ogive). Moments can be obtained formally by standard mathematical procedures (see eq. 21a) but the result may have an ambiguity in the interpretation for an angular variate. In the past it has been common practice in meteorology to split the wind vector into components and study their relationship with other elements. Since the wind component comprises wind speed and direction, most results reflect the combined effect rather than direction alone. Sometimes this may be an added benefit, but at other times the influence of the direction alone is of interest and is difficult to discover.
The "prevailing" wind direction has occasionally been employed as a substitute to solve the above mentioned deficiency. In the bimodal case the "prevailing" wind direction may not lead to a better solution than the separation of the wind vector into components. Other statistical techniques have been introduced by GUMBEL (1950, 1954), GUMBEL et al.

(1953), or GREENWOOD (1958, 1959). These methods may be adequate for some studies; correlation and curve fitting problems cannot easily be solved with unequivocal outcome, although GOULD (1969) treated regression techniques for angular variates with the circular distribution (see eq. 159b) and JOHNSON and WEHRLY (1977) recommended the canonical correlation. A circular distribution as statistical background was utilized by JONES et al. (1976). It also was summarized by SUZUKI (1980). ESSENWANGER (1961) suggested definition of the mean and variance for an angular variate which is presented in the following sections. A proper mean value is neccssary as the basis for the calculation of a correlation coefficient. Recently, FISHER and LEE (1983) also developed a method to define a mean, and FISHER and LEWIS (1983) expanded it for the estimation of the common mean of several circular or spherical distributions.

Statistical background for the definition of a mean wind direction

The problem of deriving a suitable mean direction was treated by the author (ESSENWANGER, 1961 and 1964). The calms are disregarded under the assumption that they are distributed like the data with non-zero wind speed or the calms can be converted into directions by postulating that they are distributed in the same ratio as low wind speeds. The latter may be the better solution in most cases. Next an ambiguity is explained.
Assume that an angular variate such as the wind direction is given by a set of two observations, 20° and 340°. Formal computation of the mean value would lead to 180°. The variance would amount to 160^2 degrees. The 20° is now converted into the equivalent of 380° as the angle of a periodic variate. Now the mean is 360° and the variance 20^2 degrees. This points out that 360 (or zero) degrees is another solution of a mean value. In fact this solution is even better because it leads to a smaller variance. This ambiguity of two solutions comes from the periodicity of the angular variates, by which we can treat the observation with its face value or its periodic extension. The only requirement is that $|\phi_i-\phi_{\mathrm{m}}|\leq 180°$, which in both cases is fulfilled (i.e., $340° = -20°$). Because the direction of the angular variate does not change by adding or subtracting 360°, i.e., the length of the cycle, determination of the mean becomes ambiguous. A definition is necessary. Mere transformation of the angle into arc units does not resolve the problem of ambiguity caused by the periodicity.
It is shown that the mean ϕ_m of the directions ϕ_i is governed by two conditions. First:

$$\sum(\phi_i-\phi_k)=0 \tag{761a}$$

From eq. 26d:

$$\sigma^2_{xm}=\sigma^2_{x0}+(x_0-x_m)^2 \tag{761b}$$

A minimum occurs for $x_0=x_m$. Thus, the variance*[1] is a minimum for the mean. This second condition implies for the periodic variate:

$$G(\phi_i,\phi_k)=N\sigma^2_{\phi_k}=\sum(\phi_i-\phi_k)^2 \tag{762a}$$

with:

$$\mathrm{d}G/\mathrm{d}\phi_k=0,\ \text{a minimum for } \phi_k=\phi_m \tag{762b}$$

*[1] The difference between biased and unbiased variance is not essential for the following discussion.

Let ϕ_k be a variable reference point, which coincides with ϕ_m when these two conditions (eqs. 760 and 762b) are met. Then, $\sigma^2_{\phi_k}$ is the usual variance $\phi_k = \phi_m$. The only restrictive condition is:

$$|\phi_i - \phi_k| \leq 180^\circ \tag{763}$$

We notice that eq. 760 is a solution of eq. 762b which implies that any minimum for eq. 762b automatically fulfills the condition of eq. 760. The function $G(\phi_i,\phi_k)$ is now a varying function of a reference point ϕ_k, but not all conditions $dG/d\phi_k = 0$ are minima. Besides, a solution of $\phi_m = \phi_k$, where $G(\phi_i,\phi_k)$ is the infimum (=lowest minimum) is needed:

$$G(\phi_i,\phi_m) < G(\phi_i,\phi_k), \quad k \neq m \tag{764}$$

Thus, the infimum location is the logical place for ϕ_m. Although for a rectangular distribution eq. 762b does not lead to a solution in practical application ϕ_m has always been obtained.

In the non-periodic case eq. 761 has no other minimum than $x_0 = x_m$. This is not the case for the periodic variate. The assumed sample of two, $\phi_i = 20^\circ$ and 340°, clearly illustrates that $dG/d\phi_k = 0$ for 180° and 360° but only 360° is the infimum.

This task of finding the infimum of eq. 762b is simple for electronic data processing. $\sigma^2_{\phi_k}$ is calculated for a variable reference point ϕ_k, e.g., for every 10 degrees of a circle. Thus:

$$g(\phi_k) = \sum (\phi_i - \phi_k)^2 \tag{765a}$$

or:

$$g(\phi_k) = \sum f_{\phi_j}(\phi_j - \phi_k)^2 \tag{765b}$$

for grouped data. Observe, however, that:

$$|\phi_i - \phi_k| \leq \phi_t/2 \tag{765c}$$

where ϕ_t is the length of the periodicity. E.g., for a circle with the observation given in one degree unit $\phi_t = 360$, for the 16 point wind rose $\phi_t = 16$, etc. The infimum $g(\phi_k)$ is then the solution for the mean ϕ_m.

$$\sigma^2_\phi = g(\phi_m)/N \tag{766a}$$

or:

$$\sigma^2_\phi = g(\phi_m)/(N-1) \tag{766c}$$

depending on whether we are satisfied with a biased or need the unbiased variance.

Calculation of the mean wind direction by desk calculator

When no electronic data processors are available, the computation of $g(\phi_k)$ within the boundaries from ϕ_{r_0} to $\phi_{r_0} + \phi_t$ may be sometimes elaborate. A shorter procedure for desk calculator application is introduced with the restating of eq. 762a:

$$G_k = G_0 - 2\phi_k\phi_0 + N\phi_k^2 + 2\phi_t\left[\sum_{\phi_r}^{\phi_r+\phi_k} n_i(\phi_i' - \phi_k + \phi_t/2)\right] \tag{767a}$$

from which the derivative is:

$$G_{k_2}-G_{k_1}=\frac{\Delta g(\phi_k)}{\Delta\phi_k}=-2\left[\bar{\phi}_0-N\phi_k\Delta\phi_k+\phi_t\sum_{\phi_r}^{\phi_r+\phi_k}n_i(\Delta\phi_k)\right] \tag{767b}$$

The original reference point $\phi_r=\phi_{r_0}$ for this equation is placed at $\phi_t/2$ (i.e. $\phi_t=360°$, $\phi_{r_0}=180°$, and ϕ_i keeps its original value from 0 to 180°, but ϕ_i from 180° to 360° will be $\phi_i'=\phi_i-360$). G_0 corresponds to the initial condition for a reference point ϕ_{r_0}. Later it is shown that G_0 does not need to be computed to determine ϕ_m. Under the assumption that $\Delta\phi_k=1$ and $\phi_{r_0}=\phi_t/2$:

$$-\frac{1}{2}\frac{\Delta g}{\Delta\phi_k}=\bar{\phi}_0-N\phi_k+\phi_t\sum_{\phi_t/2}^{\phi_t/2+\phi_k}n_i. \tag{768a}$$

Then:

$$\bar{\phi}_0=\sum_{0}^{\phi_t/2}\phi_i+\sum_{\phi_t/2}^{\phi_t}(\phi_i-\phi_t) \tag{768b}$$

which merely defines the variate ϕ_i for an initial condition. Eq. 767a is written for ungrouped data and can be modified for grouped data by the customary procedure. The initial mean value is $\phi_{m_0}=\bar{\phi}_0/N$.

Eq. 767a can be interpreted that an initial mean $\bar{\phi}_0$ is chosen which is modified by progressing terms in k. While the first term is merely a linear change proportional to the shift of the reference point, the second term is generally a nonlinear contribution. It comprises the number of observations exceeding $|\phi_t/2|$ as ϕ_r progresses. Assuming a finite abscissa of length ϕ_t, this term contains the number of observations which are cancelled from one side and reappear on the other side of the abscissa. The calculation by differences is much shorter than the calculation by eq. 762a. This is possible because we are only interested in $\Delta g/\Delta\phi=dg/d\phi=0$.

The parameter ϕ_k and the reference point ϕ_r are related by:

$$\phi_k=\phi_r-\phi_t/2 \tag{768c}$$

i.e., $\phi_{k_0}=0$ for $\phi_r=\phi_t/2$, or in this example $\phi_{k_0}=0$ for $\phi_{r_0}=180°$.

Eq. 767b can also be solved graphically by plotting the left hand side versus the right hand side of:

$$\bar{\phi}_0-N\phi_k=-\phi_t\sum_{\phi_t/2}^{\phi_t/2+\phi_k}n_i \tag{769a}$$

The left hand side is a straight line. The intersection between the line of the left hand side and the curve at the right hand side provides the solutions $dg/d\phi=0$. The summation of n_i is the cumulative distribution of the frequency of ϕ_i starting at $\phi_t/2=\phi_{r_0}$. Consequently, the analytical form of eq. 769a is:

$$\bar{\phi}_0-N\phi_k=-\phi_tNF(\phi_i) \tag{769b}$$

The computation on a desk calculator can be reduced further by introducing the second derivative:

$$\Delta H(\phi_k)=\frac{dg_i}{d\phi}-\frac{dg_{i+1}}{d\phi}=-\Delta\phi_1+\phi_t\left(\sum_{\phi_1}^{\phi_2}n_i\right)\Big/N \tag{770a}$$

with $\phi_1=\phi_r$; $\phi_2=\phi_{r+1}$, or $\phi_1=\phi_t/2+\phi_k$ and $\phi_2=\phi_1+\Delta\phi_k$. For simplicity $dg_i/d\phi$ is denoted by δ_i. Then:

$$\delta_i-\delta_{i+1}=-\Delta\phi_i+n_\delta \qquad (770b)$$

Regrouping renders:

$$\delta_{i+1}=\delta_i\pm\Delta\phi_i\mp n_\delta \qquad (770c)$$

The lower sign goes for $\phi_{r+1}>\phi_r$, a mathematical positive turn from 0° to 180° etc. From eq. 770a the following three conditions are deduced:

$$\Delta\phi_i=\phi_r-\phi_{r+1}=\Delta\phi_k \quad \text{(class width)} \qquad (771a)$$

$$n_\delta=\phi_t n_j/N=\phi_t f_j=n_j(\phi_t/N) \qquad (771b)$$

$$\delta_1=\left(\sum_{\phi_0}^{\phi_t}\phi_i n_i\right)\Big/N=\sum_{0}^{\phi_t}f_j\phi_j \qquad (771c)$$

where n_j stands for the observed frequency in the class interval from ϕ_r to ϕ_{i+1}, f_j is the corresponding probability density. After the initial δ_1 we compute δ_{i+1} by eq. 770c. The terms of eq. 770c which are known a priori are combined by setting:

$$\varepsilon_i=\delta_i\pm\Delta\phi_i \qquad (772a)$$

while n_δ must be calculated in every step. Now:

$$\delta_{i+1}=\varepsilon_i\mp n_\delta \qquad (772b)$$

Recall that δ_{i+1} stands for $d(g_{i+1})/d\phi$. Then solutions $dg/d\phi=0$ occur when:

(*1*) $\varepsilon_i=0$ and/or $\delta_{i+1}=0$ (direct solution) (773a)

(*2*) $\varepsilon_i-n_\delta/2=0$ ($\delta_{i+1}=-n_\delta/2$, accuracy zero) (773b)

(*3*) a change is from $-\delta_i$ to $+\varepsilon_i$ (solution is between $-\delta_i$ and ε_i). (773c)

Eq. 771a permits adjustment of the class interval to any size, and empty classes can be combined if $\Delta\phi_i$ and n_j are properly determined. More details can be seen from Example 68.
The variance σ_ϕ^2 needs to be computed only for solutions $dg/d\phi=0$ to judge the infimum. The method saves considerable time compared with the computation of $g(\phi_k)$ by eq. 765a. In the first computation of the $\bar{\phi}_0$ the addition of the observations in the class interval $\phi_r\pm\phi_t/2$ can be omitted, assuming that half the observations in that class would be accounted with plus, the other half with a negative sign. Before a continuation of the calculations with the next reference ϕ_r this class must be added with the proper sign. For simplicity one should count the last class interval with positive sign. This requires an adjustment of the mean by half of the observations, $(n_i\cdot 180)/2$. Otherwise confusion may arise with regard to the exact location of ϕ_m. For more details see Example 68.

Mean wind direction calculations by runs

This method is a shortcut for the calculation of the mean wind direction by desk calculation. The calms are treated as outlined in the statistical background. The procedure is presented for 16 classes of the wind direction. The angular data are grouped into classes and the probability density of the classes f_i is converted into code 0 or 1 as follows. A zero code is given when $f_i < 0.05$ and code 1 when $f_i \geq 0.05$, i.e., the dividing line is the 5% frequency. Now the runs (sequence of same numbers) are examined. Of interest are the runs of 1 only. The midpoint of the major run of ones is determined as the initial mean ϕ_{m_0} and the angular ϕ scale is adjusted to range from $-\phi_t/2 + \phi_{m_0}$ to $\phi_{m_0} + \phi_t/2$. Now $\bar{\phi}_0$ is computed (eq. 727a) utilizing the adjusted angular scale, i.e.:

$$\bar{\phi}_0 = \sum_{-\phi_t/2}^{\phi_{m_0}} (\phi_i - \phi_t) + \sum_{\phi_{m_0}}^{\phi t/2} \phi_i \tag{774a}$$

Now:

$$n_\delta = \phi_t \left(\sum_{\phi_1}^{\phi_2} n_i \right) \Big/ N = \phi_t \cdot \sum_{\phi_1}^{\phi_2} f_i = (\phi_t/N) \sum_{\phi_1}^{\phi_2} n_i \tag{774b}$$

$$\phi_1 = (\phi_t/2 + \phi_0) \quad \text{and} \quad \phi_2 = (\phi_t/2 + \phi_0) + \phi_u \tag{774c}$$

where ϕ_u is the upper boundary of the next class interval following ϕ_1 in analogy with eq. 771b. We subtract or add, depending whether ϕ_u decreases or increases. When we subtract (going towards the negative side) we must judge:

$$\phi'_0 = \bar{\phi}_0 - n_\delta + \Delta\phi \tag{775a}$$

and:

$$\phi_m = \phi'_0 - n_\delta/2 + \phi_r \tag{775b}$$

If:

$$-0.5\Delta\phi \leq \phi'_0 \leq 0.5\Delta\phi \tag{775c}$$

the mean has been found and is ϕ_{m_i}. Adjustment must be made that half of the observations in the class $\phi_r = \phi_{m_i} + \phi_t/2$ were counted as positive.

If $|\phi'_0| > 0.5$, then the next $\phi_{m_{i+1}}$ must be computed, etc. until eq. 775c is fulfilled. If we add (going towards the positive side), we must judge:

$$\phi'_0 = \bar{\phi}_0 + n_\delta - \Delta\phi \tag{775d}$$

Although an adjustment must be made for half of the number of observations in the class $\phi_{m_i} + \phi_t/2$, at the final step, the adjustment is not necessary as an interim step. (See Example 68.)

The sequential process can be shortened by adding (or subtracting) more than one class interval by:

$$\phi'_0 = \bar{\phi}_0 - \sum n_\delta + c_{i-1}\Delta\phi \tag{775e}$$

or:

$$\phi'_0 = \bar{\phi}_0 + \sum n_\delta - c_i\Delta\phi \tag{775f}$$

where c_i stands for the number of classes to be shifted, $c_{i-1} = c_i - 1$ and $\sum n_\delta$ accounts for the changed positions opposite the reference point ϕ_r.

After ϕ_m has been determined, σ_ϕ^2 can readily be calculated as given by eq. 762a with $\phi_k = \phi_m$.

Example 68. Computation of the mean wind direction (unimodal case). The first example (see Table LXXX) illustrates the computation of the mean direction for a set of angular values (the average wind direction over a layer from surface to 5 km) at Albrook in March (1956–1964). The frequency distribution n_i of the angular variate is listed in the column next to the class interval. (The column i is omitted as trivial, $i=1$ for the class interval 0 to 10, etc.) Following is the class reference value ϕ_r employed to judge the condition of eq. 763. The subsequent columns list the resulting ϕ_{m_i} and the standard deviation $\sigma_{\phi_{m_i}}$ for this reference value ϕ_r. ϕ_{m_i} has not been obtained by electronic data processing:

$$\phi_{m_i}=(\sum \phi_i)/N=\sum (\phi_i-\phi_r)/N+\phi_r \qquad (776)$$

TABLE LXXX

COMPUTATION OF THE WIND DIRECTION MEAN (UNIMODAL)

Class (degr.)	n_i	ϕ_r	ϕ_{m_i}	$\sigma_{\phi_{m_i}}$	n_j^{*1}	n_δ	δ_{i+1}	n'_j	δ'_{i+1}	Runs
0–10	11	5	27.7	60.3	0	0	22.80	0	22.68	0
10–20	21	15	28.5	57.2	1	0.84	13.64	1	13.52	0
20–30	22	25	28.5	55.68	1	0.84	4.48	0	3.52	1
30–40	42	35	33.6	55.69	5	4.20	−1.32	6	−1.44	1
40–50	63	45	34.4	56.8	3	2.52	−8.80	1	−10.60	1
50–60	82	55	38.6	59.2	6	5.03	−13.77	5	−16.41	1
60–70	46	65	41.1	62.4	1	0.84	−22.93	3	−23.89	1
70–80	13	75	43.6	66.7	2	1.68	−31.25	3	−31.37	0
80–90	11	85	43.6	71.9	1	0.84	−40.41	0	−41.37	0
90–100	8	95	46.2	78.0	8	6.71	−43.70	3	−48.85	0
100–110	8	105	52.0	84.1	4	3.36	−50.34	7	−52.98	0
110–120	4	115	57.0	90.4	8	6.71	−53.63	6	−57.95	0
120–130	0	125	62.9	96.7	8	6.71	−56.92	7	−62.07	0
130–140	2	135	72.2	103.0	12	10.07	−56.85	11	−62.84	0
140–150	0	145	82.2	108.9	9	7.55	−59.30	12	−63.77	0
150–160	2	155	87.3	114.7	5	4.20	−65.10	6	−67.74	0
160–170	2	165	92.3	120.7	5	4.20	−70.90	6	−72.70	0
170–180	0	175	101.5	126.7	13	10.91	−69.99	11	−73.47	0
180–190	0	185	108.2	132.5	11	9.23	−70.76	8	−76.76	0
190–200	1	195	123.4	138.1	21	17.62	−63.14	18	−71.65	0
200–210	1	205	139.3	143.0	22	18.46	−54.68	19	−65.71	0
210–220	5	215	168.7	147.0	42	35.25	−29.43	35	−46.34	0
220–230	3	225	214.8	149.1	63	52.87	13.44	55	−10.18	0
230–240	6	235	270.2	148.4	82	68.82	72.26	66	32.20	0
240–250	1	245	334.8	143.9	46	38.61	100.87	77	89.82	0
250–260	2	255	353.3	137.2	13	10.91	101.78	22	98.28	0
260–270	1	265	364.2	129.9	11	9.23	100.01	13	99.19	0
270–280	8	275	369.2	122.3	8	6.71	96.72	6	94.22	0
280–290	4	285	375.1	114.5	8	6.71	93.43	7	90.10	0
290–300	8	295	380.1	106.5	4	3.36	86.79	6	85.13	0
300–310	8	305	382.6	98.5	0	0	76.79	3	77.65	0
310–320	12	315	384.3	90.7	2	1.68	68.47	2	69.33	0
320–330	9	325	384.3	83.4	0	0	58.47	0	59.33	0
330–340	5	335	385.2	76.5	2	1.68	50.15	1	50.17	0
340–350	5	345	386.8	70.2	2	1.68	41.83	2	41.84	0
350–360	13	355	387.7	64.7	0	0	31.83	1	32.68	0
	$\sum=429$									

$n_\delta=n_j\cdot 360/429$

*[1] n_j is n_i for a class interval 180° apart from ϕ_r. It has been symbolized by n_i in eqs. 767a, 768a and 769a. It is denoted n_j for this table to differentiate from the observation n_i.

In order to accommodate condition 763 the right hand side of eq. 776 must be used. Without condition 763 the sum $(\sum \phi_i)/N$ remains constant and is independent of the reference point.
The correct ϕ_m can be picked from the minimum standard deviation, in our case $\sigma_{\phi_m}=55.68$. Hence ϕ_m would be $\phi_r+\delta'_{i+1}=25.0+3.52=28.52$. It can be seen that the standard deviation with the class reference $\phi_r=35^\circ$ is almost the same low value, with 55.69. If this class had rendered the minimum standard deviation, the true mean would be $35-1.44$ or 33.56.
The example was especially chosen to illustrate to the reader that sometimes the minimum can be very broad. The correct mean lies between the boundaries 28.5 and 33.6. ϕ_{m_i} does not coincide with either $\phi_r=25$ or 35 degrees. The exact value depends on the frequency distribution within the class intervals 200°–210° or 210°–220° (opposite 25° or 35°). The interval 200°–220° contains six values. (See also column n'_j at reference $\phi_r=35^\circ$.) Assume that no observation between 205 and 208.5 had occurred. Then we have no misclassification from condition 763. For reference $\phi_r=25^\circ$ we find: $\phi_j=\phi_i-\phi_m$ is negative for $0\le\phi_i<25^\circ$, ϕ_j is positive for $25^\circ\le\phi_i<205$ and ϕ_j is negative, i.e. $\phi'_i=\phi_i-360$ for $205<\phi_i<360$. Hence, ϕ_i for the class 205 to 215 would be $-180<\phi_i\le-170$. For a mean value of $\phi_m=28.5$ the ϕ_j should not be negative in the interval $205<\phi_i<208.5$. Consequently, the exact mean value depends on the frequency density in the class interval 205°–215°. In electronic data processing ungrouped data (e.g., units of one degree) are utilized. Calculating mean and standard deviation by reference ϕ_r of one degree progression in the interval between 25 and 35° easily solves the problem. The exact location of the minimum can be established with an error of less than one degree.*[1]
Assume that the same value of $\sigma_{\phi_{m_i}}$ for 25° and 35° is obtained from grouped data or assume $\sigma_{25}=\sigma_{35}$. A proper mean ϕ_m can be found by the following analysis: $n_i=1$ for 200 to 210 and $n_i=5$ for 210 to 220. Assuming an equal distribution within the classes, $n_i=0.5$ from 205 to 210 and $n_i=2.5$ from 210 to 215. Thus, the total between 205 and 215 is $n_j=3.0$. The maximum shift of the mean 28.5 could be 2.52, i.e. to 31.0 (namely $\phi_m+360\cdot n_j/N=28.5+360\cdot 3/429=28.5+2.52$). The calculation with a shift from the other side provides $33.6-360\cdot 3/429=31.1$. The most likely ϕ_m is 31.05. It is rarely found that standard deviations for neighboring class references are exactly equal for individual observations used in one degree units. In this case, the continuation of electronic data processing of ϕ_r in degree units between 25° and 35° led to $\phi_m=29.4$ with $\sigma_{\phi_m}=55.67$.
It may seem somewhat puzzling that the precise location for the mean direction requires that much diligence. It may be simpler to adopt the solution from $dg/d\phi=0$, which in this case is based on the column δ_{i+1}. We could linearly interpolate with the ratio $4.48/(4.48+1.32)$ between $\phi_r=25$ and 35, which renders $25^\circ+0.77\Delta\phi=32.7$. This provides a third value ϕ_m. Although the assumption of a linear interpolation is not necessarily valid the existence of three mean values ϕ_m may appear as an ambiguity. This discrepancy has a simple explanation.
The standard error of the mean is $\varepsilon_{\phi_m}=\sigma/\sqrt{N}=55.68/\sqrt{429}=2.69$. Consequently, all three solutions, 29.4, 31.05 or 32.7 are within the $\pm$ one sigma range. The main issue is not the existence of three close numerical values for the mean but the formalistic summation of $(\sum \phi_i)/N$ over the scale 0°–360° which provides $\phi_m=105^\circ$, about 65° apart from the true mean with minimum variance. The standard deviation for $\phi_m=105^\circ$ is $\sigma_{\phi_m}=84.1$, which is considerably larger than the 55.67 for the true ϕ_m.

Example 69. Short method of calculating the mean. The three columns subsequent to the standard deviation list n_j, n_δ, and δ_{i+1}, the latter is identical with the function $dg_i/d\phi$. We extract from column δ_{i+1} that one zero solution lies between the 20°–40° class interval, another between 210° and 230°. Although the first answer leads to the defined mean $\phi_m=29.4$, the second solution shows a maximum for the variance.
The two adjacent columns contain the result for a slightly shifted class division, based on $\phi_r+\Delta\phi=\phi_r+10$, i.e. 5 to 15°, etc. While n'_j is the summation corresponding to the change in ϕ_{m_i}, δ'_{i+1} is the corresponding function to δ_{i+1}. Comparison between δ_{i+1} and δ'_{i+1} indicates that the fluctuations of $dg/d\phi$ may be caused by the empirical distribution (in degrees as units) because ϕ_{m_i} is based on δ'_{i+1}.
The last column "runs" is needed for the shortcut method. Since 5% of 429 is 21.45 all values below 21.45 are designated as zero, classes with more than 21.45 are given as one. Only one run is found.

---

*[1] Note, this "data accuracy" should not be mistaken for the "estimation inaccuracy".

We select the middle class ($\phi_r = 45°$). From the frequency distribution:

$\sum \phi_i = \delta_{i+1} = -8.80$

Application of eq. 775a yields:

$\phi'_0 = -8.80 - 2.52 + 10.0 = -1.32$

This value is below $|0.5\Delta\phi|$, which implies that $\phi_m = 35 - 1.32 = 33.7$ is the solution which needs correction for the class distribution from 200° to 220°. From the distribution of n_i (second column) n_j is 5 for the class interval 180° apart from the mean $\bar{\phi}'_0$. Hence:

$\phi_m = \phi'_0 - n_\delta/2 + \phi_r = -1.32 - 2.10 + 35 = -3.42 + 35 = 31.58$

This value is close to the mean determined from the individual data. It should be reiterated that the difference between 29.4 and 31.6 by the shortcut method is partly due to the unequal density distribution of the individual observations (one degree units) and the random error attached which cannot be properly assessed for grouped data. The true population mean lies, however, within $\pm 2\varepsilon_{\phi_m}$ with 95% confidence. This 95% interval is $\pm 5.38°$, i.e., the total range of 10.8° is of the magnitude of a class interval and twice the difference between 28.5 and 33.6.
It is reiterated that the example was chosen to illustrate the individual problem areas. The author encountered no problems in most computations of the defined mean.

Example 70. Computation of the mean wind direction in the bimodal case. The frequency distribution (Table LXXXI) represents average wind directions over a layer from surface to 3 km at Chateauroux (France) in December (1956–1964). The sequence of columns is the same as disclosed in Table LXXX except that n_δ has been omitted.
Since the frequency distribution is bimodal, two minima are found, at 195.9 and 303.3. The standard deviations are 97.6 and 95.8, respectively, and the solution with the lower variance is selected namely $\phi_m = 303.3$. Columns δ_{i+1} and δ'_{i+1} indicate two other zero points, around 57° and 255°, which in both cases are solutions with maximum variance. In the bimodal case the shortcut method by runs fails. This can be readily explained because in the non-periodic bimodal case the mean is placed between the two peaks. Analogously in the case of an angular variate the mean is expected between modes. This is confirmed by the regular procedure developed by the author (see Table LXXXI).
The minimum standard deviation is 95.8°. This may seem rather high. However, the frequency distribution is bimodal, and the large value is not surprising, but is typical for a frequency distribution of an angular variate with two peaks. It resembles the non-periodic case. The mean from the analysis of 1° class units yields $\phi_m = 299.9$ with $\sigma_{\phi_m} = 95.75$.

The cumulative distribution

The establishment of a cumulative distribution is no problem for a distribution with defined boundaries or a defined reference point. This is now the case for an angular variate. We may now define:

$$F(\phi_a) = 0 \quad \text{for } \phi_a = \phi_m - \phi_t/2 \qquad (777a)$$

and:

$$F(\phi_b) = 1.0 \quad \text{for } \phi_b = \phi_m + \phi_t/2. \qquad (777b)$$

This furnishes the boundaries of the cumulative distribution and we should not have any difficulty computing $F(\phi_i)$ or graphing the cumulative distribution (see Example 1).
With the definition of ϕ_m it is possible to treat the angular distribution like any other non-periodic variate and apply statistical techniques and tests as appropriate according to the shape of the distribution. Although other statistical concepts are available, the resemblance to the non-periodic variate simplifies many problems. ϕ_t defined on p. 329.

TABLE LXXXI

COMPUTATION OF THE WIND DIRECTION MEAN (BIMODAL)

Class (degr.)	n_i	ϕ_r	ϕ_{m_i}	σ_{ϕ_m}	n_j	δ_{i+1}	n'_j	δ'_{i+1}	Runs
0–10	9	5	−22.3	104.4	6	−27.4	4	−27.3	0
10–20	4	15	−14.6	107.2	4	−34.0	9	−29.6	0
20–30	10	25	−3.4	110.0	11	−34.6	13	−28.4	0
30–40	7	35	7.8	112.6	11	−35.1	13	−27.2	0
40–50	16	45	21.5	114.8	19	−28.8	16	−23.5	0
50–60	14	55	42.1	116.4	21	−20.7	24	−12.8	0
60–70	13	65	66.2	117.0	20	−13.6	28	1.2	0
70–80	20	75	83.4	116.7	29	1.4	20	8.4	0
80–90	17	85	102.3	115.5	23	11.1	22	17.3	0
90–100	17	95	113.5	114.0	15	14.0	13	18.5	0
100–110	4	105	127.2	112.1	16	17.8	16	22.2	0
110–120	2	115	142.7	109.9	17	22.4	18	27.7	0
120–130	8	125	153.0	107.4	12	22.7	12	28.0	0
130–140	3	135	164.2	104.7	16	26.5	13	29.2	0
140–150	8	145	168.4	102.2	7	22.5	5	23.4	0
150–160	12	155	171.0	100.2	5	16.8	3	16.0	0
160–170	5	165	174.5	99.0	2	8.5	4	9.5	0
170–180	6	175	180.5	98.3	6	3.6	7	5.5	0
180–190	4	185	189.9	97.8	10	2.2	11	4.9	0
190–200	11	195	195.9	97.6	9	−0.05	7	0.9	0
200–210	11	205	200.2	97.9	4	−6.6	5	−4.8	0
210–220	19	215	207.1	98.4	10	−8.0	8	−7.9	0
220–230	21	225	218.3	99.1	7	−12.0	13	−6.7	1
230–240	20	235	230.3	99.7	16	−8.3	14	−4.7	0
240–250	29	245	245.8	99.9	4	−6.2	18	0.8	1
250–260	23	255	257.8	99.9	13	−5.1	14	2.8	1
260–270	15	265	274.1	99.3	20	2.1	19	9.1	0
270–280	16	275	289.6	98.2	17	6.7	18	14.6	0
280–290	17	285	296.5	96.7	17	11.3	8	11.4	0
290–300	12	295	299.9	95.9	4	4.8	4	4.9	0
300–310	16	305	303.3	95.8	2	−3.5	4	−1.7	0
310–320	7	315	308.5	96.2	8	−6.6	6	−6.5	0
320–330	5	325	313.7	97.2	3	−14.1	6	−11.4	0
330–340	2	335	317.9	98.6	8	−17.2	5	−17.1	0
340–350	6	345	327.3	100.1	12	−16.9	11	−17.6	0
350–360	10	355	334.3	102.0	5	−22.6	8	−20.8	0
	$\sum=419$								

Explanations in text.

Other techniques may involve the von Mises distribution, based on:

$$f(k,\theta)=[2\pi I_0(k)]^{-1}\cdot\exp[k\cos(\theta-\theta_0)] \tag{778}$$

where $I_0(k)$ is the Bessel function of purely imaginary argument of order zero. This sophisticated statistical tool is not trivial and a detailed discussion is omitted. Another topic, curve fitting with regression techniques on surfaces of spheres with given angles, was discussed by GOULD (1969). JONES et al. (1976) fit the histogram with the aid of harmonic analysis (see eq. 384a).

The wind shear

The wind shear is defined as the difference between two wind vectors, usually vectors at different altitudes. We may define:

$$\Delta V = V_1 - V_2 \tag{779a}$$

The magnitude ΔS of the wind shear is customarily calculated from the difference of the horizontal wind components:

$$\Delta S^2 = (\Delta V_x)^2 + (\Delta V_y)^2 \tag{779b}$$

where V_x and V_y are the zonal and meridional components, respectively, or other rectangular horizontal components. The split into rectangular components does not provide an answer to the question whether the wind shear is produced by an increase (decrease) of the wind speed with altitude or a turn of the wind vector. This judgement can be made from the following formula:

$$(\Delta S)^2 = (V_1 - V_2)^2 + 4V_2 V_1 \cdot \sin^2(\Delta\phi/2) \tag{779c}$$

The first term represents the change of the wind speed and becomes zero when the speed remains constant, i.e., $V_1 = V_2$. The second term is zero when $\Delta\phi = \phi_1 - \phi_2 = 0$. Thus, the relative contribution by the change of wind speed is:

$$P_V = (V_1 - V_2)^2 / \Delta S^2 \tag{779d}$$

and the relative share of the vector turn is:

$$P_\phi = [4V_1 V_2 \sin^2(\Delta\phi/2)] / \Delta S^2 \tag{779e}$$

The turn contribution is not independent from the "average wind speed" expressed here as the product $V_1 \cdot V_2$. Notice, if one wind speed is zero $P_\phi = 0$.
The angular turn has its strongest contribution in the first km and in the upper atmosphere around 16–20 km in summer (see Montgomery, Alabama and Thule, Greenland, in ESSENWANGER, 1974).
For more details on wind shear and the relation with turbulence see ESSENWANGER (1963, 1965, 1967), ESSENWANGER and BILLIONS (1965) and ESSENWANGER and REITER (1969).

The distribution of cloud cover

The frequency distribution of cloud cover has a peculiar shape. Most data fall into the two boundary classes zero or overcast, and the p.d.f. looks like the letter U and, therefore, is often called U-distribution, occasionally a V-distribution. None of the ordinary distribution types presented in the previous sections resemble this shape. The author treated the U-distribution extensively in a previous text (ESSENWANGER, 1976, p. 63). The beta-function or Pearson's system gives an appropriate description of U-shaped distributions (FALLS, 1974). In this text a simple approach by a transformed distribution is presented, which may not be satisfactory from the point of theoretical statistics, but which may solve some of the practical problems and is very simple. The suggestion was made by JOHNSON (1949) and also was described by KENDALL and STUART (1958).

Assume the cloud cover distribution is represented by:

$$f(x)=(x_i-a_1)/[R_x-(x_i-a_1)],\ a_1<x_i<a_2 \qquad (780a)$$

with:

$$R_x=a_2-a_1 \qquad (780b)$$

where a_2 is the upper and a_1 the lower boundary (see details after eq. 788b). Then the transformation:

$$y_i=(x_i-a_1)/R_x \qquad (781)$$

leads to:

$$f(y)=y_i/(1-y_i) \qquad (782)$$

We now perform a comparison with the Gaussian distribution z and postulate

$$(z_i-a_z)/\sigma_z=\ln\,[y_i/(1-y_i)] \qquad (783a)$$

or:

$$z_i=a_z+\sigma_z\ln\,[y_i/(1-y_i)] \qquad (783b)$$

The constants a_z and σ_z must be determined by appropriate estimators. According to Johnson we may determine z_i from the frequency of the two boundary classes.
The cumulative distribution for y is transformed to the Gaussian distribution:

$$F(y_i)=F(z_i) \qquad (784a)$$

In particular for the eleven cloud cover classes from $i=1$ to 11:

$$F(y_1)=F(z_1)=f(x_{c1}), \qquad (784b)$$

$$F(y_{10})=F(z_{10})=1.0-f(x_{c11}) \qquad (784c)$$

It is evident that $F(y_1)$ is equal to the frequency density of the first class and $F(y_{10})$ is equal to 1.0 minus the last class. Since the cumulative Gaussian distribution is given in tables, one can easily find z_1 and z_{10} for σ_z' for 1.0 and then determine σ_z, the scale factor.
The following two equations are obtained:

$$z_1=a_z+\sigma_z\ln\,[y_1/(1-y_1)] \qquad (785a)$$

and:

$$z_{10}=a_z+\sigma_z\ln\,[y_{10}/(1-y_{10})] \qquad (785b)$$

which can be solved for $\bar{z}$ and σ_z.
For the cloud cover:

$$y_{10}=1-y_1 \qquad (786a)$$

Hence:

$$\ln\,[y_{10}/(1-y_{10})]=\ln\,[(1-y_1)/y_1]=-\ln\,[y_1/(1-y_1)] \qquad (786b)$$

The two solutions are:

$$(z_1 + z_{10})/2 = a_z, \quad (786c)$$

$$(z_1 - z_{10})/(2 \ln [y_1/(1-y_1)]) = \sigma_z \quad (786d)$$

Eq. 786, c and d provide a total match in the boundary classes but the other classes may not show a good agreement. The author suggests therefore an estimation by an expanded order statistics. The system of eq. 785a, b is extended and the other classes are included. After some arithmetic (with n_j the number of classes, $n-1$, hence $n_j = 10$):

$$a_z = (\sum z_i)/n_j \quad (787a)$$

The second equation contains the differences $z_1 - z_{10}$, $z_2 - z_9$ etc., which can be written $z_i - z_{n-i}$. Finalizing gives:

$$5\sigma_z = \sum_1^5 (z_i - z_{n-i})/(2 \ln [y_i/(1-y_i)]) \quad (787b)$$

Eq. 787a, b is a more elaborate scheme than the system of eq. 786c, d because z_i must be determined for every class interval of the cumulative distribution.

The reader may question whether something is gained by the transformation other than the simple reconstruction of the frequency distribution from the Gaussian distribution. However, there are other benefits. Estimators for a_z and σ_z can be compared with other data samples. A threshold y_{th} or the ranges of y_a–y_b for thresholds can be obtained from the Gaussian distribution, and other tasks, for which knowledge of a frequency distribution is required, can be performed. E.g., the threshold y_{th} is:

$$y_{th} = e^{Z_{th}}/(1 + e^{Z_{th}}) \quad (788a)$$

where:

$$Z_{th} = (z_{th} - a_z)/\sigma_z \quad (788b)$$

is the normalized variate. Notice, although z_{th} for one sigma is 1.0, $Z_{th} \neq 1.0$. Eqs. 786c, d and 787a, b are applied first to a system of cloudiness with the assumption that the class center is 0, 1, 2, ... 10 tenths sky cover. Then the first class ranges from -0.5 to $+0.5$, the last class from 9.5 to 10.5 (Table LXXXII). This provides $a_1 = -0.5$ and $a_2 = 10.5$, with $R_x = 11.0$. The first $y_1 = 1/11$ and $y_{10} = 10/11$ etc., as listed in Table LXXXII. The second alternative assumes the same class center, but the first and last class interval extends from 0 to 0.5 and 9.5 to 10.0, respectively. This affects the y-variate as illustrated in Table LXXXII. For an even number of class intervals the logarithm of the center class is zero and must be omitted from eq. 787b.

Example 71. Suppose we are interested in representing the cloudiness distribution at Hampton, VA, January 1946–1964, summarized over all hours. The method is illustrated in Tables LXXXIII and LXXXIV. In these tables the first column, x, is the cloudiness scale (in tenths). This column is followed by the frequency density and the cumulative frequency distribution in Table LXXXIII. The column z_x lists the scale corresponding to a Gaussian distribution, etc. The estimators for the system of eq. 786c, d and the class intervals -0.5 to 0.5 in the boundary class have been computed as $a_z = -0.2385$ and $\sigma_z = 0.1809$. This provides the results of column z_1. Calculation by the order statistics of eq. 787a, b leads to $a_z = -0.2290$, $\sigma_z = 0.1808$ with the subsequent column z_2. In this case the solution has not been forced by a match in the boundary classes. Thus, the recomputation of the frequency from the estimators discloses differences in the boundary classes, too.

TABLE LXXXII

CLASS DIVISION AND y-VARIATE FOR CLOUD COVER

i	Cloudiness x_{c_i}	Class boundary x_i	$R_x y_i$	$y_i/(1-y_i)$	$\ln[y_i/(1-y_i)]$	Class boundary x_i	$R_x y_i$	$y_i/(1-y_i)$	$\ln[y_i/(1-y_i)]$
1	0	−0.5–0.5	1	1/10	−2.30259	0.0–0.5	0.5	1/19	−2.94444
2	1	0.5–1.5	2	2/9	−1.50408	0.5–1.5	1.5	3/17	−1.73460
3	2	1.5–2.5	3	3/8	−0.98083	1.5–2.5	2.5	5/15	−1.09861
4	3	2.5–3.5	4	4/7	−0.55962	2.5–3.5	3.5	7/13	−0.61904
5	4	3.5–4.5	5	5/6	−0.18232	3.5–4.5	4.5	9/11	−0.20067
6	5	4.5–5.5	6	6/5	0.18232	4.5–5.5	5.5	11/9	0.20067
7	6	5.5–6.5	7	7/4	0.55962	5.5–6.5	6.5	13/7	0.61904
8	7	6.5–7.5	8	8/3	0.98083	6.5–7.5	7.5	15/5	1.09861
9	8	7.5–8.5	9	9/2	1.50408	7.5–8.5	8.5	17/3	1.73460
10	9	8.5–9.5	10	10/1	2.30259	8.5–9.5	9.5	19/1	2.94444
11	10	9.5–10.5	11	–		9.5–10.0	–		
		$R_x y_i=(x_i-a_1)$ $a_1=-0.5,\quad R_x=11.0$				$R_x y_i=(x_i-a_1)$ $a_1=0,\quad R_x=10$			

TABLE LXXXIII

CLOUDINESS DISTRIBUTION, HAMPTON, VA., JANUARY 1946–1964, ALL HOURS

Cloud-iness (x)	Empirical $f(x)$	$F(x)$	Analytical z_x	z_1	z_2	z_3	z_4	$F(z_1)$	$F(z_2)$	$F(z_3)$	$F(z_4)$
0	25.6%	25.6%	−0.655	−0.655	−0.645	−0.655	−0.692	25.62	25.94	25.62	24.45
1	4.0	29.6	−0.536	−0.510	−0.500	−0.484	−0.501	30.50	30.85	30.82	30.82
2	4.1	33.7	−0.420	−0.416	−0.406	−0.394	−0.402	33.87	34.23	34.69	34.37
3	3.6	37.3	−0.324	−0.340	−0.330	−0.326	−0.326	36.69	37.07	37.22	37.22
4	2.7	40.0	−0.253	−0.271	−0.262	−0.267	−0.260	39.32	39.66	39.47	39.74
5	2.1	42.1	−0.199	−0.206	−0.196	−0.210	−0.197	41.84	42.33	41.68	42.19
6	2.7	44.8	−0.129	−0.137	−0.128	−0.151	−0.131	44.55	44.91	44.00	44.79
7	3.5	48.3	−0.042	−0.061	−0.051	−0.083	−0.056	47.57	47.97	46.69	47.77
8	5.3	53.6	0.090	0.034	0.043	0.007	0.044	51.36	51.72	50.28	51.76
9	3.4	57.0	0.178	0.178	0.187	0.178	0.234	57.06	57.41	57.06	59.26
10	43.0	100.0	–								

TABLE LXXXIV

DIFFERENCES OF THE CUMULATIVE DISTRIBUTION $F(z_i)$ WITH THE EMPIRICAL $F(x)$

x	$F(x)-F(z_1)$ (%)	$F(x)-F(z_2)$ (%)	$F(x)-F(z_3)$ (%)	$F(x)-F(z_4)$ (%)
0	0.0	−0.34	0	1.15
1	−0.90	1.25	−1.22	−1.22
2	−0.17	−0.53	−0.99	−0.67
3	0.61	0.23	0.08	0.08
4	0.68	0.34	0.53	0.26
5	0.26	−0.13	0.32	−0.09
6	0.25	−0.11	0.80	0.01
7	0.73	0.33	1.61	0.53
8	2.24	1.88	3.32	1.84
9	0	−0.41	0	2.26

The next two columns list z_3 and z_4, which are calculated with the assumption that the first class interval ranges from 0.0 to 0.5 or the last class from 9.5 to 10.0. The next four columns contain the respective cumulative frequencies for the four solutions.

The differences between empirical and analytical distributions are reflected in Table LXXXIV. Although this example alone does not permit complete judgment of the merits of the method, the example illustrates that the differences appear smaller for the assumption of a wider marginal class. As expected, the differences are more balanced in z_2 rather than z_1. The absolute differences are smaller in the non-forced boundary solutions. This gains importance in statistical testing because the absolute maximum is related to the Kolmogorov-Smirnov significance test. In this case the difference is significant at the 5% level (the reader may compute the exact significance level for $N = 14125$). However, the deviation in the margin classes, which contributes largely to the signficance, may be due to observer misclassification as was earlier pointed out by BROOKS and CARRUTHERS (1953). Another explanation is the inhomogeneity of data. The example demonstrates that for certain problems the simple transformation suggested by JOHNSON (1949) may serve quite well.

Statistical models of precipitation frequencies

Unlike the temperature, precipitation data seldom follow the Gaussian distribution law, except in the rare case where the central limit theorem is applicable (e.g., annual precipitation sums, etc.). Even then the frequency distributions may deviate. It is therefore not surprising that numerous articles have been written in the past with suggested solutions (e.g., almost 50 papers came to the attention of the author in 1973–74). The scope of this section does not permit the inclusion of all the topics on statistical representation of precipitation data. A selected number of methods will be treated, however, to familiarize the reader with various choices and the problems involved. A limited survey also was given by SUZUKI (1967, 1980).

Precipitation frequencies must be distinguished by types of data. Most commonly known is the amount of precipitation (rainfall, snow, etc.) within a certain time period. Daily sums from which monthly or annual summaries are derived are widely used. Another type of special interest is the hourly amount. Daily and hourly amounts exhibit frequency density distributions with exponential decline towards higher amounts, although generally a straight exponential model may not provide the optimum fit. In hydrology often a logarithmic transformation can be found; in meteorology the gamma function and negative binomial has been tried (see details below). SEVRUK and GEIGER (1981) discussed the selection of distribution types for extreme precipitations.

Dry and wet spells have been derived from records of precipitation amounts. Several models have been suggested and will be commented on later. Several authors have attempted to link precipitation models and various schemes of urns, e.g.:

(*a*) Bernoulli urn: no persistence (binomial). A ball is chosen at random from an urn with white and black balls, is recorded, and returned (no persistence, seldom valid, see p. 29).

(*b*) Polya urn: persistence (negative binomial). A ball is chosen at random, is recorded, and is replaced by the same color, but additional balls of the same color are added (see p. 33).

(*c*) First order Markov urn: persistence is limited to one time intervals. This resembles the drawing of balls from 3 Bernoulli urns, urn one with a general ratio of white and black balls, urn two with predominance of white and urn three with black balls. A first ball is drawn from urn one and according to the color the next ball is drawn from either urn 2 or urn 3. The results are recorded and the balls placed back into their respective urns (see p. 349).

(*d*) Friedman urn: modified Polya urn, persistence. The urn contains white and black balls. After a ball is drawn, it is placed back and n_1 balls of the same color are added, n_2 balls of the opposite color (see p. 349).

(*e*) WISER (1965) modified the simple Markov chain by stipulating a specific rule: the contents of an urn can vary by adding balls as long as the sequence of balls of the same color is not interrupted. Any drawing of a ball of the opposite color interrupts the sequence and the urn is restored to its initial state. This resembles higher order Markov chains.

The various schemes of statistical modelling lead to different approaches for proper representation, and no uniform specification can be given. Some details on the frequency models follow in the subsequent sections.

Furthermore, a noted interest exists in special precipitation types (such as thunderstorms, storm frequency, hail occurrence), specific characteristics (such as droplet size, precipitable water) or other miscellaneous observations of the moisture field and their calculations from precipitation records. In summary, primarily amount, intensity and duration are of importance.

The negative binomial and Poisson distribution for precipitation frequencies

In recent years the treatment of precipitation amounts by the gamma distribution (e.g., THOM, 1957a, etc.) or logarithmic transformation (e.g., CHOW, 1954; ESSENWANGER, 1956a, b) has found widespread practical application. For historical reason and the relation with urn models the application of the negative binomial is discussed first.

After the exponential law (J-shaped frequency) had been fitted to precipitation amounts with variable success, WANNER (1939, 1942) or GREEN (1964) suggested approximations by the adoption of a negative binomial frequency distribution. This recommendation also appeared in BROOKS and CARRUTHERS (1953). THOM (1957a) and the author (ESSENWANGER, 1956a, b) have pointed out, however, that data of precipitation amounts constitute a collective from a continuous variate. This statistical background contrasts with the basis of the negative binomial theory which requires discrete steps. Grouping of data into classes or rounding to whole numbers, as Wanner suggested, creates the image of a discrete frequency. However, the difficulty in establishing a uniform system was pointed out by the author (ESSENWANGER, 1956a, b), and the curve fitting to the negative binomial density distribution, therefore, is strictly descriptive.

The utilization of the negative binomial law for runs of precipitation data, such as number of dry or wet days also was attempted by WANNER (1939, 1942) although with more justification, because in this case a real division into two separate groups exists which may resemble Polya's urn scheme. Successful applications of the Markov chain have been discussed (e.g., GABRIEL and NEUMANN, 1957, 1962), although computations may be more elaborate than the application of the negative binomial model. The Poisson and negative binomial frequency distribution as applied to thunderstorm data was presented in Example 8.

The application of the negative binomial law to persistence of rainfall for data from Japan was illustrated by DOI (1959). The interesting feature in his article is the derivation of relationships between hourly data and n-hourly data. Although the additive property of the gamma function should automatically lead to a solution for composite sums, the difficulty of incorporating the dry hours into the additive gamma function scheme makes Doi's results valuable. (See later eq. 794a.) The data must first be converted into class-intervals, e.g. equivalent to whole millimeter amounts, etc.

In the notation of eq. 70a for a combination of n periods:

$$f_n(x) = \binom{nk+x-1}{x}\left(\frac{1}{1+\gamma_n}\right)^{nk}\left(\frac{\gamma_n}{1+\gamma_n}\right)^{x} \tag{789}$$

This equation is a modified form of eq. 70 written for n-units of the basic period (e.g., hourly precipitation amounts). The identification of parameters k and γ follows eq. 75a, b. Estimators can be determined from the basic unit period (e.g., hourly amounts) by methods described on p. 35ff. Doi suggested an estimation of γ_n by:

$$[(1-\alpha\beta^{n-1})(1+\alpha\gamma)/[(1-\alpha)\beta^n]]^{1/n\gamma} = (1+\gamma_n)^{1/\gamma_n} \tag{790a}$$

with:

$$\beta = (1+\alpha\gamma)/(1+\gamma) \tag{790b}$$

and:

$$\alpha = [\bar{x}/\bar{x}(x|0) - 1]/\gamma \tag{790c}$$

where $\bar{x}(x|0)$ denotes the mean of x for the selected sample of x after a dry interval (e.g., the average of the hourly precipitation amount after the previous hour has been dry, etc.). Furthermore, $0<\alpha<1$. Eq. 790a can be stated in logarithmic form:

$$[(1/(n\gamma)][\log(1-\alpha\beta^{n-1}) + \log(1+\alpha\gamma) - \log(1-\alpha) - n\log\beta] = (1/\gamma_n)\log(1+\gamma_n) \tag{790d}$$

Since γ is known, α can be obtained from eq. 790c, β from eq. 790b, and finally γ_n from eq. 790a. The parameter γ_n could also be determined from one station in an homogeneous climatic area and then applied to other stations. This may be useful when sample data from n-hourly observations are available and the distribution for the unit-period is sought. Solving eq. 790a for α and β is not a simple task, however. Since the assumption can be made that $\bar{x}_n = n\bar{x}_1$ where the subscript 1 stands for the unit period, the fraction $\bar{x}/\bar{x}(x|0)$ remains approximately the same for n-periods as for the unit period. Then the factor:

$$A = \alpha\gamma = \bar{x}/\bar{x}(x|0) - 1 \tag{791a}$$

can be determined. This leads to:

$$\beta = (1 + A)/(1 + \gamma) \tag{791b}$$

After some lengthy arithmetic we finally obtain:

$$[(\gamma - A(1 + a)^n)/(\gamma - A)(1 + A)^n]^{1/n\gamma} = (1 + \gamma_n)^{1/\gamma_n} \tag{791c}$$

This expression is an equation in γ alone, because the right side of the equation and A are known. Unfortunately, it cannot be solved very easily. DOI (1959) suggested graphical solutions.
The underlying $f_n(x)$ is an approximation by a negative binomial distribution. The author has previously cautioned against its use, but the gamma function is an approximation, too. Doi's method is an alternative which some readers may prefer.
Doi also expanded this formula for the runs of dry days:

$$f(d_n) = N(f_n - 2f_{n+1} - Nf_{n+2}) \tag{792a}$$

The calculation of f_i follows from:

$$f_i = \{(1 - \alpha)\beta^{i-1}/[(1 - \alpha\beta^{i-1})(1 + \alpha\gamma)]\}^{\bar{x}/\gamma} \tag{792b}$$

where $i = n$, $n + 1$ and $n + 2$. γ is deduced from the records of the time period whose frequency distribution is desired, e.g., daily amounts, etc., but $\bar{x}$ and α for the daily rainfall must also be known. Doi's results for Fukuoka agree with the observed runs of dry days, but the scheme fails for wet runs. One other interesting result in Doi's paper is noteworthy. His studies reveal that the exponential type of frequency (J-shaped curve) transforms into the bell-shaped form (bounded or unbounded) for a summation of precipitation amounts of more than ten-day periods. More details on dry and wet runs are presented on p. 352.
A study by ALEXANDERSSON (1983) is based on the compound Poisson-exponential distribution. According to his findings, this type of distribution is superior to other distribution models for monthly and annual precipitation amounts, if only a two-parameter model is used. A compound Poisson model is also described by RODRIGUEZ-ITURBE (1983) for storm data.

Logarithmic scale and other transformations

Besides the curve fitting by straight exponential types $a_1\, e^{-a_2 x}$ for either amount or runs of dry or wet spells (GREEN, 1964) the logarithmic transformation often can be found in hydrological practice (CHOW, 1954, 1964). This transformation was also suggested by SCHNEIDER-CARIUS (e.g., 1955) who designed several schemes of class intervals in logarithmic progression for grouping of precipitation data in practical work (see JUNGHANS, 1968). CLARK (1976) has even recommended the logarithmic distribution for droplet spectra.

The author (ESSENWANGER, 1956b) pointed out that the complexity of physical processes rendering precipitation generally do not lead to one homogeneous population in the frequency density of precipitation amounts but rather a mixture of collectives. This mixture cannot readily be separated by ordinary means, because in most cases not enough information is available to perform even a simple separation, e.g., into convective, frontal, orographic or local type of precipitation, etc.

A separation into Gaussian subgroups (partial collectives) for daily rainfall amounts has been attempted. The problems involved and the physical background for these Gaussian components were delineated by the author in two articles (ESSENWANGER, 1960a, b) in which the frequency density of the individual months was set up in class intervals with logarithmic progression. The author (1960a) has expanded the concept to the bivariate scale (duration and intensity), an idea which has been pursued recently by HIEMSTRA (1983) for floods from rain storms.

In a special research project on rainfall modification experiments SCHICKEDANZ and HUFF (1971) collected areal data and determined precipitation groups. They also fitted a log-normal distribution to these areal storm precipitation data stratified by ten groups of precipitation processes (seven basic synoptic weather types and three precipitation types). For samples of the storm network where the mean rainfall was ≥ 0.005 inch but ≤ 0.10 inch and for the data of maximum point rainfall a non-truncated log-normal distribution was fitted. For samples with a network mean > 0.10 but ≤ 1.0, and for > 1.0 inch, a truncated distribution was employed by making the transformation $x = (X - 0.1)$ and $(X - 1.0)$, respectively, where X denotes the network mean rainfall. They concluded that the log-normal distribution fits these data samples well as verified by the Kolmogorov-Smirnov test for samples < 40, and the χ^2-test for ≥ 40 in size. This confirms the hypothesis of a mixture of Gaussian distributions in a logarithmic scale towards which the author has directed attention in his 1960a, b articles. The log-normal distribution was treated by the author (1976). BOWMAN and SHENTON (1970) have suggested a logarithmic series random variate for the duration of rainfall storms (see eq. 136a).

Another transformation of the frequency of precipitation amount into a variate with approximate Gaussian distribution was suggested by STIDD (1953, 1969, 1973). In his studies the precipitation amount was divided into classes with cubic progression. Thus the transformed variable employs the cube root of the precipitation amount. This transformation leads to a straight line in probability paper (ordinate Gaussian scale), but as ESSENWANGER (1956b) pointed out, the straight line has validity from the range of 15–20% to about 99% of the cumulative distribution, but outside of that range deviations from the straight line proved a significant discrepancy between the Gaussian frequency and the observed data. For most hydrological problems or other practical application this disagreement may be negligible, because small precipitations are usually of little interest, and extreme values should be examined separately.

SCHICKEDANZ (1971) and SCHICKEDANZ and HUFF (1971) tested the application of the log-normal and the incomplete gamma functions to distributions of areal rainfall data. For a network of stations within 400 square miles the log-normal distribution fitted about 70% of the samples at the 0.05 confidence level, while the number was slightly lower for the gamma distribution. The comparable figures for the 200 square miles area network were around 90% for the log-normal, about 80% for the gamma distribution. This indicates a decrease in the homogeneity of gage rainfall amounts with increasing size of the area,

evidently due to the increase in heterogeneity of the rainfall processes with increasing area, although a 400 square mile area is only of the size of some of our larger cities.
The assumption of a log-normal distribution leads to an interesting connection between the shape parameter of the gamma and the log-normal distribution for the average rainfall on rainy hours. Since $\hat{\alpha}$ of the gamma distribution is a function of a parameter A (see eq. 99b), we can write:

$$A = \ln \bar{X} - \bar{y} = \sigma_y^2/2 \tag{793a}$$

where $y = \ln X$. Consequently, the scale parameter β is related:

$$\beta = \bar{X}/\alpha \tag{793b}$$

SIMPSON (1972) studied the radar-evaluated rainfall data from cumulus clouds in Florida. In her findings the gamma distribution emerged as the most suitable model although she utilized the fourth root of the rainfall amounts.

The incomplete gamma function

The application of the incomplete gamma function (see eq. 91) was suggested by BARGER and THOM (1949) and since then has been adapted to precipitation data by various researchers. Recall that $f(x=0)=0$, thus the dry periods (e.g., dry hours or days, etc.) cannot be accommodated. FRIEDMAN and JONES (1957) introduced a model such as:

$$G(x) = p_d + (1 - p_d)F(x) \tag{794a}$$

where $G(x)$ represents the probability of occurrence of any precipitation of the amount x or less and p_d denotes the probability of dry periods. $F(x)$ is a suitable function for precipitation amounts, in this case the incomplete gamma function. The function $G(x)$ was called the mixed gamma distribution by THOM (1968) because zero and non-zero values of x are mixed, but the terminology does not imply a mixture of various precipitation processes.
An estimate for the parameter p_d can be gained from:

$$p_d = n_d/N \tag{794b}$$

where n_d denotes the number of dry periods, e.g., dry days out of N days. This estimation lies already within tolerable limits for a reasonably large sample. The standard error for p is given by $\varepsilon_p^2 = p_d(1-p_d)/N$. Assume that $N = 100$, and dry and wet days are equal ($p=0.5$), then $\varepsilon_p = 0.05$. At the 95% level of confidence it provides $2\varepsilon_p = 0.1$. Hence, the error limits for p_d with $N = 100$ imply that $0.4 < p_d < 0.6$ with 95% confidence. This result corresponds with the binomial limits. At $N = 1000$ the limits range from 0.47 and 0.53. Any other probability $p_d \neq 0.5$ has a smaller error range (e.g., $p_d = 0.9$, $\varepsilon_p = 0.03$, etc.).
The parameters of $F(x)$ can be estimated as previously outlined (eq. 91).
The gamma function was engaged in MOOLEY and CRUTCHER's (1968) study on Indian rainfall and WIHL and NOBILIS (1975) calculated 2.5 and 97.5 percentiles in Austria based on the gamma distribution. MOOLEY (1973) found the gamma distribution the most suitable model for fitting monthly rainfall amounts in Asia. He has compared several Pearsonian models (see Pearson's system in ESSENWANGER, 1976).
SUZUKI (1964, 1980) recommended the use of the "hyper-gamma distribution" (see

eq. 106). According to Suzuki, the comparison between analytical and observed frequency distributions from one and ten minutes up to the annual precipitation amount displays satisfactory results for Tokyo and selected data for Niiguta. It is evident that a three-parameter model has one more degree of freedom for adjustment to the observed data. The approximations of the observed data ought to be better than with a two-parameter model. It must be left to the reader to decide whether the gain by usage of one additional parameter such as for the hypergamma distribution is justified. In some cases it may pay to use a three-parameter model, in other cases expenses and computer time can be saved, Suzuki further pointed out that the climatological and synoptic meaning of the parameters of the hypergamma function must be investigated in some future research.

In the above referenced literature on the use of the gamma distribution little indication of the reliability of precipitation estimates has been given. BRIDGES and HAAN (1972) addressed this problem. Their findings correspond with the trivial expectation that the error range for estimates of rainfall threshold decreases with increasing N. They deduced that the error distribution follows a log-normal distribution rather than a linear scale.

BARGER and THOM (1949) have adapted the incomplete gamma distribution to determine the likelihood of receiving less than a specified amount of rainfall, which in turn can be interpreted as the occurrence of drought.

DOI (1959) has related the frequency distribution of an initial time interval to longer periods based on the negative binomial distribution (see eq. 789). KOTZ and NEUMANN (1963, 1964) developed a formula for the gamma function as follows:

$$\alpha_n = \alpha \cdot n^2/(n+2f[\rho]) \tag{795a}$$

and:

$$\beta_n^{-1} = \beta^{-1} n/(n+2f[\rho]) \tag{795b}$$

where $f[\rho]$ is a function of the correlation coefficient which disappears for $\rho = 0$; for α and β see eq. 91. Furthermore, $n \leq 1$ is the ratio of the time interval to the original interval. For $n \gg 2f[\rho]$ the equations simplify to:

$$\alpha_n = n\alpha \tag{795c}$$

$$\beta_n = \beta \tag{795d}$$

Because $f[\rho]$ is the autocorrelation function it depends in the case of stationarity only on the lag. Consequently, eqs. 795c and d are valid where the autocorrelation ρ is small. The above authors suggested that for an exponential decline $\rho_\kappa = \rho^\kappa$, $\rho > 0$. The following approximation is valid for $n \gg (1-\rho^n)/(1+\rho)$:

$$\alpha_n = \alpha n(1-\rho)/(1+\rho) \tag{795e}$$

and:

$$1/\beta_n = (1-\rho)/[(1+\rho)\beta] \tag{795f}$$

KOTZ and NEUMANN (1964) later described the exact distribution for the expanded time interval under the assumption of an exponential autocorrelation. They stated that the discrepancies between the exact and approximate distribution can be neglected for large n and small $\rho > 0$. Since the exact distribution requires an elaborate mathematical scheme the interested reader may refer to the quoted literature.

A bivariate model of the gamma distribution was designed and defined by CROVELLI (1973).

Beta distribution for precipitation data

A variety of frequency models has been introduced in this section on precipitation. MIELKE (1973) discussed an additional family of frequency distributions which in principle is based on a modified beta function. This family of distributions is supposed to describe certain frequencies for precipitation better than the incomplete gamma distribution. In a later article JOHNSON and MIELKE (1973) concluded, however, that only a three-parameter model performs quite well (PHONSOMBAT and LEDUC, 1977). This three-parameter model has been presented in ESSENWANGER's 1976 text while the two-parameter model was treated here (eq. 128a).

Markov chain models

Models based on the gamma function largely solve problems of the frequency density for precipitation amounts. Questions like the probability of a dry day after a dry or wet day or the probability for a run of dry or wet days are more appropriately answered by other models. Several authors (e.g., GABRIEL and NEUMANN, 1957, 1962; GREEN, 1964, 1970; WEISS, 1964; WISER, 1965; FEYERHERM and BARK, 1967, 1973; BAYNE and WEBER, 1973; SNEYERS 1978; SUZUKI, 1980; PALUMBO and MAZZARELLA, 1980, etc.) have pointed out that a first order Markov chain model may provide good results (see ESSENWANGER, 1976, p. 289).

A wet period (i.e., any period where a specified amount of precipitation or more is observed) is denoted with W, a dry period with D. Assume that the probability of the W or D depends only on the preceding period and not on earlier periods, i.e., the probability of precipitation on a particular day depends only on whether the previous day was wet or dry. An analogy exists for the probability of a dry day (first order Markov chain). If the previous state is denoted by J, the present state by I, we can write the probability:

$$P_{IJ}=P(I|J) \qquad (796a)$$

This leads to the following conditional probabilities (with W and D). The sequence of days are classified by w and d for wet and dry, respectively. Then:

$$P_{11}=P(W|W)=p_{ww} \qquad (796b)$$

$$p_{12}=P(D|W)=p_{wd} \qquad (796c)$$

$$p_{21}=P(W|D)=p_{dw} \qquad (796d)$$

$$p_{22}=P(D|D)=p_{dd} \qquad (796e)$$

The following summations add up to unity:

$$p_{11}+p_{12}=p_{ww}+p_{wd}=1 \qquad (796f)$$

$$p_{21}+p_{22}=p_{dw}+p_{dd}=1 \qquad (796g)$$

Eqs. 796, b–e can be written in matrix form. This matrix is called the transition matrix.

More details on Markov chains can be found in texts by FELLER (1968), KARLIN (1968), or BHARUCHA-REID (1960), GODSKE (1962, 1965), etc. The transition matrix is:

$$\mathbf{T}=\begin{pmatrix} P(W|W) & 1-P(W|W) \\ 1-P(D|D) & P(D|D) \end{pmatrix}=\begin{pmatrix} p_{ww}p_{wd} \\ p_{dw}p_{dd} \end{pmatrix} \tag{797}$$

Any combination of two given probabilities except in the same row, such as eq. 796f, g, determines the total matrix entries in **T**. The probability p_w and p_d is then the probability of wet and dry days irrespective of the history.

From a theoretical point of view the two estimates of the probability in the matrix 797 should be determined by maximum likelihood. ANDERSON and GOODMAN (1957) proved that the empirical probabilities for p_{ww} and p_{dw} are good approximations of the likelihood estimators and can be taken.

Under the assumption of a first order Markov chain the following probabilities can be derived:

$$np_{ww}=P+(1-P)d^n \tag{798a}$$

$$np_{wd}=P+Pd^n \tag{798b}$$

Eq. 798a provides the probability of precipitation n days after a wet day, eq. 798b the probability n days after a dry day. The following abbreviations have been employed:

$$P=p_{21}/(1-d)=p_{dw}/(1-d)=p_w \tag{798c}$$

and:

$$d=p_{11}-p_{21}=p_{ww}-p_{dw} \tag{798d}$$

Notice that P also is the absolute probability of a wet day and thus can be replaced by p_w. Now the probabilities (or the frequency density in terms of a frequency distribution) for runs of wet or dry spells are needed. The definition of a wet spell requires that it is a run of wet days preceded and followed by a dry day. Analogously a dry spell is a sequence of dry days with a wet day before and after. Hence the probability p_{ws} of a wet spell of length L is:

$$p_{ws}=(1-p_{11})p_{11}^{L-1}=(1-p_{ww})p_{ww}^{L-1} \tag{799a}$$

A dry spell of length M results in the probability p_{ds}

$$p_{ds}=p_{21}(1-p_{21})^{M-1}=p_{dw}(1-p_{dw})^{M-1} \tag{799b}$$

If a cycle is defined as the sequence of a wet and an adjacent dry spell, then for the length N of the cycle ($N=L+M$) the following probability is derived:

$$p_{cy}=p_{21}(1-p_{11})\frac{(1-p_{21})^{N-1}-p_{11}^{N-1}}{1-p_{21}-p_{11}} \tag{799c}$$

where p_{11} and p_{21} can be replaced again by p_{ww} and p_{dw}, respectively.

The probability that exactly L wet days are among the N days, following a wet day is given by:

$$p(L, N|W)=p_{11}^L(1-p_{21})^{N-L}\sum_{c=1}^{c_1}\binom{L}{A}\binom{N-L-1}{B-1}\left(\frac{1-p_{11}}{1-p_{21}}\right)^B\left(\frac{p_{21}}{p_{11}}\right)^A \tag{800a}$$

with the notation:

$$c_1 = \begin{cases} N+0.5-|2L-N+0.5| & \text{for } L<N \\ 0 \quad \text{(only one term)} & \text{for } L=N \end{cases} \qquad \begin{matrix}(800b)\\(800c)\end{matrix}$$

In this formula A and B are the next possible integers after 0.5 (c_1-1) and 0.5 c_1, respectively. Likewise the probability L of wet days following a dry day is:

$$p(L, N|D)=p_{11}^{L}(1-p_{21})^{N-L}\sum_{c=1}^{c_0}\binom{L-1}{B-1}\binom{N-L}{A}\left(\frac{1-p_{11}}{1-p_{21}}\right)^{A}\left(\frac{p_{21}}{p_{11}}\right)^{B} \qquad (800d)$$

with the boundary:

$$c_0 = \begin{cases} N+0.5-|2L-N-0.5| & \text{for } L>0 \\ 0 \quad \text{(only one term)} & \text{for } L=0 \end{cases} \qquad \begin{matrix}(800e)\\(800f)\end{matrix}$$

where A and B designate the same as for eq. 800a.
To determine the probability of any number of L wet days among N days, we must compute:

$$P(L, N)=P\cdot p(L, N|W)+(1-P)p(L, N|D) \qquad (801a)$$

For large N the distribution of the number of wet days N approaches normality (unless $d>0.5$) with mean and variance as follows:

$$\bar{L}=E(L)=NP \qquad (801b)$$

$$\sigma_L^2=\text{Var}\,(L)=NP(1-P)(1+d)/(1-d) \qquad (801c)$$

The above model was tested by GABRIEL and NEUMANN (1962) on rainfall data for Tel Aviv and was found in good agreement with the observations (see also JURCEC, 1975).
Eq. 801a provides the probability of wet days among N days, i.e., for $N=7$ the wet days in a week or for $N=30$ the wet days in a month, etc.
The procedure by GABRIEL and NEUMANN (1962) which is based on eqs. 801a and 800a, d is elaborate. KATZ (1974) has pointed out that a recursion formula exists which was developed by HELGERT (1970). The statistical background for the probabilities (eq. 801a) can be found in the article by Gabriel and Neumann. They derived maximum likelihood estimates for their model. BILLARD and MESHKANI (1980) described a variety of estimators for the model and EIDSVIK (1980) discussed the identification of models. Furthermore:

$$p(L, N|D)=P_{00}p_0(L, N-1)+Pp_1(L-1, N-1) \qquad (802a)$$

$$p(L, N|W)=P_{10}p_0(L, N-1)+P_{11}p_1(L-1, N-1) \qquad (802b)$$

where:

$$P_{00}=p_{dd}; P_{01}=p_{dw}; P_{10}=p_{wd}; P_{11}=p_{ww}$$

See eq. 797. Notice that p_0 and p_1 are the conditional probabilities for dry and wet periods (i.e., $p_0(1, h|D)$ or $p_1(k, h|W)$. Since $h=N-1$, and $k=L-1$, p_0 or p_1 are the conditional probabilities from the preceding time interval L or N. The recursion formula permits the calculation of $P(L,N)$ with relative ease with the aid of the transition matrix $\mathbf{T}$ (i.e., eq. 797). An expanded model by Green will be discussed (eq. 803a, b). FITZPATRICK and KRISHNAN

(1967) investigated rainfalls of six stations in Central Australia and applied a first order Markov chain model to pentads.

The simplicity of the Markov model is quite evident. Only two conditional probabilities (and the probability of wet or dry days) need to be known. All other probabilities for any combinations can be derived. This Markov chain model may not replace tabulations of sequences such as those prepared by FEYERHERM et al. (1965), but it would be very economical and easy to calculate these on electronic data processing equipment.

The application of orders greater than one was studied by LOWRY and GUTHRIE (1968). They concluded that for estimation of dry spells and a sequence of various kinds the simple Markov chain is sufficient. Areas with climatological diversity within a season may require higher orders. The upper Midwest of the United States may be such a diverse area, as FEYERHERM and BARK (1967) pointed out. These two authors later (1973) expanded their model to include prediction of maximum and minimum temperatures given the *i*-th precipitation sequence.

CHIN and MILLER (1980) attempted to predict the daily precipitation amount with the aid of a Markov model.

Dry–wet runs

Some models of dry and wet runs have been mentioned previously (DOI, 1959; GABRIEL and NEUMANN, 1962; KATZ, 1974), but the intricate problem attracted the attention of various authors and various other models have been suggested (e.g., BLAIR-FISH, 1975; DYER and TYSON, 1977; LUND and GRANTHAM, 1977, etc.). All cannot be included, but some interesting approaches may be singled out.

A binomial (negative binomial) model may be helpful but discrepancies between observed and analytical data have been found (see p. 343). One handicap of the binomial model is the fact that the total series of runs must be known a priori before parameters can be computed. The subsequently described models require only limited information.

Green's model, 1964

GABRIEL and NEUMANN (1957, 1962) attempted a solution with the aid of a first order Markov chain (see eqs. 799a, b). These equations provide the probability of runs of dry and wet days.

GREEN (1964) proposed an alternative model, which assumes an exponential distribution for the length L of spells. It can be deduced from the transition matrix of a first order Markov chain.

Suppose that a frequency density distribution of runs (dry and wet spells) is:

$$f(d) = a\,\mathrm{e}^{-at} \tag{803a}$$

$$f(w) = b\,\mathrm{e}^{-bt} \tag{803b}$$

where the first equation represents the dry and the second the wet days, and t denotes the time period (length of run).

The transition matrix $\mathbf{T}_{Gr}$ (by Green) of a Markov chain model is (see eq. 797):

$$\mathbf{T}_{Gr} = \begin{pmatrix} 1-p_{12}, p_{12} \\ p_{21}, 1-p_{21} \end{pmatrix} = \begin{pmatrix} p_{dd}p_{dw} \\ p_{wd}p_{ww} \end{pmatrix} \qquad \begin{array}{c} \text{final} \\ d \; w \end{array} \; \text{(columns)}, \quad \text{initial: } d, w \text{ (rows)} \tag{804}$$

The arrangement of columns and rows is different from eq. 797.

The task is now to compute estimators for p_{12}, p_{21}, a and b. $P(W)$ and $P(D)$ denote the general probability of a wet and dry day, respectively. We further assume, that the conditional probabilities $P(W|W)$, $P(D|W)$, and $P(D|D)$ are known. The computation follows Anderson and Goodman (1957) who showed that the empirical probabilities can be taken as estimators for the probability. Auxiliary parameters are defined as:

$$d = b/(a+b) \tag{805a}$$

$$w = a/(a+b) \tag{805b}$$

$$A = e^{-a}d[1-e^{-(a+b)}] \tag{805c}$$

$$B = e^{-a}(1-e^{-b}) \tag{805d}$$

$$C^2 = (1-B)C + (B-A) \tag{805e}$$

The positive root of C is the limiting value of Q_n, since $B > A$ (Q_n see eq. 808a). Then the following solution can be found:

$$e^{-a} = P(D|d) = P(D|D) \tag{806a}$$

consequently:

$$a = -\ln P(D|D) \tag{806b}$$

Further:

$$P(D) = d \cdot P(D|D) \tag{806c}$$

or:

$$d = P(D)/P(D|D) \tag{806d}$$

with:

$$w = 1 - d \tag{806e}$$

Note that d represents the probability of a dry instant and w the one for a wet instant. Now:

$$b = da/(1-d) \tag{807a}$$

$$s = e^{-(a+b)} \tag{807b}$$

and:

$$p_{12} = w(1-s) \tag{807c}$$

with:

$$p_{21}=d(1-s) \tag{807d}$$

In Green's model p_{12} and p_{21} are not merely the empirical conditional probabilities $P(W|D)$ or $P(D|W)$ (see Example 72).
Now turn to the conditional probability for a wet day*[1]:

$$Q_n=P(W|W^n)=P(W^{n+1})/P(W^n) \tag{808a}$$

and:

$$P_n=P(W|DW^n)=P(DW^{n+1})/P(DW^n) \tag{808b}$$

where a run of n wet days is preceding. (For $P(W^n)$ or $P(DW^n)$ see later eq. 811a, e.) The difference between Q and P is the starting day, a dry day for P_n, a wet day for Q_n. The sequence of four consecutive wet days could thus be classified by either Q_3 or P_3, but P_3 comprises five consecutive days.
For $n=0$ we can write:

$$Q_0=P(W) \tag{809a}$$

$$P_0=P(W|D) \tag{809b}$$

After these definitions P_n and Q_n are computed by the recursion formula:

$$P_n=1-B+(B-A)/P_{n-1} \tag{810a}$$

$$Q_n=1-B+(B-A)/Q_{n-1} \tag{810b}$$

(Definition of A and B see eqs. 805c, d.)
There is one difference between the GABRIEL and NEUMANN (1962) and the GREEN (1964) model. Under the assumption of a first order Markov chain only the four conditional probabilities (eqs. 796b, c, d, e) are taken into account in the Gabriel-Neumann model, e.g., one wet day in a sequence $DDDW$ would be treated by the probability $P(W|D)$ only, and for $DWWW$ by $P(W|W)$.
The Green model includes prior runs from eqs. 808a, b, 809a, b, and 810a, b although the runs are only for wet days. Now $DDDW$ would still be $P(W|D)$, but $DWWW$ is P_2. The sequences $WWWW$, $DWWW$, $WDWW$, $DDWW$ emerge with the same probability in the Gabriel-Neumann model, namely $P(W|W)$, but the respective probabilities in the Green model are Q_3, P_2, P_1 and P_1. Furthermore, $P_1=P(W|DW)$, $Q_1=(W|W)$, $P_2=P(W|DW^2)$, $Q_2=P(W|W^2)$ and $Q_3=P(W|W^3)$ would all display the same probability in the Gabriel-Neumann model, i.e. $P(W|W)$, while in Green's model:

$$P_2<Q_2<Q_3<Q_1<P_1 \tag{810c}$$

These sequences have been confirmed on Tel Aviv data (see also Example 72). As Green pointed out, however, this relationship may not generally hold (see Example 72 for rainfall data from W. Germany).
The conditional probability of wet runs could be computed from eqs. 808a, b. Green

*[1] The nomenclature W^n stands for the sequence of n wet days, i.e., $W^3=WWW$.

deduced another formula. The conditional probability of a sequence of $n+1$ wet days is given by:

$$P(W^{n+1}) = P(W^n) - P(DW^n) \quad (n=0, 1, 2, \dots) \tag{811a}$$

$$P(W^{n+1}) = P(W^n) - P(W^n D) \tag{811b}$$

Furthermore:

$$P(W^{n+1} D) = AP(W^n) - BP(DW^n) \tag{811c}$$

and:

$$P(DW^{n+1}) = AP(W^n) - BP(DW^n) \tag{811d}$$

The reversals from dry to wet or vice versa in the last term of eqs. 811a, b and the left side of eqs. 811c, d are part of the assumptions in Green's model (i.e., the exponentially distributed density function).

In Green's model conditional probabilities of runs of dry and wet spells follow the equations:

$$P(D^{n-1}W|WD) = P(WDD^{n-1}W) = P^{n-1}(D|d)[1 - P(D|d)] \tag{812a}$$

Earlier $P(D|d)$ was replaced by $P(D|D)$ in eq. 806a. Consequently, the probability transforms to:

$$P(WDD^{n-1}W) = P^{n-1}(D|D)P(W|D), \quad n>0 \tag{812b}$$

This formula is identical with eq. 799a.

It should be noticed that a "spell" in this sense is defined by a preceding and following day of the opposite event. The formula for the conditional probability of a wet spell is different from eq. 799a. We find:

$$P(W^{n-1}D|DW) = P(DWW^{n-1}D) = P(W^{n-1}|DW) - P(W^n|DW) \quad (n=1, 2, 3, \dots) \tag{813a}$$

or:

$$P(DWW^{n-1}D) = [P(DW^n) - P(DW^{n+1})]/P(DW) \quad (n=1, 2, 3, \dots) \tag{813b}$$

Consequently, one can recognize that the distribution of runs of dry days is independent from the runs of wet days in Green's model.

Example 72. The precipitation records of four neighboring stations around Hamburg (W. Germany) have been combined and the sequence of dry and wet days for July–August has been computed (ESSENWANGER, 1956a):

$P(D) = 0.461$

$P(W) = 0.539$

$p_{11} = P(W|W) = 0.706$

$p_{12} = P(D|W) = 0.294$

$p_{21} = P(W|D) = 0.354$

$p_{22} = P(D|D) = 0.646$

The following results are obtained for the transition matrix $\mathbf{T}_{Ga}$ of the Gabriel-Neumann model:

$$\mathbf{T}_{Ga}=\begin{pmatrix}0.706 & 0.294\\ 0.354 & 0.646\end{pmatrix}=\begin{pmatrix}p_{ww} & p_{wd}\\ p_{dw} & p_{dd}\end{pmatrix}.$$

The calculations for Green's model are:

$$a=-\ln P(D|D)=0.43696$$

$$d=P(D)/P(DD)=0.461/646=0.7136$$

$$w=1-d=0.2864$$

$$b=da(1-d)=(0.7136)(0.43696)/(0.2864)=1.08869$$

$$a+b=1.52565$$

$$s=e^{-(a+b)}=0.2176$$

$$p_{12}=w(1-s)=(0.2864)(0.7824)=0.2240$$

$$p_{21}=d(1-s)=(0.7136)(0.7824)=0.5583$$

The transition matrix is:

$$\mathbf{T}_{Gr}=\begin{pmatrix}0.776 & 0.224\\ 0.558 & 0.442\end{pmatrix}$$

We compute:

$$e^{-a}=0.6463,\quad e^{-b}=0.3365,$$

$$A=(0.6463)(0.7136)(1-0.2176)=0.3603;\ B=(0.6463)(0.6635)=0.4288$$

The following sequences are needed:

$$Q_0=P(W)=0.539$$

$$Q_1=1-B+(B-A)/Q_0=0.5712+0.0685/0.539=0.6982$$

$$Q_2=0.5725+0.0685/0.6982=0.6706$$

$$Q_3=0.5725+0.0685/0.6696=0.6748$$

$$P_0=P(W|D)=0.354$$

$$P_1=1-B+(B-A)/P_0=0.5725+0.0685/0.354=0.7660$$

$$P_2=0.5725+0.0685/0.7640=0.6622$$

Now the models can be compared. The additional probabilities for dry days at the end of a preceding wet sequence, e.g., three or four days, can be computed as the complement, e.g., the sequence $WWWWW$, $Q_3=0.675$; then the $WWWD$ probability would be $1-Q_3=0.325$ (see Table LXXXV).

Example 73. Computation of runs by several methods. In the interest of better understanding several models for computing dry and wet runs will be discussed and compared with one another. In order to enable a judgment of the Markov chain background the dry and wet run frequency is computed for the same data as Example 72, the areal rainfall data around Hamburg, W. Germany, during July–August. Unfortunately, the number of dry and wet runs from the observed data for Hamburg was not available to the author but GABRIEL and NEUMANN (1962) and GREEN (1964, 1970) illustrated the validity of their models at least for one climatic regime (see also Table LXXXV). Thus, the observed number of runs is not an essential part of this example.
The probabilities for dry and wet runs calculated by the Gabriel-Neumann and Green models are listed in the first two columns of the respective parts of Table LXXXVI. Both equations provide identical results except for rounding. It should be stressed that the exponential distribution for dry days has been obtained by $a=0.43696$ with the assumption of central class intervals from

TABLE LXXXV

COMPARISON OF PROBABILITY OF SEQUENCES OF DRY AND WET DAYS BY GREEN'S (1964) AND GABRIEL AND NEUMANN'S (1962) MODELS

Sequence of days	Green	P	Gabriel-N.	Observed
W	Q_0	0.539	0.539	0.539
D		0.461	0.461	0.461
WW	Q_1	0.698	0.706	0.706
WD		0.302	0.294	0.294
DW	P_0	0.354	0.354	0.354
DD		0.646	0.646	0.646
WWW	Q_2	0.671	0.706	0.717
DWW	P_1	0.766	0.706	0.677
WDW	P_0	0.354	0.354	0.430
DDW	P_0	0.354	0.354	0.315
$WWWW$	Q_3	0.675	0.706	0.732
$DWWW$	P_2	0.662	0.706	0.678
$WDWW$	P_1	0.766	0.706	0.686
$DDWW$	P_1	0.766	0.706	0.675
$WWDW$	P_0	0.354	0.354	0.419
$DWDW$	P_0	0.354	0.354	0.417
$WDDW$	P_0	0.354	0.354	0.344
$DDDW$	P_0	0.354	0.354	0.301

Note. The inequality 810c provides the theoretical values correctly, namely: $0.662 < 0.671 < 0.675 < 0.698 < 0.766$, but empirically: $0.678 < 0.717 < 0.732 \nless 0.706 \nless 0.677$.

TABLE LXXXVI

PROBABILITY FOR SEQUENCE OF WET AND DRY RUNS

Day	Wet: eq. 799a (Gab.-Neu.)	eq. 803a (Green)	eq. 813b (Green)	Dry: eq. 799b (Gab.-Neu.)	eq. 803b (Green)	eq. 812b (Green)	Conditional probability $P(W^n)$	$P(DW^n)$
1	0.294	0.294	0.234	0.354	0.353	0.354	0.539	0.163
2	0.208	0.208	0.260	0.229	0.228	0.228	0.376	0.125
3	0.147	0.146	0.164	0.148	0.147	0.148	0.252	0.082
4	0.104	0.103	0.113	0.095	0.095	0.095	0.170	0.056
5	0.073	0.073	0.075	0.062	0.061	0.062	0.114	0.037
6	0.052	0.052	0.050	0.040	0.040	0.040	0.077	0.025
7	0.036	0.036	0.034	0.026	0.026	0.026	0.052	0.017
8	0.026	0.026	0.023	0.017	0.016	0.017	0.035	0.011
9	0.018	0.018	0.015	0.011	0.011	0.011	0.023	0.008
10	0.013	0.013	0.010	0.007	0.007	0.007	0.016	0.005
11	0.009	0.009	0.007	0.004	0.004	0.004	0.011	0.003
12	0.006	0.006	0.005	0.003	0.003	0.003	0.007	0.002
13	0.004	0.004	0.003	0.002	0.002	0.002	0.005	0.002
14	0.003	0.003	0.002	0.001	0.002	0.001	0.003	0.001
15	0.002	0.002	0.002	0.001	0.001	0.001	0.002	0.001
16	0.002	0.002	0.001	0.001	0.001	0.001	0.001	
17	0.001	0.001	0.001				0.001	
18	0.001	0.001					0.001	
$\sum$	0.999	0.997	0.999	1.001	0.997	1.000	(1.685)	(0.538)

0.5, 1.5, 2.5, ... 17.5. This is in agreement with procedures of recomputing frequencies from exponential distributions (see ESSENWANGER, 1976).
The series of wet runs (eq. 803b) cannot be based on $b = 1.08869$ as provided by eq. 807a. The parameter b coordinates the dry and wet series in particular relationship with the Markov chain model as assumed under eq. 804, the transition matrix. Thus a and b are related for the purpose of computing the Q and P series. If the series of wet runs alone is the goal, an equation analogous to eq. 806a must be utilized:

$$b = -\ln P(W|W) \tag{814}$$

which renders $b = 0.34814$, and leads to the identical series as eq. 799a and the displayed probabilities of Table LXXXVI.
The third columns in the respective dry and wet sections list the probabilities as obtained from eqs. 813b and 812b. As anticipated from the formulae, the result for the dry runs resembles the previous series but the wet runs deviate. While obviously the formulae are based on the same concept for dry days, the probability for a wet spell provides the chances after a combination of dry–wet days. The conditional probability $P(DW)$ of a sequence dry–wet, can be computed from eq. 811d:

$$P(DW) = AP(W^0) - BP(DW^0) = A - BP(D)$$

This can be transformed (introduction of eqs. 806a, b and 805a, d) to:

$$P(DW) = P(D)[1 - P(D|D)] = P(D) \cdot P(W|D) = 0.163$$

The probability which is computed for the runs of wet days represents therefore the probability of wet runs from the overall total days, while the conditional probability $P(W|D) = 0.354$ refers to the conditional probability when a dry day has occurred. Therefore, $P(DW)$ expresses the chances how often this combination would occur in the given data. This concept is different from the question of how many runs develop, once the number of wet days is given. In fact, the same formula applies to the dry spells.

Green's model, 1970

WILLIAMS (1952) suggested a general logarithmic series, $p_1 p^2/2, \ldots p^n/n$, for runs of dry or wet days for which the series must be normalized by $-1/\ln(1-p)$, because $\sum f(x) = 1$. The previous model of the Markov chain progresses by a power series $p, p^2, \ldots p^r$ with normalization by $(1-p)/p$ (see eqs. 799a, b or 800a).
GREEN (1970) proposed a third model $p/(1+c), p^2/(2+c), \ldots p^n/(n+c)$. We must determine c between zero and infinity. A normalizing constant C must also be obtained from:

$$C \sum_{1}^{n} p^n/(n+c) = 1 \tag{815}$$

For $c = 0$ Williams' model appears, when $c = \infty$ the Markov chain emerges.
The derivation of estimators for $\hat{c}$ and $\hat{p}$ (maximum likelihood estimators) is based on:

$$\frac{1}{N} \sum x_n/(n+\hat{c}) = C \sum \hat{p}^n/(n+\hat{c})^2 \tag{816a}$$

where x_n denotes the observed runs of wet or dry days, and:

$$\frac{1}{N} \sum nx_n = C \sum n\hat{p}^n/(n+\hat{c}) \tag{816b}$$

Furthermore:

$$N = \sum x_n \tag{816c}$$

No explicit solution for the parameters $\hat{c}$ and $\hat{p}$ can be found, but an iterative procedure will succeed, which can be readily carried out by electronic data processing. The constant C must be determined from eq. 815.

This model by Green can be utilized for fitting given runs. In the previous models (Markov chain or exponential) the distribution of the runs need not be known a priori.

Green has suggested the fitting by minimum χ^2 which leads to a third model. A selected number from the series $\hat{p}/(1+\hat{c})$, $\hat{p}^2/(2+\hat{c})$, etc. is matched against the observed number of runs x_n with assumed $\hat{p}$ and $\hat{c}$. Then the χ^2-test is performed to determine the difference between analytical and observed frequency distributions. When χ^2 is less than the preselected level of significance, the full series of runs can be employed and tested, and possible corrections for $\hat{p}$ and $\hat{c}$ can be made. According to Green, the proper estimators can be found in a relatively short time.

Other models for wet and dry runs

Various additional models can be found in the literature (e.g., WEISS, 1964; WISER, 1965; etc.) so that the reader may refer to the references, partly because of the similarity to the presented methods, partly to keep this section within established bounds. A few of these models show great simplicity.

BEER et al. (1946) suggested a technique which is mainly applicable for the number of dry and wet runs for months. The months are split into two categories by calling a month dry when its precipitation amount is less than the long-term average for that month. Any precipitation amount equal to or above the mean value makes the month wet.

If the distribution of monthly precipitation sums follows the Gaussian law, the probability p_A and p_B for dry or wet months, respectively, is 1/2, i.e., $p_A = p_B = 0.5$. Since the frequency density distributions of monthly precipitation sums are not Gaussian or symmetrical with reference to the mean, $p_A \neq p_B$. Beer et al. have derived that the number of runs with a sequence of at least r consecutive months of the same category with p for occurrence and q for non-occurrence of the event can be represented by the binomial law:

$$N_r = Np^r q \tag{817a}$$

where N_r has the property of a cumulative function, summed up by beginning with the longest run, and N represents the total number of months. The frequency density of an isolated run of r months is n_r

$$n_r = N_r - N_{r+1} = Np^r q^2 \tag{817b}$$

For the runs of dry months $p = p_A$, for wet months $p = p_B$. The equation above can be transformed to:

$$\ln N_r = \ln N + \ln q + r \ln p \tag{817c}$$

This relationship provides a straight line in a graph in which the abscissa ($z_1 = r \ln p$) and the ordinate ($z_2 = \ln q + \ln N$) are taken in logarithmic progression. Since for $r = 1$ the equation becomes identical for dry and wet runs:

$$N_1 = Np_A p_B \tag{817d}$$

both lines start with the same point.

For $N=1.0$ the cumulative distribution or probability of having runs of the length r or more is obtained. Because the summation starts at the maximum length of r, the supplement $1-F(r)$ instead of $F(r)$ should be substituted for N_1. Then:

$$\ln[1-F(r)]=\ln q+r\ln p \tag{817e}$$

This equation is related to eq. 799a, b with the only difference that the exponent r is replaced by $L-1$ or $M-1$ in eq. 799a, b. BEER et al. (1946) found no significant correlation between rainfall at successive months for Kew (England). Hence, his model postulates independence from month to month. This may not be correct for other climate regimes or other classifications, where persistence can cause deviations of the probabilities especially for longer runs of r (see Example 74). Beer's formula does not include persistence. The presence of any annual cycle is eliminated, however, by the splitting of the month into two categories based on the long-term mean of the individual months.

The above formula is applicable when the length of the longest run is considerably shorter than the number of total observations (e.g., number of months). If this is not the case, GOLD's (1929) expression for $q=p$ or the expanded form by COCHRAN (1938) for $q\neq p$ should be used (see below).

The expected number of runs r of *either* event is (after GOLD, 1929):

$$n_r=(N+3-r)/(2^{r+1}) \quad \text{with } 1\leq r\leq(N-1) \tag{818a}$$

or:

$$n_N=4/(2^{r+1}) \quad \text{for } r=N \tag{818b}$$

Cochran has derived for $q\neq p$:

$$n_r=2(p^r q+pq^r)+(N-1-r)(p^r q^2+p^2 q^r) \quad \text{with } 1\leq r\leq(N-1) \tag{819a}$$

and:

$$n_N=p^r+q^r \quad \text{for } r=N \tag{819b}$$

Eq. 819a, b lead to the model by Gold for $p=q=1/2$.

Cochran's equation is symmetric in p and q and dry and wet runs have been combined. When $p=q$ the individual run of wet or dry events can be easily obtained by dividing n_r by 2. For $p\neq q$ the components must be split. The runs of a dry or wet event of length r is then:

$$n_r=2p^r q+(N-1-r)p^r q^2 \tag{820a}$$

This formula was also given by BROOKS and CARRUTHERS (1953).

The total number of runs can be found by:

$$N_T=2(N-1)pq+1 \tag{820b}$$

Eqs. 818a through 820b can be expanded to three or more events, provided these events are independent. For runs of three or more events, e.g., p_A, p_B, p_C etc., we can set $p=p_A$ and $q=p_B+p_C$ etc.

Sometimes it may be helpful to estimate the average number of runs (in a random series) which can be expected. This problem was treated by MAHALANOBIS (1944):

$$E(n)=\bar{n}=(N-1)pq+p \tag{821a}$$

with:

$$\text{Var}(n) = \sigma_n^2 = (N-1)(1-3pq)pq + (1-2p^2)pq \quad (821\text{b})$$

The second term in both equations can be neglected for large N. Comparison with eq. 820b reveals that $N_T \sim 2E(n)$. Eq. 821a provides the total number of runs for either event, while $E(n)$ renders the information on one single category only. Consequently:

$$N_T = \bar{n}_w + \bar{n}_d \quad (821\text{c})$$

where $\bar{n}_w$ and $\bar{n}_d$ stand for the average runs of wet or dry events, respectively.

Example 74. Number of runs. The various models introduced in the preceding section will be compared employing the precipitation data in Examples 72 and 73. Beer's model is computed by eq. 817b. Gold's model was introduced by eq. 818a, Cochran requires eq. 819a, while Brooks and Carruthers have discussed eq. 820a. In this example computation of runs is based on $N = 100$, $P_A = 0.461$ (dry days) and $P_B = 0.539$ (wet days); P and q in the various formulae are replaced by the pertinent p_A or p_B.

A first glance at Table LXXXVII reveals that the differences between the models are small. This should be expected, because p_A and p_B are close to 0.5. The number of runs by eq. 819a is the combined number of dry and wet runs by eq. 820a as expected. Multiplying and summing $\sum rn_r$, yields 54.0 and 45.1 for the model by BROOKS and CARRUTHERS (1953). Although 54.0 is exactly the number of wet days among $N = 100$, the number of dry days, 45.1, is slightly short, an effect of rounding. The columns in Beer's model render 53.6 and 45.7, also slightly short of the expected number due to rounding.

Little difference can be discovered between the models of the first seven columns of Table LXXXVII. The last two columns are significantly different, however. In these columns the data from

TABLE LXXXVII

NUMBER OF RUNS ($p_A = 0.461$; $p_B = 0.539$, $N = 100$)

Days r	Eq. 818a*[1] n_r	Eq. 819a	Eq. 820a*[2] wet	Eq. 820a*[2] dry	Eq. 820a*[2] total	Eq. 817a*[3] wet	Eq. 817a*[3] dry	Dry*[4] $a\,e^{-a}$	Wet*[4] $b\,e^{-b}$
1	25.5	25.3	11.7	13.6	25.3	11.5	13.4	5.78	4.70
2	12.6	12.5	6.3	6.2	12.5	6.2	6.2	3.76	3.32
3	6.2	6.2	3.3	2.8	6.1	3.3	2.8	2.42	2.29
4	3.1	3.1	1.8	1.3	3.1	1.8	1.3	1.56	1.82
5	1.5	1.5	1.0	0.6	1.6	1.0	0.6	1.02	1.16
6	0.7	0.8	0.5	0.3	0.8	0.5	0.3	0.65	0.82
7	0.4	0.4	0.3	0.1	0.4	0.3	0.1	0.42	0.58
8	0.2	0.2	0.2	0.0	0.2	0.2	0.1	0.28	0.42
9	0.1	0.1	0.1			0.1		0.17	0.30
10	0.0	0.0	0.0					0.11	0.22
11								0.07	0.15
12								0.05	0.10
13								0.03	0.07
14								0.02	0.05
15								0.01	0.03
16								0.01	0.02
17									0.01
$\sum n_r$	50.3	50.1	25.2	24.9	50.1	24.9	24.8	16.36	16.06
$\sum rn_r$			54.0	45.1		53.6	45.7	56	46

References: *[1]GOLD, 1929; *[2]BROOKS and CARRUTHERS, 1953; *[3]BEER et al., 1946; *[4]GREEN, 1970.

Table LXXXVI based on the exponential model were converted to the scale of the other models. The dry or wet runs have been weighted so that $\sum rn_r$ will conform to 46 and 54 for the dry and wet runs, respectively. The differences between the models in the last two columns and the first seven columns must be attributed to the consideration of persistence in the exponential models, while the other models postulate independence. Hence, persistence leads to more runs of longer length than based on independence. Therefore, BROOKS and CARRUTHERS (1953) suggested to sum the number of runs, and accept for n_1 and n_2 an empirical value while the remaining runs are computed by adopting an average probability $p_k = p_2$. This is a modification of eq. 817a. We compute $\sum_{r=i}^{m} n_r = (1-p_i)N$, where N is the total number of days, p_i the probability to be sought, n_r the number of runs, summed up from i to the maximum. (The summation from m to i could be substituted instead.) Generally for $i=2$ a constant ratio can be found between preceding and subsequent probability, $k = p_r/p_{r+1}$. This ratio can then be taken to compute the series:

$$N_i p_i,\ N_i p_i^2,\ N_i p_i^3,\ \dots\ N_i p_i^{r-i}$$

The $N_i = \sum n_r = (1-p_i)N$.

Table LXXXVIII serves as an illustration of the differences between the four models when p_A discloses a larger deviation from 0.5. The assumption is made that $P_A = 0.7$, $p_B = 0.3$, $N = 100$.

Conditional and unconditional probabilities

Climatic tables contain usually the empirical probability of days with precipitation (or above a certain threshold of precipitation amount). The conditional probability $P(W|W)$ or $P(D|D)$ is mostly not listed. It has been illustrated in the preceding section, however, that these probabilities are quite useful. HERSHFIELD (1970) addressed this problem. He studied 33 stations located in the U.S. and has established a relationship:

$$P_c = a + bP_u \tag{822}$$

where P_c denotes the conditional probability, P_u the unconditional probability. The constants and correlation coefficients are given in Table LXXXIX.

TABLE LXXXVIII

NUMBER OF RUNS ($p_A = 0.3$, $p_B = 0.7$, $N = 100$)

r	Gold, 1929	Brooks and Carruthers, 1953			Beer et al., 1946	
		wet	dry	total	wet	dry
1	25.5	6.6	14.8	21.4	6.3	14.7
2	12.6	4.6	4.4	9.0	4.4	4.4
3	6.2	3.2	1.3	4.5	3.1	1.3
4	3.1	2.2	0.4	2.6	2.2	0.4
5	1.5	1.5	0.1	1.6	1.5	0.1
6	0.7	1.1		1.1	1.1	
7	0.4	0.7		0.7	0.7	
8	0.2	0.5		0.5	0.5	
9	0.1	0.3		0.3	0.4	
10	0.0	0.2		0.2	0.3	
11		0.2		0.2	0.2	
12		0.1		0.1	0.1	
13		0.1		0.1	0.1	
$\sum n_r$	50.3	21.3	21.0	42.3	20.9	20.9
$\sum rn_r$						

TABLE LXXXIX

CONSTANTS FOR EQ. 822
(From HERSHFIELD, 1970)

Threshold (inches)	Dry–dry				Wet–wet			
	a	*b*	*r*	std. error	*a*	*b*	*r*	std. error
0.01	0.172	0.846	0.991	0.009	0.291	0.545	0.825	0.030
0.10	0.132	0.873	0.994	0.005	0.206	0.573	0.721	0.030
0.25	0.102	0.900	0.997	0.003	0.157	0.558	0.609	0.030
0.25	0.078	0.922	0.997	0.002	0.094	0.740	0.466	0.040

The probabilities for the transition matrix, eq. 797, can be derived from:

$$P(D|D) + P(D|W) = 1.0 \tag{823a}$$

and:

$$P(W|W) + P(W|D) = 1.0 \tag{823b}$$

Miscellaneous models

Duration of rainstorms

In the preceding sections the duration of rainfall other than the length of runs was not treated. SHENTON and SKEES (1970) examined the probability density distributions of the duration of storms. They fall into the group of so-called J-shaped distributions. Several suitable discrete distributions may be chosen. Shenton and Skees suggested six distribution types, of which the first three are relatively easy to handle. Two of these are one-parameter models, however, and therefore less flexible for fitting of the frequency distribution.

(*1*) The logarithmic series distribution (one parameter):

$$f(x) = \theta^x(bx) = a\theta^x/x \tag{824}$$

This distribution has already been treated (see eq. 136a).
(*2*) The negative binomial distribution (see eq. 70a).
(*3*) The geometric distribution (one parameter):

$$f(x) = (1-p)p^{x-1} \quad 0 < p < 1 \tag{825a}$$

$$\bar{x} = 1/(1-p) \tag{825b}$$

$$\sigma^2 = p/(1-p)^2 \tag{825c}$$

From the remaining three only the "logarithmic negative mixture" is of importance (see eq. 140a). According to SHENTON and SKEES (1970), the negative binomial emerged as a suitable distribution for storms in units of days, the logarithmic negative mixture for units of an hour.

SHARON (1983) has delineated that storms may not be distributed randomly in space.

A model of n-day precipitation

While precipitation sums for certain time periods are usually readily accessible, frequency distributions of the amount or the largest daily amount within a specified time interval are difficult to obtain. TODOROVIC and WOOLHISER (1975) developed models which permit some approximate answers, although their models are presently not precise.
A random variable y_i which is either 0 or 1 is defined depending whether the day is dry or wet, respectively. Thus:

$$N_w = \sum_{i=1}^{n} y_i \qquad (826a)$$

denotes the number of days with precipitation in a period of n days. N_w is usually available for many stations of record and may range from 0 to n.
Assume that x_j is the daily amount of precipitation on the j-th day with precipitation (i.e. where $y_j = 1$). Then:

$$S_n = \sum_{j=0}^{N_w} x_j \qquad (826b)$$

is the total precipitation amount within a given period of n days, with $x_0 \equiv 0$. This information usually is given, too. Mean and variance of S_n can be deduced as:

$$\bar{S}_n = a\bar{N}_w \qquad (827a)$$

$$\text{Var}\,(S_n) = b\bar{N}_w + a^2 \text{Var}\,(N_w) \qquad (827b)$$

where:

$$a = \bar{x} = S_n/N_w \qquad (827c)$$

and:

$$b = \sigma_x^2 \qquad (827d)$$

$$\bar{N}_w = \sum^{n} y_i/n \qquad (827e)$$

$$\sigma_x^2 = \sum (x_j - \bar{x})^2/N_w \qquad (827f)$$

Although Var (N_w) may be unknown it probably can be inferred from N_w for given periods n, provided the data sample comes from a stationary time interval. This leaves σ_x^2 undetermined, but this parameter is not needed in the models.
TODOROVIC and WOOLHISER (1975) demonstrated that the distribution function of the largest daily amount within the period n can be written

$$\phi_n(x) = P(N_0) + \sum_{k=1}^{n} [H(x)]^k \cdot P(N_k) \qquad (828)$$

where N_0 is the symbol for $N_w = 0$ and N_k the symbol for $N_w = k$ in the n-day period. $P(N_j)$ denotes probabilities for the designated events, and $H(x)$ is a cumulative frequency distribution for the daily precipitation amounts (KATZ, 1977).
The distribution function:

$$F_n(x) = P(S_n \leq x) \qquad (829a)$$

can be interpreted as the cumulative frequency of $S_n \leq x$. Todorovic and Woolhiser have deduced that:

$$F_n(x) = P(N_0) + \sum_{k=0}^{n} P(X_k \leq x) \cdot P(N_k) \tag{829b}$$

where:

$$X_k = \sum_{j=1}^{k} x_j \tag{829c}$$

and $X_0 = 0$. Eq. 829a is the distribution function for n-day precipitations. It was postulated that: (*1*) the observations z_i are independent of N_w; and (*2*) the data set x_i is independent and identically distributed with $H(x) = P(X_k \leq x)$ where $k = N_w \leq n$.
It is evident that the probabilities $P(X_k < x)$, $P(N_k)$, $P(N_0)$ and the function $H(x)$ must be known in order to determine $F_n(x)$ or $\phi_n(x)$. The above authors postulated:

$$H(x) = 1 - \exp(-\lambda x) \tag{830a}$$

which corresponds to an exponential decline of the frequency density of precipitation amounts. Although the authors pointed out that discrepancies with this assumption exist, it is a simple approximation because λ is the only parameter. The moments estimator is:

$$\lambda = 1/\bar{x} = 1/a \tag{830b}$$

Other estimators have been discussed (see eq. 111c) but $\bar{x}$ is readily available.
With the definition of $H(x)$ through eq. 830a and postulation (*2*) the probability $P(X_k \leq x)$ can be derived as:

$$P(X_k \leq x) = [\lambda^k / \Gamma(k)] \int_0^x \omega^{k-1} \mathrm{e}^{-\lambda\omega} \, \mathrm{d}\omega \tag{831}$$

The other probability $P(N_k)$ depends on the statistical background. Two cases were considered:
(*1*) The sequence of $y_i \dots y_n$ is independent. Then:

$$P_B = P(N_k) = \binom{n}{k} p^k (1-p)^{n-k} \tag{832a}$$

with:

$$p = P(y_i = 1) = N_w / n \tag{832b}$$

This assumption is often unrealistic because most meteorological elements, including daily precipitations, show persistence.
(*2*) The sequence of $y_i \dots y_n$ follows a Markov chain model which is more realistic. Consequently, two probabilities can be established, with $k = 1, 2, \dots n$:

$$q_0 = P(W_k | D_{k-1}) = \sum s_{DW} / n_D \tag{833a}$$

and:

$$q_1 = P(W_k | W_{k-1}) = \sum s_{WW} / n_W \tag{833b}$$

where s_{DW} denotes any sequence of a dry–wet day, and s_{WW} the sequence of two wet days; q_0 and q_1 are conditional probabilities for a dry–wet and wet–wet succession. Note that

$\sum s_{DD} + \sum s_{DW} = n_k$ the number of dry days, etc. Then:

$$w_k = P(N_k | W_0) \tag{834a}$$

$$d_k = P(N_k | D_0) \tag{834b}$$

i.e., w_k and d_k are the conditional probabilities of having $N_w = k$ rainy days in the n-day period after the day before was wet (W_0) or dry (D_0), respectively. In conclusion:

$$P_{M_k} = P(N_k) = Rw_k + (1-R)d_k \tag{835a}$$

for this model, where:

$$R = P(W_0) \tag{835b}$$

is the probability of rainy days before the n-day period, i.e., $y_0 = 1$. (See analogy to eq. 801a.) The expected number of wet days in the n-day interval is $E(N_w) = \bar{N}_w$:

$$\bar{N}_w = nQ + (R-Q)(1-q^n) \cdot q/(1-q) \tag{836a}$$

where:

$$q = q_1 - q_0 \tag{836b}$$

and:

$$Q = q_0/(1-q) \tag{836c}$$

The distribution functions $\phi_n(x)$ and $F_n(x)$ are now known. After some simplification we find from eqs. 828 and 829a by substituting $H(x)$ and $P(N_k) = P_B$ the two functions:

$$\phi_B(x) = (1 - p\,\mathrm{e}^{-\lambda x})^n \tag{837a}$$

and:

$$F_B(x) = (1-p)^n \left[1 + \int_0^x \mathrm{e}^{-\lambda\omega} f(p,\omega)\, \mathrm{d}\omega/\omega \right] \tag{837b}$$

where:

$$f(p,\omega) = \sum_{\nu=1}^{n} \binom{n}{\nu} [\lambda p\omega/(1-p)]^{\nu}/\Gamma(\nu) \tag{837c}$$

TODOROVIC and WOOLHISER (1975) called this the "binomial-exponential" precipitation model.

The "Markov-chain-exponential model" shows:

$$\phi_M(x) = (1 - q_0 - Rq)(1-q_0)^{n-1} + \sum_{k=1}^{n} P_{Mk}(1 - \mathrm{e}^{-\lambda x})^k \tag{838a}$$

and:

$$F_M(x) = (1 - q_0 - Rq)(1-q_0)^{n-1} + \sum_{k=1}^{n} P_{M_k} \cdot P(X_k \leq x) \tag{838b}$$

The means: $\bar{S}_n$, $\bar{N}_w$ and a, are related (see eq. 827a).

Todorovic and Woolhiser expanded their models by including a truncation at $x = z - T$:

$$H(z) = 1 - \exp[-\lambda(z-T)] \tag{839}$$

where $T \leq z \leq \infty$, and T is a truncation point, e.g. $T \geq 0.005$ inch. Truncation affects $P(X_k \leq z)$, i.e., eq. 831, where the integration is now over $x = z - kT$ with $kT \leq z$. Consequently, a substitution of the new $P(X_k \leq z)$ must be made in eqs. 837a, b and 838a, b and p must be replaced by:

$$p_T = p \cdot \exp(-\lambda T) \tag{840a}$$

for ϕ_B and F_B and:

$$R_T = R \exp(-\lambda T) \tag{840b}$$

for ϕ_M and F_M.
The original transition matrix for the Markov chain:

$$\mathbf{M} = \begin{vmatrix} 1 - q_0, & q_0 \\ 1 - q_2, & q_1 \end{vmatrix} \tag{841a}$$

must be replaced by an approximation:

$$\mathbf{M}' = \begin{vmatrix} 1 - q_0', & q_0' \\ 1 - q_1', & q_2' \end{vmatrix} \tag{841b}$$

where:

$$q_0' = e^{-\lambda T}[q_0(1 - q_1) + q_0 q_1(1 - e^{-\lambda T})]/[1 - q_1 + q_0(1 - e^{\lambda T})] \tag{841c}$$

and:

$$q_1' = q_1 \exp(-\lambda T) \tag{841d}$$

Todorovic and Woolhiser illustrated that the Markov-chain-exponential model is slightly superior to the binomial-exponential model. They intended to expand their model by attempting to use functions other than the exponential for $H(x)$.
The sophisticated systems, especially P_{M_i} need information which is not readily available. However, ϕ_B and F_B require only p and λ, which can be obtained from eq. 826a, b. Given w_k, d_k, q_0 and q_1, the maximum daily amount within n days can be estimated from ϕ_M. Although it may be more economical to derive $F(x)$, and consequently $F_F(x)$, or $F_M(x)$ from empirical data the models by Todorovic and Woolhiser provide solutions when no individual records are available.

Dropsize distributions, spectra and total rainfall

Previous distributions have largely dealt with precipitation amounts. Sometimes the distribution of raindrop-size may be required. MARSHALL and PALMER (1948) derived a relationship between N_D, the number of particles of unit size-range, and the dropsize diameter D:

$$N_D = N_0 \, e^{-\lambda D} \tag{842a}$$

where N_0 is a constant and λ a parameter depending on the intensity. With $D_0 = 0.09R^{0.21}$ in rain (D_0 is the diameter of the median volume particles, in centimeters). $D_0 = 0.14R^{0.48}$

for snow (melted diameter for snow particles) and R the precipitation rate (in mm h^{-1}) we can rewrite:

$$N_D = N_0 \, e^{-(3.67D/D_0)} \qquad (842b)$$

the number of particles per cm^3. In rain, $N_0 = 0.08$ cm^{-4}, in snow $N_0 = 0.038R^{-0.87}$. The distribution will give a straight line in semi-logarithmic coordinates. N_D has the property of a frequency density function. More details can be found in the cited reference (MARSHALL and PALMER, 1948) or in VALLEY (1965). DINGLE and HARDY (1962) added sequential raindrop-size distributions, which they called drop-size spectra.

Although Marshall-Palmer's formula is in widespread usage, GRIFFITHS (1975) cautioned that for discrete values of the curve N_D this frequency may be overestimated due to the exponential decline, and the dependence of N_D on D cannot always be neglected. Griffiths recommended to work with the integral form of eq. 842a.

Although it was traditionally assumed that the Marshall-Palmer relationship is applicable only to surface raindrop distributions in extratropical rains, MERCERET (1974) concluded from data of hurricane Ginger that the relationship is also a good model for airborne measurements from hurricanes. The slope of the distribution can be directly related to the rainfall rate R:

$$\lambda = 4.1R^{-0.21} \qquad (842c)$$

where λ is given in units per mm and R in mm per hour.

In contrast, STRANTZ (1971) found from 817 raindrop spectra in Karlsruhe that spectra of raindrops generally do not agree with the Marshall-Palmer formula. Consequently, he developed a classification scheme of seven prototypes of which six types display a secondary maximum. According to Strantz the Marshall-Palmer distribution is best suited for rainfall rates between 12 and 30 mm h^{-1}, especially if N_0 is larger than 2000 [$m^{-3} \cdot 0.25$ mm^{-1}] (i.e., $N_0 = 0.08$ cm^{-4} in formula 842a) as the reference value by Marshall-Palmer. More details on the classification of raindrop spectra can also be found in DIEM and STRANTZ (1971). CZERWINSKI and PFISTERER (1972) have studied 10,650 spectra on a worldwide basis and conclude that the Marshall-Palmer distribution fits only a few spectra because it produces too low a number of small droplets while overestimating the number of large droplets. The peculiarities of dropsize spectra were also investigated by AUSTIN and GEOTIS (1979). They concluded that tropical ocean showers show a heavy concentration of medium-sized drops while large drops are rare.

CATANEO and STOUT (1969) added spectra from humid continental climates obtained by a raindrop camera and relate rainfall rate to radar reflectivity. JEON-JANG (1966) formulated a statistical theory of precipitation processes from clouds, expanding Bergeron's and Langmuir's theory of the thirties. He also presented some distributions of water content.

MALLOW (1975) addressed the problem of a frequency distribution for the droplet size in fog, and generalized the Deirmendjian-Chu-Hogg formula. The frequency distribution is given by:

$$f(x) = Cx^{\alpha}\exp(-\beta x^{\gamma}) \qquad (843a)$$

where $f(x)$ is the number density of droplets and is mostly replaced in the literature by $N(x)$. Furthermore $\beta = \alpha/\gamma$, and the variate x is the relative droplet size $x = R/R_r$ with R_r denoting a reference droplet size. This reference is an arbitrary definition; it could be the maximum R. Since the maximum may fluctuate from sample to sample a replacement as suggested by Mallow is appropriate. He defined $R_1 < R_r < R_2$, with $x_1 = R_1/R_r$ and $x_2 = R_2/R_r$, R_1 and R_2 are selected from the data sample so that the following boundary condition is fulfilled:

$$f(x_1) = f(x_2) = 10^{-n} N_r \tag{843b}$$

where $N_r = f(x=1)$, i.e., $R = R_r$, and n is an arbitrary positive number. According to Mallow frequency distributions of droplet size in warm fog follow eq. 843a but multimodal distributions were observed by ELDRIDGE (1966).
According to Mallow, the parameters α, γ and C can be estimated:

$$\ln x_1^\gamma - x_1^\gamma = \ln x_2^\gamma - x_2^\gamma \tag{844a}$$

This is an equation in γ, and can be solved by numerical or graphical methods. Then α may be obtained from:

$$\alpha = -n \ln 10/[\ln x_i - (x_i^\gamma - 1)/\gamma] \tag{844b}$$

where i is either 1 or 2. Furthermore:

$$C = \pm (N\gamma/R_r)(\beta)^\delta/\Gamma(\delta) \tag{844c}$$

where:

$$\delta = (\alpha + 1)/\gamma \tag{844d}$$

The positive sign for C applies to α, γ positive, the negative sign for α, γ negative.
The solutions for eq. 844a fall into two categories:
(1) $x_2 < 1/x_1$, viz., $R_2/R_r < R_r/R_1$. In this case γ and $\alpha > 0$.
(2) $x_2 > 1/x_1$. In this case γ and $\alpha < 0$.
From a theoretical point of view the derivation of estimators from two frequency classes (or order statistics) may be insufficient unless it has been proven that the system can produce an optimum estimator for γ or has a higher efficiency than other estimators (e.g., MURTHY and SWARTZ, 1975). Therefore, the frequency density eq. 843a can be written as:

$$f(x) = K \cdot A x^{c-1} \exp(-b x^a) \tag{845}$$

in which form it is exactly the "hyper-gamma distribution" (see eq. 106, or ESSENWANGER, 1976, p. 116) which was previously discussed where $K = N/R_r$, $\alpha = c - 1$, $\beta = b$ and $\gamma = a$ (α, β, γ) of eq. 843a.
In order to avoid any loss of information caused by the discrepancies between eq. 842a and the observed distributions, JOSS and GORI (1976) recommended the calculation of sets of parameters which provide sufficient details, but make it unnecessary to keep the detailed frequency distributions. They based their system on:

$$P(n) = C \int_0^\infty N_D D^\delta \, \mathrm{d}D \tag{846a}$$

where C is a constant and N_D and D have been defined previously (eq. 842a). The parameter δ is an integral parameter to be selected arbitrarily. Joss and Gori selected $\delta = 2, 3, 4$ and 6. This leads to the optical extinction cross-section σ, the total volume of water W, the rainfall rate R and the radar reflectivity factor Z, respectively.

Now the median parameters for these four distributions and finally the shape parameters are defined as:

$$S(\xi \cdot \eta) = Q(\xi \cdot \eta)/Q(\xi \cdot \eta)_{\text{exp.}} \tag{846b}$$

where:

$$Q(\xi \cdot \eta) = (M_\xi - M_\eta)/(M_\xi + M_\eta) \tag{846c}$$

ξ, η represent the four parameters, either σ, W, R or Z (e.g., $\xi = W$, $\eta = \sigma$ etc.) and M_ξ or M_η stand for the median value; $Q(\xi \cdot \eta)_{\text{exp.}}$ is the quotient of the median values for the exponential distribution. According to Joss and Gori all necessary parameters for answering practical questions can be calculated from these sets of parameters. The parameters permit us interpretations in physical terms.

Areal precipitation and patterns

In the previous discussions it was generally assumed that "point" precipitation data were treated. It is well known, however, that maps of precipitations are constructed, delineating the variability of precipitation within areas, even small areas (see also areal persistence, p. 19). In recent time the analysis of areal data has been aided by electronic data processing. Several data quality control techniques have been developed for this purpose. Basic procedures were suggested by BLEASDALE and FARRAR (1965). This method was expanded by ALLEN (1972). His criterion is very simple: after some basic checks (missing data, etc.) a control parameter C_p is calculated:

$$C_p = [S - (A + 2\sigma_d)]/S, \tag{847a}$$

where:

$$A = a_d/Y \tag{847b}$$

and a_d denotes the daily means of the areal precipitation divided by the annual average of the area Y (i.e. A is expressed in percentage); σ_d stands for the standard deviation of the station values used in finding the mean (percentage), and S represents the daily value of the station's annual average. If $C_p > 0.25$ the value is flagged as too high. Values of $S < (A - 2\sigma_d)$ are considered as suspiciously low. The control system is then expanded to months.

A modification was suggested by SHEARMAN (1975). Instead of the control parameter C_p he recommended:

$$D = R_j - R_{\text{int}} \tag{848a}$$

where R_j is the rainfall at station j and R_{int} an interpolated rainfall from six neighboring stations out of eight within a circle of 25 km from the station. These six station values can be considered homogeneous data, because the freedom exists to eliminate two suspicious rainfall amounts. No more than two stations per octant of the circular area are included for the selection of the eight stations. This restriction avoids clustering.

$$R_{\text{int}} = (\textstyle\sum R_i/d_i^n)/\sum (1/d_i^n) \tag{848b}$$

with $1 \leq n \leq 2$. Shearman used the exponent $n = 2$ for the United Kingdom rain-gauge net work, but other exponents, e.g., $n = 1.65$ have been recommended (KELWAY, 1974). R_i stands for the individual rainfall amount of the station i and d_i for the distance between the two respective neighboring stations j and i. Topographic influences are eliminated by converting R_j and R_i to percentages of the annual total rainfall. Then R_j is accepted if either one of the conditions occurs:

$$|D| \leq 2.5 \text{ mm} \tag{848c}$$

$$|D| \leq c \cdot \varepsilon \tag{848d}$$

Shearman suggested $c = 2$ for daily rainfall, $c = 4$ for monthly values, and ε is an appropriate error estimate (e.g., the standard error of R_{int}).

An areal scheme for gridpoint analysis was developed by ENGLISH (1973). Rainfall amounts are computed at regular gridpoints from a scattered distribution of rain-gauge values. This leads to an objective method of calculating area rainfall as compared with a summation of observations from rain gauges alone. The technique is based on a least square solution for:

$$\mathbf{r} = \mathbf{D} \cdot \mathbf{a} \tag{849a}$$

where $\mathbf{r}$ is the $N \times 1$ matrix with elements r_i/d_i, $\mathbf{D}$ is the $N \times 3$ matrix of displacement elements (see below), and $\mathbf{a}$ is the 3×1 matrix of coefficients with elements a, b and c. In the individual case:

$$r/d = aX/d + bY/d + c/d \tag{849b}$$

The matrix $\mathbf{D}$ comprises the displacement elements:

$$\mathbf{D} = \begin{pmatrix} x_1 & y_1 & z_1 \\ x_2 & y_2 & z_2 \\ \vdots & \vdots & \vdots \\ x_N & y_N & z_N \end{pmatrix} \tag{849c}$$

where $x_i = X_i/d_i$, $y_i = Y_i/d_i$ and $z_i = 1/d_i$. Furthermore, d_i denotes the distance of the rain gauge from the grid point, X_i and Y_i are rectangular displacement distances of the rain gauge from the grid point, r is the precipitation amount at the gauge. The solution follows standard procedures in matrix algebra (see ESSENWANGER, 1976). According to English the model allows that areal rainfalls can be calculated with sufficient accuracy.

Other contributions to areal rainfall are studies by SALTER (1972), EDWARDS (1972), VAHL (1972), WINKLER and MURPHY (1976), MURPHY (1978), and SCOTT and SHULMAN (1979), etc. A further expansion of the statistical analysis for areal precipitation was given by ZAWADZKI (1973) who defined a storm coordinate system moving with the storm. His normalized system does not require stationarity and homogeneity of the autocorrelation function of rainfall as is the case with regular autocorrelation patterns.

A technique of delineating highs and lows in rainfall patterns was developed by SCHICKEDANZ (1973) whose method is based on a trend surface analysis. He started with a linear regression model:

$$\hat{R}_{ij} = A + Bx_i y_j + B_2 x_i y_j \tag{850a}$$

where x_i is the north–south coordinate, y_j the east–west axis (increasing to the south and east, respectively). $\hat{R}_{ij}$ is the estimate of the mapped rainfall variate at location i, j, A is the intercept, and B_1, B_2 are slope parameters. Then a basic residual is defined and converted into a relative residual:

$$R_r = (R_{ij} - \hat{R}_{ij})/R_{ij} = R_b/R_{ij} \quad (850b)$$

where R_{ij} is the actual measured amount at the location i, j. Afterwards a standardized residual:

$$R_s = (R_{ij} - \hat{R}_{ij})/S_R \quad (850c)$$

is computed for comparison. S_R stands for the standard error estimate of the two-dimensional regression surface. Of interest are only the extreme deviations (rain cells or low rainfall) which arc mapped.

Brandes (1975) or Drufuca (1977) described the aid of radar for areal precipitation measurements and Patrinos et al. (1979) related spatial correlation and weather modification experiments.

Other models of area precipitation have been developed by Gringorten (1983), Gabriel (1983), Rodriguez-Iturbe (1983), Sharon (1983), and others. The coupling between synoptic scale dynamics and statistical description of precipitation processes as an important consideration for the solution to space-time modelling of precipitation has been suggested by Gupta (1983).

Average annual precipitation and daily amounts

Thomson (1971) described a method for estimating y, the (average) annual frequency of days with at least a specified amount of rainfall x when only the average amount of rainfall is available.

His method is based on Brooks and Carruthers' (1953, p. 119) relationship:

$$\log (N - N_x) = ax + b \quad (851a)$$

or:

$$\log y = ax + b \quad (851b)$$

where N is the total number of observations for $x = 0$, N_x the number of observations *not* exceeding the threshold x and a and b are constants.

$N_x = 0$ for $x = 0$ and $N_x = N$ for $x = x_{max}$

Standardizing of the cumulative frequency leads to:

$$\log (1 - F_x) = ax + b \quad (851c)$$

As Thomson stated in his fitting of the data to British rainfall maps, a straight line (with logarithmic ordinate) gives good representation except for high and low (less than 0.08 inch = 2 mm) values of x. The small amounts are of little interest to most users and for the large amounts an extreme value statistic would be more appropriate.

Brooks gave a solution for rainfall data at Kilmarnock with the constants $a = 3.76$ and $b = -2.05$. These constants can be obtained by any of the fitting methods for straight lines previously introduced.

Thomson expanded the scheme for Great Britain and Northern Ireland data (about 100 stations) and found the relationship between the average annual precipitation amount and the number of days with 0.4 inch (10 mm) or more. He derived:

$$N_{0.4} = 1.00x_a - 10.69 \qquad (852a)$$

or in general:

$$N_x = Ax_a - B \qquad (852b)$$

In this equation x_a stands for the average annual precipitation amount of a station. Eq. 852a has validity for the climatic regime of the British Isles, but other constants for (homogeneous) climatic regions could be developed.

Eq. 852a can now be introduced into eq. 851b together with another relationship, which connects the constant a and the mean daily rainfall $\bar{x}_d$.

$$b = a \cdot \bar{x}_d \qquad (853)$$

We obtain:

$$\log y = bx/\bar{x}_d + c \qquad (854a)$$

In order to determine c, we set $N_x = y$, and write:

$$\log N_x = bx/\bar{x}_d + c \qquad (854b)$$

or:

$$c = \log (Ax_a - B) - bx/\bar{x}_d \qquad (854c)$$

Once c is known N_x could be computed for any threshold x.

Setting $\log N_x = 0$, i.e., $N_x = 1$, renders the intercept on the x-axis. Thus the fraction:

$$x = -c\bar{x}_d/b \qquad (854d)$$

represents the value of x occurring "once a year".

Total rainfall and number of days

Olascoaga (1950) related y, the total rainfall (cumulative distribution) with x, the number of days with rain (cumulative) for Argentina rainfall. His formula:

$$F(y) = a\, e^{bx}\, F(x) \qquad (855a)$$

apparently has validity for the climatic regime in Argentina, but may not find generalization in all climate types. The fitting of eq. 855a is best performed by transformation:

$$Y = \ln F(y) - \ln F(x) = A + bx \qquad (855b)$$

where $A = \ln a$. This equation is a straight line in x and the constants A and b can easily be estimated.

Rainfall intensity and rainfall rates

The rate at which rain accumulates within a short time interval is usually called the intensity of rain or the rainfall rate. Although it is customary to convert rainfall rates into mm h^{-1} or inch h^{-1}, they should be given precisely for the time period during which they were actually measured. A rainfall of 5 mm in 5 min does not necessarily amount to 60 mm in one hour unless this amount was observed in this one-hour time interval.
Because short time interval measurements often are not available, CHEN (1976) developed a method for estimating the distribution of 5-min rainfall based on the climatological data of excessive short duration rainfall published by the National Oceanic and Atmospheric Administration (US). These include rainfalls with threshold >6.25 mm per 5-min interval and 20 mm h^{-1} for a one-hour interval.
LIN (1976a) suggested an extension to records where only averages are available. The method provides the 20-year distribution of 5-min rain rates based on the average 60-min rain rate $\bar{R}_{60}$. Lin derived for a rainfall rate x of a specified time interval T:

$$x_T = R_T / R_c \qquad (856a)$$

where R_T is the normalized rain rate. Lin substituted $\bar{R}_{60}$, the average 60-min rain rate, for R_c. Then:

$$x_T = c_1 (x_{60})^{c_2} \qquad (856b)$$

where c_1 is a coefficient and c_2 an exponent depending on T. The values for c_1 and c_2 were plotted by LIN (1976b) as function of T.
FLETCHER (1950) derived a simpler relationship:

$$Y_t = \sqrt{R_{60} t / 60} \qquad (857a)$$

where Y_t is the maximum rainfall rate for time $t \leq 60$ min, t is the duration time in minutes, and R_{60} is the one-hour rainfall. The average rainfall rate is:

$$\bar{Y}_t = R_{60} t / 60 \qquad (857b)$$

This relationship can be expanded for storms of longer duration than one hour if the maximum rainfall amount (depth) and the duration of storms are observed:

$$Y_t = k \sqrt{t / (60\, h_T)} \qquad (858a)$$

where h_T is the number of hours and:

$$k = R / \sqrt{h_T} \qquad (858b)$$

The average is then:

$$\bar{Y}_t = R t / (60\, h_T) \qquad (858c)$$

WINNER (1968) and MCMORROW (1978) used this technique to derive estimates of the year for rainfall rates exceeding a certain threshold. This topic was also investigated by BRIGGS (1968) and JACKSON (1975). The latter derived a probability for the number of hours exceeding a certain rainfall rate in the London (England) area.
Various other authors have dealt with rainfall rates. Only a selected number is included here. WILHEIT et al. (1977) investigated the use of satellite data for mapping rainfall rates

over the oceans. ZAWADSKI and RO (1978) correlated maximum rates and mesoscale parameters such as parcel convective energy, upper air humidity and height of parcel convection, etc. They found a correlation coefficient around 0.8 with convective energy. CHAUZY and DESPIAU (1980) related rainfall rate, electric charge and droplet size distribution. STEINHAUSER (1966), ZEDLER (1967) and DIEM (1968) dealt with the structure of precipitation, intensity, and duration in general, and REED (1979) suggested a methodology to obtain amount and intensity over the ocean.
Another study by HERSHFIELD (1972) related 5-min and 1-min rainfalls and established a method to obtain the probabilities of extreme value 1-min rainfalls.

Precipitable water

Sometimes it is of interest to determine the total moisture content of the atmosphere. REITAN (1960, 1963) developed a linear relationship between the monthly total precipitable water W and the mean monthly surface dewpoint temperature t_d:

$$\ln(W) = c_1 + c_2 t_d \tag{859}$$

For t_d in °F and W in inches Reitan derived the constants as $c_1 = 0.0981$ and $c_2 = 0.0341$ based on a correlation coefficient of $r = 0.98$. The coefficients are $c_1 = 3.345$ and $c_2 = 0.0614$ for t_d in °C and W in mm.
BOLSENGA (1965) expanded this application to mean daily and mean monthly observations although the correlation coefficient is somewhat lower. For hourly values $c_1 = 3.176$, $c_2 = 0.0691$ and for daily values $c_2 = 3.320$, $c_2 = 0.0769$ for the metric units. SMITH (1966) pointed out, however, that c_1 is a function of the moisture profile. Later RAO et al. (1979) utilized the mean monthly dewpoint values from surface to 500 m for Brazil.
SOLOT (1939) recommended to use the formula:

$$\Delta W = q\rho . \Delta h \tag{860a}$$

where ΔW is a small element of humid air, q the specific humidity, ρ the air density and Δh the vertical interval. This leads to:

$$W = c_3 \int_{p_h}^{p_0} q \, \mathrm{d}p \tag{860b}$$

where p_0 is the surface pressure and p_h the pressure at altitude h. The constant $c_3 = 0.0004$ for W in inches and $1/g$ for metric units, where g is the gravitational constant. According to Solot the precipitable water above 500 mbar is negligible and may cause an error of less than 2 mm but the calculation of the integral may be laborious. RAO et al. (1979) gave a formula equivalent to eq. 859 for dewpoints at 850 mbar.

Weather modification

Attempts to modify the weather go as far back in history as the old customs of rain dances seeking the relief of droughts or the ringing of church bells to suppress hail or severe thunderstorms. The scientific approach began much later. Agricultural practices (such as frost prevention by burning fires in orange groves in Florida, or wind breaking devices in snowdrift areas) may be considered as simple methods to modify the "effect of the weather" but cannot be treated in detail here. Other problems such as thermal pollution by towers of nuclear plants or pollution effects of industrial products and transportation means also cannot be included. Most scientists accept agricultural practices or pollutions as modifications of the atmosphere, although the debate continues on how large the influence may be and what could be the long term effects.

For the following discussion the term weather modification is limited to the alteration of the precipitation process by cloud seeding. This particular field of scientific studies has its roots in fundamental investigations about precipitation processes and cloud physics. A complete bibliography of scientists who contributed to this field in this century is not provided here. The reader may refer to the literature such as BERGERON (1935, 1949, 1960), SCHAFER (1946), VONNEGUT (1947), AUFM-KAMPE and WEICKMANN (1957), WEICKMANN (1957, 1960) or MASON (1971). In addition, a comprehensive literature survey on weather modification or a historical review of fundamental studies can be found in PETTERSSEN et al. (1957), NATIONAL ACADEMY OF SCIENCE (1964, 1966, 1973), MALONE (1966), FLEAGLE (1969), SEWELL (1973), WMO/IAMAP (1973, 1976), HESS (1974) or DENNIS (1980).

This section serves to call the reader's attention to the controversy in the statistical analysis of augmentation or enhancement of precipitation, the suppression of hail or storms, and the evaluation of possible effects of cloud seeding. Despite hundreds of projects in various countries and serious efforts by meteorologists and statisticians, little agreement has been reached whether cloud seeding has produced the desired effects. Only a few studies have held up under crucial scrutiny by statisticians utilizing a variety of statistical methodology (GABRIEL and BARAS, 1970; GABRIEL and NEUMANN, 1978; BRADLEY et al., 1979; BRAHAM, 1979; MASON, 1980; or GAGIN and NEUMANN, 1974, 1981). Others apparently have found unexpected effects (e.g., ELLIOTT and BROWN, 1971; NEYMAN et al., 1973, etc.).

The controversy started with the first report of the Advisory Committee on Weather Control (ORVILLE, 1957). THOM (1957a, b) based the evaluation on a regression method and a parametric transformation of the gamma distribution to the Gaussian frequency. (Most statistical tests postulate this type as the underlying background for testing data samples.) The basic data for the regression method were derived from the historical records. This approach was criticized by BROWNLEE (1960b) and NEYMAN and SCOTT (1961) who pointed out that the cloud seeding projects lacked randomized sampling design and were subject to various biases.

Later data samples were randomized, e.g., BRAHAM (1965), ELLIOTT et al. (1978), and various authors suggested methods for design and evaluation (e.g., SCHICKEDANZ et al., 1969; SCHICKEDANZ and HUFF, 1971; CHANGNON and SCHICKEDANZ, 1971; SCOTT, 1973; OLSEN et al., 1973; OLSEN, 1975; NEYMAN, 1975, 1977a, 1980, or NEYMAN and SCOTT, 1974; DENNIS, 1980, etc.). However, evaluation of operational cloud seeding projects (CHANGNON et al., 1979) remains problematic because operational seedings were not controlled experiments, but commercial undertakings. Randomization is rendered difficult due to persistence in meteorological precipitation processes (e.g., BOWEN, 1966). Thus, statistical techniques became more and more sophisticated (GABRIEL and HSU, 1981; HSU et al., 1981a, b; CROW, 1978; NEYMAN, 1977b, 1979a, 1980; BRADLEY et al., 1979).

The controversy has not been resolved. BRAHAM (1979) pointed out that meteorologists and statisticians look at weather modification projects from different points of view (e.g.,

NEYMAN, 1977a, 1980) and some statisticians recommended special tests (e.g., NEYMAN, 1979b; see eq. 744a).

At the present the economical value in the increase of precipitations has been small (see SWANSON, 1978, or MASON, 1980) despite tangible proof of statistical significance in some weather modification projects (GABRIEL, 1967; GABRIEL and BARAS, 1970; GAGIN and NEUMANN, 1974, 1981). Furthermore, augmentations which had been claimed to be statistically significant appeared later with the opposite result in reanalysis (GELHOUS et al., 1974; NEYMAN, 1977b, with reply by MIELKE, 1978; RANGNO, 1979; MASON, 1980; etc.).

In recent years, the trend in statistical methodology was towards more sophistications (e.g., HSU et al., 1981a, b), but the latest investigations by GABRIEL and PETRONDAS (1981) pointed towards a return of a simplification in techniques. These authors studied the usefulness of historical records for the evaluation of cloud seeding projects and concluded that despite earlier objections, standard statistical tests may be robust against non-randomness in precipitation data. They hope that these tentative findings hold up under the scrutiny of an expanded investigation (see also HSU and CHANGNON, 1983).

In summary, the history of past cloud seeding experiments discloses a fundamental weakness in experimental designs and a problem in the comparison of data samples. Can precipitation data samples from cloud seeded areas be compared with precipitation data from non-seeded areas? Evidently, comparison can only be perfect if sampling from target area and non-target area is made under equal physical conditions except for seeding. This ideal circumstance is very difficult to achieve as is deduced from the areal and temporal variability of precipitations. HSU et al. (1981a, b) recommended various steps to avoid inadequate comparisons. The most important precept is the proper definition of the experiment. What is being measured (e.g., storms, 12 hourly precipitations, seasonal amounts, etc.)? What statistical tests are commensurate with the experiment in order to eliminate or at least minimize any possible bias? Any method of statistical evaluation should be selected or determined prior to any analysis of data from seeded areas. These precautions could lead to some clarification about possible augmentation of precipitations by cloud seeding. Close cooperation between statisticians and meteorologists is essential, but the evaluation of the physics must remain with the meteorologist. A bibliography on statistical evaluation methods has recently been compiled by HSU (1981).

Concluding remarks

The literature on precipitation is so extensive that many excellent articles have not been included in this section. The selection was made with emphasis on statistical techniques rather than pure merits of an article for the advancement of the state-of-the-art on precipitation, rainfall, or physical processes. Some readers, therefore, may miss references which they would have liked to see included. Some citations may be added, however.

Several authors have discussed time series analysis, e.g., JENKINSON (1975b, 1977), DYER (1976), HSU and WALLACE (1976), TABONY (1979), etc. Numerous authors have investigated forecasting of precipitations and forecasting the probability of precipitations (e.g., LOWRY and GLAHN, 1976) but MURPHY (e.g., 1977) repeatedly has cautioned about the possible misinterpretation of these precipitation probability forecasts by the public.

Other articles deal with the analysis of variance (e.g., COURTNEY, 1980) or principal components analysis (e.g., DYER, 1976).

Finally, the distribution model of the relative humidity may be of interest. YAO (1974) deduced from his extensive investigation that the beta distribution is suitable for this representation.

Chapter 8

References

ABRAMOWITZ, M. and STEGUN, I. A. (Editors), 1964. *Handbook of Mathematical Functions* (6th ed., 1967). Nat. Bur. Standards, Appl. Math. Ser., 55, Washington, DC, 1045 pp.

ALEXANDERSSON, H., 1983. A general stochastic model of the precipitation process with applications to integrated precipitation, maximum daily precipitation, etc. *2nd Int. Meet. Stat. Climatol.*, pp. 3.2.1–8.

ALLEN, P. G., 1972. The routine processing of current rainfall data by computer. *Meteorol. Mag.*, 101: 340–345.

ALSOP, L. E., 1966. Faster Fourier series. *J. Geophys. Res.*, 71 (22): 5482–5483.

ANDERSON, E. B., 1971. The asymptotic distribution of conditional likelihood ratio tests. *J. Am. Stat. Assoc.*, 66: 630–633.

ANDERSON, T. W., 1962. *Introduction to Multivariate Statistical Analysis* (2nd ed., 1962). Wiley, New York, NY, 374 pp.

ANDERSON, T. W., 1960. A modification of the sequential probability ratio test to reduce the sample size. *Ann. Math. Stat.*, 31: 165–197.

ANDERSON, T. W. and DARLING, D. A., 1952. Asymptotic theory of certain goodness-of-fit criteria based on stochastic processes. *Ann. Math. Stat.*, 23: 193–212.

ANDERSON, T. W. and GOODMAN, L. A., 1957. Statistical inference about Markov chains. *Ann. Math. Stat.*, 28: 89–110.

ANDREWS, D. F. and PREGIBON, D., 1978. Finding the outliers that matter. *J. R. Stat. Soc., Ser. B*, 40: 85–93.

ANSCOMBE, F. J., 1960. Rejection of outliers. *Technometrics*, 2: 123–147.

ANSCOMBE, F. J., 1967. Topics in the investigation of linear relations fitted by the method of least squares. *J. R. Stat. Soc., Ser. B*, 29: 1–52.

ANSCOMBE, F. J. and TUKEY, J. W., 1963. The examination and analysis of residuals. *Technometrics*, 5: 141–160.

ATKINSON, A. C., 1973. Testing transformations to normality. *J. R. Stat. Soc., Ser. B*, 35: 473–479.

AUFM-KAMPE, H. J. and WEICKMANN, H. K., 1957. Physics of clouds. *Meteorol. Monogr.*, 3 (18): 182–225.

AUSTIN, P. M. and GEOTIS, S. G., 1979. Raindrop size and related parameters for GATE. *J. Appl. Meteorol.*, 18: 569–575.

BARGER, G. L. and THOM, H. C. S., 1949. Evaluation of drought hazard. *Agron. J.*, 41: 519–527.

BARHAM, P. M. and HUMPHRIES, D. E., 1970. Derivation of the Kalman filtering equations from elementary statistical principles. In: C. T. LEONDES, (Editor), *Theory and Applications of Kalman Filtering. AGARDograph*, 139: 45–49.

BARTELS, J., 1943. Gesetz und Zufall in der Geophysik. *Naturwissenschaften*, 31: 421–435.

BARTELS, J., 1948. Anschauliches über den statistischen Hintergrund der sogenannten Singularitäten im Jahresgang der Witterung. *Ann. Meteorol.*, 1: 106–127.

BARTLETT, M. S., 1937a. Some examples of statistical methods of research in agricultural and applied biology. *J. R. Stat. Soc., Suppl.*, 4: 137–183.

BARTLETT, M. S., 1937b. Properties of sufficiency and statistical tests. *Proc. R. Soc., London, Ser. A*, 160: 268–282.

BÅTH, M., 1974. *Spectral Analysis in Geophysics*. Elsevier, Amsterdam, 563 pp.

BATTJES, J. A., 1972. Long-term waveheight at seven stations around the British Isles. *Dtsch. Hydrol. Z.*, 25: 179–189.

BATTYE, D. G. H., 1980. A note on singularities. *Meteorol. Mag.*, 190: 358–362.

BAUR, F., 1950. Über falsche und richtige Statistik in der Meteorologie. *Ann. Meteorol*, 3: 74–83 (*Z. Meteorol.*, 5: 200–204.)

BAUR, F., 1953. *Linke's Meteorologisches Taschenbuch, II.* Geest and Portig, Leipzig, 724 pp.

BAYNE, Ch. K. and WEBER, A. H., 1973. Statistical analysis of North Carolina precipitation data. *3rd Conf. Probability and Statistics in Atmos. Sci., Boulder, Colo**[1]., pp. 250–251.

BECHHOFER, R. E. and SOBEL, M., 1954. A single sample multi-decision procedure for ranking variances of normal populations. *Ann. Math. Stat.*, 25 (2): 273–289.

BECHHOFER, R. E., KIEFER, J. and SOBEL, M., 1968. *Sequential Identification and Ranking Problems.* Chicago Univ. Press, 420 pp.

BEDI, H. S. and BINDRA, M. M. S., 1980. Principal components of monsoon rainfall. *Tellus*, 32: 296–298.

BEER, A., DRUMMOND, A. J. and FÜRTH, R., 1946. Sequences of wet and dry months and the theory of probability. *Q. J. R. Meteorol. Soc.*, 72: 74–86.

BEHBOODIAN, J., 1977. A note on functional forms of order statistics. *Am. Stat.*, 31 (4): 161–162.

BENDAT, J. S. and PIERSOL, A. G., 1971. *Random Data: Analysis and Measurement Procedures.* Wiley, New York, NY, 407 pp.

BERGER, A. and GOLD, R. Z., 1973. Note on Cochran's Q-Test for the comparison of correlated proportions. *J. Am. Stat. Assoc.*, 68: 989–993.

BERGERON, T., 1935. On the physics of cloud and precipitation. *Proc. 5th Assem. UGGI, Lisbon*, 2: 156–175.

BERGERON, T., 1949. The problem of artificial control of rainfall on the globe. *Tellus*, 1: 32–43.

BERGERON, T., 1960. Problems and methods of rainfall investigations. In: H. WEICKMANN (Editor), *Physics of precipitation. Geophys. Monogr.*, 5. Am. Geophys. Union, pp. 5–30.

BERRETTONI, J. N., 1964. Practical application of the Weibull distribution. *Ind. Qual. Contr.*, 21: 71–79.

BERTRAM, G., 1960. Sequenzanalyse für zwei Alternativfolgen. *Z. Angew. Math. Mech.*, 40: 185–189.

BESSON, L., 1924. On the probability of rain. *Mon. Weather Rev.*, 52: 308.

BEST, D. J. and GIPPS, P. G., 1974. An improved gamma approximation to the negative binomial. *Technometrics*, 16: 621–624.

BETTGE, TH. W. and BAUMHEFNER, D. P., 1980. A method to decompose the spatial characteristics of meteorological variables within a limited domain. *Mon. Weather Rev.*, 108: 843–854.

BEYER, W. H., 1966. *Handbook of Tables for Probability and Statistics.* Chem. Rubber Co., Cleveland, Ohio, 502 pp.

BHARUCHA-REID, A. T., 1960. *Elements of the Theory of Markov Processes and Their Application.* McGraw-Hill, New York, NY, 468 pp.

BILLARD, L. and MESHKANI, M. R., 1980. Modelling weather data as a Markov chain. In: S. IKEDA, E. SUZUKI, E. UCHIDA and M. M. YOSHINO (Editors), *Statistical Climatology.* Elsevier, Amsterdam, pp. 149–163.

BIRNBAUM, Z. W., 1952. Numerical distribution of Kolmogorov's statistic for finite sample size. *J. Am. Stat. Assoc.*, 47: 425–440.

BIRNBAUM, Z. W. and TINGEY, F. H., 1951. One-sided confidence contours for probability distribution functions. *Ann. Math. Stat.*, 22: 592–596.

BLACKMAN, R. B. and TUKEY, J. W., 1958. *The Measurement of Power Spectra.* Dover Publ., New York, NY, 190 pp.

BLAIR-FISH, J. A., 1975. An investigation into spells of wet and dry days by region and season for Great Britain. *Meteorol. Mag.*, 104: 360–375.

BLEASDALE, A. and FARRAR, A. B., 1965. The processing of rainfall data by computer. *Meteorol. Mag.*, 94: 98–109.

BLOCH, F. E., 1978. Measurement error and statistical significance of an independent variable. *Am. Stat.*, 32: 26–27.

BLOM, G., 1976. When is the arithmetic mean Blue. *Am. Stat.*, 30: 40–42.

BLOOMFIELD, P., 1976. *Fourier Analysis of Time Series: an Introduction.* Wiley, New York, NY, 258 pp.

BOFINGER, E., 1973. Goodness-of-fit test using sample quantiles. *J. R. Stat. Soc., Ser. B*, 35: 277–284.

BOLCH, B. W., 1968. More on unbiased estimation of the standard deviation. *Am. Stat.*, 22 (3): 27.

BOLSENGA, S. J., 1965. The relationship between total atmospheric water vapor and surface dew point on a mean daily and hourly basis. *J. Appl. Meteorol.*, 4: 430–432.

*[1] Proceedings of these conferences published by Am. Meteorol. Soc.

BONDY, W. H. and ZLOT, W., 1976. Standard error and the mean and the difference between means for finite populations. *Am. Stat.*, 30 (2): 96–97.

BORGMAN, L. E., 1961. The frequency distribution of near extremes. *J. Geophys. Res.*, 66: 3295–3307.

BOSWELL, M. T. and PATIL, G. P., 1969. *Chance Mechanism Generating Negative Binomial Distributions.* Tech. Rep. Preprints, 15, Penn. State Univ., 25 pp.

BOWEN, E. G., 1966. The effects of persistence in cloud-seeding experiments. *J. Appl. Meteorol.*, 5: 156–159.

BOWMAN, K. O. and SHENTON, L. R., 1968. *Properties and Estimators for the Gamma Distribution.* Rep. CTC 1 Union Carbide Corp., Nav. Div., Oak Ridge, Tenn., 50 pp.

BOWMAN, K. O. and SHENTON, L. R., 1970. Properties of the maximum likelihood estimator for the parameter of the logarithmic series distribution. In: G. P. PATIL (Editor), *Random Counts in Models and Structures*, pp. 127–150.

BOWMAN, K. O. and SHENTON, L. R., 1975. Omnibus test contours for departures from normality based on $\sqrt{b_1}$ and b_2. *Biometrika*, 65: 243–250.

BOX, J. E. P. and JENKINS, G. M., 1970. *Time Series Analysis, Forecasting, and Control.* Holden-Day, San Francisco, CA, 553 pp.

BOYD, J. P., 1978. The choice of spectral functions on a sphere for boundary and eigenvalue problems: a comparison of Chebyshev, Fourier and associated Legendre expansions. *Mon. Weather Rev.*, 106: 1184–1191.

BRADLEY, J. V., 1969. A survey of sign tests based on the binomial distribution. *J. Qual. Technol.*, 1 (2): 89–101.

BRADLEY, J. V., 1973. The central limit effects for a variety of populations and the influence of population moments. *J. Qual. Technol.*, 5 (4): 171–177.

BRADLEY, R. A. and SRIVASTAVA, S. S., 1979. Correlation in polynomial regression. *Am. Stat.*, 33: 11–14.

BRADLEY, R. A., SRIVASTAVA, S. S. and LANZDORF, A., 1979. *Some Approaches to Statistical Analysis of Weather Modification Experiments.* Florida State Univ., Tallahassee, Tech. Rep., M491: 67 pp.

BRAHAM, R. R., Jr., 1965. *Project Whitetop.* Final Report to Nat. Sci. Found., G-22419, Univ. Chicago, IL.

BRAHAM, R. R., Jr., 1979. Field experimental in weather modification. *J. Am. Stat. Soc.*, 74; 57–104.

BRANDES, E. A., 1975. Optimizing rainfall estimates with the aid of radar. *J. Appl. Meteorol.*, 14: 1339–1345.

BRIDGES, T. C. and HAAN, C. T., 1972. Reliability of precipitation probabilities estimated from the gamma distribution. *Mon. Weather Rev.*, 100 (8): 607–611.

BRIER, G. W., 1961a. A test of the reality of rainfall singularities. *J. Meteorol.*, 18: 242–246.

BRIER, G. W., 1961b. Reply. *J. Meteorol.*, 18: 705–707.

BRIER, G. W., 1962. Reply. *J. Appl. Meteorol.*, 1: 429–430.

BRIER, G. W., SHAPIRO, R. and MACDONALD, N. J., 1963. A search for rainfall calendaricities. *J. Atmos. Sci.*, 20: 529–532.

BRIER, G. W., SHAPIRO, R. and MACDONALD, N. J., 1964. A test for the period of 18 cycles per year in rainfall data. *J. Appl. Meteorol.*, 3: 53–57.

BRIER, G. W., SIDDIQUI, M. M., HAURWITZ, M. W. and BIONDINI, R., 1983. High-resolution frequency analysis and applications to the prediction of almost-periodic functions. *2nd Int. Meet. Stat. Climatol.*, pp. 11.2.1–8.

BRIGGS, G., 1968. Estimating the duration of high-intensity rainfall. *Meteorol. Mag.*, 97: 289–293.

BRIGHAM, E. O., 1974. *The Fast Fourier Transform.* Prentice-Hall, Englewood Cliffs, NJ. 252 pp.

BROOKS, C. E. B. and CARRUTHERS, N., 1953. *Handbook of Statistical Methods in Meteorology.* H.M. Stationary Office, London, 412 pp.

BROOKS, C. E. P., DURST, C. S., CARRUTHERS, N., DEWAR, D. and SAWYER, J. S., 1950. Upper winds over the world. *Geophys. Mem.*, 10 (85).

BROWN, P. S. and ROBINSON, G. D., 1979. The variance spectrum of tropospheric winds over Eastern Europe. *J. Atmos. Sci.*, 36 (2): 270–286.

BROWN, R. G., 1963. *Smoothing, Forecasting and Prediction of Discrete Time Series.* Prentice-Hall, Englewood Cliffs, NJ, 468 pp.

BROWNLEE, K. A., 1960a. *Statistical Theory and Methodology in Science and Engineering.* Wiley, New York, NY, 570 pp.

BROWNLEE, K. A., 1960b. Statistical evaluation of cloud seeding operations. *J. Am. Stat. Assoc.*, 55: 446–453.

BRUGGER, R. M., 1969a.A note on unbiased estimation of the standard deviation. *Am. Stat.*, 23 (4): 32.

BRUGGER, R. M., 1969b. Letter to editor on Fisher's exact test. *Am. Stat.*, 23 (2): 35.

BRYANT, G. W., 1979. Archiving and quality control of climatological data. *Meteorol. Mag.*, 108: 309–315.

BRYSON, R. A. and KUHN, P. M., 1956. *Half-Hemisphere 500-mb Topography Description by Means of Orthogonal Polynomials, 1.* Sci. Rep. 4, USAF, Contrib. AF19(604)-992, Univ. Wisc., Madison, WI.

BUELL, C. E., 1978. The number of significant proper functions of two-dimensional fields. *J. Appl. Meteorol.*, 17: 717–722.

BUISHAND, T. A., 1983. The effect of seasonal variation and serial correlation on the extreme value distribution of rainfall data. *2nd Int. Meet. Stat. Climatol.*, 10.4.1–6.

BURINGTON, R. S. and MAY, D. C., 1953. *Handbook of Probability and Statistics with Tables.* Handbook Publ., Sandusky, OH, 332 pp.

BURR, I. W., 1942. Cumulative frequency functions. *Am. Math. Stat.*, 13: 215.

BURR, I. W., 1976. *Statistical Quality Control Methods.* Marcel Dekker, New York, NY, 522 pp.

BUSCH, N. E., 1973. On the mechanics of atmospheric turbulence. In: D. A. HAUGEN (Editor), *Workshop on Micrometeorology*. Am. Meteorol. Soc., Boston, Mass., pp. 1–65.

CAMPBELL, S. W. and TSOKOS, C. P., 1973. The asymptotic distribution of maxima in bivariate samples. *J. Am. Stat. Assoc.*, 68: 734–739.

CANFIELD, N. L., SMITH, O. E. and VAUGHAN, W. W., 1966. Progress in circumventing limitations of upper wind records. *J. Appl. Meteorol.*, 5: 301–303.

CATANEO, R. and STOUT, G. E., 1968. Raindrop size-distributions in humid continental climates, and associated rainfall-rate–radar-reflectivity relationships. *J. Appl. Meteorol.*, 7: 901–907.

CEHAK, K., 1963. Eine statistische Theorie der Böigkeit des Windes. *Arch. Meteorol. Geophys. Bioklimatol., Ser. A*, 13, H 3/4: 343–359.

CEHAK, K., 1967. Über die Häufigkeitsverteilung meteorologischer Elemente in der freien Atmosphäre bis 30 km über Wien. *Arch. Meteorol. Geophys. Bioklimatol., Ser. A*, B16, H 1: 44–57.

CHAKRAVARTI, I. M., LAHA, R. G. and ROY, J., 1967. *Handbook of Methods of Applied Statistics, I.* Wiley, New York, NY, 460 pp.

CHANG, L.-CH., 1956. On the exact distribution of the statistics of A. N. Kolmogorov and their asymptotic expansion. *Acta Math. Sin.*, 6: 55–81.

CHANGNON, S. A. and SCHICKEDANZ, P. T., 1971. Statistical studies of inadvertent modification of precipitation. *Int. Symp. Probability and Statistics in Atmospheric Science, Honolulu, Hawaii.* pp. 137–142.

CHANGNON, S. A., HUFF, F. A. and HSU, CH-F., 1979. On the need to evaluate operational weather modification projects. *Bull. Am. Meteorol. Soc.*, 60: 770–774.

CHARLES, B. N., 1959. On some limitations of upper wind records. *J. Geophys. Res.*, 64 (3): 343–346.

CHAUZY, S. and DESPIAU, S., 1980. Rainfall rate and electric charge and size of raindrops of six spring showers. *J. Atmos. Sci.*, 37: 1619–1627.

CHEN, W. Y. S., 1976. A simple method for estimating five-minute point rain-rate distribution based on available climatological data. *Bell System Tech. J.*, 55: 129–134.

CHIN, E. H. and MILLER, J. F., 1980. On the conditional distribution of daily precipitation amounts. *Mon. Weather Rev.*, 108: 1462–1464.

CHOW, V. T., 1954. The log-probability law and its engineering application. *Proc. Am. Soc. Civ. Eng.*, 80 (536): 1–25.

CHOW, V. T. (Editor), 1964). *Handbook of Applied Hydrology.* McGraw-Hill, New York, NY, 1453 pp.

CHOW, W. K. and HODGES, Y. L., 1975. An approximation for the distribution of the Wilcoxon one-sample statistic. *J. Am. Stat. Assoc.*, 70 (351): 648–655.

CLARK, T. L., 1976. Use of log-normal distributions for numerical calculations of condensation and collection. *J. Atmos. Sci.*, 33: 810–821.

CLEMMER, B. A. and KRUTCHKOFF, R. G., 1968. The use of empirical Bayes estimators in a linear regression model. *Biometrika*, 55: 525–534.

COCHRAN, W. G., 1936. The χ^2 distribution for the binomial and Poisson series with small expectations. *Ann. Eugen. London*, 7: 207–217.

COCHRAN, W. G., 1938. An extension of Gold's method of examining the apparent persistence of one type of weather. *Q. J. R. Meteorol. Soc.*, 64: 631–634.

COCHRAN, W. G., 1950. The comparison of percentages in matched samples. *Biometrika*, 37: 256–266.

COCHRAN, W. G., 1952. The χ^2 test of goodness-of-fit. *Ann. Math. Stat.*, 23: 315–345.

COCHRAN, W. G., 1954. Some methods of strengthening the common χ^2 tests. *Biometrics*, 10: 417–451.

COCHRAN, W. G. and COX, G. M., 1957. *Experimental Designs*. Wiley, New York, NY, 611 pp.

CONOVER, W. J., 1973. On methods of handling ties in the Wilcoxon signed-rank test. *J. Am. Stat. Assoc.*, 68: 985–988.

CONOVER, W. J., 1980. *Practical Non-Parametric Statistics*. Wiley, New York, NY, 2nd edn., 462 pp.

CONRAD, V., 1948. A new criterion of relative homogeneity of climatological series. *Arch. Meteorol. Geophys. Bioklimatol., Ser. B*, H.1: 948–955.

CONRAD, V. and POLLAK, L. W., 1950. *Methods in Climatology*. Harvard Univ. Press, Cambridge, MA, 458 pp.

COOLEY, J. W. and TUKEY, J. W., 1965. An algorithm for the machine calculation of complex Fourier series. *Math. Comp.*, 19: 297–301.

COROTIS, R. B., SIGL, A. B. and KLEIN, J., 1978. Probability models of wind velocity magnitude and persistence. *Sol. Energy*, 20: 483–493.

COURTNEY, F. M., 1980. The use of analysis of variance in the assessment of rainfall variability. *Meteorol. Mag.*, 109: 268–271.

CRADDOCK, J. M., 1965. The analysis of meteorological time series for use in forecasting. *Statistician*, 15: 167–190.

CRADDOCK, J. M., 1968. *Statistics in the Computer Age*. Engl. Univ. Press, London, 214 pp.

CRADDOCK, J. M. and GRIMMER, M., 1960. The estimation of mean annual temperature from the temperature of preceding years. *Weather*, 15: 340–348.

CRAMER, H., 1928. On the composition of elementary errors. *Skand. Akt.*, 11: 13–74; 141–180.

CRAMER, H., 1946. *Mathematical Methods of Statistics*. Princeton Univ. Press, Princeton, NJ, 575 pp.

CROMER, F. E., 1975. A subroutine for computing exact probabilities of F-ratios. *Proc. Stat. Comp. Sect., Annu. Meet., Am. Stat. Assoc.*, pp. 96–98.

CROOKS, W. M., HOBLIT, F. M. and MITCHELL, F. A., 1968. *Project HICAT: High-Altitude Clear Air Turbulence Measurements and Meteorological Correlations, I and II*. Tech. Rep. AFF DL-TR-68-127, Lockheed-Calif., 960 pp.

CROVELLI, R. A., 1973. A bivariate precipitation model. *3rd Conf. Probability and Statistics in Atmos. Sci., Boulder, Colo.*, pp. 130–134.

CROW, E. L., 1978. Confidence limits for seeding effects in single-area weather modification experiments. *J. Appl. Meteorol.*, 17: 1652–1660.

CRUTCHER, H. L. and JOINER, R. L., 1978. Gamma distribution bias and confidence limits. *NOAA Tech. Rep., EDIS*, 30: 104 pp.

CRUTCHER, H. L. and JOINER, R. L., 1980. Gamma distribution shape parameter bias. *NOAA Tech. Mem., EDIS*, 9: 37 pp.

CRUTCHER, H. L., BARGER, G. L. and MCKAY, G. F., 1973. A note on a gamma distribution computer program and graph paper. *NOAA Tech. Rep., EDS*, 11: 91 pp.

CRUTCHER, H. L., MCKAY, G. F. and FULBRIGHT, D. C., 1977. A note on a gamma distribution computer program and computer produced graphs. *NOAA Tech. Rep. EDS*, 24: 104 pp.

CRUTCHER, H. L., FULBRIGHT, D. C. and MCKAY, G. F., 1980. A note on a gamma distribution computer program. *NOAA Tech. Mem., EDIS*, 28: 49 pp.

CURETON, E. E., 1968. Unbiased estimation of the standard deviation. *Am. Stat.*, 22 (3): 22 pp.

CURRIE, R. G., 1981. Solar cycle signal in air temperature in North America. Amplitude, gradient, phase distribution. *J. Atmos. Sci.*, 38: 808–818.

CUTTER, G. R., 1976. Some examples for treating regression toward the mean from a sampling view point. *Am. Stat.*, 30: 194–197.

CZEPA, O., 1967. Filter zur Glättung und Trendextrapolation geophysikalischer Zeitreihen. *Gerlands Beitr. Geophys.*, 76: 334–342.

CZERWINSKI, N. and PFISTERER, W., 1972. Typen von Regentropfenspektren von polaren bis zu tropischen Zonen und ihre Abhängigkeit von Elementen des Regens. *Meteorol. Rundsch.*, 25 (3): 88–94.

DAHIYA, R. C. and GURLAND, J., 1972. Pearson chi-squared test of fit with random intervals. *Biometrika*, 59: 147–153.

DARLING, D. A., 1957. The Kolmogorov-Smirnov, Cramer-von Mises tests. *Ann. Math. Stat.*, 28: 823–838.

DARLINGTON, R. B., 1970. Is kurtosis really peakedness? *Am. Stat.*, 24: 19–20.

DARTT, D. G., 1972. Automated streamline analysis utilizing "optimum interpolation". *J. Appl. Meteorol.*, 11 (6): 901–908.

DAUGHERTY, T. F., 1980. Two apparent contradictions in testing hypotheses. *J. Qual. Tech.*, 12: 154–157.

DAVIES, O. L., 1961. *Statistical Methods in Research and Production.* Hafner, New York, NY, 3rd edn., 393 pp.

DAVIS, A. W., 1967. Percentile approximations for ordered F ratios. *Biometrika*, 57: 457–459.

DEMING, W. E. and BIRGE, R. T., 1934. On the statistical theory of errors. *Rev. Mod. Phys.*, 6: 119–161.

DENNIS, A. S., 1980. *Weather Modification by Cloud Seeding.* Acad. Press, New York, NY, 267 pp.

DIEHL, H., 1948. Die Annäherung einer Funktion durch eine halbe Sinusschwingung. *Meteorol. Rundsch.*, 1: 400–401.

DIEM, M., 1968. Zur Struktur der Niederschläge, III. *Arch. Meteorol. Geophys. Bioklimatol, Ser. B*, 16: 347–390.

DIEM, M. and STRANTZ, R., 1971. Typen der Regentropfenspektren, II. Abhängigkeit von der Regenintensität. *Meteorol. Rundsch.*, 24 (1): 23–26.

DINGLE, A. N. and HARDY, K. R., 1962. The description of rain by means of sequential raindrop-size distribution. *Q. J. R. Meteorol. Soc.*, 88: 301–314.

DIXON, R. E., 1969. Orthogonal polynomials as a basis for objective analysis. *Sci. Pap.*, 30, *Meteorol. Off., London*, 20 pp.

DIXON, R. E., SPACKMAN, A., JONES, I. and FRANCIS, A., 1972. The global analysis of meteorological data using orthogonal polynomial base functions. *J. Atmos. Sci.*, 29: 609–622.

DOANE, D. P., 1976. Aesthetic frequency classifications. *Am. Stat.*, 30 (4): 181–183.

DOI, K., 1959. Persistence of rainfall. *Geophys. Mag., Tokyo*, X: 307–332.

DORMAN, C. E. and BOURKE, R. H., 1978. A temperature correction for Tucker's ocean rainfall estimates. *Q. J. R. Meteorol. Soc.*, 104: 765–773.

DOWNTON, F., 1966. Linear estimates of parameters in the extreme value distribution. *Technometrics*, 8 (1): 3–17.

DRUFUCA, G., 1977. Radar-derived statistics on the structure of precipitation patterns. *J. Appl. Meteorol.*, 16: 1029–1035.

DUCHON, C. E., 1979. Lanczos filtering in one and two dimensions. *J. Appl. Meteorol.*, 18: 1016–1022.

DUCKWORTH, W. G. and WYATT, G. K., 1958. Rapid statistical techniques for operational research workers. *Oper. Res. Q.*, 9: 218–233.

DUDEWICZ, E. G. and DALAL, S. R., 1972. On approximations to the t-distribution. *J. Qual. Tech.*, 4 (4): 196–197.

DUNCAN, A. J., 1958. Design and operation of a double limit variable sampling plan. *J. Am. Stat. Assoc.*, 53: 543–550.

DURBIN, J., 1975. Kolmogorov-Smirnov tests when parameters are estimated with applications to tests of exponentiality and tests on spacings. *Biometrika*, 62: 5–22.

DURBIN, J. and KNOTT, M., 1972. Components of Cramer-von Mises statistics. *J. R. Stat. Soc., Ser. B*, 34: 290–307.

DWYER, P. S., 1941. The solution of simultaneous equations. *Psychrometrika*, 6: 101–129.

DYER, T. G. J., 1975. The assignment of rainfall stations into homogeneous groups: an application of principal components analysis. *Q. J. R. Meteorol. Soc.*, 101: 1005–1012.

DYER, T. G. J., 1976. On the components of time series: the removal of spatial dependence. *Q. J. R. Meteorol. Soc.*, 102: 157–165.

DYER, T. G. J., 1977. On the application of some stochastic models to precipitation forecasting. *Q. J. R. Meteorol. Soc.*, 103: 177–189.

DYER, T. G. J. and TYSON, P. D., 1977. Estimating above and below normal rainfall periods over South Africa, 1972–2000. *J. Appl. Meteorol.*, 16: 145–147.

EDWARDS, A. W. F., 1971. Science, statistics and society. *Nature (London)*, 233 (Sept. 3): 17–19.

EDWARDS, K. A., 1972. Estimating areal rainfall by fitting surfaces to irregularly spaced data. *Distribution of Precipitation in Mountain Areas, II.* WMO, Geneva, pp. 565–587.

EDWARDS, P. J., 1980. Comments on "Run duration analysis of surface wind speeds for wind energy applications". *J. Appl. Meteorol.*, 19: 757–758.

EIDSVIK, K. J., 1980. Identifications of models for some time series of atmospheric origin with Akaike's information criterion. *J. Appl. Meteorol.*, 19: 357–369.

ELDERTON, W. P., 1953. *Frequency Curves and Correlation*, (Chapter IV contains description of Pearson types developed in 1895–1916). Harren Press, Washington, DC, 4th edn., 272 pp.

ELDRIDGE, R. G., 1966. Haze and fog aerosol distribution. *J. Atmos. Sci.*, 23: 605–613.

ELLIOT, R. D. and BROWN, K. J., 1971. The Santa Barbara II Project-downwind effects. *Int. Conf. Weather Modification*, preprint, pp. 179–184.

ELLIOT, R. D., SHAFFER, R. W., COURT, A. and HANNAFORD, J. F., 1978. Randomized cloud-seeding in the San Juan mountains, Colorado. *J. Appl. Meteorol.*, 17: 1298–1318.

ENGLISH, E. J., 1973. An objective method of calculating areal rainfall. *Meteorol. Mag.*, 102: 292–298.

ESSENWANGER, O. M., 1950. Wahre Expektanz und Erhaltungsneigung beim Luftdruck. *Meteorol. Rundsch.*, 3: 62–65.

ESSENWANGER, O. M., 1951. Beiträge zur Statistik mittellanger Luftdruckwellen in Mitteleuropa. *Ber. Dtsch. Wetterdienstes*. 20: 19 pp.

ESSENWANGER, O. M., 1956a. Wahrscheinlichkeitsansteckung und Erhaltungsneigung beim Niederschlag. *Meteorol. Rundsch.*, 9: 13–25.

ESSENWANGER, O. M., 1956b. Zur Verwendung eines logarithmischen Maszstabes bei der Niederschlagsstatistik. *Meteorol. Rundsch.*, 9: 197–206.

ESSENWANGER, O. M., 1960a. Linear and logarithmic scale for frequency distribution of precipitation. *Geofis. Pura Appl.*, 45 (1): 199–214.

ESSENWANGER, O. M., 1960b. Frequency distributions of precipitation. *Geophys. Monogr.*, 5: 271–278.

ESSENWANGER, O. M., 1961. On defining and computing the mean and the standard deviation for wind directions. *AOMC Rep.*, RR-TR-61-1: 75 pp.

ESSENWANGER, O. M., 1963. On the derivation of frequency distributions of vector shear values for small shear intervals. *Geofis. Pura Appl.*, 56: 216–224.

ESSENWANGER, O. M., 1964. The cumulative distribution of wind direction frequencies. *Meteorol. Rundsch.*, 17: 131–135.

ESSENWANGER, O. M., 1965. Statistical parameters and percentile values for vector wind shear distributions of small increments. *Arch. Meteorol. Geophys. Bioklimatol., Ser. A*, 15: 50–61.

ESSENWANGER, O. M., 1966. Profile types of sound ,eed in the lower atmosphere and their relationships to acoustic focusing. *U.S. Army Missile Command Rep.*, RR-TR-66-6: 35 pp.

ESSENWANGER, O. M., 1967. Comments on "mesoscale structure of 11–20 km winds." *J. Appl. Meteorol.*, 6 (3): 591–593.

ESSENWANGER, O. M., 1968. On deriving 90–99% wind and wind shear thresholds from statistical parameters. *Proc. 3rd Conf. Aerospace Meteorol., New Orleans, May 1968*, pp. 145–154.

ESSENWANGER, O. M., 1970. Analytical procedures for the quality control of meteorological data. (Proc. Symp. Meteorol. Observ. Instrum., Febr., 1969). *Meteorol. Monogr.*, II (33-I): 141–147.

ESSENWANGER, O. M., 1972. On maximum likelihood fits of upper air extreme values. *Proc. 17th Conf. Design Exper.*, ARO-D 72-2: 427–444.

ESSENWANGER, O. M., 1974. The structure of the wind profile from surface to 25 km in various climatic zones. *Klimatol. Forsch., Bonner Meteorol. Abh.*, 17: 523–539.

ESSENWANGER, O. M., 1975. Eigenvector representation of wind profiles. *4th Conf. Probability Stat. Atmos. Sci., Boston, Mass.*, pp. 206–210.

ESSENWANGER, O. M., 1976. *Applied Statistics in Atmospheric Science, A. Frequency Distribution and Curve Fitting*. Elsevier, Amsterdam, 400 pp.

ESSENWANGER, O. M., 1977. Red noise analysis in autocorrelogram and power spectrum at atmospheric temperature. *Preprints, 5th Conf. Probability Stat., Atmos. Sci.*, pp. 283–288.

ESSENWANGER, O. M., 1980. On red noise and quasi-periodicity in the time series of atmospheric temperature. In: S. IKEDA, E. SUZUKI, E. UCHIDA and M. M. YOSHINO (Editors), *Statistical Climatology*. Elsevier, Amsterdam, pp. 165–181.

ESSENWANGER, O. M. and BILLIONS, N. S., 1965. The stationary and non-stationary wind profile. *PAGEOPH*, 60: 160–166.

ESSENWANGER, O. M., and REITER, E. R., 1969. Power spectrum, structure function, vertical wind shear and turbulence in troposphere and stratosphere. *Arch. Meteorol. Geophys. Bioklimatol., Ser. A*, 18: 17–24.

ESSENWANGER, O. M., HORN, L. H. and BRYSON, R. A., 1958. *Half-Hemispheric 500 mb Topographic*

Description by Means of Orthogonal Polynomials, 2. Sci. Rep., 11, ASTIA, AD-152-511 (AF 19(604)-992).

FALLS, L. W., 1974. The beta distribution: a statistical model for world cloud cover. *J. Geophys. Res.*, 79: 1261–1264.

FELLER, W., 1968. *An Introduction to Probability and its Applications, I and II.* Wiley, New York, NY, I, 510 pp., II, 669 pp.

FEYERHERM, A. M., BARK, L. D., and BURROWS, W. C., 1965. Probability of sequences of wet and dry days in Wisconsin. *Kans. Tech. Bull.*, 139: 55 pp.

FEYERHERM, A. M. and BARK, L. D., 1967. Goodness of fit of a Markov chain model for sequences of wet and dry days. *J. Appl. Meteorol.*, 6 (5): 770–773.

FEYERHERM, A. M. and BARK, L. D., 1973. Probability models for simulating temperatures and precipitations. *3rd Conf. Probability Stat. Atmos. Sci., Boulder, Colo.*, pp. 248–249.

FILIPPOV, V. V., 1968. Quality control procedures for meteorological data. *WMO World Weather Watch Rep.*, 26: 1–38.

FINKELSTEIN, J. M. and SCHAFER, R. E., 1971. Improved goodness-of-fit tests. *Biometrika*, 58: 641–645.

FINNEY, D. J., 1941. The joint distribution of variance ratios based on a common error mean square. *Ann. Eugen. London*, 11: 136–140.

FISHER, N. I. and LEE, A. J., 1983. A correlation coefficient for circular data. *Biometrika*, 70 (2): 327–332.

FISHER, N. I. and LEWIS, T., 1983. Estimating the common mean direction of several circular or spherical distributions with differing dispersions. *Biometrika*, 70 (2): 333–341.

FISHER, R. A., 1922. On the mathematical foundations of theoretical statistics. *Phil. Trans., Ser. A*, 222: 309–368.

FISHER, R. A., 1924. On a distribution yielding the error functions of several well known statistics. *Proc. Int. Math. Congr., Toronto*, pp. 805–813.

FISHER, R. A., 1950. The significance of deviations from expectations in a Poisson series. *Biometrics*, 6: 17–24.

FISHER, R. A., 1951. Properties of Hh functions. In: *Brit. Assoc. Math. Tables, XXVIII–XXXVII.* Cambridge Univ. Press, 3rd ed.

FISHER, R. A., 1966. *The Design of Experiments.* Hafner, Darien, Conn., 248 pp.

FISHER, R. A., 1970. *Statistical Methods for Research Workers.* Hafner, Darien, Conn., 14th edn., 362 pp.

FISHER, R. A. and TIPPETT, L. H. C., 1928. Limiting forms of the frequency distribution of the largest or smallest member of a sample. *Proc. Cambridge Phil. Soc.*, 24 (2): 180–190.

FISHER, R. A. and YATES, F., 1963. *Statistical Tables for Biological, Agricultural and Medical Research.* Hafner, New York, 6th edn., 146 pp.

FISZ, M., 1963. *Probability Theory and Mathematical Statistics.* Wiley, New York, NY, 3rd edn., 677 pp.

FITZPATRICK, E. A. and KRISHNAN, A., 1967. A first-order Markov model for assessing rainfall discontinuity in Central Australia. *Arch. Meteorol. Geophys. Bioklimatol., Ser. B*, 15 (3): 242–259.

FLEAGLE, R. G., 1969 (Editor). *Weather Modification, Science and Public Policy.* Univ. Washington Press, Seattle, WA, 147 pp.

FLEISS, J. L. and TANUR, J. M., 1971. A note on the partial correlation coefficient. *Am. Stat.*, 25: 43–45.

FLETCHER, R. D., 1950. A relation between maximum observed point and areal rainfall values. *Trans. Am. Geophys. Union*, 31: 344–348.

FLOHN, H., 1964. Zur Interpolation und räumlichen Verteilung statistischer Parameter der Höhenwindverteilung. *Beitr. Phys. Atmos.*, 37 (1): 17–29.

FREEMAN, D. and WEISS, L., 1964. Sampling plans which approximately minimize the maximum expected sample size. *J. Am. Stat. Assoc.*, 59: 67–88.

FRIEDMAN, D. G. and JONES, B. E., 1957. Estimation of rainfall probabilities. *Rep. Conn. Agric. Exp. Stn.*, pp. 3–21.

FRIEDMAN, M., 1937. The use of ranks to avoid the assumption of normality implicit in the analysis of variance. *J. Am. Stat. Assoc.*, 32: 675–701.

FRITSCH, J. M., 1971. Objective analysis of a two-dimensional data field by the cubic spline technique. *Mon. Weather Rev.*, 99: 379–386.

FUJIKOSHI, Y. and VEITCH, L. G., 1979. Estimation of dimensionality in canonical correlation analysis. *Biometrika*, 66: 345–351.

GABRIEL, K. R., 1967. The Israeli rainfall stimulation experiment, statistical evaluation for the period 1961–1965. *Proc. 5th Berkeley Symp. Math. Stat. Probability–Univ. Calif. Press*, pp. 91–113.

GABRIEL, K. R., 1983. An approach to analysis and modeling of multivariate spatial data in meteorology and climatology. *2nd Int. Meet. Stat. Climatol.*, p. 4.1.1–8.

GABRIEL, K. R. and BARAS, M., 1970. The Israeli rainmaking experiment 1961–1967. Final statistical tables and evaluation. *Tech. Rep., Hebrew Univ., Jerusalem*, 47 pp.

GABRIEL, K. R. and FEDER, P., 1969. On the distribution of statistics suitable for evaluating rainfall stimulation experiments. *Technometrics*, 11: 149–160.

GABRIEL, K. R. and HSU, CH-F., 1981. Evaluation of the power of re-randomized tests. *Dep. Stat., Biostat., Univ. Rochester, NY, Tech. Rep.*, 26 pp.

GABRIEL, K. R. and NEUMANN, J., 1957. On a distribution of weather cycles by length. *Q. J. R. Meteorol. Soc.*, 83: 375–380.

GABRIEL, K. R. and NEUMANN, J., 1962. A Markov chain model for daily rainfall occurrence at Tel Aviv. *Q. J. R. Meteorol. Soc.*, 88 (375): 90–95.

GABRIEL, K. R. and NEUMANN, J., 1978. A note of explanation on the 1961–1967 Israeli rainfall stimulation experiment. *J. Appl. Meteorol.*, 17: 552–554.

GABRIEL, K. R. and PETRONDAS, D., 1981. On using historical comparisons in evaluating cloud seeding operations. *Preprint 7th Conf. Probability Stat. Atmos. Sci., Monterey, Calif.*, pp. 13–18.

GAGIN, A. and NEUMANN, J., 1974. Rain stimulation and cloud physics in Israel. In: W. N. HESS (Editor), *Weather and Climate Modifications.* Wiley, New York, NY, pp. 454–494.

GAGIN, A. and NEUMANN, J., 1981. The second Israeli randomized cloud seeding experiment: evaluation of the results. *J. Appl. Meteorol.*, 20: 1301–1311.

GAIL, M. H. and GREEN, S. B., 1976. Critical values for the one-sided two-sample Kolmogorov-Smirnov statistic. *J. Am. Stat. Assoc.*, 71: 757–760.

GANDIN, L. S., 1963. *Objective Analysis of Meteorological Fields.* Leningrad. Transl. Isr. Progr. Sci. Transl., Jerusalem, 1965, 242 pp.

GASTWIRTH, J. L. and OWENS, M. E. B., 1977. On classical tests of normality. *Biometrika*, 64: 135–139.

GELHAUS, J. W., DENNIS, A. S. and SCHOCK, M. R., 1974. Possibility of a type I statistical error in analysis of a randomized cloud seeding project in South Dakota. *J. Appl. Meteorol.*, 13: 383–386.

GILMAN, D. L., FUGLISTER, F. J. and MITCHELL, J. M., Jr., 1963. On the power spectrum of red noise. *J. Atmos. Sci.*, 20: 182–184.

GILMAN, J. J., 1981. Small company–big contribution in inventivity. *Ind. Res. Dev.* 23 (June): 124–126.

GLAHN, H. R., 1979. Comments on "The number of significant proper functions of two-dimensional fields". *J. Appl. Meteorol.*, 18: 713. (Reply, C. E. BUELL, *J. Appl. Meteorol.*, 18: 714–717.)

GODOLPHIN, E. J. and STONE, J. M., 1980. On the structural representation for polynomial-projecting predictor models based on Kalman filter. *J. R. Stat. Soc., Ser. B*, 42: 35–45.

GODSKE, C. L., 1962. Contributions to statistical meteorology, I. *Geophys. Norv.*, XXIV: 161–210.

GODSKE, C. L., 1965. *Statistics of Meteorological Variables.* Final Rep., AF 61(052)-416, pp. 1–115.

GOLD, B. and RADER, C. M., 1969. *Digital Processing of Signals.* McGraw-Hill, New York, NY, 269 pp.

GOLD, E., 1929. Note on the frequency of occurrence of sequences in a series of events of two types. *Q. J. R. Soc.*, 55: 307–309.

GOLUB, G. H. and WILKINSON, J. H., 1976. Ill-conditioned eigensystems and the computation of the Jordan canonical form. *SIAM Rev.*, 18: 578–619.

GORDON, A. H. and WELLS, N. C., 1976. Changes in temperature from month to month for Central England for a quintile distribution. *J. Appl. Meteorol.*, 15: 928–932.

GOSH, B. V., 1972. On Lehmann's test for homogeneity of variances. *J. R. Stat. Soc., Ser. B*, 34: 221–235.

GOULD, A. L., 1969. A regression technique for angular variates. *Biometrics*, 25 (4): 683–700.

Goutereau, C., 1906. Sur la variabilité de la température. *Annu. Soc. mét. Fr.*, 54: 122–127.

Govind, P. K., 1974. Intercomparison of meteorological measurement systems by data-adaptive complementary filtering. *J. Appl. Meteorol.*, 13: 615–624.

Graham, R. J., 1963. Determination and analysis of numerical smoothing weights. *NASA Tech. Rep.*, TR-R-179, 28 pp.

Graybill, F. A., 1961. *An Introduction to Linear Statistical Models.* McGraw-Hill, New York, NY, 463 pp.

Green, J. R., 1964. A model for rainfall occurrence. *J. R. Stat. Soc., Ser. B,* 26 (2): 345–353.

Green, J. R., 1970. A generalized probability model for sequences of wet and dry days. *Mon. Weather Rev.*, 98 (3): 238–241.

Green, J. R., 1979. Modified Wilcoxon test for two different distributions. *Biometrika*, 66: 645–653.

Green, J. R. and Hegazy, Y. A. S., 1976. Powerful modified-EDF goodness-of-fit tests. *J. Am. Stat. Assoc.*, 71: 204–209.

Green, R. F., 1976. Outlier-prone and outlier-resistant distributions. *J. Am. Stat. Assoc.*, 71: 502–505.

Greenwood, I. A., 1958. Dissection of a circular frequency distribution into two rolled-up classical Cauchy distributions. *Iowa State Coll., Tech. Rep.*, 1.7. 42 pp.

Greenwood, I. A., 1959. Distribution theory of some angular variates. *Iowa State Coll., Tech. Rep.*, 1.13, 144 pp.

Greville, T. N. E., 1969. *Theory and Applications of Spline Functions.* Acad. Press, New York, NY, 212 pp.

Griffiths, R. F., 1975. Sources of error in the use of the Marshall-Palmer drop-size distribution equation. *Q. J. R. Meteorol. Soc.*, 101: 181–184.

Gringorten, I. I., 1973. A stochastic model of areal persistence. *Preprints 3rd Conf. Probability Stat. Atmos. Sci., June 19–22, Boulder, Colo.*, pp. 244–247.

Gringorten, I. I., 1983. Modeling climatology of areal coverage. *2nd Int. Meet. Stat. Climatol.*, pp. 2.1.1–8.

Grubbs, F. E., 1950. Sample criteria for testing outlying observations. *Ann. Math. Stat.*, 21: 27–58.

Grubbs, F. E., 1969. Procedures for detecting outlying observations in samples. *Technometrics*, 11: 1–21.

Guenther, W. C., 1972. A simple approximation to the negative binomial (and regular binomial). *Technometrics*, 14: 385–389.

Guenther, W. C., 1977. Power and sample size for approximate chi-square tests. *Am. Stat.*, 31: 83–85.

Gumbel, E. J., 1943. On the reliability of the classified chi-square test. *Ann. Math. Stat.*, 14: 253–263.

Gumbel, E. J., 1950. The cyclical normal distribution (abstract). *Ann. Math. Stat.*, 21: 143 pp.

Gumbel, E. J., 1954. Applications of the circular normal distribution. *J. Am. Stat. Assoc.*, 49: 267–297.

Gumbel, E. J., 1958. *Statistics of Extremes.* Columbia Univ. Press, New York, NY, 375 pp.

Gumbel, E. J., Greenwood, J. A. and Durand, D., 1953. The circular normal distributions: theory and tables. *J. Am. Stat. Assoc.*, 48: 131–152.

Gupta, V. K., 1983. Stochastic modeling of rainfall in space and time. *2nd Int. Meet. Stat. Climatol.*, pp. 6.2.1–6.

Gurland, J. and Tripathi, R. C., 1971. A simple approximation for unbiased estimation of the standard deviation. *Am. Stat.*, 25: 30–32.

Guttman, L., 1977. What is not what in statistics. *Statistician*, 26: 81–107.

Haberman, Sh. J., 1973. The analysis of residuals in cross-classified tables. *Biometrics*, 29: 205–220.

Hajek, J. and Sidak, Z., 1967. *Theory of Rank Tests.* Acad. Press, New York, NY, 297 pp.

Hald, A., 1952. *Statistical Tables and Formulas.* Wiley, New York, NY, 97 pp.

Hald, A., 1957. *Statistical Theory with Engineering Application.* Wiley, New York, NY, 783 pp.

Haldane, I. B. S., 1941. The fitting binomial distributions. *Ann. Eugen. London*, 11: 179–181.

Hall, C. D., 1975. The simulation of particle motion in the atmosphere by a numerical random-walk model. *Q. J. R. Meteorol. Soc.*, 101: 235–244.

Hamdan, M. A., 1963. The number and width of classes in the chi-square test. *J. Am. Stat. Assoc.*, 58: 678–689.

Hannan, E. J., 1962. Rainfall singularities. *J. Appl. Meteorol.*, 1: 426–429.

Hannan, E. J., 1970. *Multiple Time Series.* Wiley, New York, NY, 536 pp.

Harley, B. I., 1957. Relation between the distribution of non-central *t* and of a transformed correlation coefficient. *Biometrika*, 44: 219–244.

HARRIS, C. M., 1968. The Pareto distribution as a queue service discipline. *Oper. Res.*, 16: 307–313.
HARSAAE, E., 1969. On the computation and use of a table of percentage points of Bartlett's M. *Biometrika*, 56: 273–281.
HARTLEY, H. O., 1949. Tests of significance in harmonic analysis. *Biometrika*, 36: 194–201.
HAUGEN, D. A., (Editor), 1973, *Workshop on Micrometeorology*. Sci. Press, Ephrata, PA, 392 pp.
HAYASHI, Y., 1977. Space–time power spectral analysis using the maximum entropy method. *J. Meteorol. Soc. Jpn., II*, 55 (4): 415–420.
HAYASHI, Y., 1979. Space–time spectral analysis of rotary vector series. *J. Atmos. Sci.*, 36: 757–766.
HAYNAM, G. E., GOVINDARAJULU, Z. and LEONE, F. C., 1962. Tables of the cumulative non-central chi-square distributions. *Case Stat. Lab. Publ.* 104, AD 426500, 22 pp.
HEGAZY, Y. A. S. and GREEN, J. R., 1975. Some new goodness-of-fit tests using order statistics. *Appl. Stat.*, 24: 299–308.
HELGERT, H. J., 1970. On sums of random variables defined on a two-state Markov chain. *J. Appl. Probability*, 7: 761–765.
HENZE, F. H. H., 1979. The exact noncentral distribution of Spearman's r and other related correlation coefficients. *J. Am. Stat. Assoc.*, 74: 459–464.
HERRERO, J. L. and WILLONER, G., 1966. *Synthesis of Filters*. Prentice-Hall, Englewood Cliffs, NJ, 192 pp.
HERSHFIELD, D. M., 1970. A comparison of conditional and unconditional probabilities for wet- and dry-day sequences. *J. Appl. Meteorol.*, 9 (5): 825–827.
HERSHFIELD, D. M., 1972. Estimating the extreme value 1 minute rainfall. *J. Appl. Meteorol.*, 11: 936–940.
HERSHFIELD, D. M., 1973. On the probability of extreme rainfall events. *Bull. Am. Meteorol. Soc.*, 54: 1013–1018.
HESS, W. N. (Editor), 1974. *Weather and Climate Modification*. Wiley, New York, NY, 842 pp.
HESSELBERG, TH. and BJORKDAL, E., 1929. Über das Verteilungsgesetz der Windunruhe. *Beitr. Phys. Atmos.*, 15: 121–133.
HIEMSTRA, L. A. V., 1983. The standardized bivariate lognormal probability distribution simplifies the storm–flood relationship. *2nd Int. Meet. Stat. Climatol.*, p. 3.6.1–2.
HILL, G. W. and DAVIS, A. W., 1968. Generalized asymptotic expansion of Cornish-Fisher type. *Ann. Math. Stat.*, 39: 1264–1273.
HILL, M. B., 1975. Aberrant behavior of the likelihood function in discrete cases. *J. Am. Stat. Assoc.*, 70: 717–719.
HINICH, M. J. and CLAY, C. S., 1968. The application of the discrete Fourier transform in the estimation of power spectra, coherence and bispectra of geophysical data. *Rev. Geophys.*, 6 (3): 347–363.
HIROH, A. and ITOH, M., 1983. Analysis of observed wind directions by statistics of directional data. *2nd Int. Meet. Stat. Climatol.*, pp. 2.4.1–6.
HOGBEN, D., PINKHAM, R. S. and WILK, M. B., 1961. The moments of the non-central t-distribution. *Biometrika*, 48: 465–468.
HOGG, R. V. and CRAIG, A. T., 1967. *Introduction to Mathematical Statistics*. MacMillan, New York, NY, 2nd edn., 383 pp.
HOLLOWAY, J. L., 1958. Smoothing and filtering of time series and space fields. *Adv. Geophys.*, IV: 351–389.
HOLMSTRÖM, I., 1970. Analysis of time series by means of empirical orthogonal functions. *Tellus*, 22: 638–647.
HOLTZMAN, W. H., 1950. The unbiased estimate of the population variance and standard deviation. *Am. J. Psychol.*, 63: 615–617.
HOOPER, J. W., 1959. Simultaneous equations and canonical correlation theory. *Econometrica*, 27: 245–256.
HOSHIAI, M., IWASHIMA, T. and YAMAMOTO, R., 1974. Quasi-biennial oscillation of the ultra-long waves at 500 mb during the years 1948–1968. *J. Meteorol. Soc., Jpn., Ser. II*, 52 (3): 283–288.
HOTELLING, H., 1936. Relation between two sets of variates. *Biometrika*, 28: 321–377.
HOYT, J. P., 1972. Generating functions in elementary probability theory. *Am. Stat.*, 26 (3): 45–46.
HSU, CH-F., 1981. An annoted bibliography on the evaluation and statistical issues of weather modification. *SWS Contr. Rep., 265, State Water Surv. Div., Ill. Inst. Nat. Resour., Champaign, IL*, 93 pp.

HSU, CH-F. and CHANGNON, S. A., 1983. Uses of historical data in weather modification evaluation. *Preprints, 8th Conf. Probability, Stat. Atmos. Sci., Nov. 1983*, pp. 45–48.

HSU, CH. P. F. and WALLACE, J. M., 1976. The global distribution of the annual and semi-annual cycles in precipitation. *Mon. Weather Rev.*, 9: 1093–1101.

HSU, CH.-F, GABRIEL, K. R. and CHANGNON, S. A., 1981a. Statistical techniques and key issues for the evaluation of operational weather modification. *J. Weather Mod.*, 13: 195–199.

HSU, CH.-F., CHANGNON, S. A., HUFF, F. A. and GABRIEL, K. R., 1981b. *The Assessment of Statistical-Physical Techniques for the Evaluation of Weather Modification Operations.* SWS Contract Rep. 286, State Water Survey Division, Champaign, IL, 135 pp.

HUGHES, L. A. and SANGSTER, W. E., 1979. Combining precipitation probabilities. *Mon. Weather Rev.*, 107: 520–524.

HURST, R. B., EDWARDS, P. J. and ROXBURGH, A. J., 1977. Characterization of wind energy sites. *Meteorol. Energy, Proc. N.Z. Meteorol. Serv., Symp.*, pp. 57–68.

HUSS, P. O., 1946. *Relation between Gusts and Average Winds for Homing Load Determination.* Daniel Guggenheim Airship Inst. Akron, OH, Rep. 140.

IMAN, R. L., 1977. Graphs for use in testing equality of two correlation coefficients. *J. Qual. Tech.* 9: 172–175.

IMAN, R. L., 1982. Graphs for use with the Lilliefors test for normal and exponential distributions. *Am. Stat.*, 36: 109–112.

JACKSON, M. C., 1975. Annual duration of any rainfall intensity. *Meteorol. Mag.*, 104: 243–248.

JACKSON, K. A., GILMER, G. H. and MATULA, R. A., 1982. Inventivity issue joined: small firm concept challenged. *Ind. Res. Dev.*, 24: 210–216.

JAESH, J. L., 1966. Understanding multiple regression. *Ind. Qual. Contr.*, 23: 260–264.

JENKINS, G. M., 1961. General consideration in the analysis of spectra. *Technometrics*, 3 (2): 133–190.

JENKINSON, A. F., 1955. The frequency distribution of the annual maximum (or minimum) values of meteorological elements. *Q. J. R. Meteorol. Soc.*, 87: 158–171.

JENKINSON, A. F., 1969. Statistics of extremes. Chapter 5 in: *Estimation of Maximum Floods, WMO Tech. Note*, 98: 183–227.

JENKINSON, A. F., 1975a. Extreme value analysis in meteorology. *4th Conf. Probability Stat. Atmos. Sci.*, pp. 83–89.

JENKINSON, A. F., 1975b. Some quasi-periodic changes in rainfall in Africa and Europe. *Proc. WMO/IAMAP Symp. Long-term Climatic Fluctuations, Norwich*, pp. 453–460.

JENKINSON, A. F., 1977. *A Powerful Elementary Method of Spectral Analysis for Use with Monthly, Seasonal, or Annual Time Series.* (Unpublished copy available in Meteorol. Off. Library, Bracknell.)

JENNRICH, R. I., 1970. An asymptotic χ^2 test for the equality of two correlation matrices. *J. Am. Stat. Assoc.*, 65 (330): 904–912.

JENSEN, D. R. and SOLOMON, H., 1972. A Gaussian approximation to the distribution of a definite quadratic form. *J. Am. Stat. Assoc.*, 67 (340): 898–902.

JEON-JANG, J., 1966. Statistical theory of precipitation processes. *Tellus*, 18 (4): 722–729.

JOHNSON, E. S. and MIELKE, P. W., 1973. Some empirical comparison of certain probability distributions used to describe precipitation amounts. *3rd Conf. Probability Stat. Atmos. Sci., Boulder, Colo.*, pp. 91–95.

JOHNSON, N. L., 1949. Systems of frequency curves generated by methods of translations. *Biometrika*, 36: 149–176.

JOHNSON, N. L., 1959. On an extension of the connexion between Poisson and χ^2 distribution. *Biometrika*, 46: 352–363.

JOHNSON, N. L. and KOTZ, S., 1969. *Discrete Distributions.* Houghton Mifflin, Boston, MA, 328 pp.

JOHNSON, N. L. and KOTZ, S., 1970a. *Continuous Univariate Distributions, 1.* Houghton Mifflin, Boston, MA, 330 pp.

JOHNSON, N. L. and KOTZ, S., 1970b. *Continuous Univariate Distributions, 2.* Houghton Mifflin, Boston, MA, 306 pp.

JOHNSON, N. L. and KOTZ, S., 1972. *Continuous Multivariate Distributions.* Houghton Mifflin, Boston, MA, 333 pp.

JOHNSON, N. L. and PEARSON, E. S., 1969. Tables of percentage points of non-central χ. *Biometrika*, 56: 255–272.

JOHNSON, N. L. and WELCH, B. L., 1940. Application of the non-central t-distribution. *Biometrika*, 31: 362–389.

JOHNSON, R. A. and WEHRLY, TH., 1977. Measures and models for angular correlation and angular-linear correlation. *J. R. Stat. Soc., B.*, 39: 222–229.

JONES, R. H., 1979. Filtering rational spectra with unequally spaced data. *Preprints 6th Probability Stat. Atmos. Sci., Oct. 9–12, 1979, Banff*, pp. 231–234.

JONES, R. H., DANIELS, A. and BACH, W., 1976. Fitting a circular distribution to a histogram. *J. Appl. Meteorol.*, 15: 94–98.

JOSEPH, P. and TOU, J. T., 1961. On linear control theory. *AIEE* Trans., 80: 193–196.

JOSS, J. and GORI, E. G., 1976. The parameterization of raindrop size distributions. *Riv. Ital. Geofis. Sci. Appl.*, 3: 275–283.

JULIAN, P. R., CARR, M. B. and STEPHENS, J. J., 1977. A simple technique for non-recursive digital filter design. *Preprints, 5th Conf. Probability Stat. Atmos. Sci.*, pp. 272–276.

JUNGHANS, H., 1968. Die statistische Bearbeitung von Niederschlagsdaten mit logarithmischen Merkmalsteilungen. *Z. Meteorol.*, 20: 351–354.

JURCEC, V., 1975. Statistical analysis of dry spells and rainfall extremes during 1947–1971. *Riv. Ital. Geofis. Sci. Appl.*, 1: 125–133.

JUSTUS, C. G., HARGRAVES, W. R., MIKHAIL, A. and GRABER, D., 1978. Methods for estimating wind speed frequency distribution. *J. Appl. Meteorol.*, 17 (3): 350–353.

KAISER, J. F. and REED, W. A., 1977. Data smoothing using low-pass digital filters. *Rev. Sci. Instrum.*, 48: 1447–1457.

KAISER, H. F. and STEFANSKY, W., 1972. A Polya distribution for teaching. *Am. Stat.*, 26 (3): 40–43.

KALBFLEISCH, J. G. and SPROTT, D. A. 1973. The comparison of Poisson-distributed observations. *Biometrika*, 29 (1): 223–224.

KALLMAN, H. E., 1940. Transversal filters. *Proc. IRE*, 28: 302–310.

KALMAN, R. E., 1960. A new approach to linear filtering and prediction problems. *J. Basic Eng.*, 82: 35–45.

KALMAN, R. E. and BUCY, R. S., 1961. New results in linear filtering and prediction theory. *J. Basic Eng.*, 83: 95–108.

KARLIN, S., 1968. *A First Course in Stochastic Processes.* Acad. Press, New York, NY, 2nd edn., 502 pp.

KATZ, L., 1975. A direct development of the correlation coefficient. *Am. Stat.*, 29: 170.

KATZ, R. W., 1974. Computing probabilities associated with the Markov chain model for precipitation. *J. Appl. Meteorol.*, 13: 953–954.

KATZ, R. W., 1977. Precipitation as a chain-dependent process. *J. Appl. Meteorol.*, 16: 671–676.

KELWAY, P. S., 1971. A scheme for assessing the reliability of interpolated rainfall estimates. *J. Hydrol.*, 21: 247–267.

KENDALL, M. G. and STUART, A., 1958. *The Advanced Theory of Statistics, 1. Distribution Theory.* Hafner, New York, NY, 433 pp.

KENDALL, M. G. and STUART, A., 1961. *The Advanced Theory of Statistics, 2. Inference and Relationship.* Hafner, New York, NY, 676 pp.

KENDALL, M. G. and STUART, A., 1966. *The Advanced Theory of Statistics, 3. Design, Analysis, and Time Series.* Hafner, New York, NY, 552 pp.

KENNEY, J. F. and KEEPING, E. S., 1954. *Mathematics of Statistics, Parts I and II.* D. van Nostrand, Princeton, NJ, 3rd ed., Vol. I, 348 pp., Vol. II, 429 pp.

KERRIDGE, D. F. and COOK, G. W., 1976. Yet another series for the normal integral. *Biometrika*, 63 (2): 401.

KERTZ, W., 1966. Filterverfahren in der Geophysik. *Gerlands Beitr. Geophys.*, 75: 1–33.

KIDSON, J. W., 1975a. Eigenvector analysis of monthly mean surface data. *Mon. Weather Rev.*, 103: 177–186.

KIDSON, J. W., 1975b. Tropical eigenvector analysis and the southern oscillation. *Mon. Weather Rev.*, 103: 187–196.

KIEFER, J. and WEISS, L., 1957. Some properties of generalized sequential probability ratio tests. *Ann. Math. Stat.*, 28: 57–74.

KIMBALL, B. F., 1956. The bias in certain estimates of the parameters of the extreme value distribution. *Ann. Math. Stat.*, 27: 758–767.

KLEINER, B., MARTIN, R. D. and THOMSON, D. J., 1979. Robust estimation of power spectra. *J. R. Stat. Soc., B*, 41: 313–351.

KLUG, W., 1964. Zur Statistik der Böigkeit des Windes. *Arch. Meteorol. Geophys. Bioklimatol., Ser. A*, 14 (3): 300–305.

KOLMOGOROV, A., 1933. Sulla determinazione empirica di una legge di distributione. *G. Ist. Ital. Attuari*, 4: 1–11.

KOROLYUK, V. S., 1960. Asymptotic analysis of the distribution of the maximum deviation in the Bernouilli scheme. *Theor. Probab. Appl.*, 4: 339–366.

KOTZ, S. and NEUMANN, J., 1963. On the distribution of precipitation amounts for periods of increasing length. *J. Geophys. Res.*, 68 (12): 3635–3640.

KOTZ, S. and NEUMANN, J., 1964. On the distribution of precipitation amounts for periods of increasing length, addendum. *J. Geophys. Res.*, 69 (4): 800–801.

KRAEMER, H. CH., 1973. Improved approximation to the non-null distribution of the correlation coefficient. *J. Am. Stat. Assoc.*, 68 (344): 1004–1008.

KRUSKAL, W. H., 1957. Historical notes on the Wilcoxon unpaired two-sample test. *J. Am. Stat. Assoc.*, 52: 356–360.

KRUSKAL, W. H. and WALLIS, W. A., 1952. Use of ranks in one-criterion variance analysis. *J. Am. Stat. Assoc.*, 47: 583–621.

KRUSKAL, W. H. and WALLIS, W. A., 1953. Errata to "use of ranks in one-criterion variance" analysis. *J. Am. Stat. Assoc.*, 48: 907–911.

KU, H. H. and KULLBACK, S., 1974. Log linear models in contingency table analysis. *Am. Stat.*, 28 (4): 115–122.

KUIPER, N. H., 1960. Tests concerning random points on a circle. *Proc. K. Ned. Akad. Wet., Ser. A*, 63: 38–47.

KULHÁNEK, O., 1975. *Introduction to Digital Filtering in Geophysics.* Elsevier, Amsterdam, 168 pp.

KULLBACK, S., 1974. The information in contingency tables. *Final Tech. Rep., Grant DAHCO-4-74-G-0164, Army Res. Off., Durham, NC*, 378 pp.

KURASHIGE, K., 1969. Numerical tables of the percent points in the F-distribution for the detailed significance levels. *Pap. Meteorol. Geophys. (Jpn.)*, 20: 253–273.

KUTZBACH, J. E., 1966. *Representation and Classification of Fields of Atmospheric Variables.* Thesis, Univ. Wisconsin, 125 pp.

KUTZBACH, J. E. and WAHL, E. W., 1965. The representation of scalar fields with functions orthogonal in polar coordinates. *J. Appl. Meteorol.*, 4: 542–544.

LAND, CH. E., 1974. Confidence interval estimation for means after data transformation to normality. *J. Am. Stat. Assoc.*, 69: 795–802.

LANDSBERG, H. E., 1969. *Physical Climatology.* Gray Printing, DuBois, PA, 2nd ed., 446 pp.

LANDSBERG, H. E., 1975. The definition and determination of climatic changes, fluctuations and outlooks. In: R. KOPEC (Editor), *Proc. Atmospheric Quality and Climatic Change.* (*Univ. NC., Studies in Geography*, 9: 52–64.

LANDSBERG, H. E., MITCHELL, Jr., J. M. and CRUTCHER, H. L., 1959. Power spectrum analysis of climatological data for Woodstock College, MD. *Mon. Weather Rev.*, 87 (8): 283–298.

LANDSBERG, H. E., MITCHELL, Jr., J. M., CRUTCHER, H. L. and QUINLAN, F. T., 1963. Surface signs of the biennial atmospheric pulse. *Mon. Weather Rev.*, 91: 549–556.

LANGLEY, R., 1970. *Practical Statistics Simply Explained.* Dover, New York, NY, 399 pp.

LAUBSCHER, N. F., 1960. Normalizing the non-central t and F distributions. *Ann. Math. Stat.*, 31: 1105–1112.

LAWAL, H. B. and UPTON, G. J. G., 1980. An approximation to the distribution of the χ^2 goodness-of-fit statistic for use with small expectations. *Biometrika*, 67: 447–453.

LAWRENCE, A. J., 1976. On conditional and partial correlation. *Am. Stat.*, 30: 146–149.

LEDSHAM, W. H. and STAELIN, D. H., 1978. An extended Kalman-Bucy filter for atmospheric temperature profile retrieval with a passive microwave sounder. *J. Appl. Meteorol.*, 17 (7): 1023–1033.

LEE, A. C. L., 1981. Smoothing and filtering of meteorological data. *Meteorol. Mag.*, 110: 115–132.

LEHMAN, E. L., 1959. *Testing Statistical Hypotheses.* Wiley, New York, NY, 369 pp.

LEITH, C. E., 1973. The standard error of time-average estimates of climatic means. *J. Appl. Meteorol.*, 12: 1066–1069.

LEONDES, C. T. (Editor), 1970. Theory and applications of Kalman filtering. *AGARDograph*, 139: 3–49.

LEPAGE, Y., 1971. A combination of Wilcoxon's and Ansari-Bradley's statistics. *Biometrika*, 58: 213–217.

LEPAGE, Y., 1973. A table for combined Wilcoxon Ansari-Bradley statistic. *Biometrika*, 60: 113–116.

LESTER, P., 1972. An energy budget for intermittent turbulence in the free atmosphere. *J. Appl. Meteorol.*, 11: 90–98.

LETTAU, H., 1962. Notes on theoretical models of profile structure in the diabatic surface layer. *Final Rep. Contr. DA-36-039-SC-80282 (USAEPG, Ft. Huachuca, Arizona).* Univ. Wisconsin, pp. 195–226.

LEVIN, J. J., 1959. On the matrix Riccarti equation. *Trans. Am. Math. Soc.*, 10: 519–524.

LIEBLEIN, J., 1954. A new method of analyzing extreme-value data. *U.S. Natl. Adv. Comm. Aero., Tech. Note*, 3053; 87 pp.

LILLIEFORS, H. W., 1969. On the Kolmogorov-Smirnov test for the exponential distribution with mean unknown. *J. Am. Stat. Assoc.*, 64: 387–389.

LIN, S. H., 1976a. Dependence of rain-rate distributions on rain-gauge integration time. *Bell System Tech. J.*, 55: 135–141.

LIN, S. H., 1976b. Rain-rate distributions and extreme value statistics. *Bell System Tech. J.*, 55: 1111–1124.

LOCKE, L. G., 1964. Bayesian statistics. *Ind. Qual. Contr.*, 21 (10): 18–21.

LOCKS, M. O., ALEXANDER, M. J. and BYARS, B. J., 1963. *New Tables of the Non-Central t-Distribution.* ARL 63-19, Contr. AF 33(616)-7372, 463 pp.

LORENZ, E., 1956. Empirical orthogonal functions and statistical weather prediction. *Sci. Rep., 1, Stat. Forecasting Proj., M.I.T., Dep. Meteorol., Cambridge, MA*, 49 pp.

LOWRY, D. A. and GLAHN, H. R., 1976. An operational model for forecasting probability of precipitations — PEATMOSPOP. *Mon. Weather Rev.*, 104: 221–232.

LOWRY, W. P. and GUTHRIE, D., 1968. Markov chains of the order greater than one. *Mon. Weather Rev.*, 96 (11): 798–801.

LUND, I. A., 1963. Map pattern classification by statistical methods. *J. Appl. Meteorol.*, 2: 56–65.

LUND, I. A. and GRANTHAM, D. D., 1975. Estimating hourly persistence and recurrence probabilities of temperature. *Preprints 4th Conf. Probab. Stat. Atmos. Sci., Nov. 18–21*, pp. 152–156.

LUND, I. A. and GRANTHAM, D. D., 1977. Persistence, runs and recurrence of precipitation. *J. Appl. Meteorol.*, 16: 346–358.

LUND, I. A. and GRANTHAM, D. D., 1979. Estimating recurrence probabilities of weather events. *J. Appl. Meteorol.*, 18: 921–930.

MACPHERSON, A. K. and KELLY, R. E., 1976. A horizontal telescoping grid model with a vertically nested layer using bi-cubic splines. *Mon. Weather Rev.*, 104: 932–941.

MADDEN, R. A., 1977. Estimates of the autocorrelation and spectra of seasonal mean temperatures over North America. *Mon. Weather Rev.*, 105 (1): 9–18.

MADDEN, R. A. and SADEH, W., 1975. Empirical estimates of the standard error of time-averaged climatic means. *J. Appl. Meteorol.*, 14: 164–169.

MAHALANOBIS, C., 1944. On large-scale sample surveys. *Phil. Trans. London, Ser. B*, 231: 329–451.

MAHRER, Y. and PIELKE, R. A., 1978. A test of an upstream spline interpolation technique for the advective terms in a numerical mesoscale model. *Mon. Weather Rev.*, 106: 818–830.

MALKOVICH, J. F. and AFIFI, A. A., 1973. On tests for multivariate normality. *J. Am. Stat. Assoc.*, 68: 176–179.

MALLOW, C. L., 1973. Some comments on Cp. *Technometrics*, 15 (4): 661–667.

MALLOW, J. V., 1975. Empirical fog droplet size distribution functions with finite limits. *J. Atmos. Sci.*, 32: 440–443.

MALONE, T. F., 1966. Weather and climate modification; problems and prospects, II, Research and development. *NAS-NRC Publ.*, 1350, 80 pp.

MALONEY, C. J., 1978. Calculation of chi-square. *Proc. Computer Sci. Stat., 11th Symp., Inst. Stat., NC State Univ.*, pp. 373–375.

MANN, H. B. and WALD, A., 1942. On the choice of the number of class intervals in the application of the chi-square test. *Ann. Math. Stat.*, 13: 306–317.

MANN, H. B. and WHITNEY, D. R., 1947. On a test of whether one of two random variables is stochastically larger than the other. *Ann. Math. Stat.*, 18: 50–60.

MARITZ, J. S. and MUNRO, A. H., 1967. On the use of the generalized extreme value distribution in estimating extreme percentiles. *Biometrics*, 23: 79–103.

MARSHALL, A. W., 1958. The small sample distribution of $n\omega^2_n$. *Ann. Math. Stat.*, 29: 307–309.

MARSHALL, J. S. and PALMER, W. MCK., 1948. The distribution of raindrop with size. *J. Meteorol.*, 5: 165–166.

MARTIN, M. A., 1962. Digital filters for data processing. *G. E. Tech. Inf. Ser.*, 62SD484: 142 pp.

MASON, B. J., 1971. *The Physics of Clouds.* Clarendon Oxford Press, 671 pp.
MASON, J., 1980. A review of three long-term cloud-seeding experiments. *Meteorol. Mag.*, 109 (1301): 335–344.
MASSEY, F. J., 1951. The Kolmogorov-Smirnov test for goodness-of-fit. *J. Am. Stat. Assoc.*, 46: 68–78.
MATHAI, A. M. and RATHIE, P. N., 1971. The problem of testing independence. *Proc. 38th Session ISI*, pp. 254–258.
MATHISEN, H. C., 1943. A method of testing the hypothesis that two samples are from the same population. *Ann. Math. Stat.*, 14: 188–194.
MCCOOL, J. I., 1970. Inferences on Weibull percentile and shape parameter from maximum likelihood estimates. *IEEE Trans. Reliability*, R-19 (Feb.), pp. 2–9.
MCLOWERY, E., 1973. Error analysis of meteorological network data. *Preprints, 3rd Conf. Probab. Stat. Atmos. Sci., June 19–22, Boulder, Colo.*, pp. 175–180.
MCMILLAN, R. G., 1971. Tests for one or two outliers in normal samples with unknown variance. *Technometrics*, 13: 87–100.
MCMILLAN, R. G. and DAVID, H. A., 1971. Tests for one or two outliers in normal samples with known variance. *Technometrics*, 13: 75–85.
MCMORROW, D. J., 1978. A technique for estimating clock two-hourly precipitation rate distributions. *USAFETAC-TN-78-002 (Scott Air Force Base, Illinois)*, 62225: 13 pp.
MERCERET, F. J., 1974. On the size distribution of raindrops in hurricane Ginger. *Mon. Weather Rev.*, 102: 714–716.
MEYER, F. and VAN ISACKER, J., 1975. The synthesis of high resolution filters. *Inst. R. Meteorol. Belg., Publ. Ser. A*, 90: 87 pp.
MIELKE, P. W., 1973. Another family of distributions for describing and analyzing precipitation data. *J. Appl. Meteorol.*, 12 (2): 275–280.
MIELKE, P. W., 1976. Simple iterative procedures for two-parameter gamma distribution maximum likelihood estimates. *J. Appl. Meteorol.*, 15 (2): 181–183.
MIELKE, P. W., 1978. On criticisms concerning the Israeli experiment. *J. Appl. Meteorol.*, 17: 555–556.
MIELKE, P. W. and JOHNSON, E. S., 1973. Three-parameter kappa distribution, maximum likelihood estimates and likelihood ratio tests. *Mon. Weather Rev.*, 101 (9): 701–707.
MILLS, F. C., 1955. *Statistical Methods.* Henry Holt, New York, NY, 3rd edn., 842 pp.
MITCHELL, J. M., Jr., 1961. The measurement of secular temperature change in the eastern United States. *U.S. Dept. Commerce, Res. Pap.*, 43: 1–80.
MITSUTA, Y. and HAYASHI, T., 1979. Wind power potential in Japan. *Climate*, 26 (10): 583–593.
MOOD, A. MCF., 1950. *Introduction to the Theory of Statistics.* McGraw-Hill, New York, NY, 433 pp.
MOOLEY, D. A., 1973. Gamma distribution model for Asian summer monsoon rainfall. *Mon. Weather Rev.*, 101 (2): 160–176.
MOOLEY, D. A. and CRUTCHER, H. L., 1968. An application of the gamma distribution function to India rainfall. *ESSA Tech. Rep., EDS 5, Silver Springs, MD.*, 48 pp.
MURPHY, A. H., 1977. On the misinterpretation of precipitation probability forecasts. *Bull. Am. Meteorol. Soc.*, 58: 1297–1299.
MURPHY, A. H., 1978. On the evaluation of point precipitation probability forecasts in terms of areal coverage. *Mon. Weather Rev.*, 106: 1680–1686.
MURTHY, V. K. and SWARTZ, G. B., 1975. Estimation of Weibull parameters from two-order statistics. *J. R. Stat. Soc., B*, 37 (1): 96–102.
NASS, C. A. C., 1959. The chi-square test for small expectations in contingency tables with special reference to accidents and absenteeism. *Biometrika*, 46: 365–385.
NATIONAL ACADEMY OF SCIENCES RESEARCH COUNCIL, 1964. *Scientific Problems of Weather Modification.* NAS-NRC Publ. 1236, Washington, D.C., 53 pp.
NATIONAL ACADEMY OF SCIENCES, NATIONAL RESEARCH COUNCIL, 1966. *Weather and Climate Modification.* NAS-NRC Publ. 1350, Washington, DC., 148 pp.
NATIONAL ACADEMY OF SCIENCES, 1973. *Weather and Climate Modification, Problems and Progress.* Washington, DC, 258 pp.
NATIONAL BUREAU OF STANDARDS, 1950. Tables of the binomial probability distribution. *Appl. Math. Ser.*, 6: 387 pp.
NELSON, L. S., 1975. Use of the range in testing heterogeneity of variance. *J. Qual. Technol.*, 7: 99–100.
NELSON, L. S., 1976. Fitting a least-square straight line. *J. Qual. Technol.*, 8: 115–116.
NELSON, L. S., 1977. Tolerance factors for normal distributions. *J. Qual. Technol.*, 9: 198–199.

NELSON, L. S., 1979. Olmstead's runs test. *J. Qual. Technol.*, 11: 100–101.

NELSON, P. R., 1974. A computer program for the Doolittle technique. *J. Qual. Technol.*, 6: 160–162.

NELSON, S. P. and WEIBLE, M. L., 1980. Three-dimensional Shuman filter. *J. Appl. Meteorol.*, 19: 464–469.

NEYMAN, J., 1959. *Optimal Asymptotic Tests of Composite Statistical Hypothesis. Probability and Statistics.* Almquist and Wiksetts, Uppsala, pp. 231–234.

NEYMAN, J., 1975. Problems and design of evaluation of rain making experiments. In: J. N. SRIVASTAVA (Editor), *A Survey of Statistical Design and Linear Models*, North-Holland, Amsterdam, pp. 443–458.

NEYMAN, J., 1977a. A statistician's view of weather modification technology (a review). *Proc. Natl. Acad. Sci.*, 74: 4714–4721.

NEYMAN, J., 1977b. Experimentation with weather control and statistical problems generated by it. In: P. R. KRISHNAIAH (Editor), *Application of Statistics.* North-Holland, Amsterdam, pp. 1–25.

NEYMAN, J., 1979a. Developments in probability and mathematical statistics generated by studies in meteorology and weather modification. *Comm. Stat. Theor. Math.*, A8 (11): 1097–1110.

NEYMAN, J., 1979b. C(α) tests and their use. *Sankhya, A.*, 41: 1–21.

NEYMAN, J., 1980. Comments on the special issue of communications in statistics concerned with weather modification experiments. *Comm. Stat. Theor. Math.*, A9: 965–992.

NEYMAN, J. and PEARSON, E. S., 1928. On the use and interpretation of certain test criteria for the purpose of statistical inference. *Biometrika*, 20 A: 175; 263.

NEYMAN, J. and PEARSON, E. S., 1933. The problem of the most efficient tests of statistical hypotheses. *Phil. Trans. R. Soc., A*, 231: 289–337.

NEYMAN, J. and SCOTT, E. L., 1961. Further comments on the Final Report of the Advisory Committee on Weather Control. *J. Am. Stat. Assoc.*, 56: 580–600.

NEYMAN, J. and SCOTT, E. L., 1965. Asymptotically optimal tests of composite hypothesis. *J. Am. Stat. Assoc.*, 60: 699–721.

NEYMAN, J. and SCOTT, E. L., 1974. Rain stimulation experiments: design and evaluation. *Proc. WMO/IAMAP Sci. Conf. Weather Modif.*, 399: 449–457.

NEYMAN, J., SCOTT, E. L. and WELLS, M. A., 1973. Downwind and upwind effects in the Arizona cloud-seeding experiments. *Proc. Natl. Acad. Sci. U.S.A.*, 70 (2): 357–360.

OGALLO, L. J., 1980. Regional grouping of rainfall stations in East Africa into homogeneous regions using the method of principal component analysis. In: S. IKEDA, E. SUZUKI, E. UCHIDA and M. M. YOSHINO (Editors), *Statistical Climatology.* Elsevier, Amsterdam, pp. 255–266.

OGAWARA, M., 1980. The use of exponential smoothing for the estimation of climatic elements. In: S. IKEDA, E. SUZUKI, E. UCHIDA and M. M. YOSHINO (Editors), *Statistical Climatology*, Elsevier, Amsterdam, pp. 217–228.

OHTAKI, J., 1977. A comparison of techniques of obtaining multiple regression equations for computing probabilities of precipitation. *Jpn. J. Meteorol. Res.*, 29: 239–243.

OLASCOAGA, M. J., 1950. Some aspects of Argentina rainfall. *Tellus*, 2 (4): 312–318.

OLBERG, M., 1972a. Statistische Beurteilung gefilterter geophysikalischer Beobachtungsreihen bei Zugrundelegung eines weissen Rauschens. *Gerlands Beitr. Geophys.*, 81: 65–72.

OLBERG, M., 1972b. Filterung und Erhaltungsneigung. *Z. Meteorol.*, 23: 11–16.

OLBERG, M., 1973. Filteranalyse und statistische Beurteilung von Filterergebnissen am Beispiel der Zeitreihen für die Komponenten des Windvektors in Potsdam. *Z. Meteorol.*, 23 (11–12): 323–331.

OLBERG, M., 1974. Signifikanzprüfung bandgefilterter geophysikalischer Beobachtungsreihen mit rotem Spektrum. *Gerlands Beitr. Geophys.*, 83: 129–140.

OLIVEIRA, J. TIAGO DE, 1983. Extreme values and meteorology. *2nd Int. Meet. Stat. Climatol.*, pp. 10.1.1–8.

OLSEN, A. R., 1975. Bayesian and classical statistical methods applied to randomized weather modification experiments. *J. Appl. Meteorol.*, 14: 970–973.

OLSEN, A. R., WORDLEY, W. L. and HERNDON, A., 1973. Investigation of the effect of natural rainfall variability and measurement errors in the detection of seeding effects. *Preprints 3rd Conf. Probab. Stat. Atmos. Sci., Boulder, Colo.*, pp. 96–103.

ORD, J. K., 1968. Approximations to distribution functions which are hypergeometric series. *Biometrika*, 55: 243–248.

ORSZAG, S. A., 1974. Fourier series on spheres. *Mon. Weather Rev.*, 102: 56–75.

ORVILLE, H. T., 1957. (Chairman). *Final Report of the Advisory Committee on Weather Control*, I, (32 pp.) and II, (422 pp.). Gov. Print. Off., Washington, DC.
OSEEN, C. W., 1930. Das Turbulenzproblem. *Proc. 3rd Int. Conf. Appl. Mech., Stockholm, 24–29 Aug., 1930*, pp. 3–22.
OSTLE, B. and MENSING, R. W., 1975. *Statistics in Research*. Iowa State Univ. Press, 3rd edn., 624 pp.
OTTEN, A., 1973. Notes on the Spearman rank correlation coefficient. *J. Am. Stat. Assoc.*, 68: 585.
OVERLAND, J. E. and PREISENDORFER, R. W., 1982. A significant test for principal components applied to a cyclone climatology. *Mon. Weather Rev.*, 110 (1): 1–4.
OWEN, D. B., 1962. *Handbook of Statistical Tables*. Adison-Wesley, Reading, MA, 580 pp.
OWEN, D. B., 1963. Factors for one-sided tolerance limits and for variable sampling plans. *Sandia Corp. Monogr.*, SCR-607.
OWEN, D. B., 1965. The power of Student's *t*-test. *J. Am. Stat. Assoc.*, 60: 320–333.
OWEN, D. B., 1968. A survey of properties and applications of the non-central *t*-distribution. *Technometrics*, 10: 445–478.
PAHL, P. J., 1969. On testing for goodness-of-fit of the negative binomial distribution when expectations are small. *Biometrics*, 25: 143–151.
PALUMBO, A. and MAZZARELLA, A., 1980. Rainfall statistical properties in Naples. *Mon. Weather Rev.*, 108: 1041–1045.
PANOFSKY, H. A. and BRIER, G. W., 1965. *Some Application of Statistics to Meteorology*. Penn. State Univ., Univ. Park, 224 pp.
PASSI, R. M., 1976. A weighting scheme for autoregressive time averages. *J. Appl. Meteorol.*, 15: 117–119.
PASSI, H. H. and PASSI, R. M., 1975. Statistical editing of meteorological data. *Preprints 4th Conf. Probab. Stat. Atmos. Sci.*, pp. 200–205.
PATIL, G. P., 1962. Some methods of estimation for the logarithmic series distribution. *Biometrics*, 18: 68–75.
PATNAIK, P. B., 1949. The non-central χ^2 and F-distributions and their applications. *Biometrika*, 36: 202–232.
PATRINOS, A. A. N., CHEN, N. C. J. and MILLER, R. L., 1979. Spatial correlation of monthly rainfall: applications in climatology and weather modification experiments. *J. Appl. Meteorol.*, 18: 719–732.
PEARSON, E. S., 1947. Choice of statistical tests illustrated on interpretation of data classed in a 2×2 table. *Biometrika*, 34: 123–169.
PEARSON, E. S., 1959. Note on an approximation to the distribution of noncentral χ^2. *Biometrika*, 46: 364.
PEARSON, E. S., 1963. Comparison of tests for randomness of points on a line. *Biometrika*, 50: 315–325.
PEARSON, E. S. and HARTLEY, H. O., 1958. *Biometrika Tables for Statisticians*, I. Cambridge Univ. Press, 240 pp.
PEARSON, E. S. and STEPHENS, M. A., 1962. The goodness-of-fit tests based on W_N^2 and U_N^2. *Biometrika*, 49: 397–402.
PEARSON, E. S., D'AGOSTINO, R. B. and BOWMAN, K. O., 1977. Tests for departure from normality: comparison of powers. *Biometrika*, 64: 231–246.
PEARSON, K., 1894. Contribution to the mathematical theory of evolution. *Philos. Trans. R. Soc., London, Ser. A*, 185: 71–110.
PEARSON, K., 1895. Contribution to the mathematical theory of evolution. *Philos. Trans. R. Soc., London, Ser. A*, 186: 383–414.
PEARSON, K., 1900. On a criterion that a given system of deviations from the probable in the case of a correlated system of variables is such that it can reasonably be supposed to have arisen in random sampling. *Phil. Mag.*, 5: 157.
PEARSON, K., 1904. On the theory of contingency and its relation to association and normal correlation. *Drapers' Co. Memoirs, Biometric Ser.*, No. 1, London.
PEARSON, K., 1932. Experimental discussion of the (χ^2, P) test for goodness-of-fit. *Biometrika*, 24: 351–381.
PEARSON, K., 1936. Method of moments and method of maximum likelihood. *Biometrika*, 28: 34–59.
PEARSON, K., 1956. *Tables of the Incomplete Beta-Function*. Cambridge Univ. Press, London, (reprinted from 1933) 494 pp.

Pearson, K., 1957. *Tables of the Incomplete Gamma Function.* Cambridge Univ. Press, London (re-issue) 164 pp.

Peizer, D. B. and Pratt, J. W., 1968. A normal approximation for binomial, F, beta, and other common related tail probabilities. *J. Am. Stat. Assoc.*, 63: 1416–1456.

Pelz, W. and Good, I. J., 1976. Approximating the lower tail-area of the Kolmogorov-Smirnov one-sample statistic. *J. R. Stat. Soc., Ser. B*, 38: 152–156.

Pennington, R. H., 1970. *Introductory Computer Methods and Numerical Analysis.* MacMillan, London, 2nd edn., 497 pp.

Petterssen, S., Spar, J., Hall, F., Braham, R. R., Jr., Battan, L. J., Byers, H. R., Kampe, H. J., Kelly, J. J. and Weickmann, H. K., 1957. Cloud and weather modification. *Meteorol. Monogr.*, 11: 111 pp.

Pettitt, A. N., 1976. Cramer-von Mises statistics for testing normality with censored samples. *Biometrika*, 63: 475–481.

Phonsombat, V. and LeDuc, Sh. K., 1977. Comparison of kappa and gamma distributions for weekly rainfall amounts in Thailand. *Preprints 5th Conf. Probab. Stat. Atmos. Sci.*, pp. 221–224.

Pieters, E. P., Gates, C. E., Matis, J. H. and Sterling, W. L., 1977. Small sample comparison of different estimators of negative binomial parameters. *Biometrics*, 33: 718–723.

Polya, G. and Eggenberger, F., 1923. Über die Statistik der Verketteten Vorgänge. *Z. Angew. Math.*, 3: 279 ff.

Posner, E. L., Rodemich, E. R., Ashlock, J. C. and Lurie, S., 1969. Application of an estimator of high efficiency in bivariate extreme value theory. *J. Am. Stat. Assoc.*, 64: 1403–1414.

Pratt, J. W., 1959. Remarks on zeros and ties in the Wilcoxon signed rank procedures. *J. Am. Stat. Assoc.*, 54: 655–667.

Prentice, R. L. and Marek, P., 1979. A qualitative discrepancy between censored data rank tests. *Biometrics*, 35: 861–867.

Purnell, D. K., 1976. Solution of the advective equation by upstream interpolation with a cubic spline. *Mon. Weather Rev.*, 104: 42–48.

Quandt, R. E., 1966. Old and new methods of estimation and the Pareto distribution. *Metrika*, 10: 55–82.

Raff, M. S., 1970. On calculating the gamma function of non-integral arguments. *Am. Stat.*, 24 (2): 22–24.

Rangno, A. L., 1979. A reanalysis of the Wolf Creek Pass cloud seeding experiment. *J. Appl. Meteorol.*, 18: 579–605.

Rao, C. R., 1973. *Linear Statistical Inference and its Applications.* Wiley, New York, NY, 2nd edn., 625 pp.

Rao, N. J. M., Viswanadham, Y. and Rao, T. V. R., 1979. A preliminary study of precipitable water over Brazil. *PAGEOPH.*, 117: 883–890.

Rayment, R., 1970. Introduction to the fast Fourier transform (FFT) in the production of spectra. *Meteorol. Mag.*, 99: 261–270.

Reed, R. K., 1979. On the relationship between the amount and frequency of precipitation over the ocean. *J. Appl. Meteorol.*, 18: 692–696.

Reisig, G. H. R., 1956. Instantaneous and continuous wind measurements up to the higher stratosphere. *J. Meteorol.*, 13: 448–455.

Reisig, G. H. R., 1977. Statistical data analysis in the information domain. *Kybernetes*, 6: 107–123.

Reitan, C. H., 1960. Mean monthly values of precipitable water over the US 1946–1956. *Mon. Weather Rev.*, 88: 25–35.

Reitan, C. H., 1963. Surface dew point and water vapor aloft. *J. Appl. Meteorol.*, 2: 776–779.

Ricketts, J. N., 1980. World surface climatological data — methods of quality control and archiving. *Meteorol. Mag.*, 109: 325–330.

Rinne, J., 1971. Investigation of the forecasting error of a simple barotropic model with the aid of empirical orthogonal functions. *Geophysica*, 11: 185–240.

Rockette, H., Antle, Ch. and Klimko, L. A., 1974. Maximum likelihood estimation with the Weibull model. *J. Am. Stat. Assoc.*, 69 (345): 246–249.

Rodriguez-Iturbe, I., 1983. Probabilistic modeling of the precipitation process. *2nd Int. Meet. Stat. Climatol.*, pp. 6.1.1–7.

Salter, P. M., 1972. Areal rainfall analysis by computer. In: *Distribution of Precipitation in Mountain Areas, II.* WMO, Geneva, pp. 479–509.

SCHAEFER, V. J., 1946. The production of ice crystals in a cloud of supercooled water droplets. *Science*, 104: 457–459.

SCHEFFÉ, H., 1959. *The Analysis of Variance*. Wiley, New York, NY, 477 pp.

SCHEFFÉ, H., 1970. Practical solutions of the Behrens-Fisher problem. *J. Am. Stat. Assoc.*, 65: 1501–1508.

SCHENZLE, D., 1979. Fitting the truncated negative binomial distribution without the second sample moment. *Biometrics*, 35: 637–639.

SCHEUER, E. M. and SPURGEON, R. A., 1963. Some percentage points of the non-central *t*-distribution. *J. Am. Stat. Assoc.*, 58: 176–182.

SCHICKEDANZ, P. T., 1971. Theoretical frequency distributions for rainfall data. *Int. Symp. Probab. Stat. Atmos. Sci., Honolulu, Hawaii*, pp. 131–136.

SCHICKEDANZ, P. T., 1973. A statistical approach to computerized rainfall patterns. *Preprints, 3rd Conf. Probab. Stat. Atmos. Sci., Boulder, Colo.*, pp. 104–109.

SCHICKEDANZ, P. T. and BOWEN, E. G., 1977. The computation of climatological power spectra. *J. Appl. Meteorol.*, 16: 359–367.

SCHICKEDANZ, P. T. and HUFF, F. A., 1971. The design and evaluation of rainfall modification experiments. *J. Appl. Meteorol.*, 10: 502–514.

SCHICKEDANZ, P. T. and KRAUSE, G. F., 1970. A test for the scale parameters of two gamma distributions using the generalized likelihood ratio. *J. Appl. Meteorol.*, 9: 13–16.

SCHICKEDANZ, P. T., CHANGNON, S. A. and LONNQUIST, C., 1969. A statistical methodology for the planning and evaluation of hail suppression experiments in Illinois. *Ill. State Water Surv. Urbana, Final Rep. NSF GA-482*, 140 pp.

SCHNEIDER-CARIUS, K., 1955. Zur Frage der statistischen Behandlung von Niederschlagsbeobachtungen. *Z. Meteorol.*, 9: 129–135, 193–202, 266–271, 299–302.

SCHOENBERG, I. J. (Editor), 1969. *Approximations with Special Emphasis on Spline Functions*. Acad. Press, London, 488 pp.

SCHÖNWIESE, C. D. (Editor), 1983. *Statistische Methoden der Klimatologie. Prometheus, 1/2*, 58 pp.

SCHUMANN, T. E. W., 1963. The graduation or smoothing of data in one and two dimensions. *C.S.I.R. Spec. Rep., Wisk 4, Pretoria, S.A.*, 22 pp.

SCHUSTER, A., 1898. On the investigation of hidden periodicities with application to a supposed 26-day period of meteorological phenomenon. *Terr. Magn. Atmos. Electr.*, 3: 13–28.

SCHUSTER, E. F., 1973. On the goodness-of-fit problem for continuous symmetric distributions. *J. Am. Stat. Assoc.*, 68: 713–715.

SCOTT, E. L., 1973. Problems in the design analysis of weather modification studies. *Preprints. 3rd Conf. Probab. Stat. Atmos. Sci.*, pp. 65–72.

SCOTT, C. M. and SHULMAN, M. D., 1979. An areal and temporal analysis of precipitation in the Northeastern United States. *J. Appl. Meteorol.*, 18: 627–633.

SEVRUK, B. and GEIGER, H., 1981. Selection of distribution types for extremes of precipitation. *WMO Bull.*, 560, 64 pp.

SEWELL, W. R. D. (Editor), 1973. Modifying the weather, a social assessment. *West. Geogr. Ser.*, 9, *Univ. Vict., B.C.*, 349 pp.

SHAKUN, M. F., 1966. Nonlinear regression analysis. *Ind. Qual. Contr.*, 23: 11–13.

SHAPIRO, R., 1970. Smoothing, filtering and boundary effects. *Rev. Geophys. Space Phys.*, 8: 359–387.

SHAPIRO, R., 1971. The use of linear filtering as a parameterization of atmospheric diffusion. *J. Atmos. Sci.*, 28: 523–531.

SHAPIRO, R., 1972. A comparison between the effects of Fourier truncation and a class of linear digital filters. *J. Atmos. Sci.*, 29: 988–990.

SHAPIRO, R. and MACDONALD, N. J., 1961. A test of the reality of rainfall singularities (correspondence). *J. Meteorol.*, 18: 704–705.

SHAPIRO, S. S. and WILK, M. B., 1965. An analysis of variance test for normality (complete samples). *Biometrika*, 52: 591–611.

SHAPIRO, S. S., WILK, M. B. and CHEN, H. J., 1968. A comparative study of various tests for normality. *J. Am. Stat. Assoc.*, 63: 1343–1372.

SHARON, D., 1983. Are "scattered" thundershowers randomly distributed in space? An appraisal based on correlation analysis. *2nd Int. Meet. Stat. Climatol.*, pp. 6.5.1–4.

SHEARMAN, R. J., 1975. Computer quality control of daily and monthly rainfall data. *Meteorol Mag.*, 104: 102–108.

SHEARMAN, R. J., 1980. The meteorological office archive of machinable data. *Meteorol. Mag.*, 109: 344–350.

SHENTON, L. R. and BOWMAN, K. O., 1970a. Remarks on Thom's estimators for the gamma distribution. *Mon. Weather Rev.*, 98 (2): 154–160.

SHENTON, L. R. and BOWMAN, K. O., 1970b. Tables of the moments of the maximum likelihood estimators of the two-parameter gamma distribution. *Rep. Stat. Appl. Res., JUSE*, 17: 117–136.

SHENTON, L. R. and BOWMAN, K. O., 1973. Comments on the gamma distribution and uses in rainfall data. *3rd Conf. Prob. Stat. Atmos. Sci., Boulder, Colo.*, pp. 91–95.

SHENTON, L. R. and SKEES, P., 1970. Some statistical aspects of amounts and duration of rainfall. Random counts in Phys. Sci., GLO Science and Business. *Penn. State Statist. Ser.*, pp. 73–94.

SHUKLA, G. K., 1972. An invariant test for the homogeneity of variances in a two-way classification. *Biometrics*, 28: 1063–1072.

SHUMAN, F. G., 1957. Numerical methods in weather predictions, II. Smoothing and filtering. *Mon. Weather Rev.*, 85: 357–361.

SIEGEL, S. and TUKEY, J. W., 1960. A nonparametric sum of rank procedure for relative spread in impaired samples. *J. Am. Stat. Assoc.*, 55: 429–445.

SIEGMUND, D., 1980. Sequential χ^2 and F tests and the related confidence intervals. *Biometrika*, 67: 389–402.

SIGL, A. B., COROTIS, R. B. and WON, D. J., 1979. Run duration analysis of surface wind speeds for wind energy application. *J. Appl. Meteorol.*, 18: 156–166.

SIMMONDS, I., 1975. On interpolation and evaluation of derivatives from a finite number of equally-spaced data points. *J. Appl. Meteorol.*, 14: 1004–1010.

SIMPSON, J., 1972. Use of the gamma distribution in single-cloud rainfall analysis. *Mon. Weather Rev.*, 100: 309–312.

SLAKTER, M. J., 1965. A comparison of the Pearson chi-square and Kolmogorov goodness-of-fit tests with respect to validity. *J. Am. Stat. Assoc.*, 60: 854–858.

SMIRNOV, N. V., 1936. Sur la distribution de ω^2. *C. R. Acad. Sci.*, 202: 449–452.

SMIRNOV, N. V., 1937. On the distribution of ω^2 criterion of von Mises. *Rec. Math.*, 2: 973–993.

SMIRNOV, N. V., 1948. Table for estimating the goodness-of-fit of empirical distributions. *Ann. Math. Stat.*, 19: 279–281.

SMITH, W. L., 1966. Note on relationship between total precipitable water and surface dew point. *J. Appl. Meteorol.*, 5: 726–727.

SMITH, W. L. and H. M. WOOLF, 1976. The use of eigenvectors of statistical covariance matrices for interpreting satellite sounding radiometer observations. *J. Atmos. Sci.*, 33: 1127–1140.

SNEDECOR, G. W. and COCHRAN, W. G., 1967. *Statistical Methods.* Iowa State Coll. Press, Ames, Iowa, 6th ed., 593 pp.

SNEYERS, R., 1960. On a special distribution of maximum values. *Mon. Weather Rev.*, 88: 66–69.

SNEYERS, R., 1969. On the climatological analysis of local series of observations in data processing. *WMO Tech. Note*, 100: 93–102.

SNEYERS, R., 1971. Sur l'estimation du nombre équivalent de répétitions. *Rev. Stat. Appl.*, XIX (2): 35–47.

SNEYERS, R., 1974. Sur les tests de normalité. *Rev. Stat. Appl.*, XXII (2): 29–35.

SNEYERS, R., 1975. Sur l'analyse statistique des séries d'observations. *Note Tech.*, 143: 192 pp.

SNEYERS, R., 1976. Application of least squares to the search of periodicities. *J. Appl. Meteorol.*, 15 (4): 387–393.

SNEYERS, R., 1977a. L'intensité maximale des précipitations en Belgique. *Inst. R. Météorol. Belg., Publ. Sér. B*, 86: 15 pp.

SNEYERS, R., 1977b. Les méthodes statistiques en climatologie. *Inst. R. Météorol. Belg., Publ. Sér. B*, 90: 34 pp.

SNEYERS, R., 1978. Über die Anwendung von Markoff'schen Ketten in der Klimatologie. *Arb. Zentralanst. Meteorol. Geodyn., Wien*, 31: 9 pp.

SNEYERS, R., 1979a. Homogenéité et stabilité des éléments météorologiques à Uccle (Belgique). *Nuovo Cimento*, 2: 101–113.

SNEYERS, R., 1979b. L'intensité et la durée maximales des précipitations en Belgique. *Inst. R. Météorol. Belg., Publ. Sér. B*, 99, 19 pp.

SNEYERS, R. and VANDIEPENBEECK, M., 1983. On the estimation in the case of an exponential distribution with two parameters with an application to the problem of large values (exceedances). *2nd Int. Meet. Stat. Climatol.*, pp. 10.3.1–2.

Sneyers, R. and Van Isacker, J., 1972. Sur l'ajustement de la loi de répartition de Fisher-Tippett du type I au moyen des estimateurs de Kimball. *Rev. Belg. Stat. Inf. Rech. Opérat.*, 12: 1–8.

Sneyers, R. and Van Isacker, J., 1980. A generalized circular distribution. In: S. Ikeda, E. Suzuki, E. Uchida and M. M. Yoshino (Editors), *Statistical Climatology*. Elsevier, Amsterdam, pp. 21–25.

Solot, S. B., 1939. Computation of depth of precipitable water in a column of air. *Mon. Weather Rev.*, 67: 100–103.

Sorenson, H. W., 1966. Kalman filtering techniques. In: C. T. Leondes (Editors), *Advances in Control Systems, 3*. Acad. Press, New York, NY, pp. 219–292.

Stearns, C. R., 1970. Determining surface roughness and displacement height. *Boundary-Layer Meteorol.*, 1: 102–111.

Steckler, H. O., 1960. On smoothing and lags. *Am. Stat.*, 14, p. 13.

Steinhauser, F., 1966. Über den Tagesgang des Niederschlags. *Arch. Meteorol. Geophys. Bioklimatol., Ser. B*, 14: 1–35.

Stephens, M. A., 1963. The distribution of the goodness-of-fit statistics U_N^2, I. *Biometrika*, 50: 303–313.

Stephens, M. A., 1964. The distribution of the goodness-of-fit statistic U_N^2, II. *Biometrika*, 51: 393–397.

Stephens, M. A., 1970. Use of the Kolmogorov-Smirnov, Cramer-von Mises and related statistics without extensive tables. *J. R. Stat. Soc., Ser. B*, 32: 115–122.

Stephens, M. A., 1979. Vector correlation. *Biometrika*, 66: 41–48.

Stern, R. D., 1983. Statistical methods for the analysis of climatic data. *2nd Int. Meet. Stat. Climatol.*, pp. 7.1.1–6.

Stern, A. C., Wohlers, H. C., Boubel, R. W. and Lowry, W. P., 1973. *Fundamentals of Air Pollution*. Academic Press, New York, NY, 442 pp.

Stevens, D. G. and LeDuc, Sh. K., 1975. Maximum likelihood estimates for parameters of the *m*-th extreme value distribution. *Preprints, 4th Conf. Probab. Stat. Atmos. Sci., 18–21 Nov., Tallahassee, Fla.*, pp. 194–196.

Stewart, D. A., 1971. Effects of data bias in the upper atmosphere at high latitudes. *U.S. Army Missile Command Rep.*, RR-TR-71-6, 20 pp.

Stewart, D. A., 1975. Turbulence measurements from the Army gas dynamic laser range. *U.S. Army Missile Command Tech. Rep.*, RR-75-8, 25 pp.

Stewart, D. A. and Essenwanger, O. M., 1978. Frequency distributions of wind speed near the surface. *J. Appl. Meteorol.*, 17: 1633–1642.

Stidd, C. K., 1953. Cube root precipitation distributions. *Trans. Am. Geophys. Union*, 34: 31–38.

Stidd, C. K., 1969. A three-parameter distribution for precipitation data with a straight line plotting method. *Proc. 1st Stat. Meteorol. Conf., Hartford, Conn.*, pp. 158–162.

Stidd, C. K., 1973. Estimating the precipitation climate. *3rd Conf. Probab. Stat. Atmos. Sci., Boulder, Colo.*, pp. 135–138.

Storch, H. von, 1983. Statistical aspects of empirical orthogonal functions based on small sample sizes. *2nd Int. Meet. Stat. Climatol.*, pp. 5.2.1–6.

Strantz, R., 1971. Typen der Regentropfen. *Meteorol. Rundsch.*, 24 (1): 19–23.

Stringer, E. T., 1972. *Techniques of Climatology*. W. H. Freeman, Reading, 539 pp.

"Student", 1908. On the probable error of a mean. *Biometrika*, 6: 1–25.

Stumpff, K., 1937. *Grundlagen und Methoden der Periodenforschung*. Julius Springer, Berlin, 332 pp.

Sturges, H. A., 1926. The choice of a class interval. *J. Am. Stat. Assoc.*, 21: 65–66.

Sukhatme, P. V., 1938. On the distribution of χ^2 in samples of the Poisson Series. *J. R. Stat. Soc.*, 5: 75–79.

Suzuki, E., 1964. Hypergamma distribution and its fitting to rainfall data. *Pap. Meteorol. Geophys.* 15: 31–51.

Suzuki, E., 1966. Correlation analysis containing discrete variables used in certain meteorological problems. *Pap. Meteorol. Geophys.*, XVII (1) (October).

Suzuki, E., 1967. A statistical and climatological study on the rainfall in Japan. *Pap. Meteorol. Geophys.*, 18: 103–181.

SUZUKI, E., 1968. Secular variations of the rainfall in Japan. *Pap. Meteorol. Geophys.*, 19: 363–399 (Meteorol. Res. Inst., Tokyo.)

SUZUKI, E., 1980. A summarized review of theoretical distributions fitted to climatic factors and Markov chain models of weather sequences with some examples. In: S. IKEDA, E. SUZUKI, E. UCHIDA and M. M. YOSHINO (Editors), *Statistical Climatology*. Elsevier, Amsterdam, pp. 1–20.

SUZUKI, E., MIYATA, M. and HONGO, S., 1980a. Statistical prediction of climatological extremes values and return period in the case of small samples. In: S. IKEDA, E. SUZUKI, E. UCHIDA and M. M. YOSHINO (Editors), *Statistical Climatology*. Elsevier, Amsterdam, pp. 207–216.

SUZUKI, E., OOHASHI, T. and HONGO, S., 1980b. An optimum linear restriction in the estimation problem for a generalized linear model and its application to climatic data. In: S. IKEDA, E. SUZUKI, E. UCHIDA and M. M. YOSHINO (Editors), *Statistical Climatology*. Elsevier, Amsterdam, pp. 229–239.

SWANSON, E. R., 1978. Weather modification: the economic context. *J. Appl. Meteorol.*, 17: 872–875.

SWED, F. S. and EISENHART, C., 1943. Tables for testing randomness of grouping in a sequence of alternatives. *Ann. Math. Stat.*, 14: 66–87.

TABONY, R. C., 1979. A spectral filter analysis of long-period rainfall records in England and Wales. *Meteorol. Mag.*, 108: 97–118.

TACKLE, E. S. and BROWN, J. M., 1978. Note on the use of Weibull statistics to characterize wind-speed data. *J. Appl. Meteorol.* 17 (4): 556–559.

TAKEUCHI, D. M. and CHEN, P. C., 1979. A technique for determining parameter estimates of the gamma distribution. *Preprints 6th Conf. Probab. Stat. Atmos. Sci., Oct. 9–12, Banff, Alta, Canada*, pp. 239–243.

TATE, M. W. and HYER, L. H., 1973. Inaccuracy of the χ^2 test of goodness-of-fit when expected frequencies are small. *J. Am. Stat. Assoc.*, 68: 836–841.

TAUBENHEIM, J., 1969. *Statistische Auswertung Geophysikalischer und Meteorologischer Daten.* Geest und Portig, Leipzig, 386 pp.

TENTER, KL. J., 1970. Die Anwendbarkeit der Differenzenmethode zwischen Berg- und Ebenenstationen. *Meteorol. Rundsch.*, 23: 118–120.

TEUBER, D. L., REICHMANN, E. J. and WILSON, R. M., 1979. Principal component analysis of solar flares in the soft X-ray flux. *Astron. Astrophys.*, 80: 218–226.

THOM, H. C. S., 1954. Frequency of maximum wind speeds. *Proc. Am. Soc. Civ. Eng.*, 80. (Separate No. 539, November.)

THOM, H. C. S., 1957a. A statistical method of evaluating augmentation of precipitation by cloud seeding. In: H. T. ORVILLE (Chairman), *Final Report of the Advisory Committee on Weather Control.* Govt. Printing Office, Washington, DC, pp. 5–25.

THOM, H. C. S., 1957b. A method for the evaluation of hail suppression. In: H. T. ORVILLE (Chairman), *Final Report of the Advisory Committee on Weather Control.* Govt. Printing Office, Washington, DC, pp. 55–69.

THOM. H. C. S., 1958a. The frequency of hail occurrence. *Arch. Meteorol. Geophys. Bioklimatol., Ser. B*, 8 (2): 185–194.

THOM, H. C. S., 1958b. A note on the gamma distribution. *Mon. Weather Rev.*, 86: 117–122.

THOM, H. C. S., 1958c. A method for the evaluation of hail suppression. *J. Appl. Math. Phys.* (ZAMP) 9: 37–64.

THOM, H. C. S., 1959. A time interval distribution for excessive rainfall. *J. Hydraul. Div.*, p. 839.

THOM, H. C. S., 1968. Approximate convolution of the gamma and mixed gamma distributions. *Mon. Weather Rev.*, 96: 883–886.

THOMSON, A. B., 1971. The average annual frequency of daily rainfall amounts. *Meteorol. Mag.*, 100: 182–187.

TIETJEN, G. L. and MOORE, R. H., 1972. Some Grubbs-type statistics for the detection of several outliers. *Technometrics*, 14: 583–597.

TIKU, M. L., 1967. Tables of the power of the *F*-test. *J. Am. Stat. Assoc.*, 62: 525–539.

TIKU, M. L., 1972a. More tables of the power of the *F*-test. *J. Am. Stat. Assoc.*, 67: 709–710.

TIKU, M. L., 1972b. A note on the distribution of the doubly noncentral *F*-distribution. *Austral. J. Stat.*, 14: 37–40.

TODHUNTER, I., 1865. *A History of the Mathematical Theory of Probability from the Time of Pascal to that of Laplace.* MacMillan, Cambridge, 624 pp.

TODOROVIC, P. and WOOLHISER, D. A., 1975. A stochastic model of n-day precipitation. *J. Appl. Meteorol.*, 14: 17–24.

TUKEY, J. W., 1949a. The sampling theory of power spectrum estimates. *Woods Hole NAVEXOS-P-735, Off. Nav. Res.*, pp. 47–67.

TUKEY, J. W., 1949b. The simplest signed-rank test. *Princeton Univ. Stat. Res. Group, Memo. Rep.*, 17.

TUKEY, J. W., 1977. *Exploratory Data Analysis.* Addison Wesley, Reading, MA, 688 pp.

VAHL, H., 1972. Computerized calculation of areal precipitation and its accuracy. In: *Distribution of Precipitation in Mountain Areas.* WMO, Geneva, pp. 510–516.

VALLEY, S. L. (Editor), 1965. *Handbook of Geophysics and Space Environment.* McGraw-Hill, New York, NY, 714 pp.

VAN DER BIJL, W., 1951. Fünf Fehlerquellen in statistischer Forschung. *Ann. Meteorol.*, 4: 183–212.

VAN EEDEN, C., 1961. Some approximations to the percentage points of the noncentral t-distribution. *Rev. Inst. Int. Stat.*, 29: 4–31.

VAN MONTFORT, M. A. J., 1970. On testing that the distribution of extremes is of type I when type II is the alternative. *J. Hydrol.*, 11: 421–427.

VAN MONTFORT, M. A. J. and OTTEN, A., 1978. On testing a shape parameter in the presence of a location and a scale parameter. *Math. Operat. Stat., Ser. Stat.*, 9 (1): 91–104.

VON MISES, R., 1918. Über die Ganzzahligkeit der Atomgewichte und verwandte Fragen. *Phys. Z.*, 19: 490–500.

VONNEGUT, B., 1947. The nucleation of ice formation by silver iodide. *J. Appl. Phys.*, 18: 593–595.

WAHBA, G., 1977a. Optimal smoothing of density estimates. In: *Classification and Clustering.* Acad. Press, New York, NY, pp. 423–457.

WAHBA, G., 1977b. A survey of some smoothing problems and the method of generalized cross-validation for solving them. In: *Applied Statistics*, North Holland, Amsterdam, pp. 507–522.

WAHBA, G., 1978. Improper priors, spline smoothing and the problem of guarding against model errors in regression. *J. R. Stat. Soc., B*, 40 (3): 364–372.

WALD, A., 1941. Asymptotically most powerful tests of statistical hypotheses. *Ann. Math. Stat.*, 12: 1–19.

WALD, A., 1947. *Sequential Analysis.* Wiley, New York, NY, 4th ed., 212 pp.

WALD, A. and WOLFOWITZ, J., 1940. On a test whether two samples are from the same population. *Ann. Math. Stat.*, 11: 147–162.

WALKER, G. T., 1914. Correlation in seasonal variation of weather, III. On the criterion for the reality of relationships or periodicities. *Ind. Meteor. Dep. (Simla) Mem.*, 21: 22 ff.

WALLIS, W. A., 1952. Rough and ready statistical tests. *Ind. Qual. Control*, 8: 35–40.

WALSH, J. E., 1962. *Handbook of Nonparametric Statistics, I.* D. van Nostrand, Princeton, NJ, 549 pp.

WALSH, J. E., 1965. *Handbook of Nonparametric Statistics, II*, D. van Nostrand, Princeton, NJ, 686 pp.

WANG, Y. Y., 1971. Probabilities of the type I errors of the Welch tests for the Behrens-Fisher problem. *J. Am. Stat. Assoc.*, 66: 605–608.

WANNER, E., 1939. Über die Frequenz der täglichen Niederschläge. *Verh. Schweiz. Naturforsch. Ges.*, pp. 27–31.

WANNER, E., 1942. Niederschlagsfrequenzkurven. *Meteorol. Z.*, 59: 92–96.

WATSON, G. S., 1961. Goodness-of-fit tests on a circle, I. *Biometrika*, 48: 109–114.

WATSON, G. S., 1962. Goodness-of-fit tests on a circle, II. *Biometrika*, 49: 57–63.

WEAST, R. C., SELBY, S. M. and HODGMAN, CH. D., 1964. *Handbook of Mathematical Tables.* Chem. Rubber Co., Cleveland, OH, 680 pp.

WEIBULL, W., 1951. A statistical distribution function of wide applicability. *J. Appl. Mech.*, 18: 293–297.

WEICKMANN, H. K., 1957. Physics of precipitations. *Meteorol. Monogr.*, 3 (19): 226–255.

WEICKMANN, H. K. (Editor), 1960. *Physics of Precipitation–Geophys. Monogr.*, 5. Am. Geophys. Union, 435 pp.

WEISS, L., 1962. On sequential tests which minimize the maximum expected sample size. *J. Am. Stat. Assoc.*, 57: 551–566.

WEISS, L. L., 1964. Sequences of wet or dry days described by a Markov chain probability model. *Mon. Weather Rev.*, 92 (4): 169–176.

WEISSBERG, A. and BEATTY, G. H., 1960. Tables of tolerance limit factors for normal distributions. *Technometrics*, 2 (4): 483–500.

WEITBRECHT, R., 1979. Wahrscheinlichkeit, Zufall und Statistik. *Phys. Blätt*, 35: 25–29.

WELCH, B. L., 1938. The significance of the difference between two means when the population variances are unequal. *Biometrika*, 29: 350–362.

WELCH, B. L., 1947. The generalization of "Student's problem" when several populations are involved. *Biometrika*, 34: 28–35.

WETHERILL, G. B., 1975. *Sequential Methods in Statistics.* Chapman Hall, London, 2nd edn, 232 pp.

WHITTAKER, E. and ROBINSON, G., 1944. *The Calculus of Observations.* Blackie, London, 397 pp.

WIENER, N., 1949. *Extrapolation, Interpolation and Smoothing of Stationary Time Series.* M.I.T. Press, Cambridge, MA, 163 pp.

WIHL, G. and NOBILIS, F., 1975. Die Verteilung und Höhenabhängigkeit von 2.5 und 97.5 Perzentilen der Niederschlagssummen in den Jahreszeiten in Österreich. *Riv. Ital. Geofis. Sci. Affini*, 1: 134–137.

WILCOXON, F., 1945. Individual comparison by ranking methods. *Biometrics*, 1: 80–83.

WILCOXON, F., 1946. Individual comparisons of grouped data by ranking methods. *J. Econ. Entomol.*, 39: 269–270.

WILCOXON, F., 1947. Probability tables for individual comparisons by ranking methods. *Biometrics*, 3: 119–122.

WILHEIT, T. T., CHANG, A. T. C., RAO, M. S. V., RODGERS, E. B. and THEON, J. S., 1977. A satellite technique for quantitatively mapping rainfall rates over the oceans. *J. Appl. Meteorol.*, 16: 551–560.

WILKS, S. S., 1935. The likelihood test of independence in contingency tables. *Ann. Math. Stat.*, 6: 190–195.

WILKS, S. S., 1948. Order statistics. *Bull. Am. Math. Soc.*, 54: 6–50.

WILLIAMS, C. G., 1952. Sequences of wet and dry days considered in relation to the logarithmic series. *Q. J. R. Meteorol. Soc.*, 78 (335): 91–96.

WILLIAMS, J. S., 1979. A synthetic basis for a comprehensive factor-analysis theory. *Biometrics*, 35: 719–733.

WILLIAMS, W. H., 1978. How bad can "good" data really be. *Am. Stat.* 32: 61–65.

WILLIAMSON, D. L., 1976. Linear stability of finite-difference approximations on a uniform latitude-longitude grid with Fourier filtering. *Mon. Weather Rev.*, 104: 31–41.

WINKLER, R. L. and MURPHY, A. H., 1976. Point and area precipitation forecasts: some experimental results. *Mon. Weather Rev.*, 104: 86–95.

WINNER, D. C., 1968. Climatological estimates of clock-hour rainfall rates. *Air Weather Serv.* (MAC) Tech. Rep., 202: 24 pp.

WIPPERMANN, F., 1961. Der Effekt der Messdauer bei der Ermittlung von Maximal-Konzentrationen eines sich in turbulenter Strömung ausbreitenden Gases. *Int. J. Air Water Pollut.*, 4: 1–23.

WISER, E. M., 1965. Modified Markov probability models of sequences of precipitation events. *Mon. Weather Rev.*, 93 (8): 511–516.

WMO, 1966. *Statistical Analysis and Prognosis in Meteorology.* Tech. Note 71, WMO-No. 178, TP 78, 197 pp.

WMO, 1968. *Data Processing for Climatological Purposes.* Tech. Note 100, WMO-No. 242, TP 132, 132 pp.

WMO/IAMAP, 1973. *Scientific Conference on Weather Modification.* WMO-Rep., 399: 538 pp.

WMO/IAMAP, 1976. *Scientific Conference on Weather Modification.* WMO-Rep., 443: 592 pp.

WOLD, S., 1974. Spline functions in data analysis. *Technometrics*, 16: 1–11.

WONG, R. K. W., 1977. Weibull distribution, iterative likelihood techniques and hydrometeorological data. *J. Appl. Meteorol.*, 6 (12): 1360–1364.

WOO, T. L., 1929. Tables for ascertaining the significance or non-significance of association measured by the correlation ratio. *Biometrika*, XXI: 1–40.

WOOLF, B., 1956. The log likelihood ratio test (the G-test). Methods and tables for the test of heterogeneity in contingency tables. *Ann. Hum. Genet.*, 21: 397–409.

WRIGHT, P. B., 1971. An erroneous use of the chi-square test. *Meteorol. Mag.*, 100: 301–303.

YAMAZAKI, K. and KINAMI, Y., 1977. Principal components analysis on daily rainfall amount for the Kanto-Kashin region. *J. Meteorol. Res. (Japan)*, 29: 27–33.

YANG, CH-H., 1974. A controlled experiment with one-dimensional interpolation. *J. Appl. Meteorol.*, 13: 625–636.

YAO, A. Y. M., 1974. A statistical model for the surface relative humidity. *J. Appl. Meteorol.*, 13: 17–21.

YATES, F., 1934. Contingency tables involving small numbers and the χ^2 test. *J. R. Stat. Soc.*, 1, Suppl. 1: 217–235.

ZAWADSKI, I. I., 1973. Statistical properties of precipitation patterns. *J. Appl. Meteorol.*, 12 (3): 459–472.

ZAWADSKI, I. I. and RO, C. U., 1978. Correlations between maximum rate of precipitation and mesoscale parameters. *J. Appl. Meteorol.*, 17: 1327–1334.

ZEDLER, P., 1967. Zur Struktur der Niederschläge, II. *Arch. Meteorol. Geophys. Bioklimatol., Ser. B*, 15: 274–286.

ZVEREV, A. I., 1967. *Handbook of Filter Synthesis*, Wiley, New York, NY, 576 pp.

Reference Index

Subject Index

List of Symbols

General symbols and abbreviations

c.d.f., cumulative distribution function, $F(x)$
coefficients, A, a, etc.
conditional probability $P(A_1|A_2)$
constants, A, a, etc.
determinants $\|\mathbf{M}_{ij}\|$
estimators $\hat{a}$, $\tilde{a}$ etc.
functions $F(x)$, $G(x)$, $\Phi(x)$, $\Psi(x)$, $f(x)$, etc.
group symbols
 element of $X \in A$
 intersection $\cap$
 sample space, A
 subset B, $B \subset A$
 union of $\cup$
ln, natural logarithm
log, logarithm, base 10
matrix, $\mathbf{M}$
max, maximum
med, median
min, minimum
mo, mode
mod, modulus, 0.43429228
MSOD, minimum square orthogonal distance
parameter A, a, σ, τ, etc.
p.d.f., probability density function, $f(x)$
statistic, x, s etc.
variate X, x
vector, $\boldsymbol{v}$

Mathematical symbols

approximate $\approx$
derivative, $d^r m/dt^r$, order r
difference (finite) Δx
factorial, $r!$
imaginary root, $i = \sqrt{-1}$
infinity, ∞
maximum likelihood estimator $\hat{}$
mean $\bar{x}$, $\bar{X}$, x_m
operator for fractional moments $x^{[r]}$, definition p. 62, eq. 147
partial derivative $\partial x/\partial y$
pi, $\pi = 3.141593$
prior parameter $\tilde{}$
products $\prod$
summation $\sum$

Special letters (not implicitly included above)

$B(m, n)$ beta function
B_p, persistence parameter, Besson
C_a, coefficient of alienation
$C(\alpha)$, Neyman test statistic
Cov, covariance
D_M, D_α, Kolmogorov-Smirnov test
$E(x)$, expectancy of x
$F(x)$, cumulative distribution function
f_d, degrees of freedom
$f(x)$, frequency density function
G, log-likelihood ratio, p. 294, eq. 674
G_p, persistence parameter, Goutereau
H_0, H_1, hypothesis
$I(\theta)$, definition on p. 73, eq. 177b
$I_0(x)$, hyperbolic modif. Bessel function, p. 70
i subscript, also $\sqrt{-1}$
k_i, cumulants
$k(t)$, cumulant generating function
k_u, kurtosis
L, likelihood function, p. 24, eq. 52a
Lco_j, co-spectral line
L_j, spectral line (power spectrum)
Lqu_j, quadrature spectral line
M_i, empirical moment, order i, central
m_i, idem, noncentral
m-th value, see distribution
N, n, number of observations (with or without subscript)
N_e, expected number
$P(x)$, p, probability
p, period (Fourier series)
$Q(x)$, probability
q, probability, $1 - p$
q, constancy of wind measurement
R, r, correlation coefficient
R, range
R_{123} etc., multiple correlation coefficient
$R_{1.23}$ etc., multiple partial correlation coefficient
Rco, cross-covariance coefficient
$R(f)$, frequency response function
R^2_{PR}, percentage reduction
r_B, coefficient, Besson
r_G, coefficient, Goutereau
r_{vw}, vector correlation, r_t turn-, r_s stretch correlation
S, s standard deviation estimators
S^2, s^2, variance estimators
$S(x)$ smoothed part of function, p. 179
S^q, shift operator
T_{HG}, test criterion, p. 313
T_T, test criterion, p. 319
$T(Z)$, return period
t, standardized variate, Student test statistic
U^2_N, Watson statistic, p. 310
V, v, windspeed
Var, variance

V_N, Kuiper test statistic, p. 311
W_N^2, defined p. 308, eq. 706, and p. 311, eq. 724a
w, class width, weighting function (factor)
X, x, observed element
x_c, central class value
x_m, empirical mean
X_{th}, threshold, cumulative distribution
Z, standard variate (extreme values)
z, Fisher transformation
$\bar{Z}$, Euler's constant, p. 76

Greek letters (not implicitly included above)

α, angle, level of significance, shape parameter $1-\alpha$, confidence limit
β, angle, scale parameter, $1-\beta$, power of test
β_1, β_2, Pearson parameters
γ, angle, reference parameter
γ_1, skewness, γ_2, kurtosis
δ, shape parameter
δ, Kronecker delta
ε, error, ε^2
ε_S, standard error
ε_{AC}^2, accounted variance, ε_{RD}^2 accounted variance Fourier term
ε_F^2, expectancy (Fourier term)
ε_F^2, expectancy, (Fourier term) with persistence
$\varepsilon(x)$, oscillation, p. 179
ζ, linearity
η_{xy}, correlation ratio
θ, parameter, scale parameter
κ, Kolmogorov constant, p. 169, 0.5 to 0.6
λ, significant threshold (correlation ratio), likelihood ratio
μ_i, noncentral moment, order i
ν_i, central moment, order i
ν_N, Nyquist frequency
ν, degrees of freedom
ξ, parameter, variate
ρ, canonical correlation, correlation coefficient
σ, standard deviation
σ, variance
σ_x, σ_x^2, standard deviation, variance of x, respectively
τ, time lag
Φ, φ, angle, phase angle (Fourier term), wind direction
φ_r, factorial moment order r, orthogonal polynomial
χ, χ^2, test statistic
ψ, angle, digamma function, ψ, trigamma function
ω_i, weighting function (factor)
ω_R, equivalent number, p. 18
Ω, wave number